Petroleum Accounting

Principles, Procedures, & Issues

6th Edition

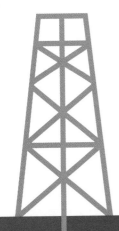

Petroleum Accounting

Principles, Procedures, & Issues

6th Edition

Horace R. Brock

Distinguished Professor Emeritus
University of North Texas

Martha Z. Carnes

Partner
PricewaterhouseCoopers LLP

Randol Justice

Partner
PricewaterhouseCoopers LLP

Editor-in-Chief
Molly McDonald-Ogden
Media Mastery

Published by
Professional Development Institute
Denton, Texas

FASB *Current Text* is copyrighted by the Financial Accounting Standards Board, 401 Merritt 7, P.O. Box 5116, Norwalk, Connecticut 06856-5116, U.S.A. Section Oi5, *Oil & Gas Producing Activities*, is reprinted with permission.

This publication is designed to provide accurate and authoritative information and explanation in regard to U.S. petroleum financial accounting principles and practices prior to publication. It is sold with the understanding that the publisher, Professional Development Institute, is not engaged in rendering legal, accounting, or other professional services, and that the book is intended to serve neither as professional advice nor conclusive guidance for a particular transaction or financial presentation. If legal, accounting, or other expert assistance is required, the services of a competent professional person should be sought.

International Standard Book Number: 978-0-940966-26-0

Professional Development Institute
University of North Texas
Denton, Texas 76205

Printed in the United States of America

In 1981 this publication appeared under the title *Accounting for Oil & Gas Producing Companies, Part I*, which was followed by *Part 2* (same title) in 1982.

In 1985 the publication appeared as *Petroleum Accounting: Principles, Procedures and Issues*.

In 1990, 1996, and 2000 the publication appeared as *Petroleum Accounting: Principles, Procedures, & Issues*.

ABOUT THE AUTHORS

Horace R. Brock, Ph.D., CPA, is the Director of Oil and Gas Programs and Director of the International Oil and Gas Accounting and Financial Management School of the Professional Development Institute. He is a Distinguished Professor Emeritus at the University of North Texas (UNT). Dr. Brock was Chair of the FASB Task Force on Financial Accounting and Reporting in the Extractive Industries. He was also a member of the FASB Task Force on Supplemental Disclosures for Oil and Gas Companies, the SEC Advisory Committee on Oil and Gas Accounting, the AICPA Oil and Gas Committee, and the Texas Commissioner's Blue Ribbon Committee on Oil and Gas Leasing. Dr. Brock has served as President of COPAS of Dallas, editor of the *Petroleum Accounting and Financial Management Journal*, and Director of the Institute of Petroleum Accounting at UNT. He holds a Ph.D. in accounting from the University of Texas at Austin.

Martha Z. Carnes, CPA, based in Houston, Texas, is the U.S. Energy Assurance Leader for PricewaterhouseCoopers. Martha's 24 years of experience in public accounting have involved serving clients primarily in the energy industry, including natural gas transmission and distribution, natural gas and power marketing, independent power producers, and oil and gas exploration and production. She has led multinational teams in conducting audits and due diligence reviews associated with mergers and acquisitions, and has completed associated filings with the SEC. Martha has served as a Risk Management Partner for the Firm and is an instructor and course writer for many of the Firm's energy and utility related Accounting and Auditing courses. She frequently speaks on current energy industry issues at Firm events and industry associations including the Federal Energy Regulatory Commission, Interstate Natural Gas Association of America, Financial Executives International, Edison Electric Institute, and American Gas Association. Martha is a member of the Texas Society of CPA's Electric, Gas and Telecommunications Committee, American Gas Association, and AICPA. Martha holds a BBA in accounting from The University of Texas at Austin.

Randol Justice, CPA, is a Partner in the Global Energy, Utilities and Mining Group of PricewaterhouseCoopers. Randol has provided professional services to companies involved in all areas of the energy industry and has also consulted on accounting and reporting matters with numerous multinational energy companies. Randol served as a partner in the Firm's national Professional, Technical, Risk & Quality Group consulting on energy accounting, reporting, and SEC issues. He is one of the primary reviewers for internal guidance on energy matters provided to engagement teams. He has been a presenter on energy topics at various conferences. Randol is a Certified Public Accountant in the states of Texas, New Jersey, and Oklahoma and is a member of the AICPA. Randol holds a BS in accounting from Southeastern Oklahoma State University.

PREFACE

Petroleum Accounting focuses on U.S. financial accounting and reporting for petroleum exploration and production activities. This book describes petroleum activities and the numerous accounting principles, practices, and procedures employed in petroleum financial reporting. *Petroleum Accounting* was written to serve as a college textbook and as a general reference source for petroleum accountants, financial auditors, and other interested parties. As with any textbook or guidance, the book is not intended to serve as professional advice nor conclusive guidance for a particular transaction or financial presentation. If legal, accounting, or other expert assistance is required, the services of a competent professional should be sought.

This 6th edition is a complete update to the 5th edition, adding a new chapter to address developments in business combinations and regulatory updates in the areas of FIN 46, FAS 141, Sarbanes-Oxley Section 404, and the accounting for impairments, asset retirement obligations, and conveyances, including discontinued operations.

Authorship. PricewaterhouseCoopers LLP is the U.S. member of PricewaterhouseCoopers, an international professional services firm that provides auditing, tax, and consulting services to many of the world's leading petroleum exploration and production companies. For this edition, PricewaterhouseCoopers partners Martha Z. Carnes and Randol Justice are the primary authors. They wish to acknowledge and thank Dr. Horace Brock for his instrumental role, particularly as the primary author of the earlier editions. For years, the book has been known in the industry as simply the "Brock Book."

Several PricewaterhouseCoopers partners and staff, alumni, and industry friends have given their assistance and advice for the 6th edition. Their backgrounds span major operational areas of petroleum exploration and production including: senior company management; property acquisition, valuation, and sale; geological and geophysical analysis; reservoir petroleum engineering; production engineering; oil & gas processing; oil & gas marketing; international operations; financial reporting; income tax reporting; and joint venture accounting.

Horace R. Brock	**Martha Z. Carnes**	**Randol Justice**
Denton, Texas	*Houston, Texas*	*Houston, Texas*

CONTRIBUTORS

The authors wish to acknowledge and thank the many people who have contributed to the writing and editing of this 6th edition:

PricewaterhouseCoopers Partners

John Brady, CPA, Assurance Partner, Houston, Texas
Rowena Cipriano-Reyes, CPA, Assurance Partner, Houston, Texas
Greg Hampton, CPA, Assurance Partner, Houston, Texas
Steve Johnson, CPA, Assurance Partner, London, U.K.
Robert R. Keehan, CPA, Assurance Partner, McLean, Virginia
James Koch, CPA, Tax Partner, Houston, Texas
Niloufar Molavi, CPA, Tax Partner, Houston, Texas
Ricardo Moreno, CPA, Assurance Partner, Houston, Texas
Jonathan Mullins, CPA, Assurance Partner, Dallas
John W. Phillips, CPA, Assurance Partner, Houston, Texas
Jodi Probst, CPA, Assurance Partner, Houston, Texas
Rick Roberge, CA, Transaction Services Partner, Houston, Texas
Keith Rowden, CPA, Assurance Partner, Houston, Texas
Kurt Sands, CPA, Assurance Partner, Houston, Texas
Rich Shappard, CPA, Assurance Partner, Houston, Texas
Thomas E. Smith, CPA, Assurance Partner, Florham Park, New Jersey

PricewaterhouseCoopers Staff

Christopher M. Bryant, CPA, Tax Senior Manager, Houston, Texas
Joseph P. Dunleavy, CPA, Assurance Senior Manager, Houston, Texas
Colleen Ernst, CPA, Assurance Senior Manager, Houston, Texas
Craig Friou, CPA, Assurance Senior Manager, Dallas, Texas
Susan G. Heitmann, MA, U.S. Energy & Mining Knowledge Manager, Houston, Texas
Anthony Hodge, CA, Assurance Senior Manager, Perth, Australia
Arthur H. Kramer, drs RA, Assurance Director, The Hague, The Netherlands
Paul Legoudes, CPA, Transaction Services Manager, Houston, Texas
Yaroslava Makalskaya, CPA, Assurance Senior Manager, Florham Park, New Jersey
Clifford Mangano, Ph.D., Transfer Pricing Senior Manager, Houston, Texas
Annette C. Morgan, MBA, Global Energy Marketing Director, Houston, Texas
Colin P. O'Beirne, CPA, Assurance Senior Manager, Houston, Texas
Denzil Rogers, CPA, Tax Associate, Houston, Texas
Todd M. Roemer, CPA, Assurance Senior Manager, Houston, Texas
Angel Salinas, CPA, Assurance Senior Manager, Houston, Texas
Robert J. Welsh, CPA, Assurance Senior Manager, Houston, Texas
Amy Whicher, CPA, Tax Senior Associate, Houston, Texas

PricewaterhouseCoopers Alumni

Curt T. Calaway, CPA, Houston, Texas
Linda J. Ibrahim, CPA, Houston, Texas
James P. Langley, CE, Houston, Texas
Jonathan McCarter, CPA, Houston, Texas
Robin Tompkins, Graphics Designer, Houston, Texas
Brent C. Willson, CPA, Houston, Texas

Other Contributing Authors

Kent Morgan, Geologist, San Antonio, Texas
Ben F. McDonald, Attorney at Law, Corpus Christi, Texas
Jim Hoffman, Professional Development Institute, Instructor and Director of Sales & Business
           Development, Denton, Texas

Editor-in-Chief

Molly McDonald-Ogden, M.A., former CPA, President Media Mastery, Austin, Texas

Graphics

Allison Easton, Graphic Artist, El Lago, Texas
Carol Wells, Graphic Manager, PricewaterhouseCoopers, Houston, Texas
Tracy Tobias, Graphic Artist, PricewaterhouseCoopers, Houston, Texas

Photographs and Exhibits

Special thanks to the **Petroleum Extension Service** at the University of Texas and the **American Association of Petroleum Geologists** *EXPLORER* publication for providing graphics and photographs used throughout the text.

CONTENTS

• • •

CHAPTER

1

AN INTRODUCTION TO THE PETROLEUM INDUSTRY

Key Concepts:

- **Hydrocarbon chemistry and measurement**

- **History of the U.S. petroleum industry**

- **Emergence of a world market**

The word **petroleum** refers to the **hydrocarbon** compounds of **crude oil** and **natural gas** that are found in underground rock **formations**. **Reservoirs** are generally thousands of feet below the surface and are made up of the remains of small marine plants and animals that lived millions of years ago. Petroleum may also seep to the earth's surface along fault lines and cracks in rocks where it pools as tar, asphalt, or bitumen. Its name is derived from the Latin terms petra (rock) and oleum (oil). In current usage, petroleum refers to both crude oil and natural gas.

Human use of petroleum is as old as recorded history. Ancient cultures used sticky crude oil to bind objects and repel water. Five thousand years ago, the Sumerians used asphalt to inlay mosaics in walls and floors. Mesopotamians used bitumen to line water canals, seal joints in wooden boats, and build roads. Chariots were greased with pitch by Egyptians, who also placed coatings of asphalt on mummies. The Chinese were the first to discover underground deposits of oil and gas, and even transported those hydrocarbons in bamboo pipelines.

Modern uses of petroleum and its byproducts include:

- Transportation fuels including gasoline, diesel fuel, jet fuel, and compressed natural gas (CNG)

- Heating fuels such as propane, heating oil, and natural gas

- Electric generation fuels such as natural gas and fuel oil

- Manufactured products such as plastics and building materials

CHEMISTRY AND MEASUREMENT

Different mixtures of hydrocarbons have varying uses and economic values. It is necessary to recognize the basic types of hydrocarbon mixtures to understand portions of this book.

Crude oil refers to unrefined hydrocarbon mixtures produced from underground reservoirs that are liquid at normal atmospheric pressure and temperature. Crude ranges in color from almost clear to green, amber, brown, or black, and is classified as light or heavy depending on the density of the mixture. Density is measured in **API gravity** as explained in Chapter 11. Heavy crude oil has more of the longer, larger hydrocarbon molecules and, thus, a greater density than light crude oil. Heavy crude is difficult to produce and transport to market, and more expensive to process into valuable products. Consequently, heavy crude oils weigh more, but sell for much less.

Natural gas refers to hydrocarbon mixtures that are not liquid, but gaseous at normal atmospheric pressure and temperature. Natural gas is largely methane, which is a clear, odorless gas. It has the smallest natural hydrocarbon molecule consisting of one carbon atom and four hydrogen atoms (CH_4). Natural gas may also contain some of the larger hydrocarbon molecules commonly found in nature:

- **Ethane (C_2H_6)**　　　　　　　- **Propane (C_3H_8)**

- **Butane (C_4H_{10})**　　　　　　- **Natural gasolines (C_5H_{12} to $C_{10}H_{22}$)**

Ethane, propane, butane, and natural gasolines are collectively called **natural gas liquids (NGL)**, and are valuable feedstock for the petrochemical industry. When removed from the natural gas mixture, these larger, heavier molecules become liquid under various combinations of increased pressure and lower temperature. Liquefied petroleum gas (LPG) usually refers to propane and butane, which are stored in a liquid state under pressure. LPG is the fuel used in portable gas barbeque grills.

Both natural gas and crude oil can contain contaminants, such as sulfur compounds and carbon dioxide (CO_2), which must be substantially removed before marketing them. The contaminant hydrogen sulfide (H_2S) is poisonous and, when dissolved in water, is corrosive to metals. Natural gas and crude oil that are high in sulfur compounds are called **sour gas** and **sour crude oil**. Two additional types of crude oil are known as **sweet crude**, which contains minimal sulphur compounds, and **intermediate crude**, which is between sour and sweet. Some crude oils contain small amounts of metals that require special equipment during the refining process.

In the U.S., natural gas is measured in two ways, and both are important in petroleum accounting:

- By the amount of energy or heating value when burned; this quantity is expressed in million **British thermal units (MMBtu)**

- By volume, which is expressed in:

  - **Mcf** (thousand cubic feet)

  - **MMcf** (million cubic feet)

  - **Bcf** (billion cubic feet)

  - **Tcf** (trillion cubic feet)

Gas volumes are necessarily measured at a standard pressure and temperature, typically at an atmospheric pressure base of 14.65 to 15.025 pounds per square inch absolute (or psia) and a temperature of 60 degrees Fahrenheit.

The ratio of MMBtu (energy) to Mcf (volume) varies from approximately 1:1 to 1.3:1. The more NGL there are in the gas mixture, the higher the ratio, the greater the energy, and the "richer" or "wetter" the gas.

Wet gas is produced to the surface and sent through a mechanical **separator** near the **well**. Some natural gasolines within the gas condense into a liquid classified as a light crude oil, and are called **condensate**. To create pipeline quality natural gas, the wet gas is sent from the **wellhead** by pipeline to a gas processing plant for removal of substantially all of the NGL, which are sold to petrochemical plants or refineries. The remaining gas mixture—called **residue gas** or **dry gas**—is more than 90 percent methane. It is the natural gas burned for home heating, electric generation, and industrial uses.

Crude oil is measured in the U.S. by volume expressed as **barrels (bbl)**. A barrel equates to 42 U.S. gallons. However, for comparison purposes, hydrocarbons may be expressed in barrels of oil equivalent **(BOE)** whereby gas volumes in Mcf are converted to barrels on the basis of energy content or sales value. Approximately 5.6 Mcf of dry gas has the same MMBtu energy content (5.8 MMBtu) as one average U.S. barrel of oil. In addition, equivalency can be expressed based on price. For example, if one Mcf of gas is selling for $6.00 when oil is selling for $60 per barrel, then 10

Mcf equate to one barrel of oil based on the given sales prices. For one million BOE of gas, the corresponding Mcf is shown for the conversion ratios provided.

Conversion Basis	Assumed Ratio	BOE	Mcf
Energy	5.6 to 1	1,000,000	5,600,000
Value	10 to 1	1,000,000	10,000,000

Many companies use an energy conversion ratio of six Mcf per barrel, which is the required ratio for certain income tax rules in Internal Revenue Code (IRC) Section 613A(c)(4).

In countries using the metric system, crude oil is measured by weight in metric tons, or by volume expressed in kiloliters (equivalent to 6.29 barrels). A metric ton of crude oil approximates 7.33 barrels of crude oil, but the ratio varies since some crude oil mixtures are heavier per barrel than others. Gas volumes are measured in cubic meters (kiloliters) and energy is measured in gigajoules. A kiloliter (or cubic meter) approximates 1.31 cubic yards and 35.3 cubic feet. A gigajoule (or a billion joules) approximates 0.95 MMBtu.

HISTORY OF THE U.S. PETROLEUM INDUSTRY

To understand the ramifications of financial accounting and reporting in the petroleum industry, it is important to know how the business of oil and gas has developed over time. This text's emphasis is on U.S. operations, and how exploration and production (E&P) companies have adapted to the emerging global marketplace.

The U.S. petroleum industry began in the early 1800s when dwindling supplies of whale oil were supplanted by illuminating oils called kerosene or coal oil. Kerosene was extracted from coal, asphalt, and surface crude seepage (known as rock oil). At the same time, settlers drilling for salt brine occasionally found crude oil mixed in.

In 1856, George Bissell, an investor in the Pennsylvania Rock Oil Company, surmised that a similar type of well could be used to produce crude oil for making kerosene. While there is mention of an oil discovery in Ontario, Canada, a year earlier, it is generally accepted that Bissell's company was the first commercial oil drilling venture. Drilling began in 1859 near Titusville, Pennsylvania, under the supervision of Colonel Edwin L. Drake, a retired railroad conductor.

A steam-powered, **cable-tool rig** with a wooden derrick was used to drill the 69-foot well, which produced approximately five barrels of crude oil per day for the Pennsylvania Rock Oil Company. Additional drilling and production in the Titusville area dramatically increased the supply and caused a decline in the price of crude oil from $10 per barrel in January 1860 to about 10 cents a barrel two years later. Shortly thereafter, a number of refineries began distilling valuable kerosene from crude oil.

Nearly four decades later in 1897, the first offshore well in the U.S. was drilled near the coast of Southern California. H.L. Williams designed a wharf and erected a drilling rig on top of it. At 300 feet in depth, the well was successful in producing oil.

THE INDUSTRIAL REVOLUTION AND THE GROWTH OF BIG OIL

At the start of the Civil War, approximately 200 wells were producing more than 500,000 barrels annually. The introduction of petroleum-based lamp fuel was the first of an increasing variety of uses for crude oil and its refined products. The Industrial Revolution and wartime manufacturing created a demand for lubricants to replace turpentine. By 1870, annual production of crude oil exceeded 25 million barrels.

Transportation was a challenge from the earliest days of oil production. The coopers' union constructed wooden barrels (with capacities of 42 to 50 gallons) that were filled with oil and hauled by teamsters on horse-drawn wagons to railroad spurs or river barge docks. At railroad spurs, the oil was emptied into large wooden tanks placed on flatbed railroad cars. The quantity of oil that could be moved by this method was clearly limited. However, the industry's attempts to construct pipelines were thwarted by railroad companies and unions that stood to lose this lucrative business. The first pipeline, built during the 1860s, was made of wood and measured less than a thousand feet long.

In 1870, John D. Rockefeller moved to the forefront of the burgeoning petroleum industry when his firm merged with four other companies to form Standard Oil Company. The goal was to be the industry leader in petroleum refining, transporting, and marketing. However, shortly after the merger, the company also moved into oil production.[1]

During the 1880s, Standard Oil controlled approximately 90 percent of the refining industry in the U.S., and it dominated the global petroleum industry as well. Standard Oil's control of refineries, as well as its ownership of railroads, pipelines, and marketing outlets, forced most petroleum customers in the U.S. to purchase products from the company.[2]

Standard Oil's dominance drew the attention of federal and state regulators. After discovery of the Spindletop **field** near Beaumont, Texas, in 1901, the Texas legislature passed laws preventing Standard Oil from becoming involved in the field. As a result of the more open market, other companies were organized. Some evolved into vertically integrated companies such as Texaco, which was founded in 1901. Between 1911 and 1915, federal antitrust laws forced the break-up of Standard Oil into several companies.

THE 1920s AND 1930s: DEMAND, SUPPLY, AND REGULATION

The 1920s witnessed increased competition in the oil industry as more companies formed and demand was spurred by economic growth and the proliferation of automobiles. Production increased to meet demand, but the industry experienced price fluctuations and regulatory change.

American companies began to search for foreign oil beginning in the early 1920s. This outbound investment was encouraged by U.S. policymakers who feared a domestic oil shortage might occur. By the mid-1920s, approximately 35 companies had invested more than $1 billion in exploring for and developing **reserves** in the Middle East, South America, Africa, and the Far East.

The 1930 discovery of the giant East Texas Oil Field resulted in a world surplus of oil. Abundant East Texas oil and the prevailing economic depression combined to temporarily reduce oil prices by 90 percent.

Offshore production added a new dynamic to the oil and gas market. While some shallow offshore drilling occurred as early as the late 1800s, it was not until the late 1930s that wells were drilled from structures resembling the offshore drilling platforms in use today.

From the earliest years of active exploration and production, states began to monitor environmental impact. For example, the Texas legislature in 1933 recognized the need for conservation measures to avoid waste and rampant overproduction of fields. Enforcement and oversight duties were given to an existing state agency, the Texas Railroad Commission. Over time, other oil-producing states created similar agencies or commissions to regulate the development and production of reserves.

In 1938, the U.S. Congress passed the Natural Gas Act which extended the jurisdiction of the Federal Power Commission to wholesale sales and transportation of natural gas. Federal regulation of the interstate movement of gas continues today under the Federal Energy Regulatory Commission (**FERC**).

WORLD WAR II: PETROLEUM FOR DEFENSE

Economic recovery from the Great Depression accelerated in the U.S. with the onset of World War II in 1939. Significant numbers of airplanes, automotive equipment, and ships were powered by petroleum. The industry easily met the Allied Forces' demands for petroleum at the start of the war; however, as the conflict progressed, the U.S. and British governments feared an eventual shortage of crude oil. As a preventive measure, huge capital investments were made to develop the enormous reserves in the Persian Gulf.

AFTER WORLD WAR II: GROWTH OF THE NATURAL GAS AND PETROCHEMICAL INDUSTRIES

At the end of World War II, two events spurred tremendous growth in the natural gas industry: the advent of longline pipe and the birth of the petrochemical industry. Large quantities of natural gas had been discovered in Texas, Louisiana, and other southwestern states. However, without reliable longline pipelines, gas transportation proved challenging. New techniques for welding large pipe joints were developed that allowed gas supplies to reach the heavily populated Midwestern and eastern regions of the country. War Emergency Pipelines, initially constructed to move crude oil from Texas to the East Coast, were sold to private enterprises and converted to natural gas transportation.

The need for synthetic rubber and chemicals for explosives during World War II prompted the development of a highly specialized petrochemical industry. With readily available feedstock, petrochemical plants flourished in tandem with broader industry growth. By the 1960s, this specialized industry segment and the range of petroleum-derived products offered to consumers grew considerably.

THE 1950s AND 1960s: IMPORTED OIL AND THE FORMATION OF OPEC

During the 1950s and 1960s, there was ample world oil production. Prices remained stable at an average of $3.00 per barrel. However, the U.S. began to rely more heavily on imported crude oil and refined products. In 1950, 10 percent of the oil used in the United States was supplied by imported oil and refined products; by 1970, imported products represented 23 percent of supplies.

In 1960, a world oil cartel, the Organization of Petroleum Exporting Countries (OPEC), was formed by Saudi Arabia, Kuwait, Iran, Iraq, and Venezuela. Later, eight other countries joined OPEC: the United Arab Emirates and Qatar from the Middle East;

the African countries of Algeria, Gabon, Libya, and Nigeria; Indonesia; and Ecuador. (Ecuador withdrew from the cartel in late 1992.) By 1973, OPEC members produced 80 percent of the world oil exports and member countries began to nationalize oil production within their borders.

THE 1970s: EMBARGO AND PRICE CONTROLS

Beginning in October 1973, OPEC members cut off all oil exports to the U.S. This action was in response to the U.S.-proposed $2.2 billion Israeli military aid package. Israel had suffered recent surprise attacks from Egypt and Syria. Saudi Arabian oil prices rose from $1.80 per barrel in 1971 to $11.65 in December 1973. World crude oil prices slowly increased until the 1979 Iranian Revolution caused prices to escalate rapidly again and peak at $42 per barrel for some U.S. crude oil.

Because of the 1973 embargo, a large portion of U.S. oil imports was cut-off for several months. In response, the federal government created the Federal Energy Administration (predecessor to the U.S. Department of Energy) in 1973 with the power to control prices of crude oil.

Price regulations were complex: a two-tier oil pricing structure was established with a low price for "old" or "lower-tier oil" and a higher price for "new" or "upper-tier oil." Lower-tier oil generally came from properties that were producing prior to 1973, while upper-tier oil came from properties that began producing after 1972. Producers often had both kinds of properties and therefore sold some oil at less than half the price of other oil of the same quality. By 1979, the U.S. allowed free market prices for U.S. oil from newly drilled properties or properties producing less than 10 barrels per day per well.

The Strategic Petroleum Reserve (SPR) was officially established in December 1975 by President Gerald Ford. The first crude oil was delivered to the SPR in July 1977, and was stored at the West Hackberry site near Lake Charles, Louisiana. Other major storage sites include Bryan Mound and Big Hill in Texas and Bayou Choctaw, the St. James Terminal, in Louisiana. Total storage capacity of the SPR is 700 million barrels, although there are plans to expand this to one billion barrels.

Foreign oil continued to be imported (at prices exceeding domestic oil prices) to meet the growth in domestic demand. By 1977, approximately 47 percent of the country's needs were met by imported oil.

ALASKAN NORTH SLOPE OIL

Prudhoe Bay, the largest U.S. oil field, was discovered in 1968 on the North Slope of Alaska bordering the Arctic Ocean. A year later, the giant Kuparuk field adjacent to Prudhoe Bay was discovered. Prior to the Prudhoe Bay discovery by Atlantic Richfield Company (ARCO), seven very expensive, but unsuccessful, **exploratory wells** had been drilled in the area. Even after discovery, development of the reservoir was stalled until the 1973 Arab oil embargo prompted Congress to allow construction of the Trans Alaska Pipeline System (or TAPS). Finally in 1977, Prudhoe Bay and Kuparuk crude oils were produced and marketed.

The North Slope fields are immense with estimated ultimate oil production of 15.8 billion barrels. However, the 32 trillion cubic feet (Tcf) of recoverable natural gas reserves from these fields cannot yet be transported economically to the lower 48 states. Advances in converting gas to liquids (GTL) offer enhanced prospects for transportation and marketing. Alternatively, the gas may be shipped as LNG to Asia's Pacific Rim in the future.

THE 1980s: BOOM AND BUST

Global market factors, coupled with U.S. regulatory actions, set the stage for a U.S. petroleum industry boom in 1981-1982, which culminated in a bust by the decade's end.

- World oil price increases in 1973 and 1979 improved exploration economics and created an expectation of substantial price increases in the future.

- Expropriations of U.S. interests in Libya and elsewhere in the 1970s encouraged U.S. companies to explore within domestic borders.

- The Natural Gas Policy Act of 1978 created incentive pricing mechanisms to stimulate the discovery and development of domestic natural gas reserves.

- U.S. price controls on crude oil were removed in 1981, which gave producers additional cash to reinvest.

- In 1981, U.S. tax laws reduced the highest individual income tax rate from 70 percent to 50 percent, and reduced windfall profit taxes on new oil fields.

Consequently, in 1981 and 1982 U.S. individuals invested billions of tax-advantaged dollars in limited partnerships for petroleum exploration and production.

All of these factors brought about a U.S. drilling boom—a total of $65 billion was spent in 1984 on exploration and production activities. When Saudi Arabia refused to further reduce its market share in 1986, world oil prices fell by 50 percent. With the 1986 oil price collapse, global and U.S. exploration and development activity substantially decreased, and oil prices hovered at $15 to $18 per barrel for the remainder of the 1980s.

THE 1990s AND ADVENT OF THE MODERN MARKET

The 1990s were marked by five trends:

1. Use of oil and gas futures

2. Growth in natural gas demand, production, and value in the U.S.

3. Continued restructuring of the U.S. gas industry

4. Increased focus by U.S. companies on foreign E&P investments

5. Continued success with offshore deepwater drilling and improvements in technological and operational efficiencies

Fluctuating Crude Oil Market. The early 1990s brought increased price volatility. Oil prices briefly spiked upward after Iraq's invasion of Kuwait, but quickly fell after the liberation of Kuwait.

In response to weakening demand in Asia and other factors, oil prices declined briefly in late 1998 to around $11 per barrel accompanied by fears of a prolonged price decline. Several major producing countries agreed to production cuts in early 1999 and oil prices more than doubled.

The new millennium brought about further price fluctuations in crude oil. February 2000 marked the $30 per barrel mark for crude oil. Prices declined to the teens and twenties in 2001, but returned to the $30+ range by the end of 2002.

Price increases that few could have predicted occurred in 2004. The ongoing war in Iraq, coupled with a fierce hurricane season in the U.S., resulted in the highest crude oil prices ever experienced in the domestic market. With Iraq's production disrupted and the weather playing havoc with offshore production, crude prices climbed over the $55 per barrel mark by late October 2004. Prices continued to increase throughout 2005 and 2006, reaching nearly $71 per barrel by early June 2006, before dropping in January 2007 to around $55 per barrel. See Figure 1-1 for an example of West Texas Intermediate crude prices for the past 22 years.

Figure 1-1
Monthly F.O.B. WTI Spot Crude Prices
1986-2007

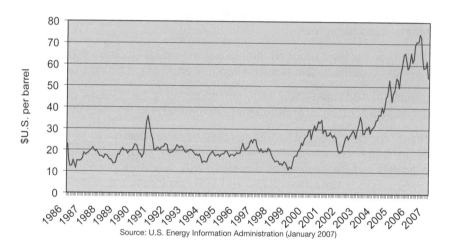

Source: U.S. Energy Information Administration (January 2007)

Futures Market Emerges. With expectations of continued price volatility, petroleum producers, processors, and end-users increased the use of commodity futures markets to hedge prices. Oil and gas futures are publicly traded standardized contracts to buy or sell specified quantities of crude oil or natural gas at set times in the future and at predetermined prices. Futures can be used to hedge or speculate on crude oil and natural gas prices as further explained in Chapter 33. Similar contracts have arisen for call (and put) options to buy (and sell) specified quantities at certain prices until agreed-upon dates.

Growth of Natural Gas Market. In 1990, natural gas began trading on the NYMEX. Worldwide demand for gas grew faster than crude oil. In 1993, for the first time in history, the value of U.S. natural gas production exceeded the value of U.S. crude oil production.

The traditional attachment of natural gas reserves to gas pipelines under long-term contracts was replaced by sales of gas at market prices to energy marketers and end-users under short term (less than one year) contracts. Average U.S. gas prices became seasonal—high in winter months when cold weather increases gas demand for space heating and relatively low in warmer summer months.

As natural gas became a more popular fuel for electricity generators, summer prices rose and year-round demand was created. Changes in federal regulation of interstate gas pipelines in the 1990s required pipelines to become providers of gas transportation and storage services only, rather than traditional first purchasers and resellers of natural gas (as further explained in Chapter 12).

Exploration Trends. In the late 1980s, the U.S. was viewed as a poor area of the world for new discoveries. It had been heavily drilled by world standards, and its most promising regions for new fields were in environmentally protected areas. However, in the 1990s, prospects were favorably reversed by technology advancements that substantially reduced exploration and development risks and costs. Expenditures for domestic petroleum exploration more than doubled from 1990 to 1999.

Offshore fields in deeper waters proved to be highly productive. As explained in Chapter 5, onshore and offshore exploration success was improved by the use of 3-D **seismic** to identify likely reservoirs. Fewer exploratory wells became necessary. The well cost per reserve volume declined with the advent of **horizontal drilling**, in which the well bore starts down vertically and bends to become a horizontal shaft through wide reservoirs.

The industry also learned to economically extract substantial natural gas and oil from non-traditional sources, including methane contained in underground coalbeds, natural gas from continuous tight sands formations, and oil recovered from mined **oil sands**, such as the vast oil sands of Alberta, Canada.

In the 1990s, U.S. petroleum companies doubled their exploration and development expenditures outside the United States. Foreign E&P opportunities emerged as a function of: (1) political restructurings within the former Soviet Union, and (2) growing sophistication and interest by countries in attracting E&P investments from around the world. By 1998, imported crude and refined products supplied over half of the U.S. demand.

Mergers. Growing prosperity for oil and gas companies was eclipsed in 1997-1998 by both the Asian economic crisis and a sharp drop in oil prices. These conditions precipitated a frenzy of cost-cutting and consolidation that led to the formation of a group of global companies known as supermajors:

- BP p.l.c. (merger of British Petroleum and Amoco)
- Exxon Mobil Corporation (merger of Exxon and Mobil)
- Royal Dutch Shell plc
- TOTAL S.A. (mergers of TOTAL, Petrofina and Elf Aquitaine)
- Chevron Corporation (merger of Chevron and Texaco)
- ConocoPhillips

Additional merger activity involving French, Spanish, Belgian, Argentine, Russian, and Ukrainian companies also marked the early 21st century. These are further indicators of the increasingly global scale of the industry's consolidated footprint.

Figure 1-2 lists the *Oil & Gas Journal's* top U.S. petroleum companies in 2005.

"Reserve replacement has been the key objective driving deals with companies looking to bring additional reserves into their company through acquisitions rather than through the drill bit."

– *Oil & Gas Deals 2006 Annual Review*, Pricewaterhouse Coopers April 2007

Figure 1-2
Oil & Gas Journal 200
Top 20 U.S. Oil & Gas Companies
As of December 31, 2005

				Worldwide		
	Market Capitalization		Liquids Reserves		Natural Gas Reserves	
Company	**Rank**	**$1,000**	**Rank**	**MM bbl**	**Rank**	**Bcf**
ExxonMobil Corp.	1	$344,490,610	2	7,813.0	1	33,355.0
Chevron Corp.	2	126,749,622	1	8,000.0	16	2,968.0
ConocoPhillips	3	82,835,598	3	6,168.0	2	19,061.0
El Paso Corp.	4	8,019,055	--	n/a	--	n/a
Devon Energy Corp.	5	27,731,112	7	895.0	5	7,296.0
Marathon Oil Corp.	6	22,360,496	8	704.0	12	3,547.0
Occidental Petroleum Corp.	7	32,121,205	4	3,478.0	19	2,127.0
Anadarko Petroleum	8	21,972,525	5	1,130.0	4	7,910.0
Apache Corp.	9	22,619,907	6	975.9	7	6,848.0
Burlington Resources	10	32,351,076	10	662.7	3	8,508.0
Hess Corp.	11	11,802,582	9	692.0	17	2,406.0
Chesapeake Energy Corp.	12	11,746,119	--	n/a	6	6,900.8
Dominion Exploration & Production	13	26,788,400	16	217.7	10	4,962.0
Kerr-McGee Corp.	14	10,558,989	12	362.0	11	3,633.0
XTO Energy Inc.	15	15,975,054	15	256.1	8	6,085.6
Noble Energy Inc.	16	7,077,670	14	290.8	15	3,091.2
Williams Cos. Inc.	17	13,285,678	--	n/a	13	3,382.0
EOG Resources	18	17,760,980	--	n/a	9	5,557.4
Pioneer Natural Resources Co.	19	6,592,725	11	429.0	14	3,346.1
Murphy Oil Corp.	20	10,039,261	18	182.0	--	n/a

Source: *Oil & Gas Journal*, Vol. 104.33, September 4, 2006.

INTO THE FUTURE

Industry leaders are pushing for rapid development of alternative fuels using existing and emerging technologies. Fuel cells could potentially replace internal combustion engines in automobiles, and such a change would rely on hydrogen-based fuels. Gasoline is a ready source of hydrogen and has an accessible distribution network (gas stations) in place.

According to the U.S. Department of Energy, "the petroleum business has transformed itself into a high-technology business." Application of new techniques has allowed the industry to produce more energy resources from increasingly remote locations with reduced environmental impact. Companies continue to seek access to huge natural gas resources that are locked in gas hydrates and are unattainable by current E&P methods. Other technologies are being studied to recover oil and gas deposits located in hot, high pressure environments deep inside the Earth.

The development of new drilling and recovery methods has been a catalyst for industry collaboration. Dozens of organizations have formed partnerships in order to share best practices and increase productivity. Companies have found competitive advantage in sharing the risks of exploration and spreading the enormous capital outlays amongst partners. For example, Chevron and its partners Devon Energy and Statoil ASA (Norway) cooperated to drill a test well in the Gulf of Mexico at a total depth of 28,175 feet. In September 2006, the group announced a highly successful production test indicating reserves between three and 15 billion barrels of oil and NGL.

Finally, many companies previously focused on fossil fuels have become major investors in renewable sources of energy. These new arenas include wind, solar, biomass, and geothermal initiatives. Although potentially useful, scientists do not expect them to be a significant part of our nation's energy mix for many years. Significant technological hurdles must be overcome to make alternative energy sources reliable, cost effective, and convenient for consumers.

• • •

1 Albert Z. Carr. *Rockefeller's Secret Weapon*. New York: McGraw-Hill Book Co., Inc., 1962.

2 J.G. McLean and R.W. Haigh. *The Growth of Integrated Oil Companies*. Boston: Harvard University Graduate School of Business Administration, 1954.

PETROLEUM ECONOMICS & ACCOUNTING DILEMMAS

Key Concepts:

- **Factors affecting oil and gas supply and demand**

- **Petroleum industry structure**

- **Financial statement challenges for petroleum accountants**

> *"As I began my business life as a bookkeeper, I learned to have great respect for figures and facts, no matter how small they were."*
>
> – **John D. Rockefeller** *(1839-1937), Founder of Standard Oil Company*

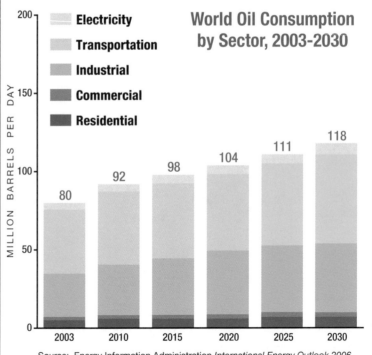

Source: Energy Information Administration *International Energy Outlook 2006*, http://www.eia.doe.gov/oiaf/ieo/figure_26.html

Transportation is a key driver of oil demand in the U.S.

HYDROCARBON SUPPLY AND DEMAND

Global supplies of petroleum appear adequate to satisfy demand for the next several decades. The U.S. Energy Information Administration predicts oil will be consumed at a rate of nearly 118 million barrels per day by 2025. Developing countries in Asia are expected to have the largest increase in demand at an average rate of three percent annually.

The American Petroleum Institute (**API**) reports that oil provides about 40 percent of the energy consumed in the U.S. With its high energy density, there are few substitutes for oil in the transportation arena. Thus, transportation is considered a key driver of the nation's oil demand.

Natural gas currently supplies about 23 percent of the energy used in the U.S. and 22 percent of energy used worldwide. In the U.S., electricity generation dominates the natural gas market. Liquefied natural gas (LNG) has garnered a critical role in worldwide supply/ demand balances, especially as: (1) North American gas reserves decline, (2) pipeline limitations continue, and (3) energy demands increase in developing countries.

Technological advancements in exploration and environmental matters have made the recovery of new reserves more economically feasible. However, the delicate balance between supply and demand has been challenged by recent conditions of price volatility, geopolitical changes, and—particularly in the U.S.—reduced downstream refining infrastructure.

Figure 2-1 summarizes the world's proved oil and gas reserves by country. More than 92 percent of the total proved oil and gas reserves are found in the 25 countries listed. Nearly 80 percent of the world's oil and gas reserves and the majority of global production occur in the top ten countries.

> *"When ranked on the basis of proved oil and gas reserves, 17 of the top 20 oil and gas companies in the world are National Oil Companies (NOCs). Nearly 75% of the oil reserves are held by OPEC members."*
>
> *— Tom Collins, PricewaterhouseCoopers*

Figure 2-1
Worldwide Oil & Gas Reserves (Estimated)
Top 25 Countries as of 1-1-2007

	Oil Reserves			Natural Gas Reserves	
Rank	Country*	(1000 bbl)	Rank	Country*	(Bcf)
1	Saudi Arabia	259,800,000	1	Russia	1,680,000
2	Canada	179,210,000	2	Iran	974,000
3	Iran	136,270,000	3	Qatar	910,500
4	Iraq	115,000,000	4	Saudi Arabia	239,500
5	Kuwait	99,000,000	5	United States	204,385
6	Abu Dhabi	92,200,000	6	Abu-Dhabi	198,500
7	Venezuela	80,012,000	7	Nigeria	181,900
8	Russia	60,000,000	8	Algeria	161,740
9	Libya	41,464,000	9	Venezuela	152,380
10	Nigeria	36,220,000	10	Iraq	112,000
11	Kazakhstan	30,000,000	11	Turkmenistan	100,000
12	United States	21,757,000	12	Kazakhstan	100,000
13	China	16,000,000	13	Indonesia	97,780
14	Qatar	15,207,000	14	Norway	82,320
15	Mexico	12,352,000	15	China	80,000
16	Algeria	12,270,000	16	Malaysia	75,000
17	Brazil	11,772,640	17	Uzbekistan	65,000
18	Angola	8,000,000	18	Egypt	58,500
19	Norway	7,849,300	19	Canada	57,946
20	Azerbaijan	7,000,000	20	Kuwait	54,500
21	India	5,624,640	21	Libya	52,650
22	Oman	5,500,000	22	Netherlands	50,000
23	Neutral Zone	5,000,000	23	Ukraine	39,000
24	Sudan	5,000,000	24	India	37,960
25	Ecuador	4,517,000	25	Australia	30,370

* OPEC members in boldface

Source: *Oil & Gas Journal*, Dec. 18, 2006, Volume: 104 Issue: 47

INDUSTRY STRUCTURE

The petroleum industry is comprised of three types of organizations: privately owned companies, investor-owned corporations, and nationalized enterprises. Each conducts business in some or all of the following operational areas:

- exploration and production
- processing and refining
- transportation
- marketing

Exploration and production (E&P) are considered upstream operations. Upstream and midstream activities are shown in Figure 2-2; downstream functions are illustrated in

Figure 2-3. The determination of whether an activity is upstream or midstream should be based on an evaluation of the specific facts and circumstances.

Companies involved only in upstream activities are referred to as **independents**, whereas **integrated companies** have both upstream and downstream operations. In the petroleum industry, the largest integrated companies are known as majors, or supermajors, as mentioned in Chapter 1.

Figure 2-2
Petroleum Production Schematic

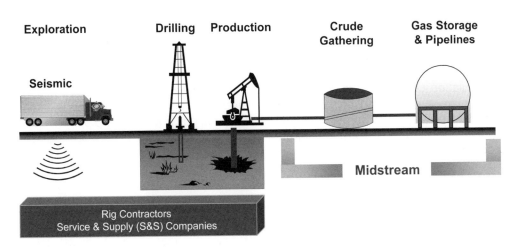

UPSTREAM

Exploration is a process of using geologic science, drilling technology, and skilled personnel to find subsurface traps that contain hydrocarbons. Production is the activity that removes oil and gas resources from reservoirs and delivers the petroleum to a transportation provider. Service and supply companies provide the specialized equipment and skills needed for exploring, drilling, testing, producing, maintaining, and reclaiming crude oil and natural gas wells.

A complex and capital intensive business, exploration and production involve the following typical processes:

- **Preliminary exploration.** Exploration of land where oil and gas reservoirs might be discovered and developed economically. (See Chapter 5)

- **Leasing of rights to find and produce.** Negotiation of **mineral rights** with surface and mineral rights owners, and structuring of the leasing agreement that may include percentages of future production. Potential identification of **joint venture** partners. (See Chapter 7)

- **Exploring leased property.** Drilling an exploratory well. May be assisted by a subcontractor who drills and/or provides drilling equipment. (See Chapter 8)

- **Evaluating and completing a well.** Testing for sufficient reserves and making subsequent expenditures to complete a well that is economically feasible.

- **Developing the property.** Drilling additional wells and installing surface equipment to create efficient and economical production. (See Chapters 8 and 11)

- **Producing the property.** Producing, surfacing, and selling separated oil and gas on an economic timetable dictated by reservoir pressure and the efficiency of equipment selected. (See Chapters 11 and 12)

- **Plugging and abandoning the property.** Plugging and sealing the well below the surface and removing surface equipment after a well reaches its economic limit. Such activities are known as **Plugging and Abandonment costs (P&A)** or **Dismantlement, Restoration, and Abandonment costs (DR&A)**. (See Chapter 20)

MIDSTREAM

Midstream processes provide a vital link between petroleum producing regions and the population centers where most end-users are located. Gathering and transmission pipelines are a major part of the midstream petroleum industry. Crude oil is typically moved by pipeline, truck, barge, or tanker, while natural gas is moved by pipeline. Refined products and natural gas are transported by various means to distribution points for consumption.

DOWNSTREAM

Downstream operations include oil refineries, petrochemical plants, fuel products distributors, and retail outlets, as well as specialty manufacturers and distributors. Thousands of products are provided downstream including: gasoline, diesel, jet fuel, heating oil, asphalt, lubricants, synthetic rubber, plastics, fertilizers, antifreeze, pesticides, natural gas, and propane.

MARKETING

Through marketing outreach, the oil and gas industry shows its public face. Advertising, customer management, product mix, and wholesale/retail strategies are employed to promote sales and brand awareness. Wholesale activities include channel choice, site management, and product expansion into convenience store and hypermarket operations.

Figure 2-3
Downstream Processing Schematic

| Crude Acquisition and Transportation | Refining | Bulk Distribution |

MARKETING

| Retailing | Final Distribution | Terminals & Wholesalers |

FACTORS IN E&P ECONOMICS

Demand for crude oil—and its value—is driven by multiple factors including world supply, product markets, refinery capacity, technological change, and the prevailing economy. To remain competitive, today's refiners need enough capacity and leading edge technology to generate operational efficiencies for withstanding fluctuating margins.

REFERENCE PRICING

Reference pricing, which ties the price of crude to market-determined or published levels, continues to dominate the international crude oil industry. A mathematical formula is used to adjust the reference price to derive a price for the specific crude oil stream being traded. The reference price should be easily obtained and reflect market conditions in the consuming area.

Two categories of reference pricing are used by the oil industry: netback and formula. First, **netback** pricing is a broad classification for crude oil pricing based on the price or value of the products derived from processing the crude oil. At the margin, crude buyers will not pay more than the value of the products, less processing and transportation costs. Netback crude oil prices are defined as the price of crude oil at the point of loading (f.o.b.) after all costs are subtracted. The general formula for calculating a netback price is:

	Gross product value
Less:	Marginal refining costs
Less:	Marginal transportation costs
Equals:	**Netback price**

The second type of reference pricing is **formula pricing**. It is any pricing methodology that ties the price of one crude oil stream to the price of one or more widely traded crude oil streams. Based on the economic theory of a single global crude oil price, all hydrocarbon streams are assumed to be from one economic pool with related prices. The value of any given crude oil stream can be calculated from another by adjusting for quality and market differences. Depending on the source price, known as the marker, a trade crude price can be calculated. The calculation for formula pricing follows:

Trade crude price = Marker crude price +/- Adjustment factor(s)

TAXATION ISSUES

Petroleum economics is influenced by taxation issues and interactions of the world's competing fiscal regimes. While considering the geologic circumstances, revenues, return on capital employed, and other production economic factors of prospective investments, companies must also consider the tax consequences.

Much depends on an oil company's tax residence and location of the investment. For example, the U.S. government has a residence-based tax system. It taxes worldwide income, and then provides foreign tax relief by means of a credit.

In order to attract foreign investment, governments must analyze their fiscal policies in relation to U.S. tax policies. These nations should assess the potential impact of any laws on U.S. oil companies, which are major participants in the global petroleum industry.

RESERVE VALUE

Petroleum exploration and production economics is based on the size and nature of oil and gas reserves in relation to oil and gas prices, i.e., reserve value. An E&P company is said to have two key assets:

1. Human capital with the ability to find (or acquire), develop, and produce oil and gas reserves profitably

2. Existing reserves and their capabilities, when produced, to generate positive cash flow

Exploration success is not measured by a success ratio (the number of producible wells versus the number of total wells drilled). This is because a ten-well program with discovery of a single large reservoir may be far more profitable than a ten-well program that discovers five marginal reservoirs.

Also, exploration success is not determined solely by the quantity of reserves found. Questions involving location, transportation, and quality play into the analysis. In many remote parts of the world, large quantities of gas reserves have been found that have relatively limited value because transportation costs to gas markets are too high for the current market. Likewise, finds of sour crude and sweet crude will yield unequal values because of higher processing costs associated with the sour crude on the downstream end.

An E&P company evaluates potential investments using sophisticated present value analyses of expected future cash flows. These tools project estimated future monthly production volumes, revenues, and production expenses per well over its economic life. From projected cash flows and investment outlays, an expected annual rate of return and other profit indicators are calculated to evaluate the investment's economic merits.

Records of historical production, revenues, and cost categories by well and by field can be instrumental in developing reasonable cash flow projections for investment decision making. Historical cost may be much greater or less than the value of reserves found. Such analysis is outlined in Chapter 31 on valuation of proved oil and gas properties.

E&P financial statement accounting recognizes the economic importance of reserves in three ways:

• Capitalized costs of properties with proved reserves (proved properties) are amortized on a **unit-of-production method** based on the ratio of volumes produced during the period to the sum of those volumes and remaining proved reserves at the end of the period. This topic is examined in Chapter 17.

• **Proved properties**' net capitalized costs are limited to certain computations of value of the underlying proved reserves as discussed in Chapters 9 and 18.

• Public companies must disclose, with audited financial statements, certain supplemental unaudited information on the **proved reserve** volumes and certain related values. These disclosures are described in Chapters 28 and 29.

Even though oil and gas reserves affect an E&P company's financial statements, the company's stock price is more closely correlated to historical and expected cash flow from current production of reserves and to the overall value of reserves than to historical earnings measured under generally accepted accounting principles (GAAP).

In this book, U.S. GAAP is the source for financial reporting of the exploration and production of petroleum. Additionally, Chapter 25 introduces accounting for international operations, and Chapters 26 and 27 address accounting for income tax reporting.

ACCOUNTING DILEMMAS

The nature of petroleum exploration and production raises numerous financial reporting issues. Some of these challenges include, but are not limited to:

- Given the modest success rates for exploratory wells, should well costs be treated as assets or expenses? Should the cost of a **dry hole** be capitalized as a cost of finding oil and gas reserves? Suppose a company drills five exploratory wells costing $1 million each, but only one well finds a reservoir worth $20 million to the company. Should the company recognize an asset for the total $5 million of cost, the $1 million cost of the successful well, the $20 million value of the productive property, or some other amount?

- The sales prices of oil and gas can fluctuate widely over time. Hence, the value of rights to produce oil and gas may fluctuate widely. Should such value fluctuations affect the amounts of the related assets presented in financial statements?

- If production declines over time and productive life varies by property, how should capitalized costs be amortized and depreciated?

- International activities have many different arrangements that give companies the right to produce oil and gas. Do these constitute oil and gas activities or are they merely services provided by the company as an agent? Do the arrangements reflect the economic ownership of reserves?

- If the oil company forms a joint venture and sells portions of the lease to its venture partners, should a gain or loss be recognized on the sale?

As discussed throughout this text, the nature, complexity, and importance of the petroleum E&P industry create an unusual and complex set of rules and practices for petroleum accounting and financial presentation.

• • •

CHAPTER

3

ORGANIZATIONAL STRUCTURE OF AN E&P COMPANY

Key Concepts:

- **Organizational structures of exploration and production companies**

- **Departmental functions in independent and integrated companies**

- **Organization of the accounting department**

- **Internal control framework**

- **Overview of related industry groups, trade associations, and key governmental agencies**

Like all enterprises, exploration and production (E&P) companies implement organizational structures to meet their needs. The structure establishes how authority is delegated and provides accountability in operations. Financial procedures, as well as the flow of paperwork, directly follow these lines of responsibility.

Petroleum accountants should become familiar with the roles and functions of various departments within an E&P company. Such information is obtained by experience and inquiry, and by reviews of organization charts and company operating manuals.

One important aspect of an organization's structure is the system of internal controls. This chapter discusses the source of internal control standards and suggests ways to assess and quantify risks.

Organizational structures of companies in the petroleum industry vary widely. Much depends on their size and diversity of activities. Oil and gas producers are classified as either independents or integrated companies. Independents are typically viewed by the public as small companies with few employees, while integrated companies are thought of as the "giants." In practice, however, several large oil companies have no refining or marketing operations, and some integrated companies are small in size.

The size of a company and its degree of integration often determine the type of structure utilized. Geographical dispersion of activities is a factor also. It makes sense that an E&P company operating in a single region would have closer managerial control from its top officials. When operations expand geographically, top management can look to regional and district managers to exert local control. The home office role becomes one of managing overall company activities. Similarly, an integrated company requires a greater degree of delegation of authority and responsibility from top management to those directly involved in its diverse operations.

SUMMARY OF KEY FUNCTIONS IN SMALLER E&P COMPANIES

Small and medium-sized oil and gas companies have much in common, especially at the executive level. Four distinct activities are represented in almost all producers:

- Exploration
- Marketing
- Drilling and production
- Administration

The organization chart in Figure 3-1 reflects this basic structure. (It should be noted that some companies have recently modified their approach by creating multidisciplinary teams of geologists, petroleum engineers, accountants, and other specialists to manage assigned fields or geographic areas of operations.)

Typically, the president of a small oil and gas company is a petroleum engineer, geologist, or geophysicist who not only serves as CEO, but may also direct the exploration, development, or production activities. Small company CEO's may negotiate joint venture agreements, major property acquisitions and divestitures, and financing arrangements.

The exploration department has the job of locating and acquiring oil and gas reserves. This includes obtaining mineral properties and conducting **geological and geophysical (G&G)** exploration, either through the use of company-owned equipment and personnel, or through contracts with exploration support companies. Many E&P companies, even very small ones, have one or more geologists on staff; most companies also hire outside professionals or organizations to provide G&G services.

The drilling and production department (or petroleum engineering department) is responsible for exploratory drilling, development drilling, **enhanced recovery** operations, and field production.

Arranging the sales of produced oil and gas is the role of the marketing division. U.S. crude oil is usually sold near the well site. Natural gas is frequently sold to large gas consumers and utilities located far from the lease. Under this arrangement, gas pipelines provide transportation services.

Various general office functions and stakeholder relations are handled by the administration department. It oversees human resources, finance, accounting, tax compliance, management information systems, public relations, and legal services. The vice president of administration may serve as the vice president of finance and chief financial officer (CFO). Some companies break these functions into separate departments, such as a finance department headed by the CFO, and have sub-departments for treasury, accounting, and taxation.

Figure 3-1
Basic Structure of an Independent Oil Company

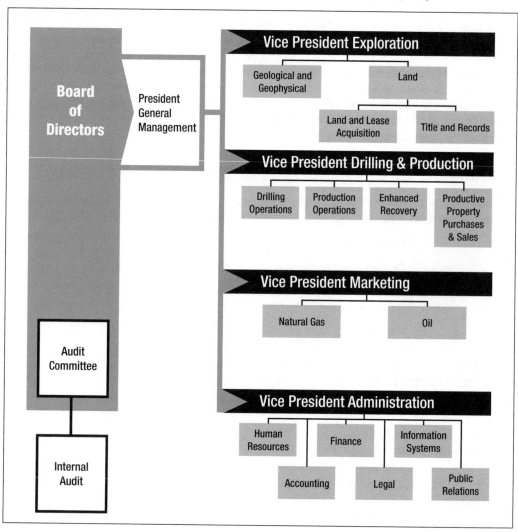

EXPLORATION DEPARTMENT

The exploration department is responsible for locating and acquiring properties that may contain oil and gas, conducting G&G studies, and in some cases, supervising the drilling of exploratory wells. Work of the exploration department is delegated to several sections as demonstrated in Figure 3-1. A brief description of the roles of each section follows.

Geological and geophysical (G&G). The G&G division accumulates and analyzes geological and geophysical information that helps to decide:

- If leases should be obtained in an **area of interest**, and

- Whether exploratory wells should be drilled and in which **locations**.

Land. Land departments have two major functions: (1) acquiring mineral properties, and (2) maintaining records of properties owned. As shown in Figure 3-1, the work is carried out by two divisions—the land and lease acquisition section and the title and records section.

The manager over the land department is called a landman. This term refers to a person who is responsible for identifying and locating mineral rights owners and negotiating leases. Landman also refers to an independent lease broker. Land departments may use independent lease brokers familiar with a particular state or region to represent the company in negotiations with owners of mineral and surface rights and to check local title records.

The land and lease acquisition section is responsible for contacting landowners and other mineral rights owners to obtain leases or other mineral rights. It advises exploration department managers on leasing activities and secures pooling and unitization agreements with lessees of properties adjoining the company's leases. The title and records section checks all new leases for legal propriety, maintains a complete file for all properties, and ensures the timely payment of all lease rentals as authorized.

DRILLING AND PRODUCTION DEPARTMENT

The overall objective of the drilling and production department is to manage the company's wells and production operations in a safe manner. This group seeks to maximize production value while complying with applicable government regulations. It is often called the petroleum engineering department, and its management and core personnel are typically petroleum engineers.

Larger companies may group petroleum engineers into categories such as exploitation engineers, reservoir engineers, and production engineers:

- Exploitation engineers address how to best exploit a field via drilling and enhanced recovery methods. They prepare or review justifications for drilling expenditures and advise on technical phases of exploitation, **completion**, fluid recovery, and remedial work.

- Reservoir engineers study oil and gas reservoir performance, calculate recovery and profitability, and devise means of increasing ultimate recovery. Internal reports of estimated reserves by well, field, region, and company are prepared. They also work with independent engineering firms that produce independent reports of the company's reserves.

- Production engineers are concerned with the everyday management of producing fields, including drilling, well completion, production handling and treatment, and equipment selection and design.

Drilling operations. In most cases, an E&P company contracts its drilling operations to outside drilling contractors rather than maintaining its own equipment. It is not unusual, however, for the owners of a producing company to organize and operate a drilling company independent of the producing company. In this case, the drilling superintendent is responsible for all drilling activities including the oversight of rigs, tools, and equipment. Drilling operations are discussed at length in Chapter 8.

Production operations. A typical oil and gas producing company has a production foreman or manager for each field. There are also **pumpers** or **gaugers** who measure and control production (discussed in Chapter 11). Maintenance, infrequent repairs, and mechanical tasks are often carried out by specialist subcontractors.

Enhanced recovery. Some companies distinguish between the routine operation of fields where normal reservoir pressure drives oil and gas into the wells, and those that supplement reservoir pressure to increase production. Enhanced recovery includes **secondary recovery** methods, such as **water flooding**, and **tertiary recovery** methods, such as steam flooding. Because of their technical natures and the extremely high costs involved, secondary and tertiary projects require special attention and supervision.

Productive property purchases and sales. A separate department often handles the buying and selling of **property** with proved reserves (proved property). In some cases, the duties may be assigned to the production department since petroleum engineers are key to evaluating potential acquisitions and sales of proved property.

Other department functions. Many support activities are necessary to efficiently operate an oil or gas company. For example, materials needed in the field are warehoused and trucks and other forms of transportation must be available. Field clerks are assigned to carry out routine functions such as correspondence and payroll. Although supervised by a production manager, field clerks are frequently under the functional supervision of the administrative department of the company.

MARKETING DEPARTMENT

Depending on the organization and size of the company, oil and gas are sold through one or more marketing departments or subsidiaries. Close coordination is required between marketing, production, and administration departments.

Oil marketing. Oil marketing is in a mature stage, especially when compared with natural gas sales. For over a decade, no structural changes have been made in the way oil marketing is done. Generally, oil is marketed under 30-day contracts and sold at the lease site at wellhead prices posted (publicized) by the oil purchaser or a major oil company.

Natural gas marketing. Many changes have occurred in recent years in how natural gas is sold. Historically, natural gas and **casinghead gas** (gas produced along with crude oil) were marketed to pipeline companies, which then sold the gas to others. Today gas is marketed by producers, large and small, to many types of gas customers (other than residential). Chapter 12 describes in more detail how both oil and gas are marketed and outlines the significant changes in these processes.

ADMINISTRATIVE DEPARTMENT

In an independent oil and gas company, the administrative department encompasses a variety of activities and may consist of a number of divisions, sections, or offices as shown in Figure 3-1. The administrative structure of an E&P company differs little from those found in other types of businesses. Accounting functions related to oil and gas companies are discussed briefly in the next section (see Figure 3-2).

ORGANIZATION OF THE ACCOUNTING FUNCTION

Figure 3-2
Organization of the Accounting Function in an Independent Company

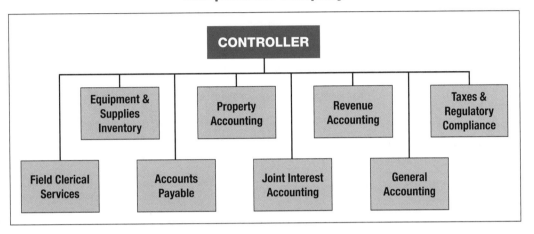

FIELD CLERICAL SERVICES

- Trains and supervises clerical personnel assigned to field operations
- Develops systems, forms, and procedures for field accounting and reporting

EQUIPMENT AND SUPPLIES INVENTORY

- Maintains equipment and supply inventory records
- Prices and records warehouse receipts, issues, and field transfers
- Oversees physical inventory taking
- Prepares reports on equipment and supplies inventory

ACCOUNTS PAYABLE

- Maintains accounts payable records
- Prepares vouchers for disbursements
- Distributes **royalty payments**
- Maintains corporate-delegated limits of authority and verifies that disbursements are made within those limits

PROPERTY ACCOUNTING

- Maintains subsidiary records for:
    - Unproved properties
    - Proved properties
    - Work in progress
    - Lease and well equipment
    - Field service units

- Accounts for property and equipment acquisition, reclassification, amortization, impairment, retirement, and sale
- Compares actual expenditures of work in progress to authorized amounts

JOINT INTEREST ACCOUNTING

- Maintains files related to all joint operations
- Prepares billings to joint owners
- Reviews all billings from joint owners
- Prepares statements for jointly operated properties
- Prepares payout status reports pursuant to farmin and **farmout** agreements
- Arranges or conducts joint interest audits of billings and revenue distributions from joint venture operations
- Responds, on behalf of the company, to joint interest audits by other joint interest owners

REVENUE ACCOUNTING

- Accounts for volumes sold and establishes or verifies prices reflected in revenues received
- Maintains oil and gas revenue records for each property
- Maintains records related to properties for purposes of regulatory compliance and production taxes
- Computes production taxes
- Maintains Division of Interests (DOI) master files with guidance from the land department as to revenue allocations among the company, royalty owners, and others
- Computes amounts due to royalty owners and joint interest owners and prepares related reports
- Invoices purchasers for sales of natural gas
- Maintains ledgers of undistributed royalty payments for owners with unsigned **division orders**, owners whose interests are suspended because of estate issues, and other undistributed **production payments**
- Prepares revenue accruals

GENERAL ACCOUNTING

- Maintains the voucher register, cash receipts and disbursement records, and general ledger
- Prepares financial statements and other special reports
- Assembles budget information; prepares budgets and budget reports

TAXES AND REGULATORY COMPLIANCE

- Prepares required federal, state, county, and local tax returns for income taxes, production taxes, property taxes, and employment taxes

- Prepares other regulatory reports as required

- Addresses allowable options for minimizing taxes

INFORMATION SYSTEMS

E&P information and accounting systems vary in the type of technology utilized. System platforms may be mainframe, mid-size, or desktop computers, and several third-party software packages are available.

An E&P information system typically employs a master file of divisions of interests known as a DOI file. This file reflects how revenues and costs are to be shared for each well or other accounting unit for a designated time period, usually several months or years. The land department is typically responsible for maintaining the accuracy and completeness of the DOI file. Departments that use the file include property, payables, revenue, and joint operations accounting.

A revenue information system must also encompass a means of distributing the incoming sales proceeds to appropriate owners, such as the company, joint venture partners, royalty owners, and **production taxing** authorities. The purchasing component of the system will include functions for distributing costs to appropriate parties, such as the company and joint venture partners. Thus, the revenue system must account for incoming cash as well as outgoing distributions of such revenue, and the purchasing system must account for the outgoing cash for purchases and the billing to other parties for their rightful shares of such costs.

The E&P information system and its chart of accounts are complicated by the need to account for:

- Revenue and cost DOI at a well or smaller level

- Tax accounting that varies from financial reporting

- Each well and each field's gross revenues and cost activity for management review and their net revenues and costs to the company for external reporting

An E&P company chart of accounts is extensive and will be addressed in the next chapter.

"The typical IT expenditure for a small E&P company is $1 million - with 49% on exploration IT, 23% on production and 28% on administrative activities.... A very large E&P company would typically commit to $37 million of IT expenditure per annum - split 36% on exploration, 32% on production and 32% on administration."*

*– **David Rose** "Trends in Information Technology Costs and Investment Levels in the Oil Industry," AUPEC Limited, http://www.iaee.org/documents/a02rose.pdf*

GENERAL ACCOUNTING STRUCTURE OF AN INTEGRATED COMPANY

The organizational structure for an integrated oil company's accounting department includes several corporate accounting sections as well as functional accounting sections as shown in Figure 3-3.

Figure 3-3
Organization of Accounting Functions in an Integrated Company

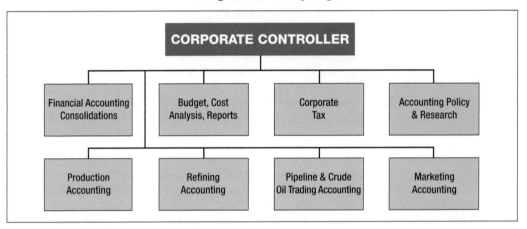

Organization of accounting activities in the production division is similar to that of an independent producing company. Figure 3-4 shows a modified organization chart of the accounting department in the production division of an integrated company.

Figure 3-4
Organization Chart of the Accounting Function in the Production Division of a Large Integrated Company

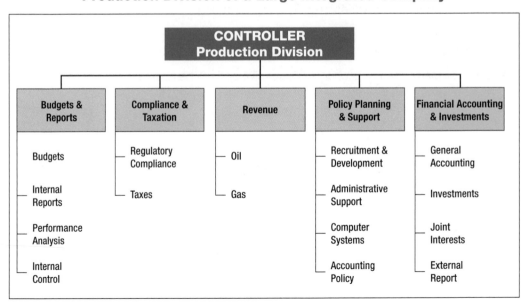

INTERNAL CONTROL FRAMEWORK

As for many enterprises, internal controls are important to an E&P company. A report called the *Internal Control—Integrated Framework* (commissioned by the Committee of Sponsoring Organizations of the Treadway Commission) documented the internal control framework standard to be followed. Known as the COSO Report[1], it defined internal control as:

> ...a process, effected by an entity's board of directors, management and other personnel, designed to provide reasonable assurance regarding the achievement of objectives in the following categories:
>
> - Effectiveness and efficiency of operations,
>
> - Reliability of financial reporting, and
>
> - Compliance with applicable laws and regulations.

The report made it clear that internal control is not a back-room function relegated to internal auditors. Instead, it should be a process that involves employees at every level of the organization. The controls play a role in meeting a company's overall objectives, such as increased profitability from greater efficiencies.

The framework addresses three hazards if internal control objectives are lacking:

- Possible material misstatement(s) of financial statements

- Possible reduction(s) in the effectiveness and efficiency of operations

- Possible violation(s) of laws and regulations

The following five components of internal control are outlined in the COSO report:

1. The control environment

2. Risk assessment

3. Control activities

4. Information and communication

5. Monitoring

Control environment. The control environment sets the tone for an organization and influences the control consciousness of its people. It is the foundation for all other components of internal control because it provides discipline and structure. Control environment factors include the integrity, ethical values, and competence of the entity's people; management's philosophy and operating style; the way management assigns authority and responsibility, and organizes and develops its people; and the attention and direction provided by the board of directors.

Risk assessment. Risk assessment is the identification and analysis of current and future risks faced by an organization. Management must identify and analyze risks, quantify them, and project their likelihoods and possible consequences. How much risk is considered tolerable and at what costs are decisions to be made at the executive level.

The following example addresses a company's risk tolerance for fluctuations in oil prices. With oil selling for $60 per barrel, the management group of ABC Petroleum expects prices to rise. However, the company recognizes it could not survive if prices fell below $20 and the two-year outlook remained in that range. Despite an expectation of rising prices, management may decide to use derivatives (discussed in Chapter 33) to hedge against falling oil prices. The derivatives' cost may be in the form of cash (via purchase of a put option) or in foregoing gains from price increases (via derivative instruments that create a price floor and a price ceiling).

Managers of E&P companies should set clear objectives and understand the risks in their areas. In too many cases, risk evaluations are done informally and controls are assumed to be adequate. One tool designed to help document organizational risks is a risk matrix. It lists major business components or processes across the top axis and related major risks down the left side. Once the risks are identified within the matrix, they can be evaluated as to the probability of occurrence and potential impact on the company.

Control activities. Control policies and procedures to minimize identified risks are established and executed in accordance with management's objectives.

Information and communication. Information and communication systems must be implemented by the company to support its risk management activities.

Monitoring. Internal control processes should be monitored and modified as necessary to allow the internal controls to respond to a changing environment.

SARBANES-OXLEY ACT: SECTION 404

The Sarbanes-Oxley Act, also known as the Public Company Accounting Reform and Investor Protection Act of 2002 (the Act), was enacted in July 2002 largely in response to major corporate and accounting scandals involving several prominent companies in the U.S. These scandals resulted in an unprecedented lack of confidence in the financial markets and a loss of public trust in corporate accounting and reporting practices. The Act has brought about the most extensive reform the U.S. financial markets have seen since the Securities Act of 1933 and the Securities Exchange Act of 1934.

The Act requires public companies to develop new practices involving corporate governance and financial reporting with the objective of restoring public trust in the capital markets. One of the most challenging aspects of the law relates to corporate responsibility for internal controls. Entitled *Management's Assessment of Internal Controls*, Section 404 of the Act requires most public companies and their auditors to report annually on the effectiveness of the company's internal control over financial reporting. As a result of the Act, regulators approved standards to provide guidance to companies and their auditors.

The impact of the Act has been felt throughout the financial markets; every industry and service sector has been—and will continue to be—impacted, including the E&P industry.

The SEC requires management to base its evaluation of the company's internal control over financial reporting on a suitable recognized control framework. The majority of public companies required to follow Section 404 used the criteria established in the *Internal Control—Integrated Framework* document previously described in this chapter.

Since these requirements became effective, regulators have closely monitored the companies and their auditors' implementation of the standards. Recently, the regulators proposed to amend the standards for auditors and provide guidance to management on evaluating internal control. These proposals were recently approved in final form.

OUTSIDE PROFESSIONAL ORGANIZATIONS

As an E&P company conducts business, it interacts with a variety of outside parties. Some provide needed technical services such as drilling rig and supply companies. Certain governmental entities also get involved as they seek to regulate aspects of the industry. Trade organizations provide membership benefits such as shared information and training opportunities. The following list – not intended to be comprehensive – identifies several organizations E&P management and personnel may encounter.

Council of Petroleum Accountants Societies   www.copas.org

The Council of Petroleum Accountants Societies, known as **COPAS**, develops educational materials and standardized forms that facilitate the practice of petroleum accounting. Guidelines and forms are issued as COPAS model form accounting procedure exhibits. Virtually every U.S. E&P joint venture **operating agreement** includes a completed COPAS Exhibit that sets forth certain billing, accounting, and auditing procedures and rights for joint venture partners. COPAS also issues interpretations of bulletins and publishes the *COPAS Accounts* newsletter. Twenty-three chapters of COPAS are active in major oil and gas producing areas of the United States. The organization's national office is located in Denver, Colorado.

American Association of Professional Landmen   www.landman.org

Petroleum accountants should be aware that the American Association of Professional Landmen (**AAPL**) develops various model industry forms, including the AAPL Form 610 for operating agreements shown in CD Reference Exhibit E.

The American Petroleum Institute   www.api.org

The American Petroleum Institute (API) fosters cooperation between industry and government agencies. A large and influential organization, it is involved in many research projects that collect data for the industry. Training films and publications are developed by API.

The Independent Petroleum Association of America   www.ipaa.org

The Independent Petroleum Association of America (**IPAA**) is the national trade association for independent producers. It takes an active part, on behalf of its members, in lobbying efforts aimed at legislative and regulatory bodies. The IPAA publishes a variety of economic and statistical information about the domestic E&P industry, including *The Oil and Gas Producing Industry in Your State*.

Society of Petroleum Engineers   www.spe.org

The Society of Petroleum Engineers (SPE), headquartered in Richardson, Texas, is an international technical and professional association of more than 50,000 members. It publishes the monthly *Journal of Petroleum Technology* (JPT). In March 2007 SPE, in conjunction with the World Petroleum Council, the American Association of Petroleum Geologists, and the Society of Petroleum Evaluation Engineers, issued a *Petroleum Resources Management System*, which replaced joint industry guidelines issued in 1997, 2000, and 2001. See Chapter 16 for additional details.

Society of Petroleum Evaluation Engineers   www.spee.org

The Society of Petroleum Evaluation Engineers (SPEE), based in Houston, Texas, consists of a few hundred experienced reservoir evaluation petroleum engineers. Each spring SPEE conducts a survey of fair market value parameters for oil and gas producing properties. SPEE and SPE jointly developed the 1987 *Definitions for Oil and Gas Reserves*, and SPEE developed the 1988 *Guidelines for Application of the Definitions for Oil and Gas Reserves*.

National Petroleum Council   www.npc.org

The National Petroleum Council (NPC) is a group of experienced industry executives, many currently employed by petroleum companies, which advises and provides studies for the U.S. Department of Energy (DOE) on petroleum issues.

Regional Trade Associations

Well-known regional associations include:

- California Independent Producers Association (CIPA)
- Independent Petroleum Association of Mountain States (IPAMS) based in Denver
- Mid-Continent Oil & Gas Association based in Washington D.C.
- Texas Independent Producers and Royalty Owners Association (TIPRO)
- Western States Petroleum Association (WSPA) based in California

Energy Information Administration and U.S. Department of Energy

The Energy Information Administration (EIA) is a division of the DOE. The agency monitors the petroleum industry and provides statistical histories, forecasts, and analyses of various domestic and international petroleum industry activities.

U.S. Department of Interior Minerals Management Service

The Minerals Management Service (MMS) oversees the receipt of royalties for oil and gas produced on federal lands and in federal offshore areas. It also conducts audits of the reports and royalties from E&P companies.

Various State Oil and Gas Conservation Commissions

Each state with petroleum production typically has an agency that issues permits for proposed oil and gas wells and also monitors drilling and production. Well operators may be required to file monthly reports with the state commission regarding each well's production of oil, gas, and water. An example of this in the state of Texas is the agency known as the Railroad Commission of Texas.

• • •

1 COSO organizations included the American Institute of Certified Public Accountants, American Accounting Association, Financial Executives Institute, Institute of Internal Auditors, and Institute of Management Accountants.

ACCOUNTING PRINCIPLES FOR OIL AND GAS PRODUCING ACTIVITIES

Key Concepts:

- **Regulatory history of successful efforts and full cost accounting methods**

- **Accounting treatment of acquisition, exploration, development, and production costs**

- **Identification of accounts used in successful efforts and full cost accounting**

- **Overview of income tax accounting**

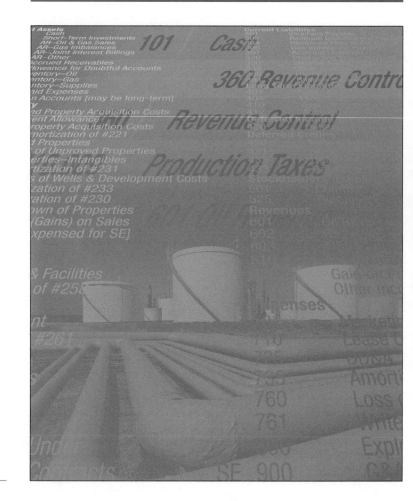

U.S. companies follow one of two methods of financial accounting for petroleum E&P activities: **successful efforts** or **full cost**. The methods are significantly different in how the costs are accounted for in acquiring, exploring, and developing oil and gas properties.

The successful efforts method capitalizes costs only when results are positive, i.e., minerals are found. Thus, the costs of exploratory dry holes, most geological and geophysical (G&G) costs, **delay rentals**, and other property-carrying costs are charged to expense in the year incurred. Costs of successful exploratory wells and all development costs are capitalized. Net unamortized capitalized costs are amortized using unit-of-production calculations where:

1. property acquisition costs are amortized over proved reserves, and

2. property development costs are amortized over **proved developed reserves**.

Amortization is computed by the lease (or property) or by certain aggregations of properties as large as a field.

Under the full cost method, all property acquisition, exploration, and development costs, even dry hole costs, are capitalized as fixed assets. These costs are amortized on a country-by-country basis using a unit-of-production method, which is based on volumes produced and remaining proved reserves. The net unamortized capitalized costs of oil and gas properties minus related deferred income taxes may not exceed a ceiling consisting primarily of a computed present value of projected future cash flows, after income taxes, from the proved reserves.

To illustrate the different financial outcomes of the two methods, assume a company drills five exploratory wells for $1 million each and only one results in proved reserves. Successful efforts accounting recognizes a $1 million asset, whereas full cost realizes a $5 million asset. (In addition, it is important for investors, analysts, and other interested parties to know the true value of proved reserves. This amount could be substantially different from capitalized historical costs.)

HISTORY OF PETROLEUM ACCOUNTING

Generally, companies follow either the successful efforts method or the full cost method of accounting. Both of these methods are part of the GAAP hierarchy, and S-X Rule 4-10 is the only published comprehensive standard for full cost accounting.

Successful efforts accounting in various forms has been used for over 65 years. Full cost accounting began to be applied in the 1950s. Currently, 70 percent of the 20 largest publicly traded U.S. petroleum companies use successful efforts. Of the next 100 largest companies, about half of them use successful efforts and half use full cost.[1]

By the mid-1960s, accountants and analysts were concerned about the diverse accounting methods in use by oil and gas producers. Not only were full cost and successful efforts methods utilized, but many variations in applying them had evolved. It became difficult to compare financial statements of oil and gas companies because of these inconsistencies. The AICPA's 1969 *Accounting Research Study No. 11* (ARS 11) suggested elimination of the full cost method of accounting and recommended successful efforts as the standard.

The next major event was the Arab oil embargo of 1973. It generated intense public and Congressional interest culminating in the Energy Policy and Conservation Act of 1975 (EPCA). EPCA called for establishing a national energy database which included financial information. Accounting practices were to be developed for use by all oil and gas producers in reports to the Department of Energy. Responsibility for compiling the practices was given to the Securities and Exchange Commission (SEC). However, the SEC was allowed to delegate the task to the Financial Accounting Standards Board (**FASB**)—as long as the final work product was acceptable to the SEC.

In December 1977, the FASB issued its Statement of Financial Accounting Standards No. 19, *Financial Accounting and Reporting for Oil and Gas Producing Companies* (FAS 19). It prescribed a version of the successful efforts method of accounting for determining capitalized costs, **conveyances** of **mineral interests**, comprehensive deferred income tax allocations, and specific audited disclosures of proved reserves of oil and gas and certain costs related to mineral activities. FAS 19 was to go into effect for fiscal years beginning after December 15, 1978.

FAS 19 was harshly criticized at SEC hearings in March and April 1978, primarily by independent producers. By August 1978, the SEC issued its *Accounting Series Release No. 253* that concluded successful efforts and full cost accounting did not provide meaningful financial statements because neither method: (1) recognized the value of the oil and gas reserves discovered, or (2) reflected the discovery activity's true income, i.e., reserve value added less related discovery costs. Within this document, the SEC proposed a new, revolutionary method to be explored known as reserve recognition accounting (RRA).

RRA would assign a value (computed under rather arbitrary rules) to proved oil and gas reserves and reflect the changes in value to these reserves in earnings as the changes occurred. Until the RRA method and standards for valuing new reserves could be developed, the SEC would allow publicly held companies and other SEC registrants to use either the FAS 19 successful efforts method or a full cost method prescribed by the SEC for audited primary financial statements. Statements based on RRA were required to be included as supplemental information.

In December 1978, the SEC issued *Accounting Series Releases 257* and *258* on rules for successful efforts and full cost accounting, respectively. Successful efforts rules were essentially the same as those in FAS 19.

Appendix 1 in this book contains the SEC rules referred to as Reg. S-X Rule 4-10.[2] The SEC amended Reg. S-X Rule 4-10 in May 1996 to delete specific successful efforts rules [i.e., Rule 4-10(b) through (h)], and add a new Rule 4-10(b) that requires those reporting entities using the successful efforts method to comply with FAS 19, as amended. The amended FAS 19 is reflected in Appendix 2, which contains the FASB Current Text, section Oi5, entitled *Oil and Gas Producing Activities* (Oi5).

Following the SEC's action to allow publicly held companies to use either the full cost or successful efforts method of accounting, the FASB issued Statement of Financial Accounting Standards No. 25 (FAS 25) in February 1979. Most of the accounting provisions of FAS 19 were suspended for an indefinite period. FAS 25 (which applies to public and private companies) made FAS 19 successful efforts method preferable, but not mandatory. Certain provisions of FAS 19 relating to deferred income taxes, mineral property conveyances, and disclosure requirements were substantially retained and became effective.

FAS 25 allowed the proved reserve disclosures to be made apart from the financial statements and thus would be unaudited information. In 1979 and again in 1980, the SEC postponed its requirement that reserve information be audited. Finally, a year later the SEC dropped the audit requirement.

In February 1981, the SEC announced that RRA had shortcomings that made it inappropriate for adoption as the primary basis of accounting. At the same time, the SEC announced that the FASB would undertake a project to develop supplemental disclosure requirements for oil and gas companies. In November 1982, FAS 69 spelled out the disclosure rules, which were adopted the next month by the SEC with only minor revisions. The rules did not include an earnings summary as required under RRA, but did include unaudited disclosures of the present value (based on specified assumptions) of future cash flows from production of proved reserves.

Controversy over the two accounting methods flared up again briefly in 1986 when the staff of the Chief Accountant's Office of the SEC recommended that the full cost method be eliminated for use by publicly held companies. Commission members rejected the proposal and both methods continue to be acceptable for financial accounting and reporting; however, there is ongoing debate within the industry as to which method is preferable.

In March 1995, the FASB issued FAS 121 on accounting for the impairment of long-lived assets. These rules were superceded by the publication in October 2001 of FAS 144, *Accounting for the Impairment of Long-Lived Assets* (discussed in Chapter 18). A long-lived asset is deemed impaired if the associated expected future cash flows (undiscounted and without interest or income taxes) are less than the asset's net book value. A loss on impairment is recognized by reducing the impaired asset's net book value to fair market value.

FAS 144 addresses impairment of proved properties under successful efforts accounting, but not under full cost. Reg. S-X Rule 4-10 is unchanged in its mandate that full cost companies meet a specific, and generally more conservative, impairment test. FAS 144 does not change FAS 19 impairment rules for unproved properties.

Prior to FAS 144 and FAS 121, informal SEC staff interpretations of generally accepted accounting principles (GAAP) held that companies using successful efforts accounting should have an impairment accounting policy and that the policy be no more liberal than limiting the oil and gas properties' aggregate net book value (less related deferred income taxes) to projected, related, undiscounted future cash flows after income taxes.

Oi5 in Appendix 2 contains the current applicable rules found in FAS 19, 25, 69, 95, 109, and 144 and in FASB Interpretation No. 36. Reg. S-X Rule 4-10 was amended in 1996 to delete its successful efforts accounting rules (i.e., old subsections (b) through (h) based on FAS 19) and adopt, by reference in new subsection (b), the successful efforts accounting rules in Oi5. Special rules for full cost accounting are found in Reg. S-X Rule 4-10's current subsection (c) reprinted in Appendix 1. Additional guidance is found in: (1) SEC Regulation S-K and SEC Financial Reporting Releases, for which excerpts are provided at the end of Appendix 1, and (2) the SEC Staff Accounting Bulletins, Topic 12, found in CD Reference Exhibit A.

Major provisions of successful efforts and full cost methods adopted by the SEC are summarized in the following pages.

> *According* to SEC filings from 2006, 47 percent of the top 100 oil and gas companies in the U.S. use the full cost method of accounting.

CLASSIFICATION OF COSTS INCURRED

The distinguishing features of successful efforts and full cost methods center around which costs are to be capitalized and how to properly amortize them. Reg. S-X Rule 4-10 classifies costs incurred in oil and gas producing activities into four categories:

- **Property acquisition costs**
- **Exploration costs**
- **Development costs**
- **Production costs**

Successful efforts and full cost accounting for each activity are summarized in Figures 4-1 and 4-2. Support facilities and equipment, such as trucks, field service units, warehouses, camp facilities, and other facilities, may serve more than one of the four activities. Facilities and equipment costs are capitalized, and related depreciation and operating costs are allocated to those functions. **Depreciation** of the capitalized facilities and equipment costs, as well as related operating expenses, is allocated as costs of acquisition, exploration, development, or production as appropriate. Accounting for support facilities and equipment is not unique to the oil and gas industry and, therefore, is not discussed in detail.

ACQUISITION COSTS

Acquisition costs include the costs incurred to purchase, lease, or otherwise acquire a property or mineral rights. For U.S. operations, these costs generally include:

- Lease bonuses
- Options to purchase or lease properties
- Costs applicable to minerals when land and mineral rights are purchased in fee
- Broker fees, recording costs, and legal expenses
- Miscellaneous costs incurred in obtaining mineral rights

Costs are initially capitalized as unproved property acquisition costs, which mean the property has not yet been evaluated as to whether it has proved reserves. After exploration, drilling, or lapse of the lease, and if no proved reserves are found, then acquisition costs are removed from the unproved property account and become costs of **abandoned** or worthless property.

Property acquisition costs for an E&P company include the costs of purchasing or leasing property.

Figure 4-1
Successful Efforts Accounting for Costs

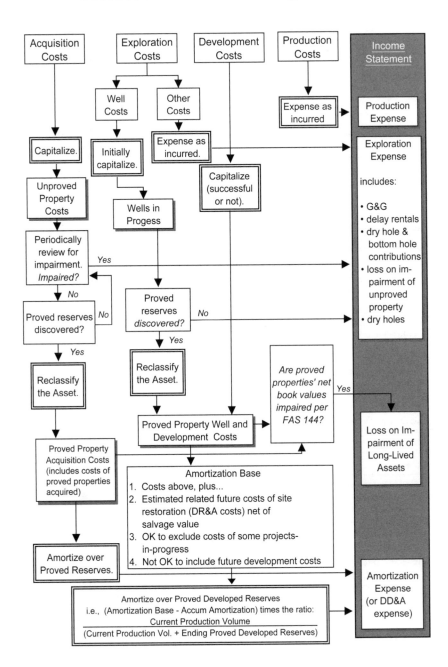

Figure 4-2
Full Cost Accounting for Costs

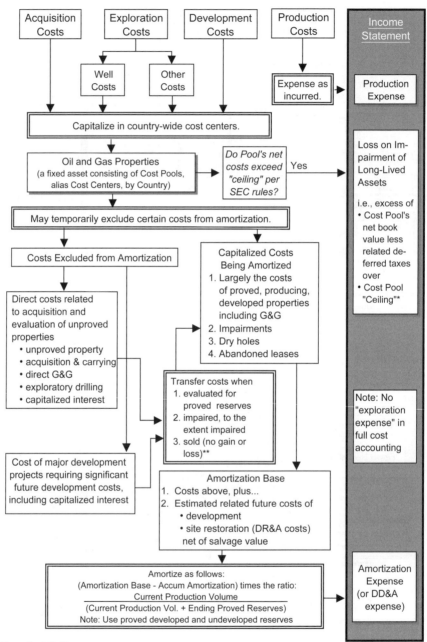

*Cost Pool Ceiling:

(a) a present value of projected future cash flow from proved reserves using hedge-adjusted prices.

(b) plus costs excluded from amortization,

(c) plus the lower of cost or fair value of unproved properties in amortization base,

(d) less estimated related income tax effects, i.e., (1) the present value of income taxes on taxable income relating to proved reserves' future cash flow, and (2) income taxes from hypothetically selling immediately the unproved properties and unevaluated projects at the values in (b) and (c) above.

**No gain or loss unless otherwise the ratio of cost to proved reserves would significantly change.

EXPLORATION COSTS

Exploration costs are incurred in:

- Identifying areas that may warrant examination

- Examining specific areas that might contain oil and gas reserves

They can include drilling exploratory wells and exploratory-type **stratigraphic test wells**. Exploration costs may be incurred both before the related property is acquired (sometimes referred to as prospecting costs) and after the property is acquired. Exploration costs can include the costs of topographical or **geophysical studies**, and salaries and expenses of geologists, geophysical crews, and others conducting the studies. Expenses of carrying and retaining undeveloped properties, such as delay rentals and **ad valorem taxes** on properties, are included in exploration costs as are dry hole and bottom-hole contributions.

DEVELOPMENT COSTS

Development costs are incurred to obtain access to proved reserves and provide facilities for extracting, treating, gathering, and storing oil and gas. They include the costs of **development wells** to produce proved reserves, as well as costs of production facilities, such as lease flow lines, separators, treaters, heaters, storage tanks, improved recovery systems, and nearby gas processing facilities.

PRODUCTION COSTS

Production costs are the costs of activities that involve lifting oil and gas to the surface, and gathering, treating, processing, and storage in the field. In a broad sense, production costs include all costs of acquisition, exploration, development, and production. However, for successful efforts and full cost accounting, the term production costs (or **lifting costs**) refers only to those costs incurred to operate and maintain wells, related equipment, and facilities that are expensed as incurred as part of the cost of oil and gas produced. Production costs include the labor to operate wells and facilities, repair and maintenance expense, materials and supplies consumed, ad valorem taxes and insurance on property, and severance or production taxes.

CAPITALIZATION OVERVIEW UNDER SUCCESSFUL EFFORTS ACCOUNTING

Figure 4-1 shows that costs of acquiring unproved properties are initially capitalized to the Unproved Property Acquisition Costs account. At least once a year, unproved properties are examined to determine whether their costs have been impaired. Impairment is recorded as an exploration expense and credited to the Allowance for Impairment account, a contra account to Unproved Property Acquisition Costs.

Capitalized costs are amortized as the petroleum is produced from the property. If an unproved property is deemed to be worthless or is abandoned, its cost is removed from the Unproved Property Acquisition Costs account and charged to Allowance for Impairment (or Exploration Expense depending on the type of impairment allowance procedure followed).

Figure 4-1 shows that under the Oi5 rules, all exploration costs, except the costs of exploratory wells, are charged to expense as they are incurred.[3] Costs of exploratory wells (including stratigraphic test wells) are initially capitalized (deferred) pending the outcome of the drilling operation. If the test well finds proved reserves, its costs are capitalized to the Proved Property Well and Development Costs account to be amortized as the related reserves are produced. If the test well is dry, accumulated drilling costs are charged to Exploration Expense.

Figure 4-1 also shows that all development costs, including the costs of development of dry holes, are capitalized to the Proved Property Well and Development Costs account. Such costs are amortized as the related proved developed reserves are produced.

Production costs are expensed as incurred with two exceptions:

- Enhanced recovery injectant costs are capitalized as deferred charges when related to future production (Chapters 13 and 31)

- Production costs are capitalized as deferred charges when associated with future gas production under the sales method of accounting for gas imbalances (Chapter 14)

A portion of production costs may also be capitalized as the cost of crude oil inventory (Chapter 13).

OVERVIEW OF AMORTIZATION UNDER SUCCESSFUL EFFORTS ACCOUNTING

Figure 4-1 summarizes the rules to be used in computing amortization of mineral property acquisition costs and the cost of wells, related equipment, and facilities under successful efforts accounting. Mineral property costs are amortized as the proved developed and undeveloped reserves from the entire property are produced. Such amortization is equivalent to depreciation and, for income tax reporting, is called cost **depletion**. Hence, amortization of oil and gas property, well, and development costs is often called DD&A, meaning depreciation, depletion, and amortization. Proved property well and development costs are amortized as the proved developed reserves are produced. In computing amortization, properties in a common geological structure (such as a reservoir or field) may be combined into a single amortization center.

If both oil and gas are produced from the same property, the capitalized costs should be amortized on the basis of total production of both minerals. This requires that the two minerals be equated to an equivalent barrel or equivalent Mcf (explained in Chapter 1). If only one mineral is produced in sufficient quantities, the other mineral is considered de minimis; since minerals produced are assumed to be in proportion to reserves in the ground, the single producing mineral may be used in the computation.

CHART OF ACCOUNTS

The illustrative uncondensed chart of accounts of ABC Oil Company is presented in Appendix 3. A condensed version of the chart appears at Figure 4-3. The abbreviations SE and FC denote accounts unique to successful efforts and full cost, respectively.

ABC Oil Company is assumed to be a medium-sized independent company using the successful efforts method of accounting. Although the company uses computerized systems, subsequent sections of this text may demonstrate the application of accounting principles through the use of manual accounting records. In practice, oil and gas companies tailor their accounts, procedures, and subsidiary records to meet overall organizational needs.

Figure 4-3
Illustrative Condensed Chart of Accounts (see Appendix 3)

ABC Oil Company -- Condensed Chart of Accounts

Current Assets			**Current Liabilities**		
	101	Cash		301	Vouchers Payable
	110	Short-Term Investments		302	Revenue Distributions Payable
	120	AR–Oil & Gas Sales		304	Revenues Held in Suspense
	121	AR–Gas Imbalances		306	Gas Imbalance Payables
	123	AR–Joint Interest Billings		307	Accrued Liabilities
	126	AR–Other		320	Production Taxes Payable
	127	Accrued Receivables		330	Income Taxes Payable
	129	Allowance for Doubtful Accounts		335	Other Current Liabilities
	130	Inventory–Oil		360	Revenue Clearing
	131	Inventory–Gas		361	Billings Clearing
	132	Inventory–Supplies	**Long Term Liabilities**		
	140	Prepaid Expenses		401	Notes Payable
	142	Margin Accounts [may be long-term]		404	Production Payments, as Debt
Oil & Gas Property				410	Asset Retirement Obligation (ARO)
	211	Unproved Property Acquisition Costs		412	Accrued Pension Liabilities
	219	Impairment Allowance	**Deferred Income Taxes**		
	221	Proved Property Acquisition Costs		420	Deferred Income Taxes
SE	226	Accum. Amortization of #221	**Deferred Credits**		
FC	227	Abandoned Properties		430	Deferred Revenue for Prepaids
FC	228	Impairment of Unproved Properties		431	Deferred Revenue for Volume Prod. Pymts.
	231	Proved Properties–Intangibles		432	Deferred Gains on Property Sales
SE	232	Accum. Amortization of #231		433	Deferred Gains on Hedging Future Production
	233	Tangible Costs of Wells & Development Costs	**Stockholders' Equity**		
SE	234	Accum. Amortization of #233		501	Common Stock
	235	Accum. Amortization of #230		525	Retained Earnings
	237	Accum. Write-Down of Properties	**Revenues**		
FC	238	Deferred Losses (Gains) on Sales		601	Oil Revenues
	240	WIP–G&G [often expensed for SE]		602	Gas Revenues
	241	WIP–Intangibles		603	NGL Revenues
	243	WIP–Tangibles		610	Gain (Loss) on Hedging Revenues
	258	Support Equipment & Facilities		620	Gain on Property Sales*
	259	Accum. Depreciation of #258		630	Other Income
Other Assets			**Expenses**		
	261	Other Plant & Equipment		701	Marketing Expenses
	269	Accum. Depreciation of #261		710	Lease Operating Expenses
	270	Notes Receivable		725	DD&A
	280	Pipeline Demand Charges		735	Amortization of Capitalized ARO
Deferred Charges				760	Loss on Impairment of Long-Lived Assets
	290	Deferred Tax Asset		761	Write-down of Cap. Costs of O&G Assets
	292	Deferred Exp. Recoverable Under		800	Exploration Expenses
		Foreign Production Sharing Contracts	SE	900	G&A Expenses
				920	Interest Expense
				924	Accretion Cost on Asset Retirement Obligations
				930	Loss on Property Sales*
	*	*Rare for FC*		940	Income Tax Provision

ANALYSIS OF ACCOUNTS FOR
SUCCESSFUL EFFORTS ACCOUNTING

Many of the accounts found in the Appendix 3 Illustrative Chart of Accounts are not unique to the petroleum industry; they apply to a variety of industries. However, accounts used to record transactions related to exploration, acquisition, development, and production are significantly different.

The following analysis of accounts is presented first for the successful efforts method followed by a brief explanation of accounts unique to full cost.

ASSETS

Accounts Receivable. Account 121, Accounts Receivable—Gas Imbalances recognizes a receivable for gas volumes owed from a joint venture partner or from the gas transporter (as further explained in Chapter 14).

Inventories. In many circumstances, the amount of crude oil located in lease tanks is not significant. Accordingly, it is not recorded as an item of inventory on the company's books. This practice has been confirmed by 63 percent of the E&P companies surveyed.[4] However, if such crude oil is a significant amount, an inventory figure would be entered based on the cost of production.

Natural gas inventory recognition is also uncommon since gas is not stored at the lease surface, like oil; however, gas injected in gas storage fields may be a significant inventory item for some companies.

Prepaid Expenses. Prepaid insurance, prepaid rents, and similar costs recognized by businesses comprise the prepaid expenses account. Although delay rentals are typically prepaid expenses in economic substance, it is industry practice to expense them under successful efforts (and capitalize under full cost) when paid.

Unproved Property Acquisition Costs. Accounts 210 through 218 are used to accumulate the costs of the company's mineral rights in unproved properties (properties on which oil or gas reserves do not exist with enough certainty to be classified as proved). There can be a general ledger account for every major type of unproved mineral interest. Detailed records are maintained to record cost data for each separate property interest. These accounts are charged with applicable costs (purchase price or leasehold bonus, option costs, and incidental acquisition costs) of unproved properties acquired. Similarly, the accounts are credited with the cost of unproved properties surrendered, sold, or transferred to proved properties when proved reserves are found. If a portion of an unproved property is sold for less than the total purchase price of the entire property, the appropriate account is credited for the proceeds up to the property's cost.

Account 210, Unproved Property Purchase Suspense, is used to accumulate costs incurred in acquiring mineral interests, but to which title has not yet been acquired. The account is credited either when the interest involved is acquired or when it is ascertained that the interest will not be acquired. For example, if ABC Oil Company pays a landowner $10,000 for the option to lease a mineral property within six months, Account 210 is charged with the option cost. Later, if the acreage is actually leased, the $10,000 option cost is credited to Account 210 and charged to Unproved Property Acquisition Costs (Account 211). If the acreage under option is abandoned, the $10,000 held in suspense is credited to Account 210 and is charged to Exploration Expense (Account 806).

The Allowance for Impairment and Amortization of Unproved Properties (Account 219) is more complex. As discussed earlier in this chapter, under Oi5 successful efforts rules unproved properties are subjected to an impairment test that is essentially a comparison between capitalized costs and value. If the value is less than the cost, an impairment must be recognized. This impairment is recorded by a charge to expense (Account 806) and a credit to the allowance account. Impairment may be measured by comparing the cost and value of individual unproved properties (this procedure must be used for properties whose costs are individually significant). Impairment of costs of groups of individually significant properties may be measured and recorded by amortization, based on prior experience, of the total cost of the group of properties. If impairment of individual properties is recorded, detailed records of the impairment of each individual property must be maintained. If group amortization is used, a single impairment allowance is kept for the entire group (or for each group if there is more than one group). If impairment is recorded on individual properties, Account 219 is charged with the accumulated impairment on a property that is sold, surrendered, or assigned or becomes proved (and the related unproved property cost account is credited to remove the sold property's cost). If impairment is based on a group method:

- For a property that becomes proved, its capitalized acquisition costs are reclassified to proved property and Account 219 is unchanged. [Oi5.120]

- For surrendered or abandoned property, its capitalized acquisition costs are charged against Account 219. [Oi5.131]

- For sold unproved property, Account 219 is charged to the extent that sales proceeds are less than the property's capitalized acquisition costs (as illustrated in Chapter 21). [Oi5.138(g) and (h)]

Proved Property Acquisition Costs. Accounts 220 through 229 reflect costs and accumulated amortization of costs of proved mineral interests, i.e., those properties that are producing oil or gas or on which, based on known geological and engineering data, oil and gas reserves are reasonably certain to exist.

When a property is found to have proved reserves, its cost is reclassified from unproved property acquisition costs to proved property acquisition costs. For a property on which impairment has been recorded individually, only net book value (i.e., cost less the impairment allowance) is transferred to the proved property account.

Account 226 reflects the cumulative amortization of the costs of proved mineral interests. When amortization is recorded, it is charged to expense (Account 726) and is credited to Account 226. Oi5.121 provides that amortization (depletion) of proved mineral interests is to be based on production and may be computed for each separate proved property, or may be computed on the total cost of properties that have been grouped together on some common geological basis, such as a field. If amortization is based on the individual property, a separate detailed record will be maintained for the amortization accumulated on that property. Similarly, if amortization is based on groups of properties, the subsidiary records must provide for accumulated amortization applicable to each group.

If amortization is based on the individual property, Account 226 is charged with the accumulated amortization on that property upon disposal. On the other hand, if proved properties are grouped for amortization purposes, Account 226 is charged with the total cost (less any proceeds realized) when disposition of a property occurs.

Proved Property Well and Development Costs. Accounts 230 through 239 reflect the cost and accumulated amortization of the costs of wells, production equipment, and facilities on proved properties.

Costs of exploratory wells that do not find proved reserves (dry holes) are not capitalized, but rather are charged to expense (Account 804 or 805). [Oi5.110].

Primarily for federal income tax determination, costs have been divided into two categories: Intangible Costs (Account 231) and Tangible (or Equipment) Costs (Account 233). Intangible costs are all those costs (such as rig rental and fuel) that have no physical existence or salvage value, but are nevertheless incurred in drilling the well as further explained in Chapter 26. For calculating federal taxable income, intangible well costs are 70 percent or 100 percent deductible when incurred, whereas **tangible costs** are depreciated over seven years or over the property's productive life (Chapter 26). Because of federal tax definitions, labor costs to install **casing** or other equipment in the well (up through the point that valves are installed to control production) are generally considered to be intangibles and are charged to Account 231. However, costs to install flow lines, separators, tanks, and other lease equipment are classified for income tax purposes as equipment and charged to Account 233.

Accounts 232 and 234 are credited with accumulated amortization of intangibles and equipment, respectively. Amortization of well and development costs may be based on individual properties (leases) or on groups of properties if the grouping is related to geological conditions such as a reservoir or field. Accounts 232 and 234 are charged with the amount of depreciation accumulated on a property that is disposed of if impairment has been recorded individually. On the other hand, if group amortization is used, Accounts 232 and 234 are charged with the total capitalized costs (less proceeds from disposition) of intangibles and equipment, respectively, when a disposition occurs for a **developed property** included in the group.

Account 235 may be used in lieu of liability Account 410 to recognize the additional cumulative depreciation from increasing the amortization base for estimated future plugging and abandonment costs noted in Figure 4-1.

Work In Progress. An important part of the accounting system of an oil and gas company is its work in progress accounts and the procedures related to them. In some companies, these accounts are referred to as work in process or incomplete construction. In ABC Oil Company, Accounts 240 through 249 in Appendix 3 are used to accumulate the costs of work in progress.

Work in progress accounts are closely related to the authorization for expenditures system under which every major construction project or asset acquisition project is controlled by a properly approved authorization for expenditures. Thus, subsidiary accounts are kept for each project and for major cost classifications for each project.

Account 240 is sometimes used to accumulate the cost of major geological and geophysical exploration projects. Each major project is approved by an **Authorization for Expenditure (AFE)**; thus, costs related to each project are properly analyzed and classified. Accumulated costs are closed at the end of the period to expense. Some companies do not use an AFE system for exploration projects, but may nevertheless have a work in progress account for such activities (see Chapter 6).

Account 241, Work in Progress—Intangible Costs, is charged for all intangible costs incurred in drilling wells. Each drilling project is properly authorized and costs are accumulated for each AFE. The detailed classification of expenditures is identical to the classification used in Account 231. If an exploratory well finds proved reserves, the accumulated costs are charged to Account 231. If, on the other hand, the exploratory well is unsuccessful, accumulated costs are charged to Exploration Expenses, Account 804 or 805.

Account 244, Work in Progress—Workovers, is used to accumulate the costs of well workovers controlled by AFEs. Most companies establish some maximum amount for workover jobs that can be expensed without an AFE. If the total cost of the workover job is estimated to be no more than the amount specified, costs will be charged directly to production expense, Account 710-002. If an AFE is required, costs are accumulated for the AFE in Account 244. Upon completion of the job, accumulated costs are removed from Account 244 and charged either to a production expense account or an asset account. A general rule is that if the workover does not increase the total proved reserves of the well, the costs are charged to expense (Account 700.002), but if the job does increase total proved reserves from the well, the costs are capitalized. Usually, the costs involved are intangible in nature, but may include well equipment.

The remaining work in progress accounts (245 through 248) in Appendix 3 are self-explanatory.

Support Equipment and Facilities. Account 258 is charged with the capitalized costs of equipment and facilities used in oil and gas operations that serve more than one property or field or more than one function (acquisition, exploration, development, or production). District camps, regional shops, trucks, barges, warehouses, and electric power systems are examples of field service equipment and facilities. Appropriate detailed records are kept for individual units and groups of assets.

Deferred Charges. Accounts 290, 291, and 292 relate to activities addressed in Chapters 27, 33, and 25, respectively.

LIABILITIES

Revenue Distributions Payable and Revenues Held in Suspense. Accounts 302 and 304 recognize liabilities to other joint interest owners or royalty owners for their share, if any, of revenues received by the company on the venture's behalf. Suspended revenues may relate to disputed or unknown ownerships or to nominal payables paid out quarterly or annually.

Production Payments and Prepaids. As production occurs, oil and gas companies are obligated to: (1) deliver specified production volumes, or (2) pay specified cash amounts. Companies may agree to make future production payments in return for receiving assets immediately, such as cash or producing property. A receipt of cash in exchange for a production payment payable in oil or gas volumes is called a Volumetric Production Payment, or VPP. It is regarded as the sale of a mineral interest and sales proceeds are credited to Account 431, Deferred Revenue for Volume Production Payments. The account's credit balance is proportionately reduced, and revenue is credited as VPP volumes are delivered.

Receipt of cash in exchange for future production payments payable in specified cash amounts is considered a borrowing: the cash account is debited and Account 404, Production Payments Payable as Debt, is credited.

Occasionally, cash is received in exchange for a production payment created from unproved mineral interests where the cash is credited to the unproved property account. Chapter 22 provides further explanation of accounting for production payments.

Account 430, Deferred Revenue for Prepaids, reflects prior cash received for an obligation to deliver oil or gas in the future regardless of production. As explained in Chapter 22, the prepaid transaction is not the sale of a mineral interest since the delivery obligation may require the company to purchase the oil or gas for delivery under the obligation.

Clearing, Apportionment, and Control Accounts. Many expenses cannot be charged readily to a single drilling operation, individual lease, or other individual operating function. They must be accumulated and subsequently distributed to other expense or asset accounts by using clearing and apportionment accounts.

Clearing accounts are used to accumulate expenses during a given period such as a month; at the end of the period, the balance of the account is allocated to other accounts on a predetermined basis. An apportionment account is also used to accumulate costs, but in this case credits to the account are made on the basis of fixed rates for services rendered. The balance of an apportionment account, which should be small if rates have been properly established, will normally be carried forward from month to month, but will be closed to miscellaneous expense or miscellaneous income at year-end.

The use of Control accounts (360 and 361) enhances accounting controls over joint venture revenues and billings received and processed. E&P companies do not normally invoice for oil and gas sales; instead, they accrue estimated receivables. When net sales proceeds are received, E&P companies should use internal information to check the accuracy of the oil (or gas) purchaser's calculations. Remittances can be reviewed for accuracy by entering the well's identity, sales month, gross production volume, and cash received by the company from the payor's remittance advice. Assume that $30,000 is received by the company for one well's oil production in June. The company's computer-generated entries are:

101	Cash		30,000	
360		Revenue Control		30,000

360	Revenue Control*		33,120	
710.009	Production Taxes		2,880	
601		Oil Revenue		36,000

* Computer calculated as 5,000 barrels sold x $60/bbl [price per company pricing file] x 12% net revenue interest [from the company's master division of interest file] x (1.0 - .08) production tax rate [from the company's tax rate file].

The control account indicates a $3,120 discrepancy which may be due to an error. A balance in the control account helps the company identify the error and correct it. Normally, control accounts have nominal balances. Some companies classify revenue control accounts in the accounts receivable section of the chart of accounts.

REVENUES

Revenue accounts unique to oil and gas production (accounts 600 through 607) are designed to reflect the company's share of revenues from each major type of mineral interest owned. Revenues applicable to mineral interests owned by other parties (for example, revenues applicable to a royalty interest owned by the lessor in a lease operated by the company) are not included in revenue.

EXPENSES

Expense accounts unique to oil and gas exploration and production are typically found in accounts 700 through 806. Direct expenses of operating producing oil and gas properties are charged to Account 710, Lease Operating Expenses. The classification of **lease operating expenses** varies by company, but in each case is designed to assist in the control of expenses. Items charged to Account 710 are generally referred to as lifting costs. Costs are accumulated for each mineral property so that net income can be computed for management oversight and income tax accounting. Depreciation, depletion, and amortization are not included in Account 710, but are separately shown in accounts 725 through 749.

OVERVIEW OF FULL COST ACCOUNTING

Under the full cost method, all acquisition, exploration, and development costs are considered necessary for the ultimate production of reserves. Many of these costs are tied to activities not directly related to finding and developing reserves. Yet, the company expects that the benefits obtained from successful prospects, together with benefits from past discoveries, will be adequate to recover all costs and yield a profit. Establishing a direct cause-and-effect relationship between costs incurred and specific reserves discovered is not relevant to the full cost concept.

COST CENTERS

Capitalized costs are aggregated and amortized by **cost center**. Under the SEC's full cost rules, cost centers are established on a country-by-country basis. A rigid interpretation of this rule prohibits the grouping of countries in a geographical area. For example, it would be improper to combine activities in the Norwegian, U.K., Dutch, and Danish territorial areas under the heading of North Sea operations. The rules would also prohibit having more than one cost center in any individual country.

COSTS TO BE CAPITALIZED

Reg. S-X Rule 4-10(c)(2) specifies the costs to be capitalized under full cost:

> **Costs to be capitalized.** All costs associated with property acquisition, exploration, and development activities (as defined in paragraph (a) of this section) shall be capitalized within the appropriate cost center. Any internal costs that are capitalized shall be limited to those costs that can be directly identified with acquisition, exploration, and development activities undertaken by the reporting entity for its own account, and shall not include any costs related to production, general corporate overhead, or similar activities.

Under these rules, all geological and geophysical costs, carrying costs (such as delay rental and maintenance of land and lease records), dry hole and bottom-hole contributions, costs of exploratory wells (both dry and successful), costs of stratigraphic test wells, costs of acquiring properties, and all development costs are capitalized. When leases are surrendered or abandoned, their costs remain a part of the net capitalized costs of the cost center.

Since all costs incurred in each country are capitalized and treated as applicable to all minerals within that country, individual properties and assets conceptually lose their identities. A single oil and gas asset account for each country can be used to accumulate the costs in that country. For example, a company with operations in four countries might maintain accounts as follows: Oil and Gas Assets—U.S.; Oil and Gas Assets—Canada; Oil and Gas Assets—Norway; Oil and Gas Assets—Trinidad.

Even if all oil and gas assets in a country are lumped into a single account, detailed records of acquisition costs, drilling and development costs, and other related costs must be maintained for federal income tax purposes. Companies using the full cost method effectively maintain subsidiary records of individual unproved and proved properties in the same way prescribed for successful efforts. In addition, the method of accounting does not alter procedures necessary for internal control of operations.

Costs to be amortized as DD&A (Figure 4-2) include the sum of three costs:

1. Capitalized costs, net of accumulated amortization, but excluding all unevaluated acreage and unevaluated exploratory costs, as well as significant investments in major development projects in progress

2. Estimated future development costs applicable to **proved undeveloped reserves**

3. Estimated dismantling and abandonment costs, net of salvage

Unproved properties and exploratory costs excluded from the amortization base should be periodically assessed for impairment until it can be determined whether proved reserves are attributable to the properties. If impairment is indicated, the impairment amount should be included in the amortization base. Unevaluated costs applicable to properties that are not individually significant may be placed in a group (or more than one group) and amortized into the amortization base.

Amortization under full cost is calculated on a unit-of-production basis using physical units of proved oil and gas reserves converted to a common unit based on relative energy (Btu) content. Economic circumstances may indicate that using gross revenues rather than physical units results in a more appropriate basis for computing amortization.[5]

Reg. S-X Rule 4-10 places a **cost ceiling** on capitalized costs for companies using the full cost method. Any excess is charged to expense. For each cost center, net unamortized costs, less related deferred income taxes, shall not exceed the sum of:

a) The present value at a 10 percent discount of future net revenues of proved reserves using hedge-adjusted prices[6]

b) Plus unproved property costs and preproduction costs not being amortized

c) Plus the lower of cost or estimated fair value of unproved properties included in costs being amortized

d) Less: income tax effects related to differences between:

     1. The sum of (a), (b), and (c), and

     2. The tax basis of the properties involved.[7]

ACCOUNTS FOR FULL COST ACCOUNTING

Chapter 19 more fully addresses the issues in applying the full cost method for an E&P company. As shown in Figure 4-3 and Appendix 3, few accounts are unique to full cost accounting. Since all costs incurred in exploration, acquisition and development activities are capitalized, there are no exploration expense accounts for a full cost company.

When an unproved lease is abandoned as unsuccessful, related costs are moved from the Unproved Property Acquisition Costs account and charged to the appropriate cost center's Account 227 as a capitalized cost of unsuccessful efforts.

Exploration costs and similar carrying costs are allocated to individual unproved properties or proved properties and become part of the cost of individual properties. Some costs, such as regional G&G costs, cannot be reasonably allocated and may simply be charged to Account 229, Unsuccessful Exploration Costs. Account 236 is used to accumulate amortization as a single figure for each cost center, and Account 725 reflects this charge. Thus, there is no separate allowance for amortization of each type of capitalized cost.

Under the full cost method, a ceiling is placed on capitalized costs. Any write-down required because a cost center ceiling is less than net capitalized costs is charged to Account 761 and credited to Account 237 with appropriate adjustment of deferred income taxes. Finally, no gain or loss is customarily recognized on the sale or abandonment of oil and gas assets under the full cost method.

OVERVIEW OF INCOME TAX ACCOUNTING

Financial accounting under successful efforts or full cost differs from the accounting required to figure income taxes and alternative minimum taxes under the Internal Revenue Code (IRC). Income tax accounting (discussed in Chapter 26) considers the following:

- Intangible drilling costs (**IDC**) for U.S. wells may be deducted when incurred except that certain integrated companies must capitalize 30 percent of the intangibles and amortize that amount over a 60-month period.

- Taxpayers who initially elect to deduct IDC have an additional annual election to capitalize all or a portion of the IDC incurred in that tax year. The capitalized portion is amortized ratably over a 60-month period beginning in the month the costs are paid or incurred.

- Dry hole costs for exploration and development wells are fully deductible when the well is determined to be dry.

- Except for certain integrated companies, a taxpayer producing oil or gas may get a **percentage depletion** deduction. It generally equals 15 percent of wellhead revenue for up to 1,000 equivalent barrels per day of production sold, but is limited by property to 100 percent of taxable income—and limited by taxpayer to 65 percent of the taxpayer's taxable income before deducting depletion. A taxpayer's recorded depletion deduction is the greater of the calculated percentage depletion deduction or a cost depletion amount. Cost depletion is similar to acquisition cost amortization under successful efforts.

- Unproved property impairments are not deductible; unproved property costs are deducted when the property is abandoned.

- Proved property impairments and ceiling write-downs are not deductible.

- Tangible well and development costs are depreciated, generally over seven years, but may be depreciated over proved reserves using the unit-of-production method.

• • •

---

1 Primary source: Hoover's Online based on SEC filings as of June 14, 2004.

2 The SEC's rules for financial accounting and reporting for oil and gas producing companies are found in Rule 4-10 of Regulation S-X (alias S-X Rule 4-10 or S-X Article 4, Section 10). Regulation App 1 is Part 210 of Title 17 of the Code of Federal Regulations. For the sake of brevity, in this book the applicable regulations will be referred to simply as Reg. S-X Rule 4-10.

3 Successful efforts accounting rules do not define the term incurred. However, FAS 71, footnote 5, defines an incurred cost as "a cost arising from cash paid out or obligation to pay for an acquired asset or service, a loss from any cause that has been sustained and has been or must be paid for."

4 Source: *2001 PricewaterhouseCoopers Survey of U.S. Petroleum Accounting Practices.*

5 Per Reg. S-X Rule 4-10(c)(3)(C)(iii) (Appendix 1) and Topic 12 F (CD Reference Exhibit A).

6 SAB 103, issued in May 2003, indicated that hedge-adjusted prices must be used in the calculation as such prices represent the "best measure of estimated cash flows from future production."

7 The tax effects formula is the short-cut approach detailed in CD Reference Exhibit A.

CHAPTER

5

GEOLOGICAL AND GEOPHYSICAL EXPLORATION

Glossary Terms

anticlines

domes

faults

geology

geophysics

igneous rocks

metamorphic rocks

sedimentary rocks

Key Concepts:

- **SEC definition of exploration costs**

- **Geologic conditions for accumulation of oil and gas**

- **Oil and gas traps**

- **Current exploration methods**

For most companies engaged in oil and gas activities, exploration costs represent a substantial portion of annual expenditures. This chapter describes the scope and nature of geological and geophysical exploration costs. Chapter 6 examines the accounting principles and procedures to be used in connection with such costs.

NATURE OF EXPLORATION COSTS

The Securities and Exchange Commission (SEC) in Reg. S-X Rule 4-10(a)(15) has defined exploration costs as follows:

Costs incurred in identifying areas that may warrant examination and in examining specific areas that are considered to have prospects of containing oil and gas reserves, including costs of drilling exploratory wells and exploratory-type stratigraphic test wells. Exploration costs may be incurred both before acquiring the related property (sometimes referred to in part as prospecting costs) and after acquiring the property. Principal types of exploration costs, which include depreciation and applicable operating costs of support equipment and facilities and other costs of exploration activities, are:

a) Studies, rights of access to properties to conduct those studies, and salaries and other expenses of geologists, geophysical crews, and others conducting those studies. Collectively, these are often referred to as geological and geophysical or G&G costs.

b) Costs of carrying and retaining undeveloped properties, such as delay rentals, *ad valorem* taxes on properties, legal costs for title defense, and the maintenance of land and lease records.

c) Dry-hole contributions and bottom-hole contributions.

d) Costs of drilling and equipping exploratory wells.

e) Costs of drilling exploratory-type stratigraphic test wells.

Five types of exploration costs have been defined by the SEC. G&G costs are explained in this chapter, while the other exploration costs are described in Chapters 7 and 8. To understand the nature of G&G exploration, this chapter presents a geologic discussion of oil and gas accumulations, followed by the techniques and methods used in exploration.

GEOLOGY AND GEOPHYSICS

Geology is the science that studies the planet earth. It addresses the materials of which the earth is made, processes that act on these materials, products formed, and the history of the planet and its life forms since its origin. Most geological studies are focused on aspects of the earth's crust because it is directly observable, and the crust is the source of energy and minerals for today's modern industrial societies. **Geophysics**, the science that studies the earth by quantitative physical methods, is used in conjunction with geology in the exploration for oil and gas.

GEOLOGIC SETTING FOR OIL & GAS ACCUMULATIONS

The outer layer of the earth is known as the lithosphere, which contains the earth's crust and overlays the upper mantle. The crust is composed of three types of rock: igneous, sedimentary and metamorphic.

Igneous rocks formed as molten rock cooled, either at the surface (e.g., lava) or well beneath it (e.g., granite).

Sedimentary rocks resulted when older rocks eroded, and the materials were transported and deposited as sediments. Through burial and compaction, these sediments were transformed into sedimentary rocks, most commonly as shales and sandstones. Other sedimentary rocks include carbonates, such as limestone, which resulted from the precipitation from water by organisms or changes in the chemistry of the water. Evaporites, primarily halite or common salt, also were precipitated from water under the right conditions of evaporation. Most oil and gas accumulations occur in sedimentary rocks.

Metamorphic rocks occurred as pressure and heat were applied to other rocks. Examples are marble, slate, and quartzite. Because organic material is destroyed in the process, these rocks tend to be poor reservoirs for hydrocarbons.

As shown in Figure 5-1, the earth has a long history. Geologists in the oil and gas industry are concerned with the more recent past—the last 500-600 million years since the Pre-Cambrian. Conditions are better preserved in these "younger" rocks for the accumulation of oil and gas. Abundant organic material was present because of the greater quantity of life forms starting in the Paleozoic. This era also is the source of more sedimentary rocks that have not been metamorphosed.

Figure 5-1
Geologic Time Periods

Era	Period	Approx. Duration in Million Years	Indicative New Life Forms
Cenozoic *Modern Life*	Quaternary	3	Large Mammals
	Tertiary	63	
Mesozoic *Middle Life*	Cretaceous	71	Large Dinosaurs
	Jurassic	54	
	Triassic	35	
Paleozoic *Ancient Life*	Permian	55	Early Reptiles, Amphibians, and Fish
	Carboniferous	65	
	Devonian	50	
	Silurian	35	
	Ordovician	70	
	Cambrian	70	
Crypotozoic or Precambrian		4,000	Bacteria, Algae, and Jellyfish

Approximate age of the earth: 4,600,000,000 years

The surface of the earth consists of several lithospheric plates, which drift slowly across the underlying asthenosphere in response to heat. The motion of these plates gives rise to the morphology of the earth's crust. At divergent boundaries such as the Mid-Atlantic ridge, new crust is being formed as the two plates, African and American, move away from each other. At convergent boundaries the plates collide. An example of this is the oceanic Nazca plate being subducted under the overriding South American plate, creating the Andes Mountains. At transform boundaries the plates grind past each other, such as occurs along the San Andreas fault. Earthquakes and volcanic activity are most common along plate boundaries. Over time, interactions of plates resulted in mountain ranges and sedimentary basins. Most oil and gas is found in these sedimentary basins.

REQUIREMENTS FOR OIL & GAS ACCUMULATIONS

For the creation and accumulation of oil and gas, several conditions were met:

- a preserved source material existed for the generation of petroleum
- right temperature and pressure occurred for the generation
- resulting oil and gas migrated into suitable rocks for production
- oil and gas were trapped by a barrier, accumulated in volume, and survived subsequent geologic history

SOURCE ROCKS

The sources of oil and gas were abundant organic materials, such as the remains of algae and plankton. Most were of marine origin, although lakes and swamps may also have contained sufficient organic remains. Over time, these organic materials were deposited along with sediment and were protected from oxidation (which would have destroyed them). With burial and increasing temperature, the organic materials generated hydrocarbons. It is often possible, through the chemical characteristics, to trace accumulations back to their source rocks. Source rocks tend to be fine-grained rocks such as shales. However, it should be noted that coal can be a source for gas.

RESERVOIR ROCKS

Reservoir rocks are those rocks possessing sufficient porosity and permeability in order for the hydrocarbons to be produced. Porosity refers to the pore space or voids between the grains of the rock as illustrated in Figure 5-2. It is measured as a percentage of the total rock volume. Permeability refers to the ability of a rock to transmit fluids. It depends on the interconnections between pore spaces. Almost all reservoirs have their grains coated with water, and the oil or gas occupies space within this water.

As sediments were buried deeper, the weight of the overburden compacted the rocks and expelled contained fluids; both porosity and permeability were generally reduced. Natural fracturing would have significantly enhanced the permeability of rocks by connecting pore spaces that would not otherwise be connected.

Conventional reservoirs are found in sandstones and various carbonates. However, oil and gas production can occur from many rock types. With improved technology, such as horizontal drilling or fracture stimulation, lower permeability rocks (shales, carbonates and coals) can serve as successful reservoirs. In some cases, circulating fluids used during exploration can dissolve certain minerals, thereby enhancing porosity and permeability.

Figure 5-2
Porosity With Reservoir Rock

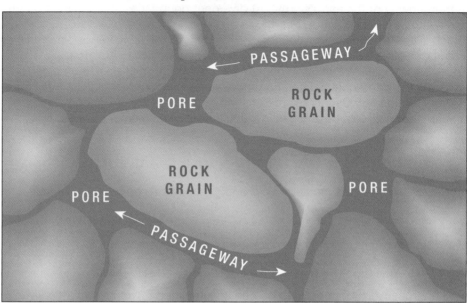

Courtesy of University of Texas Petroleum Extension Service

MIGRATION OF OIL AND GAS TO RESERVOIRS

As rocks were buried and subjected to compaction, most of the original fluid—salt water for the dominant marine sediments—was expelled from them. These fluids carried with them much of the oil or gas that had been generated. Seeking lower pressure, the fluids moved to more permeable reservoir-quality rocks. Oil and gas have buoyancy compared to the more dense formation fluids (salt water) and rose to the top of any permeable layer they encountered.

Over-pressured conditions occurred when the fluids could not escape, and they functioned to support some of the weight of the overburden. As an example, U. S. Gulf Coast sediments are often over-pressured at depth. Recovery factors for natural gas, due to its compressibility, are greatly increased in an over-pressured environment. However, drilling and completion costs increase significantly in over-pressured sediments.

With many low permeability reservoirs, the source rock and the reservoir are the same, such as with coalbed methane reservoirs; thus, no migration occurs.

TRAPPING OF OIL AND GAS

Once the oil or gas encountered a barrier to its migration, it was trapped and could no longer migrate. The overlying impermeable layer, the cap rock, prevented upward migration from the reservoir. Within the reservoir, migration was prevented by either its structural configuration, or by a loss of permeability that created a barrier.

Many trapped accumulations have been lost over time. Subsequent erosion or structural activity may have breached traps. For example, the large tar sands deposits are accumulations that have been breached and degraded, leaving only the residual heavy ends.

Several types of traps are discussed in the next section. Much exploration work focuses on the identification of oil and gas traps.

TYPES OF OIL AND GAS TRAPS

Hydrocarbon traps can be classified in many ways, and a detailed explanation is beyond the scope of this book. Petroleum accountants should be aware that traps differ in size, shape, and type due to the manner in which they were formed. A simple classification for conventional oil and gas traps includes: (1) structural traps, (2) stratigraphic traps, (3) truncation traps, and (4) combination traps. Additionally, a trap that describes many of the tight formation plays active today is called the continuous formation.

STRUCTURAL TRAPS

Structural traps were formed by geological structures resulting from horizontal and/or vertical movements in the earth's crust related to plate motions. The most common types of structural traps are **anticlines**, **faults**, and **domes**.

Anticlines were formed by the folding of strata into a dome or arch as the result of upthrusts from below or by lateral compressive forces. Anticlines, which retain hydrocarbons, are covered with a cap rock or an impervious layer. The anticline was filled by the movement of water, oil, gas, or some combination of these through porous strata until it was halted by the seal or cap rock. Figure 5-3 is a simplified illustration of an anticline.

Figure 5-3
Anticline

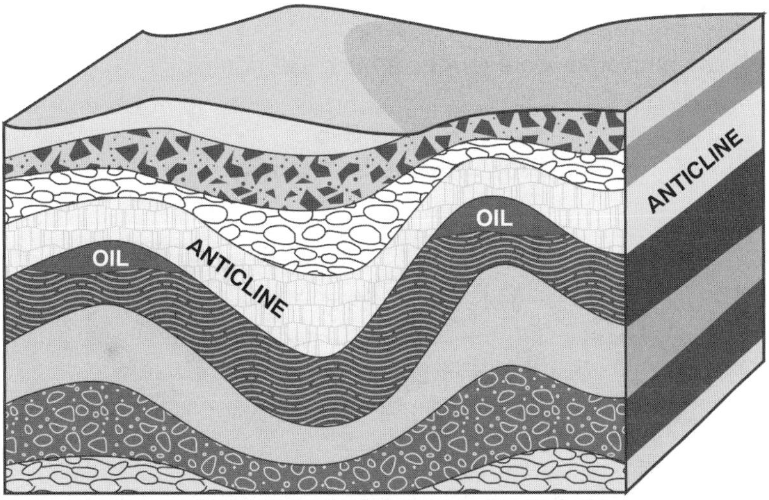

Courtesy of University of Texas Petroleum Extension Service

Historically, anticlines have been the most significant traps containing oil and gas reserves. Much of the world's oil and gas comes from anticlines. An example of an anticlinal reservoir is the giant Sadlerochit reservoir at Prudhoe Bay field in Alaska.

Another type of structural trap is known as a fault. Faults are formed by the breaking or shearing of strata as the result of significant shifting or movement within the earth's crust. When faulting occurs, the relative placement of the strata is changed to the extent that a porous bed holding hydrocarbons can be sealed off by an impermeable formation, thus establishing a seal or trap. Most individuals think of faults in connection with earthquakes, yet few realize that these shifts have resulted in the accumulation of oil and gas deposits. A typical fault is illustrated in Figure 5-4.

Figure 5-4
Simple Fault

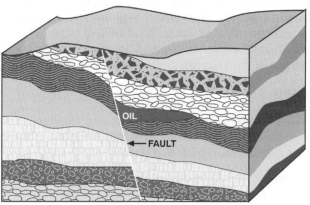

Courtesy of University of Texas Petroleum Extension Service

Domes are a third form of structural trap, and were among the first formations to be associated with the accumulation of oil. Salt domes typify this type of formation. A nonporous bed of salt, which is less dense than overlying rocks, is pushed upward and pierces or otherwise deforms weak points in the overlying formations. Where there has been a piercing of one or more formations, faults form on each side of the salt dome. When upper strata are merely deformed or lifted, anticlines or domes become part of the overall formation. This process is generalized in Figure 5-5. Some of Texas' most famous oil fields, such as Spindletop, were formed around salt domes.

Figure 5-5
Piercement Salt Dome

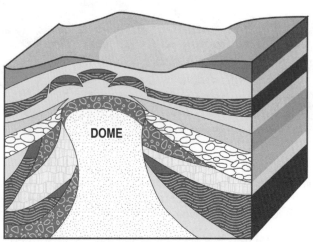

Courtesy of University of Texas Petroleum Extension Service

Oil can be trapped above salt domes when an anticline is formed, alongside salt domes, or in some cases beneath salt pillows or salt sills. The presence of salt is considered very favorable for oil provinces in many regions because of its inherent instability causing domes or anticlines to form, and its high sealing potential for migrating hydrocarbons. Subsalt formations in the Gulf of Mexico provide an important area for exploration today.

STRATIGRAPHIC TRAPS

Stratigraphic traps were formed by differences in the characteristics of strata at various points. Oil and gas became trapped in the porous and permeable portions of the formation and were surrounded by impermeable sections. Stratigraphic traps may have been caused by abrupt changes in the porosity and permeability of the formation, irregular depositions of sand and shale, or changes in certain of the carbonate rocks. Typical stratigraphic traps are shown in Figures 5-6 and 5-7.

Figure 5-6
Stratigraphic Trap

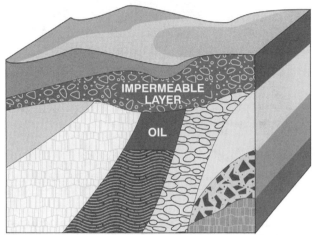

Courtesy of University of Texas Petroleum Extension Service

Figure 5-7
A Second Type of Stratigraphic Trap

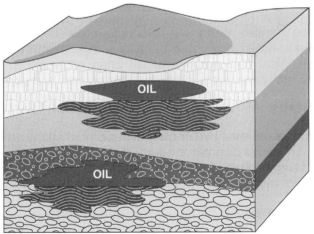

Courtesy of University of Texas Petroleum Extension Service

Some stratigraphic traps are called truncation traps or unconformities because they are associated with erosional unconformities in the strata. Erosion may have cut off portions of the sedimentary strata. Subsequently, an impermeable cap rock was deposited over this cutoff (see Figure 5-8). As oil and gas migrated upward, movement was halted by the cap rock. A classic example of a truncation trap is the East Texas field. Others include the West Edmond field in Oklahoma and part of the Central Kansas Uplift.

Figure 5-8
Unconformity

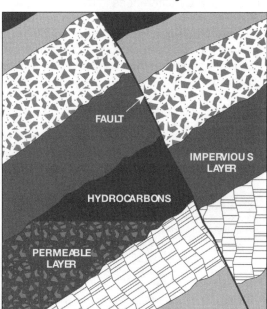

Courtesy of University of Texas Petroleum Extension Service

Many of the world's largest accumulations of hydrocarbons occurred due to enhanced porosity development along unconformities, or sealing of underlying porous reservoirs truncated and overlain by impermeable rocks. Examples include: (1) the major oil fields of Saudi Arabia such as at Ghawar, the world's largest oil field (porosity enhancement); and (2) the largest oil field in the United States, Prudhoe Bay (truncation), along major unconformities.

Stratigraphic traps are also common in carbonate rocks. The original deposition can be variable resulting in abrupt changes in porosity and permeability. Reefs are the most dramatic examples. Also, carbonate rocks are often subjected to post-depositional changes caused by circulating fluids, which can alter porosity and permeability.

COMBINATION TRAPS

Combination traps result when two or more types of formations are combined due to folding, faulting, and other conditions in the subsurface. These often involve a stratigraphic or truncation trap being combined with a structural trap. The Oklahoma City field is an example of this type of reservoir, as well as the Rangely oil field in Colorado.

CONTINUOUS FORMATIONS

Chapter 1 introduced the 1990s development of gas production from tight (low permeability) reservoirs and coalbeds—two types of continuous formations that were generally uneconomic to develop prior to that time. This has led to significant new exploration in areas previously considered unlikely for recoverable hydrocarbons, such as the deeper centers of petroleum basins. As conventional traps become more difficult to find with mature exploration, development of these new reservoirs has become very important, especially for natural gas.

Substantial quantities of oil and gas are contained in tight formations with typically poor permeability. The formations may be vast and continuous, but because of low permeability, production rates are low and usually need to be enhanced.

Examples of tight sands are the Codell and Niobrara formations in northeastern Colorado, which produce gas and some condensate from thousands of wells drilled over the years. Such formations are opened up by fracturing the rock with fracing material temporarily pumped under high pressure into the reservoir. Flow can be enhanced by horizontal drilling, which is described in Chapter 8. In this case, the well bore starts vertically, but runs horizontally through the reservoir (sometimes for several hundred feet) to expose much more of the reservoir to the well than traditional drilling.

The Austin Chalk formation in southeastern Texas and Louisiana, characterized by faulting, is an example of a continuous oil producing formation that was rejuvenated in the 1990s by horizontal drilling.

In the Fort Worth Basin, the Barnett Shale is another example of a low permeability or tight reservoir with a dramatic level of activity from the late 1990s to the present.

The two largest U.S. coalbed methane producing basins are the giant San Juan Basin in southern Colorado and New Mexico, and the Black Warrior Basin in Alabama.

GEOLOGICAL AND GEOPHYSICAL EXPLORATION METHODS

The goal of oil and gas exploration is to locate new hydrocarbon reserves that can be produced at a profit. However, the geologist, geophysicist, or reservoir engineer cannot look directly for oil and gas. Hydrocarbons are usually found only through drilling. G&G exploration is undertaken to locate areas where it is believed that conditions are favorable for the accumulation of oil and gas. Many different techniques to explore both the surface and subsurface are used for this purpose. These techniques can employ geology, geophysics, geochemistry, and even satellite imagery techniques. The dominant form of exploration relates to an integrated geologic-seismic approach.

The method used depends on the level of previous exploration in a basin. If undrilled, a basic regional study must be done to determine the geologic setting and favorability for the accumulation of oil or gas. At the other extreme is the intensely drilled basin where the primary concern is to identify any remaining traps missed by previous explorers. Improved technologies have given the current explorationists tools that offer advantages over earlier methods.

Computers have transformed exploration by incorporating various sources of data, especially seismic data, and allowing the data to be manipulated and analyzed in various ways.

SURFACE MAPPING

Surface mapping is most common in unexplored, undrilled areas where direct subsurface information on the rocks is not available. Aerial photography, satellite imaging, and geochemical surveys assist a geologist in interpreting the surface geology. The goal is to better understand the geologic setting, structural style, source rocks, and reservoir rocks. However, the extrapolation of surface data to predict subsurface conditions can be risky.

GRAVITY AND MAGNETIC SURVEYS

Gravity and magnetic surveys both measure small deviations in the gravitational attraction and magnetic fields caused by variations in the density and magnetic properties of underlying rocks. They are generally used as low cost tools to assist in the regional structural reconstruction of a basin.

EXISTING WELL DATA

The primary source for information on subsurface conditions is the data available on previously drilled wells. Various downhole logging surveys are run as wells are being drilled. See Figure 5-9. These logs provide a wealth of information on the rock characteristics and fluid content. Tests run at the site and core samples taken add to the data set. With this information, data can be extrapolated into undrilled areas, particularly when incorporated into seismic data. Several types of mapping are used including structure maps, which show the elevation of a particular geologic formation, and maps of various aspects of the geologic formation, such as porosity and sand-shale ratios. Depending on governmental rules, well data are generally released to others after a prescribed amount of time and provide low cost information to the industry.

Figure 5-9
Well-Site Log

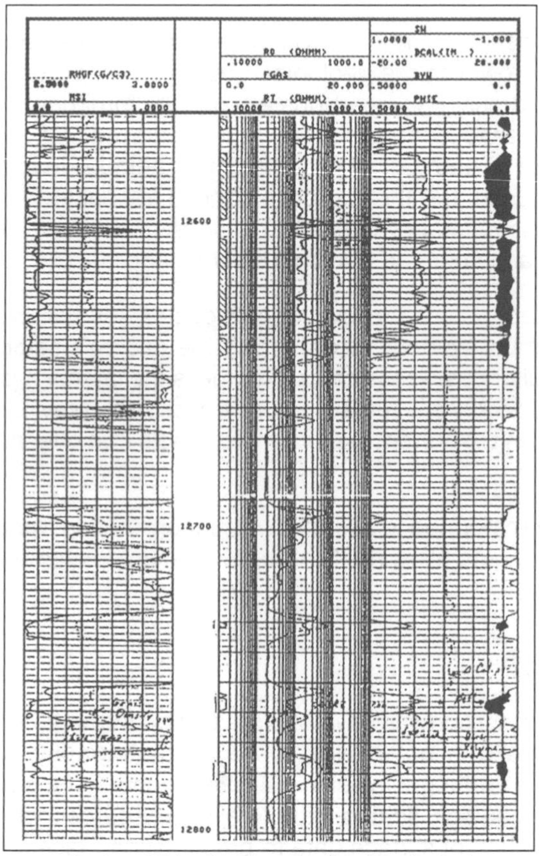

Courtesy of University of Texas Petroleum Extension Service

SEISMIC SURVEYS

The word seismic means of, or having to do with, an earthquake or earth vibration. In the oil industry, the term relates specifically to oil and gas exploration by measurement of man-made sound waves reflected from subsurface formations. Several methods generate an energy source for seismic activities including dynamite, vibroseis and air guns.

No matter the source of energy used, seismic sound waves travel downward through the earth's crust. Upon striking a layer with different acoustic properties, caused by differences in the density or velocity of the rock, a portion of the wave is reflected back to the surface. The reflected seismic waves are detected at the surface by devices called geophones and are recorded digitally for later computer processing. See Figure 5-10.

Many geophones are placed around each shot point, the location where energy is transmitted to the subsurface. This provides subsurface coverage over a large area. By building in redundancy with multiple shot points and arrays of geophones, the same subsurface point is recorded multiple times from different surface positions. The signal-to-noise ratio of the recorded sound waves increases, as does the clarity of the recording.

For many years seismic recording was limited to two-dimensional profiles through the earth, with time in the vertical axis and distance in the horizontal. Because of the increased capability in computer processing, it is now possible to record large areas, instead of linear profiles. The processing can provide a three dimensional look at the recorded data. On a computer work station, it is possible to slice the data set in multiple ways, from horizontal slices to vertical profiles in any direction. Resolution of the subsurface data is greatly enhanced by 3-D processes (see Figure 5-11).

Figure 5-10
Illustration of Seismic Surveying

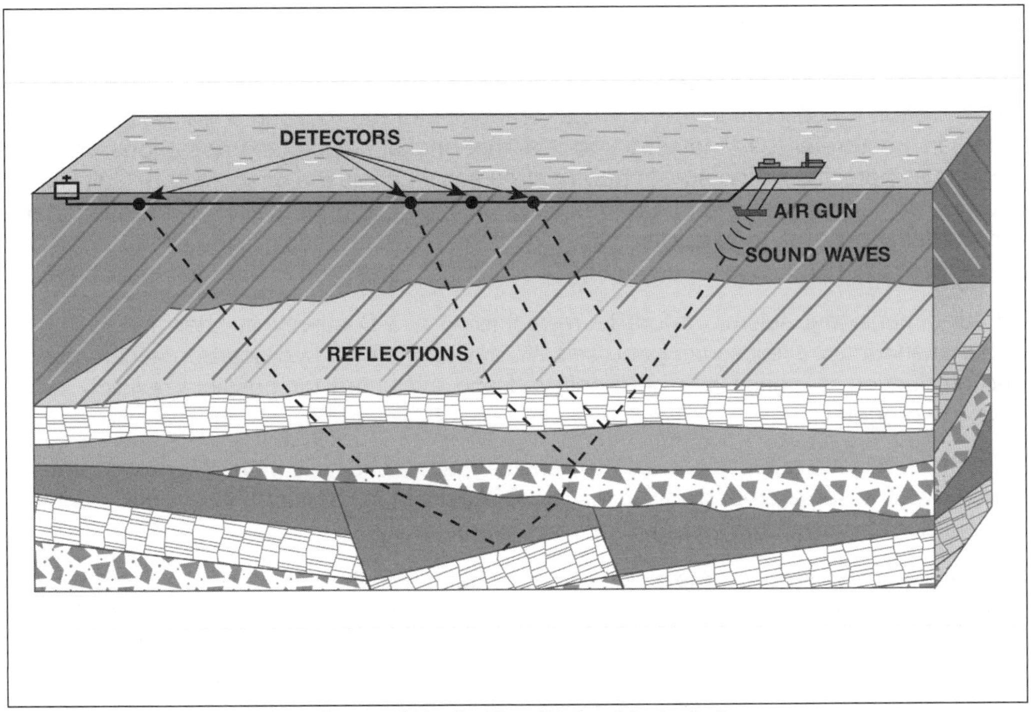

Courtesy of University of Texas Petroleum Extension Service

Figure 5-11
Three-Dimensional Seismic Survey

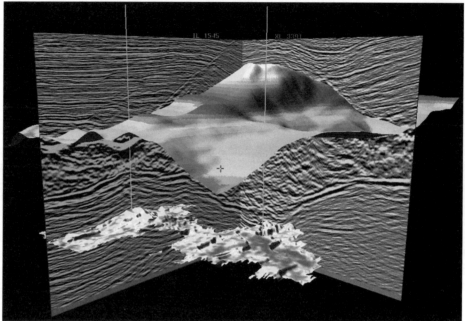

Image courtesy of the American Association of Petroleum Geologists EXPLORER magazine.

Converting the time scale to depth requires information on the velocity of the rocks through which the sound wave passes. This information is available from well data as well as by computer analysis of the recorded data itself.

In addition to the traditional use of seismic data to define the structural configuration of various layers or formations, much can be learned about the rock properties and fluid content from the seismic data, particularly when well data can be integrated into the seismic data. By calibrating the acoustic properties of the rocks in a well to the seismic data, an interpreter can develop models that make reliable extrapolations of such aspects as porosity or lithology. In good data areas, such as the offshore U.S. Gulf Coast, hydrocarbon accumulations can be mapped with great accuracy from the seismic data. With larger surveys of good quality data, a geologist can view sedimentary sequences and relate them to seismic sequence stratigraphic models that predict the likely rock types.

Four-dimensional seismic refers to re-recording a 3-D survey at later times. This is undertaken for large fields with good seismic definition of the hydrocarbon accumulation. The production response can be monitored and evaluated for possible revision in the recovery program.

Offshore seismic surveys are less expensive than onshore surveys. More area can be covered in the same amount of time. Onshore permitting problems are more common, and surface damages such as for crops can be expensive.

Seismic surveys can be done on a proprietary basis with the recorded data available only to the sponsor. Group shoots are done with several companies sponsoring and sharing the data to reduce costs. Costs can be lowered still more if, after a period of exclusivity, the data can be purchased by anyone. Some seismic companies also do speculative or "spec" shoots in anticipation of a favorable response from the industry in purchasing the data.

As the search continues for more hydrocarbons, the tools available to the explorationist have become much more precise and versatile. With improved computing power and sophisticated programs to analyze and integrate the data, a geologist can lower the risk. Reduced risks and improved production techniques make it possible to economically access smaller accumulations and lower quality reservoirs. However, as it has been said, oil and gas are only found by the drill bit.

• • •

6

ACCOUNTING FOR EXPLORATION COSTS

Key Concepts:

- **Financial and tax treatments of exploration costs**

- **Authorization for expenditure related to exploration**

- **General ledger accounts for recording exploration activities**

- **Work in progress transactions**

- **Special accounting problem areas**

Principles and procedures used in accounting for exploration costs are examined in this chapter. General financial accounting principles are covered first, followed by details of control systems, recording procedures, and special accounting problem areas.

These discussions assume that successful efforts is the chosen accounting method. Except for costs of exploratory wells, all exploration costs are correctly charged to expense as incurred. Full cost companies must capitalize their exploration costs. However, the accounting systems and procedures employed by both types of oil and gas companies are nearly identical.

GENERAL TREATMENT OF EXPLORATION COSTS

Exploration costs incurred in geological and geophysical (G&G) activities include the following: costs of topographical, geological and geophysical studies; rights of access to properties to conduct those studies (commonly referred to as shooting rights); and salaries and expenses of geologists, geophysical crews, or others conducting studies. Exploration costs also include the expenses of carrying and retaining **undeveloped properties**, drilling and equipping exploratory wells, making dry hole and **bottom-hole contributions**, and drilling exploratory-type stratigraphic test wells.

Under the successful efforts method, exploration costs are expensed when incurred. The only exceptions are those costs for exploratory wells, including exploratory-type stratigraphic test wells. Exploratory well costs are initially capitalized as work in progress until the outcome is known. At that time, exploratory wells that do not find proved reserves are charged to expense, while successful exploratory wells are capitalized.

Special rules determine the proper treatment of costs of exploratory wells in progress or wells for which drilling has been completed, but the existence of proved reserves remains uncertain. These special rules are discussed more fully in Chapter 9.

Under the full cost method, all exploration costs are capitalized as part of the oil and gas assets in the cost pool.

The following case illustrates the financial accounting treatment of exploration costs. Assume that a broad exploratory study is undertaken by an E&P company at a cost of $150,000. As a result of the reconnaissance survey, two areas of interest are designated as Area A and Area B. Before attempting to acquire acreage, the company conducts detailed surveys on the areas. Survey costs are $20,000 for Area A and $10,000 for Area B. Exploration activities reveal little likelihood of oil or gas in Area B, and the area is abandoned. However, results for Area A are positive, and two leases are acquired. One contains 320 acres and the other encompasses 480 acres. The company uses successful efforts accounting and charges all costs to current expense as noted in the following entry:

801	Exploration Expense (Geological and Geophysical)	180,000	
	101 Cash		180,000
	To record exploration costs associated with exploratory study and surveys of Areas A and B.		

GENERAL TAX TREATMENT OF EXPLORATION COSTS

Current tax laws treat exploration costs differently than GAAP. Exploration costs for tax purposes do not include carrying costs, test well contributions, drilling of exploratory wells, or drilling of exploratory-type stratigraphic test wells.

According to the IRS, G&G expenditures are essentially capital in nature and are not immediately deductible. Recent tax law changes require such costs incurred after August 8, 2005, to be amortized over 24 months. Costs paid or incurred after May 17, 2006, by major integrated oil companies, as defined in I.R.C. §167(h)(5), are amortized over a period of five years. G&G that is part of a broad reconnaissance-type survey to find smaller areas of interest must be allocated equally to each area of interest found. If no area of interest is found, the costs are classified as expenses in the year such a determination is made.

Reconnaissance survey costs allocated to an area of interest, along with the cost of any detailed survey on that area, are capitalized to any leases acquired in the area. If no leases are acquired in the area of interest, the accumulated costs are charged to expense in the year the area is abandoned. If more than one lease is acquired in an area of interest, the deferred charges are allocated among the leases in proportion to the acreage in each lease. Costs applicable to projects and areas of interest include an allocable portion of overhead, which should be applied on a logical and consistent basis. Capitalized exploration costs, together with lease acquisition charges (such as bonuses), become the leasehold cost for federal income tax purposes as further illustrated in Chapter 26.

RECORDKEEPING PROCEDURES

The accounting system is designed to capture exploration costs for an E&P company's financial statements. However, it must also furnish data to meet other business needs.

- Exploration focuses on specific projects undertaken to locate structures favorable to hydrocarbons. Management must know the cost of each project in order to determine its ultimate profitability.

- Development of a budget for exploration is dependent on accounting system information.

- Cost control depends on an adequate accounting and reporting system.

- Regulatory agencies, such as the Department of Energy, impose specific requirements on how data is classified and accumulated.

- Treatment of various costs for federal income taxes differs from financial reporting purposes, and these differences require additional detailed records.

- Frequently, detailed historical cost records are required for legal and contractual purposes.

Obviously, accounting and record-keeping procedures must be designed to serve a number of persons and users. No single system serves the needs of all E&P companies; however, the procedures discussed in the following pages are typical in the industry.

THE AUTHORIZATION SYSTEM

Exploring for oil and gas is done on a project basis. Projects may extend over a considerable period of time, often years. Management approvals are required because of the large expenditures, length of time involved, and need to maintain tight controls over cash. Company policies dictate the dollar threshold for approvals of specific expenditures. Signatures are usually required from one or more individuals with functional responsibilities for exploration. Larger expenditures in an E&P company may require an authorization for expenditure (AFE), which contains a description of the project, a listing of proposed expenditures, and spaces for appropriate approvals.

Many in the industry reserve the term AFE for those expenditures where exploratory or developmental wells are drilled. Different procedures and forms, such as project approvals, are used for other activities. Because the procedures involved are basically the same, no attempt is made in this chapter to distinguish between types of authorizations. In any case, an expenditure of a major amount requires approval of one or more individuals in an organization and, for a joint venture, approval by all working interest owners. Thus, the term AFE is used in this book for any planned expenditures where approval is required.

For example, assume that ABC Oil Company contemplates exploring a certain area. Direct expenditures are estimated to be $50,000, and an approved AFE is necessary for work to commence. The form illustrated in Figure 6-1 is initiated by a district geologist.

Detailed items specified on the exploration AFE correspond to subsidiary accounts for exploration expense, which are discussed later in this chapter. The amount for overhead is an estimate (in this case, 20 percent of direct costs) and does not indicate expected cash expenditures on the project.

Approval of the AFE does not require an entry in the formal accounting records; instead, it provides internal control procedures for expenditures. Even though exploration budgets are somewhat flexible, an AFE encumbers a portion of the company budget. Costs are accumulated for each project and compared with the amounts authorized. Columns entitled Actual Cost and Variance provide the means for making these comparisons when the project is completed, as shown in Figure 6-1.

ACCOUNTS AND SUBACCOUNTS FOR EXPLORATION EXPENSE

The accounting system must ensure that transactions are properly recorded. It also accumulates information to enhance internal control, provide management information, and collect data for filing federal, state, and local tax returns and regulatory reports. Thus, the elements of each financial transaction are not classified merely by the general ledger accounts involved, but by other categories as well. For these reasons, oil and gas producing companies use a complex coding system in their recording procedures.

How data is recorded depends on several things: management needs, organizational structure, and operational requirements. In this chapter, a typical coding system is used to classify data. Because it is cumbersome to demonstrate, this system is not used consistently in the remainder of the book.

> *"OPEC* *has the lowest average production costs in the oil industry. This is partly because some OPEC Member Countries have large amounts of oil in reasonably accessible locations. Yet, OPEC Members will still need to spend tens of billions of dollars in the future to meet the growing need for oil."*
>
> *– Organization of the Petroleum Exporting Countries,*
> *April 2007, http://www.opec.org/library/FAQs/PetrolIndustry/q9.htm*

Figure 6-1
Completed Authorization for Expenditure (AFE)

AUTHORIZATION FOR EXPENDITURE – EXPLORATION			
REQUEST FOR AUTHORITY		AFE NO.	06008
J. Smith, Exploration Dept.		DATE	05/12/06
LOCATION: T7N, R21E, Haskell Co., Oklahoma			
PURPOSE: To conduct exploration activities for possible leasing and subsequent drilling and development.			
ITEM	ESTIMATED COST	ACTUAL COST	VARIANCE
01 – G&G Contract	$40,000	$38,000	$2,000
02 – G&G Services – Other	0	0	0
03 – Field Party Salaries	7,000	7,400	(400)
04 – Field Party Supplies	0	0	0
05 – Field Party – Other	1,000	1,200	(200)
06 – Support Facilities	0	0	0
07 – Shooting Rights and Damages	2,000	2,300	(300)
08 – Mapping Expense	0	0	0
09 – Equipment Rental	0	0	0
10 – Other Geological and Geophysical Costs	0	0	0
11 – Purchased Geological and Geophysical Data	0	0	0
TOTAL DIRECT	$50,000	$48,900	$1,100
12 – OVERHEAD	10,000	9,780	220
TOTAL	$60,000	$58,680	$1,320

APPROVALS: *M. Jones 05/20/06*

Under Oi5, a company using the successful efforts method must charge all exploration costs to expense as incurred, except for costs of successful exploratory wells, wells in progress, and certain circumstances specifically addressed in Oi5.111. The general ledger accounts used by ABC Oil Company to record exploration expenses are listed below. In general, the accounts correspond to categories found in Oi5.108.

801	Geological and Geophysical Costs
802	Carrying and Retaining Undeveloped Properties
803	Test Well Contributions
804	Unsuccessful Exploratory Wells
805	Unsuccessful Exploratory Stratigraphic Wells

Various subaccounts related to carrying and retaining undeveloped properties (Delay Rentals, Ad Valorem Taxes, Legal Expenses, and Record Maintenance Costs) are discussed in Chapter 7. Accounts related to exploratory drilling activities (Unsuccessful Exploratory Wells and Unsuccessful Exploratory Stratigraphic Wells) are examined in Chapter 9.

G&G SUBACCOUNTS

Costs related directly to G&G exploration are charged by ABC to Account 801, Geological and Geophysical Costs, regardless of whether the amount involved is associated with an AFE. Subsidiary accounts are maintained to provide information for analysis and control of costs including the following:

801	001	Geological and Geophysical Contract Work
	002	Geological and Geophysical Services Other
	003	Field Party Salaries and Wages
	004	Field Party Supplies
	005	Other Field Party Expenses
	006	Charges for Support Facilities
	007	Shooting Rights and Damages
	008	Mapping Expenses
	009	Equipment Rental
	010	Other Geological and Geophysical Costs
	011	Purchased Geological and Geophysical Data
	012	Overhead

Although companies using the full cost method capitalize all G&G costs, most will maintain subsidiary accounts similar to those above in order to control and analyze costs.

CHARGING COSTS DIRECTLY TO G&G EXPENSE

To illustrate costs charged directly to exploration expense, assume an invoice for $38,000 is submitted for seismic work on AFE 06008 (shown in Figure 6-1). It is entered in the system and assigned voucher number 02098. Coding for charges included in the invoice is as follows:

801-001-02098-06008	G&G Expense		38,000	
	301-742-02098-06008	Vouchers Payable		38,000
	To record voucher payable for seismic work on AFE 06008.			

The amount due is coded according to the company's criteria:

- 801 indicates that the general ledger account charged is G&G costs.

- 001 is a sub-account that shows the charges are for G&G contract work.

- 02098 specifies that the charge is from voucher number 02098, the 98th voucher number assigned in February.

- 06008 indicates that the costs are incurred on the project covered by AFE 06008, the eighth AFE approved in 2006.

- 301 is the account number for Vouchers Payable.

- 742 is the vendor number.

When vouchers are prepared for G&G costs not covered by an AFE, the number 00000 is assigned to the AFE code block. For example, a payment of $2,000 was made on voucher number 02099 to a geologist to analyze well abandonment records filed with the state regulatory commission. This job is for Area MM in which the company is not presently operating. No AFE was prepared since the amount involved was below the cutoff point specified by company policy (for example, $20,000). This expenditure is recorded as follows:

801-002-02099-00000	*G&G Expense*		*2,000*	
	301-750-02099-00000 *Vouchers Payable*			*2,000*
	To record costs of geological service for Area MM.			

This entry indicates that a charge has been made to G&G expenses (G&G Services—Other), no AFE is involved, and the voucher number is 02099 (coding numbers and details of subsidiary records will not be used in subsequent illustrations in this book).

Periodic computer runs show the costs accumulated for each AFE. When a project is completed, a comparison is made between approved and actual costs for each subaccount. This comparison for AFE 06008 is shown in Figure 6-1. The costs related to the completed project are then removed from the active AFE file and transferred to a completed AFE file.

CHARGING COSTS TO WORK IN PROGRESS

Some companies prefer to charge costs incurred under an AFE to a deferred charge asset account, such as Work in Progress or Exploration in Progress. Costs pertaining to each AFE are accumulated in a single account. When work is completed, G&G costs are charged to Exploration Expense and credited to Work in Progress. This procedure offers additional internal control in that all costs pertaining to an AFE are initially collected in one general ledger account, as opposed to being spread among multiple accounts. Furthermore, as long as the amounts are included in Work in Progress, it is evident that the project is not yet finished.

If this method is followed, successful efforts companies make adjustments when preparing financial statements at the end of a period. Work in Progress Exploration accounts are closed into Exploration Expense. To illustrate such an entry, assume from the earlier example that ABC records voucher number 02098 as follows:

240	*Work In Progress—Geological and Geophysical Exploration*		*38,000*	
	301 *Vouchers Payable*			*38,000*
	To record voucher payable for seismic work on AFE 06008.			

Note that the only difference in recording this charge is that it is assigned to a Work in Progress account (Account 240) rather than an expense account. If the project has not been completed at the end of the accounting period, an adjustment closes the accumulated costs into exploration expense for financial statement presentation. For example, if at the end of the accounting period $45,400 of costs are accumulated on an exploration project, and the project is not complete, the following entry is made:

801	*Geological and Geophysical Expenses*		*45,400*	
	240 *Work In Progress—Geological and Geophysical Exploration*			*45,400*
	To reclassify exploration costs in Work In Progress to expense.			

Since the project is not complete, a successful efforts company must reverse the adjusting entry at the beginning of the following accounting period in order to continue the project in progress as follows:

240	Work In Progress—Geological and Geophysical Exploration	45,400	
801	Geological and Geophysical Expenses		45,400
	To reverse adjusting entry for G&G costs on unfinished projects.		

After the reversal, additional costs under the AFE are accumulated in the Work in Progress account in the usual manner until the project is completed.

The two preceding entries can be eliminated if a company's chart of accounts and general ledger simply classify G&G Work in Progress accounts within the Exploration Expense section (Accounts 800 to 899). This approach is a practical solution since G&G costs are almost always expensed as incurred under successful efforts.

To complete this example, assume the AFE has been completed and is ready to be closed. The total cost as shown in Figure 6-1 is $58,680. Under the successful efforts method, the journal entry is:

801	Geological and Geophysical Expenses	58,680	
240	Work In Progress—Geological and Geophysical Exploration		58,680
	To close AFE 06008 and record exploration expense for the project.		

Each subsidiary account under Work in Progress is also credited. An analysis of estimated and actual costs can be prepared for managerial use with greater assurance that all charges applicable to the AFE have been included. While other procedures appear in some illustrations in this book, the use of a Work in Progress account for AFEs is assumed to be standard policy for ABC Oil Company.

SPECIAL PROBLEM AREAS IN ACCOUNTING FOR EXPLORATION COSTS

Although Oi5 clearly defines exploration costs and explains how they are to be accounted for, certain problems of interpretation arise. The most common issues are discussed in this section.

EXPLORATION PERMITS (SHOOTING RIGHTS)

In either onshore or offshore activities, permission is required to conduct exploration. Before an onshore mineral lease is signed, an exploration permit called shooting rights is obtained from property owners. For offshore exploration, a permit is typically sought from the U.S. Department of the Interior Minerals Management Service (MMS). In this case, payment of a fee to the government is not usually required.

Onshore **exploration rights** may take one of two forms. Under a shooting rights only contract, the rights holder is allowed to access the property and conduct exploratory activities up to, but not including, drilling an exploratory well. Costs involved with such a contract are properly classified as exploration expense under successful efforts (assuming the use of a Work in Progress account) as noted in the following entry:

240.007	*Work in Progress—Shooting Rights and Damages*	2,300	
301	*Vouchers Payable*		2,300
	To record exploration permits for AFE 06008.		

In other cases, the contract may not only grant shooting rights, but also contain an option for the grantee to lease all or any part of the mineral acreage covered by the contract for a specified sum, usually expressed in dollars per acre.

ACREAGE SELECTION OPTIONS

An option agreement may specify the amount applicable to shooting rights and separately state the cost of the option. In this case, the cost of exploration rights is treated in the same manner as any other exploration cost. Accounting for option payments is discussed in greater detail in Chapter 7. If none of the acreage covered by the option is leased, the entire amount of the option cost is charged to expense, both for financial accounting purposes by a company using the successful efforts method and for tax purposes. If the entire acreage is leased, all of the option cost is capitalized as the cost of the mineral rights; if only part of the acreage is leased, a portion of the cost is capitalized when using successful efforts accounting. A full cost company capitalizes all option costs in every case for financial accounting purposes and would later expense the option if no acreage was leased for tax purposes.

TEST WELL CONTRIBUTIONS

Frequently, the owner or lessee of a property will agree to contribute cash to the operator of a nearby lease to defray a portion of the drilling costs of a test well. The property owner or lessee is entitled to receive certain information in return, such as cuttings, core samples, and logs obtained in drilling the well.

In the case of a dry hole contribution, funds are paid to the drilling party only if the well is dry or does not result in a producing well. Bottom-hole contributions are paid upon the drilling party's reaching the proposed depth or a specific geological formation, regardless of the outcome.

For financial accounting purposes, the recipient of test well contributions treats the amount received as a reduction in well costs. For federal income tax purposes, the IRS requires the recipient to include the amount received as income.

The payor of either type of test well contribution treats it as an exploration cost for financial accounting purposes. For example, payment of a dry hole contribution by ABC Oil Company of $10,000 to the operator of a nearby lease is recorded as follows under successful efforts accounting:

803	*Test Well Contributions Dry Hole Costs*	10,000	
301	*Vouchers Payable*		10,000
	To record dry hole contribution by ABC.		

When using the full cost method, all test well contributions are capitalized as part of the cost pool. Costs may be allocated to nearby individual properties or may be charged to Account 229, Unsuccessful Exploration Costs.

For federal income tax purposes, all test well contributions made must be capitalized and added to the cost of other acreage owned by the contributor in that area.

EXPLORATION PERFORMED IN RETURN FOR ACREAGE

An operator owning lease rights in unproved acreage may agree to contribute a portion of its interest in that acreage (either an undivided interest in the entire acreage or divided interest in a fractional share of the tract) to another company in return for an agreement to perform specified exploration work. Accounting for this pooling of assets is addressed in Oi5.138(c). The successful efforts company that is conducting the exploration will charge the costs incurred to exploration expense, while a full cost company will capitalize such costs. The company assigning the acreage will record its total acreage cost as the cost of its retained interest. Proper notations of the reduction of ownership in the acreage are made in the land department records of the assignor of the interest.

Assume that ABC Oil Company holds leases on 5,000 acres in Wilson County, Texas, that were acquired at a total cost of $800,000. A contract is executed with XYZ Company, a successful efforts company, under which it agrees to conduct specified exploration activities. On completion of the work, and regardless of whether the outcome is successful, XYZ is to be assigned a one-fourth interest in the property. It spends a total of $360,000 for the exploration activities. XYZ records exploration costs and the earning of an interest in the properties as follows:

801	Geological and Geophysical Expense	360,000	
	301 Vouchers Payable		360,000
	To record the cost of work performed for an interest in ABC Oil Company's leases in Wilson County, Texas.		

XYZ assigns no cost to the leasehold interest acquired, although most companies would assign some nominal amount, such as $1, to the property for control purposes. If this were done in the example, $1 would be charged to Unproved Property Acquisition Costs, Account 211, and $359,999 would be charged to Geological and Geophysical Expense. ABC makes no entries in the accounting records. It would, however, record the new reduced interest in the properties in the detailed lease records.

Under a different type of arrangement, the contract may specify that the party performing the work acquires an interest in the property only if the work indicates the existence of reserves. This is known as a conditional pooling of assets. However, the accounting treatment is the same: a successful efforts company performing the work charges all costs to exploration expense, and the party owning the property makes no entry.

A third type of exploration arrangement is accorded special treatment by Oi5.111. G&G studies may be conducted on a property owned by another person in exchange for an interest in the property if proved reserves are found or for reimbursement of the costs if proved reserves are not found. In such cases, G&G costs are accounted for as a receivable when incurred by the party performing the services; if proved reserves are found, G&G costs become the cost of the unproved property acquired.

A literal interpretation of Oi5.111 is shown by the following illustration. ABC Oil Company owns a lease covering 10,000 acres. By contractual agreement, XYZ agrees to conduct certain exploration activities on the property. If proved reserves are found, XYZ is to be assigned a one-sixth working interest in the property. If no proved reserves are found, ABC is to reimburse XYZ for costs incurred of $80,000.

As XYZ performs services, its charges are posted to a receivable account on XYZ's books:

130	Accounts Receivable	80,000	
	301 Vouchers Payable		80,000
	To record exploration costs incurred on ABC lease.		

If no proved reserves are found, ABC reimburses XYZ for the $80,000. XYZ records receipt of the payment as follows:

101	Cash	80,000	
	130 Accounts Receivable		80,000
	To record reimbursement from ABC for exploration activities conducted.		

Reimbursement of costs to XYZ is recorded as an exploration expense on ABC's books as follows:

801	Geological and Geophysical Expense	80,000	
	101 Cash		80,000
	To record reimbursement to XYZ for exploration activities conducted.		

The treatment required by Oi5.111 in this situation is somewhat inconsistent. Presumably, exploration work would have to include exploratory drilling because it would be rare for proved reserves to be discovered otherwise. However, if drilling is undertaken in return for an interest in a mineral property, the driller is required to treat the entire amount spent for drilling as the cost of wells and related facilities. If proved reserves are found, presumably that part of costs incurred for exploration other than drilling (and reimbursable if proved reserves are not found) would be treated as mineral property costs, while the drilling costs would be treated as the costs of wells and related facilities. If the well is successful, the costs of drilling and equipping the site are capitalized; if the drilling is unsuccessful, any costs, net of salvage value, are charged to expense.

Alternatively, if proved reserves are found, XYZ records the receipt of the mineral interest on its books as follows:

221	Proved Leaseholds	80,000	
	130 Accounts Receivable		80,000
	To record mineral interest in ABC lease.		

ABC makes no accounting entry if proved reserves are found; rather, it merely reduces its share of ownership in the property.

PURCHASED G&G LIBRARY

Sometimes oil and gas operators purchase a library of G&G data. The information may relate to a specific area of interest, basin, or trend, or it may encompass many areas. Oi5 appears to require that the costs of all purchased exploration data be charged to expense at the time the costs are incurred.

Nevertheless, some successful efforts companies have proposed to treat such costs as deferred charges—if the information is expected to be used over a period of years and to the extent the library itself can be resold and its capitalized costs readily recovered in cash (analogous to the exception in Oi5.111). These companies argue that if the costs can be allocated to specific areas, then related costs may be charged to expense when the information is used. If the costs cannot be identified with specific areas, the deferred costs are amortized over their estimated useful life (perhaps two or three years) using straight-line amortization. Such treatment would rarely be appropriate. If this method is used, care should be taken to ensure that deferred costs are truly for a saleable library and recoverable by sale of the data. If not, such costs should be expensed at the time they are incurred.

SEISMIC SURVEYS FOR PROVED PROPERTY DEVELOPMENT

Three-dimensional (3-D) or four-dimensional (4-D) seismic surveys are widely used for performing subsurface G&G analysis on both proved and unproved acreage. Costs of seismic surveys used to assist production, increase total recoverability, and determine the desirability of drilling additional development wells within a proved area can be capitalized under the successful efforts method. To be capitalized, these costs should meet the definition of development activities. All seismic survey costs that are not development costs should be expensed as incurred. Any seismic expenses related to both proved and unproved acreage should be allocated between exploration and development costs.

SUPPORT FACILITIES AND OVERHEAD COSTS

Expenses related to support facilities and activities should be allocated to the particular activities receiving benefits. Thus, costs of depreciation, taxes, repairs, and operation of equipment (such as seismic equipment, construction and grading equipment, drilling equipment, vehicles, repair shops, warehouses, supply points, camps and division, district, or field offices) may relate in whole or in part to exploration work; the identifiable part should be treated as an exploration cost. Procedures for apportioning, allocating, and assigning common costs to specific activities are discussed in Chapter 3. Under successful efforts accounting, only costs directly related to activities whose direct costs are capitalized should themselves be capitalized.

Under the full cost method, internal costs that are capitalized are limited to costs, including overhead, which can be directly identified with acquisition, exploration, and development activities undertaken by the reporting entity for its own account. For example, costs of operating the undeveloped properties section, costs of exploration management, and costs of scouts and landmen are properly capitalized; general corporate overhead or similar costs should not be capitalized. In many cases, under both full cost and successful efforts accounting, the decision as to whether costs should be capitalized is an exercise of professional judgment.

• • •

7

UNPROVED PROPERTY ACQUISITION, RETENTION, AND SURRENDER

Key Concepts:

- Basic terms and provisions of mineral lease agreements

- Illustrative oil and gas lease

- Distinction between operating and nonoperating mineral interests

- Treatment of cost for unproved mineral leasehold acquisitions

- Accounting for rentals, property taxes, and other carrying costs of unproved properties

- Effects of impairment or abandonment of unproved leases: individual and group accounting

- Full cost accounting treatment of individual properties

Petroleum companies seek to secure the rights to drill for and produce subsurface and surface minerals. Whether minerals actually exist in an area is uncertain until a drilling rig probes to depths where deposits may be found. Despite the risks, a company must negotiate in advance with owners of mineral rights for permission to drill wells and produce any minerals discovered.

Occasionally, rights are secured by simply purchasing the **fee interest** in a property—resulting in outright ownership of both surface and minerals. In nearly every case, though, the right to explore and produce is obtained through an oil and gas lease and/or a mineral lease. This chapter focuses on leasing in the United States. Chapter 25 addresses property rights outside the U.S.

Mineral rights can be severed from surface rights and are often divided among, and owned by, more than one person. For example, one person or group of persons may own the minerals to a depth of 4,000 feet; another person may own the minerals from 4,000 feet to 8,000 feet. In this situation, a potential lessee must negotiate with owners of the subsurface footage to which the lessee wishes to drill. Even more common is a situation in which many people (frequently heirs of a decedent) own undivided interests (e.g., 20 percent share) in mineral rights in a property.

If mineral rights are obtained by lease, the rights conveyed from the mineral owner to the oil and gas company are more extensive than merely the right to drill wells and produce oil and gas. Typical lease agreements grant oil and gas companies the rights to explore, drill, survey, lay pipelines, build facilities, dispose of salt water, and own the minerals during the term of the lease.

When different parties own the surface and minerals, and after securing rights from the mineral owner, an oil and gas company makes a separate agreement with the surface owner. Surface owners cannot legally deny the lessee access to land on which the minerals are leased. Thus, the mineral estate is held to be dominant over the surface estate.

Surface owners are paid for damages that occur to surface areas as petroleum operations are carried out. Road construction and brush clearing are examples of how an oil and gas company converts a portion of the surface from the landowner's use. Such changes call for adequate compensation to the landowner. If compensation cannot be agreed upon, the matter may be taken to court. In this case, a judicial rule of reasonable accommodation between mineral and surface owners is typically applied.

Acquisition of mineral rights is a crucial activity for a petroleum company. This function is typically handled by personnel in the land department who have responsibility to:

- Contact other oil and gas operators, lease brokers, and land and mineral owners for the purpose of obtaining leases covering the minerals.
- Advise the exploration department on leasing activities.
- Negotiate **joint operating agreements** with other operators.
- Secure pooling or unitization agreements.
- Negotiate the drilling of promotional test wells, farmouts, and royalty overrides.
- Check lease contracts on all newly purchased leases for proper signatures, notarization, dates, and other key information.
- File the lease contract in the county clerk's office where the leased land is located; alternatively, a memorandum may be filed to protect confidentiality of lease terms.

- Maintain a complete record on all properties including leases, royalty agreements, fee lands, and any other rights.

- Verify that the title to a lease is clear before drilling commences by obtaining a drilling opinion from an attorney qualified to examine titles based on abstracts.

- Prepare division orders for proper payment of proceeds.

- Make timely payment of all lease rentals as authorized.

THE LEASE CONTRACT

In the U.S., oil and gas operators normally acquire rights in mineral properties through mineral leases. It is essential that petroleum accountants understand the basics of mineral lease contracts.

The lease may cover oil, gas, related hydrocarbons, and other minerals or a combination thereof. A mineral is usually defined as a substance having value in excess of the existing dirt. Mineral owners who grant rights to others through a lease contract are referred to as **lessors**, while the entities acquiring such leasehold rights are known as **lessees**.

Lease forms vary considerably. Figure 7-1 demonstrates a lease agreement. Sample forms for federal and state mineral leases are found in CD Reference Exhibits B and C. Regardless of the printed lease form used, the lessor and lessee may strike certain provisions or add additional language to the document as a final agreement is reached.

LEASE BONUS *(Figure 7-1, article 1)*

A lease **bonus** is cash or other consideration paid to a lessor by the lessee in return for the rights to explore for minerals, drill wells, and produce any minerals found. The actual amount of the bonus is not normally recorded on the lease form; instead, wording such as $10.00 and other valuable consideration appears on the document.

The amount of lease bonus paid is the result of bargaining between the parties and is affected by such factors as proximity of the property to proved production, number of years in the primary term of the lease, competition among potential lessees, and the amount of royalty retained by the lessor. Bonuses are usually computed on a per-acre basis and range from a few dollars per acre in wildcat locations to thousands of dollars per acre for locations near producing properties. Leases on state and federally owned properties are normally awarded as the result of a bidding process with leases granted to the highest bidder. Offshore tracts often cover 5,000 or more acres, and a lease bonus of millions of dollars for a single block is not uncommon. Some offshore bidding requirements include royalty or net profit bids in addition to or in lieu of bonus bids.

PRIMARY TERM *(Figure 7-1, article 2)*

The maximum period of time allowed for a lessee to commence drilling a well is referred to as the primary term. Lessors are anxious for an oil company to drill as quickly as possible and generally prefer a short primary term. The company acquiring the rights would prefer a longer period of time to evaluate the property, review the drilling budget, and obtain other parcels nearby. In a wildcat area, five-year to seven-year terms may be negotiated. If the property is located near producing properties, the primary term may be two years or less.

DELAY RENTALS *(Figure 7-1, article 5)*

The payment made to defer commencement of drilling activities for an additional year is called a delay rental. Delay rentals are stated on a per-acre basis and are normally much smaller than a lease bonus. For example, if a lease contract called for a lease bonus of $50 per acre, the delay rental might be $1, $2, or $5 per acre depending on conditions in the geographic area and the negotiating ability of the parties.

Many short-term leases (i.e., two to three years) are referred to as paid-up leases whereby only bonus payments are made until production begins.

DRILLING OBLIGATION *(Figure 7-1, article 5)*

Payment of a bonus and signing of the lease ordinarily keeps the contract in force for one year. If drilling does not begin within 12 months, the lease terminates (regardless of the length of the primary term) unless the lessee makes a specified payment of delay rental to the lessor. In succeeding years, a similar drilling obligation exists—but can be deferred and the lease retained—for successive periods of one year each by making an annual delay rental payment. However, no contract provisions extend the lease beyond the stated primary term. A lease is extended only by production in paying amounts.

ROYALTY PROVISIONS *(Figure 7-1, article 3)*

Lessors retain a royalty interest in the minerals. This entitles a lessor to receive cost-free a specified portion of the oil and gas produced or a specified portion of the value of such production. Royalty payments to mineral owners are reduced only by applicable state severance taxes, production taxes, or other costs necessary to get the product into salable condition. Historically, royalties on oil and gas properties are a one-eighth share, although it may be larger if the property is located near existing oil or gas production. A royalty share is negotiable; in the past, landowners have executed leases calling for a royalty interest of one-fifth or more.

To illustrate how royalty interests work, suppose that ABC Oil Company acquired a mineral lease on a property in which Lessor Jones retained a one-eighth royalty interest. During the current year, 4,000 barrels of oil were produced and sold for $60 per barrel. The state severance tax is 10 percent of the value of the oil. The purchaser will remit to Lessor Jones the sum of $27,000 (1/8 of $240,000 x 90%), which represents the net value of Jones' one-eighth royalty share after withholding severance taxes.

ABC, the lessee, must pay all lifting costs and other production costs on the lease. The lease contract may call for the lessor to bear a proportionate share of costs to make the product salable.

PRODUCTION HOLDS LEASE *(Figure 7-1, article 6)*

Once a successful well has been drilled and commercial production is obtained, the lease remains in effect for as long as there is production without extended and indefinite interruption. If production ceases, the operator must act in good faith to resume the extraction of oil or gas within a reasonable time as specified in the lease contract. Prolonged inactivity will result in termination of the lease, in which case all mineral rights revert to the mineral owner, and the lessee must restore the surface of the land to its prior condition.

OFFSET CLAUSE *(Figure 7-1, article 6)*

A common provision is an offset clause which requires operators to drill **offset wells** on the property as a prudent operator would drill under similar circumstances. The offset clause comes into play when a successful well is drilled on adjacent land within a specified distance of the property covered by the lease contract.

SHUT-IN ROYALTIES *(Figure 7-1, article 3)*

Many lease contracts provide for shut-in royalties, which represent payments by the operator to the royalty owner if a successful well is: (1) drilled and completed, (2) capable of producing in commercial quantities, and (3) production has not begun within a specified time. Shut-ins frequently occur on properties containing gas and may be due to the absence of a market, lack of transportation, or necessity to obtain permission from a governmental unit. Normally, shut-in payments cannot be recovered by the operator out of future amounts accruing to the royalty owner. Frequently, lease contracts specify that shut-in royalties will be equal in amount to the delay rentals. In many instances, the lessor may restrict the number of years of shut-in availability.

RIGHT TO ASSIGN INTEREST *(Figure 7-1, article 8)*

Lease contracts typically grant each party the right to assign, without approval of the other party, any part or all of its rights and obligations. Federal leases are an exception as shown in section 20 of the federal lease form in CD Reference Exhibit B. The right to assign is extremely important to an oil and gas company.

POOLING PROVISIONS *(Figure 7-1, article 4)*

Most leases contain a provision that allows the operator to combine (pool or unitize) the leased property with properties owned by others. After properties are combined, each former owner of an interest in an individual property owns an interest in the total of the pooled minerals. Ownership shares in the pooled undeveloped properties are normally in proportion to the acreage contributed.

In the secondary and tertiary development of fields, it may be advantageous to unitize the operation. Royalties are divided in accordance with the production capabilities of each producing well (rather than on a contributed acreage basis) with the best wells receiving enhanced portions of total royalty.

Unitization may result in increased and more efficient production. Pooling or unitization is advantageous to lessees because it usually results in cost savings. Finally, certain governmental units may require pooling as a conservation measure.

Volume Of Oil & Gas Leases Managed By The U.S. Government ▬▬▬▬▬▬▬

"The Department of the Interior agency manages 261 million acres of federally owned land, mostly in 12 western states. It also administers 700 million acres of subsurface mineral holdings throughout the U.S."

– *Nick Snow,* "Producers, surface landowners confront split-estate issues." *Oil & Gas Journal* 104:3, Jan. 16, 2006.

Figure 7-1
Illustrative Oil and Gas Lease

OIL, GAS AND MINERAL LEASE

THIS AGREEMENT made this _____ day of _____ 20___, between
_____ Lessor (whether one or more) whose address is
_____ and
_____ Lessee.

WITNESSETH:

1. Lessor, in consideration of _____ Dollars ($____), in hand paid, of the royalties herein provided, and of the agreement of Lessee herein contained, hereby grants, leases, and lets exclusively unto Lessee for the purpose of investigating, exploring, prospecting, drilling, and mining for and producing oil, gas and all other minerals, laying pipelines, building roads, tanks, power stations, telephone lines, and other structures thereon to produce, save, take care of, treat, transport, and own said products, and housing its employees, the following described land in _____ County, to wit:

This lease also covers and includes all land owned or claimed by Lessor adjacent or contiguous to the land particularly described above, whether the same be in said section or sections, grant or grants, or in adjacent sections or grants, although not included within the boundaries of the land particularly described above. For the purpose of calculating the rental payments hereinafter provided for, said land is estimated to comprise _____ acres, whether it actually comprises more or less.

2. Subject to the other provisions herein contained, this lease shall be for a term of _____ years from this date (called *primary term*) and as long thereafter as oil, gas, or other minerals is produced in paying quantities from said land or lands with which said land is pooled hereunder.

3. The royalties to be paid by Lessee are: (a) on oil, one-eighth (1/8) of that produced and saved from said land, the same to be delivered at the wells or to the credit of Lessor into the pipeline to which the wells may be connected. Lessee may from time to time purchase any royalty oil in its possession, paying the market price prevailing for the field where produced on the date of purchase, in either case such interest to bear its proportion of any expense of treating unmerchantable oil to render it merchantable as crude; (b) on gas, one-eighth (1/8) of the market value at the well of the gas used by Lessee in operations not connected with the land leased or any pooled unit containing all or a part of said land; the royalty on gas sold by Lessee to be one-eighth (1/8) of the market value at the well; (c) one-eighth (1/8) of the market value at the mouth of the well of gas used by Lessee in manufacturing gasoline or other by-products, except that in computing such value, there shall be excluded all gas components thereof used in lease or unit operations; and (d) on all other minerals mined and marketed, one-tenth (1/10) either in kind or value at the well or mine, at Lessee's election, except that on sulphur mined and marketed, the royalty shall be fifty (50) cents per long ton. In the event that any well on the land or on property pooled therewith (or with any part thereof) is capable of producing oil or gas or gaseous substances in paying quantities but such minerals are not being produced, then Lessee's rights may be maintained, in the absence of production or drilling operations, by resuming rental payments within the primary term or the making of shut-in royalty payments of $ _____ amount

Figure 7-1
Illustrative Oil and Gas Lease
(continued)

per well per year as hereinafter provided in paragraph 6. Should conditions occur or exist at the end of or after the primary term or within sixty (60) days prior to the expiration thereof, Lessee's rights may be extended beyond and after the primary term by the commencement, resumption, or continuance of such payments at the rate and in the manner herein provided for rental payments during the primary term, and each anniversary date thereof shall be considered as a fixed rental paying date, and if such payments are made, it will be considered that oil or gas or gaseous substance is being produced within the meaning of paragraph 2 hereof. Lessee shall have free use of oil, gas, coal, wood, and water from said land, except water from Lessor's wells, for all operations hereunder, and royalty on oil, gas, and coal shall be computed after deducting any so used.

4. Lessee, at its option, is hereby given the right and power to pool or combine the acreage covered by this lease or any portion thereof with other land, lease, or leases in the immediate vicinity thereof, when in Lessee's judgment it is necessary or advisable to do so in order to properly develop and operate said premises in compliance with any lawful spacing rules that may be prescribed for the field in which this lease is situated by any duly authorized authority, or when to do so would, in the judgment of Lessee, would promote the conservation of the oil and gas in and under and that may be produced from said premises. Lessee shall execute in writing an instrument identifying and describing the pooled acreage. The entire acreage so pooled into a tract or unit shall be treated, for all purposes except the payment of royalties on production from the pooled unit, as if it were included in this lease. If production is found on the pooled acreage, it shall be treated as if production is had from this lease, whether the well or wells be located on the premises covered by this lease or not. In lieu of the royalties elsewhere herein specified, Lessor shall receive on production from a pool only such portion of the royalty stipulated herein as the amount of his acreage placed in the pool or his royalty interest therein on an acreage basis bears to the total acreage so pooled in the particular pool involved.

5. If operations for drilling are not commenced on said land or on acreage pooled therewith as above provided on or before one year from this date, the lease shall then terminate as to both parties, unless on or before such anniversary date Lessee shall pay or tender to Lessor or to the credit of Lessor in _____ Bank at _____ _____, (which bank and its successors are Lessor's agent and shall continue as the depository for all rentals payable hereunder regardless of changes in ownership of said land or the rentals) the sum of _____ Dollars ($_____), (herein called rental), which shall cover the privilege of deferring commencement of drilling operations for a period of twelve (12) months. In like manner, and upon like payment or tenders annually the commencement of drilling operations may be further deferred for successive periods of twelve (12) months each during the primary term. The payment or tender of rental may be made by the check or draft of Lessee mailed or delivered to Lessor or to said bank on or before such date of payment. If such bank (or any successor bank) should fail, liquidate, or be succeeded by another bank or for any reason fail or refuse to accept rental, Lessee shall not be held in default for failure to make such payment or tender of rental until thirty (30) days after Lessor shall deliver to Lessee a proper recordable instrument, naming another bank as agent to receive such payments or tenders. The cash down payment is consideration for this lease

Figure 7-1
Illustrative Oil and Gas Lease
(continued)

according to its terms and shall not be allocated as mere rental for a period. Lessee may at any time or times execute and deliver to Lessor or to the depository above named or place of record a release or releases covering any portion or portions of the above described premises and thereby surrender this lease as to such portion or portions and be relieved of all obligations as to the acreage surrendered, and thereafter the rentals payable hereunder shall be reduced in the proportion that the acreage covered hereby is reduced by said release or releases.

6. If prior to discovery of oil, gas, or other mineral on said land or on acreage pooled therewith, Lessee should drill a dry hole or holes thereon, or if after discovery of oil, gas, or other mineral, the production thereof should cease from any cause, this lease shall not terminate if Lessee commences additional drilling or reworking operations within sixty (60) days thereafter or if it be within the primary term, commences or resumes the payment or tender of rentals, or commences operations for drilling or reworking on or before the rental paying date next ensuing after the expiration of 60 days from date of completion of dry hole or cessation of production. If at any time subsequent to sixty (60) days prior to the beginning of the last year of the primary term and prior to the discovery of oil, gas, or other mineral on said land or on acreage pooled therewith, Lessee should drill a dry hole thereon, no rental payment or operations are necessary in order to keep the lease in force during the remainder of the primary term. If at the expiration of the primary term, oil, gas, or other mineral is not being produced on said land or on acreage pooled therewith, but Lessee is then engaged in drilling or reworking operations thereon or shall have completed a dry hole thereon within sixty (60) days prior to the end of the primary term, the lease shall remain in force so long as operations are prosecuted with no cessation of more than sixty (60) consecutive days, and if they result in the production of oil, gas, or other mineral, so long thereafter as oil, gas, or other mineral is produced from said land or acreage pooled therewith in paying quantities. In the event a well or wells producing oil or gas in paying quantities should be brought in on adjacent land and within one hundred fifty (150) feet of and draining the leased premises or acreage pooled therewith, Lessee agrees to drill such offset wells as a reasonably prudent operator would drill under the same or similar circumstances.

7. Lessee shall have the right at any time during or after the expiration of this lease to remove all property and fixtures placed by Lessee on said land, including the right to draw and remove all casing. When required by Lessor, Lessee will bury all pipelines below ordinary plow depth, and no well shall be drilled within two hundred (200) feet of any residence or barn now on said land without Lessor's consent. Lessee shall be responsible for all changes caused by Lessee's operations hereunder other than damages necessarily caused by the exercise of the rights herein granted. Abandoned wells shall be properly plugged.

8. The rights of either party hereunder may be assigned in whole or in part, and the provisions hereof shall extend to their heirs, successors, and assigns; but no change or division in ownership of the land, rentals, or royalties, however accomplished, shall operate to enlarge the obligations or diminish the rights of Lessee; and no change or division in such ownership shall be binding on Lessee until thirty (30) days after Lessee shall have been furnished by registered U.S. mail at Lessee's principal place

Figure 7-1
Illustrative Oil and Gas Lease
(continued)

of business with a certified copy of recorded instrument or instruments evidencing same. In the event of assignment hereof in part, liability for breach of any obligations hereunder shall rest exclusively upon the owner of this lease or of a portion thereof who commits such breach. In the event of the death of any person entitled to rentals hereunder, Lessee may pay or tender such rentals to the credit of the deceased until such time as Lessee is furnished with proper evidence of the appointment and qualifications of an executor or administrator of the estate, or if there be none, then until Lessee is furnished with evidence satisfactory to it as to the heirs or devisees of the deceased and that all debts of the estate have been paid. If at any time two or more persons are entitled to participate in the rental payable hereunder, Lessee may pay or tender said rental jointly to such persons or to their joint credit in the depository named herein; or, at Lessee's election, the proportionate part of said rental to which each participant is entitled may be paid or tendered to him separately or to his separate credit in said depository; and payment or tender to any participant of his portion of the rentals hereunder shall maintain this lease as to such participants. In event of assignment of this lease as to a segregated portion of said land, the rentals payable hereunder shall be apportionable as between the several leasehold owners ratably according to the surface area of each, and default in rental payment by one shall not affect the rights of the other leasehold owners hereunder. If six or more parties become entitled to royalty hereunder, Lessee may withhold payment thereof until furnished with a recordable instrument executed by all such parties designating an agent to receive payment for all.

9. The breach by Lessee of any obligation hereunder shall not work a forfeiture or termination of this lease nor be cause for cancellation hereof in whole or in part save as herein expressly provided. If the obligation should require the drilling of a well or wells, Lessee shall have ninety (90) days after the receipt of written notices by Lessee from Lessor specifically stating the duty and time alleged by Lessor within which to begin operations for the drilling of any such well or wells; and the only penalty for failure to do so shall be the termination of this lease save as to forty (40) acres for each oil well and 640 acres for each gas well being worked on or producing oil or gas, to be selected by Lessee so that each forty (40) acre tract will embrace one such well. After the discovery of oil, gas, or other mineral in paying quantities on said premises, Lessee shall reasonably develop the acreage retained hereunder, but in discharging this obligation it shall in no event be required to drill more than one well per forty (40) acres of the area retained hereunder and capable of producing oil and 640 acres per gas well, or such other proration area as be prescribed by regulatory agency or applicable field rules.

10. Lessor hereby warrants and agrees to defend the title to said land and agrees that Lessee at its option may discharge any tax, mortgage, or other lien upon said land, either in whole or in part, and in event Lessee does so, it shall be subrogated to such lien with right to enforce same and apply rentals and royalties accruing hereunder toward satisfying same. Without impairment of Lessee's rights under the warranty in event of failure of title, it is agreed that if Lessor owns an interest in said land less than the entire fee simple estate, then the royalties and rentals to be paid Lessor shall be reduced proportionately. Failure of Lessee to reduce rentals paid hereunder shall not impair the right of Lessee to reduce royalties.

Figure 7-1
Illustrative Oil and Gas Lease
(continued)

11. Should Lessee be prevented from complying with any express or implied covenant of this lease, from conducting drilling or reworking operations thereon, or from producing oil or gas therefrom by reason of scarcity of or inability to obtain or to use equipment or material, or by operation of **force majeure** [bold added], or any federal or state law or any order, rule, or regulation of governmental authority, then while so prevented, Lessee's obligation to comply with such covenant shall be suspended and Lessee shall not be liable in damages for failure to comply therewith; and this lease shall be extended while and so long as Lessee is prevented by any such cause from conducting drilling or reworking operations on or from producing oil or gas from the leased premises; and the time while Lessee is so prevented shall not be counted against Lessee, anything in this lease to the contrary notwithstanding.

12. The undersigned Lessor, for himself and his heirs, successors and assigns, hereby surrenders and releases all rights of homestead in the premises herein described, in so far as said rights of homestead may in any way affect the purpose for which this lease is made as recited herein, and agrees that the annual drilling deferment rental payments made to Lessor as herein provided will fully protect this lease as to the full interests of the undersigned.

[Signatures of Parties]

[Notary Public]

⊙ *(Note: See CD Reference Exhibit B and C for other illustrative lease forms.)*

RIGHTS TO FREE USE OF RESOURCES FOR LEASE OPERATIONS *(Figure 7-1, article 3)*

Operators are customarily given the right to use, without cost or royalty payment, oil and gas from the land in carrying out all operations under the lease contract. However, the royalty owner is entitled to a royalty on any oil or gas used on properties in which the royalty owner has no interest.

MISCELLANEOUS PROVISIONS OF LEASES

The foregoing are potential provisions in oil and gas contracts. However, many other provisions are inserted into leases that give parties special rights or impose selected obligations on them. Several of these provisions are examined in the following section.

Option Payment. Frequently, a company will initiate a pre-leasing agreement with a mineral owner that gives the company a stated period of time within which to lease the property. An option payment made by the operator may include the cost of rights to explore, or a separate payment may be required for those rights. The option typically specifies the amount of the bonus per acre to be paid if and when the lease is subsequently executed.

Fixed or Mandatory Rentals. The lease contract may provide for rental payments that cannot be avoided even though the property is **abandoned** or drilling has begun. In effect, these payments are **deferred bonuses** paid on an installment basis.

Compensatory Royalties. Compensatory royalties are paid by petroleum companies to royalty owners as compensation for loss of income during periods when the company has not fulfilled its obligation to drill. Examples of situations leading to compensatory royalty payments include failure to drill an offset well or failure to follow an agreed-upon plan for development of the property.

Guaranteed or Minimum Royalties. On properties with a high probability of being productive, mineral owners may negotiate a provision in the lease requiring lessees to guarantee a specified **minimum royalty** payment each month or each year. If a royalty owner's share of net proceeds from production is less than the specified amount, the lessee must pay the difference. Guaranteed payments may be nonrecoverable or recoverable out of future royalties accruing to the royalty owner. This provision is typically found in federal leases, but may be negotiated in fee leases, i.e. leases of private lands.

Right to Take in Kind. When a lessor owns a significant amount of minerals or is involved in activities that might require quantities of oil or gas (such as manufacturing or farming), the lessor may reserve the right to take its royalty in kind. In this case, a lessor takes its royalty share of actual production, and then secures a market or transportation for its own account. This provision requires additional metering or volume monitoring by the operator of the lease.

Call on Production. Some lessors are in the business of refining or purchasing oil, or marketing gas. An option to purchase or a call on production may be negotiated in their lease contracts. This provision guarantees the lessor has the first opportunity to purchase production for terms equivalent to market rates. This provision is often used by lessors that are vertically integrated oil and gas companies.

Executive Rights. Of increasing importance in oil, gas, and mineral transactions is the use of executive rights. These arise when a person or entity assigns or delegates exclusive rights to lease and handle the minerals belonging to another person. Executive rights can occur in a number of situations, including when several parties own undivided interests in minerals or when an oil and gas company requests it for convenience purposes. Executive rights are created much like a power of attorney and a holder of the rights does not have to own minerals in the tract.

Observations About Leases ━━━━━━━

There is no such thing as a standard or statutory oil and gas lease, except for those used by governmental authorities. Most oil and gas laws are made by the interpretations of the courts and become part of the common law.

The interest conveyed or transferred under an oil and gas lease varies greatly from state to state. In many states (and in the sample lease), the interest conveyed is a determinable fee simple in the minerals that terminates when the primary term expires or at the cessation of production. In other locales, an oil and gas lease creates only a license to explore and search, much like a hunting lease for game animals.

OPERATING AND NONOPERATING MINERAL INTERESTS

The lessee in a mineral lease has rights and obligations associated with drilling and equipping wells and producing the oil and gas. Lessees possess what is known as an operating interest or **working interest** in the property.

Lessors have the right to receive a specified fractional share of the minerals produced or the value thereof. The lessor or royalty owner has no right or obligation to carry out exploration, drilling, or production activities; lessors also bear no part of the costs incurred, except their proportionate share of production taxes or severance taxes and, where applicable, a share of costs necessary to make the oil or gas salable. Thus, the lessor, or royalty owner, is said to possess a **nonoperating interest**.

A basic royalty is not the sole nonoperating interest that may be created out of mineral rights in a property. Three other types of nonoperating interests exist which are created out of the working interest. These are: (1) **overriding royalties**, (2) production payments (oil or gas payments), and (3) **net profits interests**. These three nonoperating interests are examined later in the text.

Petroleum accountants should distinguish between the terms mineral rights and mineral interests. Mineral rights usually refer to fee ownership rights that are not created by a lease. However, for applying FAS 19, 25, and 69, the term mineral interests means more than fee ownership and encompasses **leasehold interests** such as working interests, royalty interests, overriding royalties, net profits interests, and some production payments.

GENERAL LEDGER ACCOUNTS FOR UNPROVED MINERAL INTERESTS

All capitalized costs related to unproved mineral properties are charged to the appropriate unproved mineral properties accounts. A single general ledger account entitled Unproved Mineral Properties may be maintained. In this instance, the company keeps appropriate subsidiary accounts for each type of unproved mineral interest owned as well as detailed records for individual properties.

Some companies choose to maintain separate general ledger accounts for each major type of unproved mineral interest. Subsidiary records are then kept for each individual property. The chart of accounts illustrated in Appendix 3 includes the following general ledger accounts for unproved mineral interests:

- **210** Unproved Property Purchase Suspense
- **211** Unproved Property Acquisition Costs (detailed by lease)
- **219** Allowance for Impairment of Unproved Properties
    (detailed by property or by groups of properties as appropriate)

Other accounts may be used for different types of **economic interests**, such as Account 212 for fee interests, 213 for royalty interests, 214 for overriding royalty interests, 215 for net profits interests, and 216 for volumetric production payments.

ACCOUNTING FOR
UNPROVED MINERAL LEASEHOLD ACQUISITIONS

Account 211—Unproved Property Acquisition Costs reflects the capitalized costs of unproved mineral leaseholds for the purpose of the following example.

BONUS PAYMENTS

A lease bonus, ordinarily the initial investment in an unproved lease, is capitalized as part of the property cost for financial accounting purposes. Assume ABC Oil Company acquires a lease on 640 acres from Landowner Smithers and pays a lease bonus of $100 per acre. The lease is assigned number 24002. The $64,000 lease bonus becomes the initial capitalized cost of the lease. Acquisition of the Smithers' lease is recorded as follows:

211	Unproved Property Acquisition Costs, Lease No. 24002	64,000	
301	Vouchers Payable		64,000
	To record lease bonus on acquisition of Smithers lease.		

INCIDENTAL LEASE ACQUISITION COSTS

Oi5.106 and Reg. S-X Rule 4-10(a)(14) provide that the cost of a mineral property includes such incidental costs as "broker's fees, recording fees, legal costs, and other costs incurred in acquiring properties." (Both Oi5 and Reg. S-X are explained in Chapter 4.) A legal fee of $400 was paid in connection with acquiring the Smithers lease and is recorded as follows:

211	Unproved Property Acquisition Costs, Lease No. 24002	400	
301	Vouchers Payable		400
	To record legal fee incurred in connection with acquisition of Smithers lease.		

Similar entries are made for recording fees and other acquisition costs, unless the amounts are insignificant. In that case, companies charge such costs to expense at the time incurred. Most companies require a minimum amount (such as $100 or $250) for expenditures to be capitalized.

Oi5 is silent on the proper treatment of overhead costs related to acquiring mineral properties. In identifying and acquiring leases, an E&P company may incur interval costs for scouting, civil engineering, surveying, and mapping. One problem faced in properly accounting for such costs, usually referred to as leasing costs, is that personnel are often engaged not only in lease activities, but also in servicing leases already acquired, assisting in drilling operations, working in exploration activities, and even working on producing leases.

Costs incurred by a company's own leasing staff can be accounted for in one of three ways:

- Expense all leasing costs at the time incurred

- Capitalize all leasing costs by allocating them on an acreage basis or equally to all leases taken during the period

- Capitalize those costs that can be associated with specific lease acquisitions and charge the balance to current operating expense

From the viewpoint of accounting theory, the third method is perhaps the most desirable; however, practical difficulties often make it prohibitive. Detailed time sheets can help determine labor costs directly applicable to specific properties. Operating costs of equipment may be charged to individual properties if adequate records are kept. In reality, the bulk of leasing costs cannot be traced to specific leases, and must be allocated on a predetermined basis if they are to be capitalized.

Several alternatives are available to the petroleum accountant. One is to accumulate all leasing costs applicable to an area of interest in a suspense account. This would occur in much the same way that exploration costs are accumulated by areas of interest for tax purposes. Then the entire amount applicable to an area can be capitalized on an acreage basis to any leases acquired. A second alternative provides for accumulated costs to be allocated between acreage leased (capitalized) and not leased (expensed) based on acreage. Finally, it might be argued that all leasing costs should be capitalized with the total outlay divided among all leases acquired during the year; however, this practice would certainly not be within the intent of Oi5 for companies using the successful efforts method.

Because of the practical difficulty involved, ABC Oil Company treats all leasing overhead costs as current operating expenses. The *2001 PricewaterhouseCoopers Survey of U.S. Petroleum Accounting Practices* reports that 16 of 16 responding companies using the successful efforts method charge a portion of internal land department costs to current expense. A full cost company typically capitalizes all overhead costs directly related to acquisition, exploration, and development activities. According to Reg. S-X Rule 4-10(c)(2):

> Any internal costs that are capitalized shall be limited to those costs that can be directly identified with acquisition, exploration, and development activities undertaken by the reporting entity for its own account, and shall not include any costs related to production, general corporate overhead, or similar activities.

OPTIONS TO ACQUIRE LEASEHOLD

An operator may not be sufficiently interested in an area to pay bonuses necessary to acquire leases; instead it may wish to acquire rights to shoot seismic with an option to lease any part or all of the acreage covered by the option. Oi5.108(a) requires that shooting rights are to be expensed and lease option costs are to be capitalized. The option agreement may specify an amount to be paid for each. Nevertheless, any costs assigned should be based on a reasonable allocation. If none of the acreage is leased, the option's entire cost is charged to expense. A full cost company capitalizes all option payments regardless of whether any acreage is taken.

As an example, on June 12, 2006, ABC Oil Company pays Landowner Klein $1 an acre for the right to explore a 1,200-acre tract and $2 per acre for the right to take five-year leases within the next six months on any part of the 1,200 acres by paying a lease bonus of $50 per acre at the time the option is exercised. On December 12, 2006, ABC exercises the option on 500 acres, acquiring one lease—No. 24019—and allows the option on the remaining 700 acres to lapse. The following journal entries illustrate these transactions.

June 12:

210	Unproved Property Purchase Suspense	2,400	
801	G&G Expenses, Shooting Rights	1,200	
	301 Vouchers Payable		3,600
	To record lease option and G&G rights on Klein tract.		

December 12:

211	Unproved Property Acquisition Costs, Lease No. 24019	26,000	
806	Impairment, Amortization, and Abandonment of Unproved Properties	1,400	
	201 Unproved Property Purchase Suspense		2,400
	301 Vouchers Payable		25,000
	To record exercise of option on 500 acres of Klein property (No. 24019) and lapse of option on the remaining 700 acres.		

If no acreage was leased by December 12, the amount held in suspense is expensed as follows:

806	Impairment, Amortization, and Abandonment of Unproved Properties	2,400	
	210 Unproved Property Purchase Suspense		2,400
	To record lapse of options on Klein 1,200-acre tract.		

ACCOUNTING FOR ACQUISITION OF FEE INTERESTS IN PROPERTY

Although an oil operator typically obtains mineral rights through an oil and gas lease, there may be occasions when a fee interest in a property (i.e., outright ownership of both minerals and the surface) is obtained. In this case, the purchase price (including incidental acquisition costs) should be equitably allocated between the minerals and surface rights. Theoretically, the allocation would be made on the relative fair market values of the two interests. However, it may be simpler to allocate to that element whose value is more clearly determinable, and then allocate the residual cost to the other property interest.

For example, assume that ABC paid $1,000 per acre for the fee interest in 500 acres, with the surface to be held for investment purposes. In recent transactions in the immediate vicinity of the property, surface rights in similar land without any minerals attached had sold for $900 per acre. The entry could be as follows:

184	Land	450,000	
212	Unproved Fee Interests	50,000	
	301 Vouchers Payable		500,000
	To record purchase of the fee interest in land and minerals.		

ACCOUNTING FOR MAINTENANCE AND CARRYING COSTS OF UNPROVED PROPERTIES

In addition to the acquisition of leases, the land department is responsible for maintaining accurate property records. Leases must be kept in force with good title until either the property becomes productive or a decision is made to surrender or abandon the acreage. Delay rentals, ad valorem taxes, legal fees for title defense, and clerical costs are considered maintenance or carrying costs, which must be expensed as incurred.

RENTALS

Assuming the lease is not a paid-up lease, on or before the first anniversary of the lease a rental (delay rental) must be paid to defer commencement of drilling operations for an additional year within the primary term. If operations have not commenced or the delay rental is not paid by the anniversary date, the lease automatically terminates on that day. For a successful efforts company, Oi5.108(b) stipulates that delay rentals must be charged to expense as incurred. A full cost company capitalizes delay rentals and all other maintenance costs of unproved properties.

For example, the 640-acre Landers lease No. 24078 calls for an annual delay rental of $1,280. Operations have not commenced on the first anniversary of the lease, but the company wishes to keep the lease in force. It pays the rental and records the following entry to record the voucher payment:

802	Carrying and Retaining Undeveloped Properties—Delay Rentals, Lease 24078	1,280	
	301 Vouchers Payable		1,280
	To record annual delay rental expense on the Landers lease.		

When unproved properties are bought or sold, it is important to realize that the industry accounting practices of fully expensing (successful efforts) or capitalizing (full cost) delay rentals are at odds with the economic substance of delay rentals being prepaid expenses. An acquired property's nominal price is typically increased for the seller's prepaid expenses at closing. If the property's nominal price is adjusted upwards for delay rentals as prepaid expenses, the rental would typically be prorated over a 12-month period. For example, an unproved, undeveloped lease with an anniversary date of March 31 is sold for a $20,000 nominal price as of June 30. The $4,000 delay rental paid in the preceding February or March provides a $3,000 ($4,000 x 9/12) prepaid expense as of June 30, and increases the sales price to $23,000.

Unless clarified in the sales agreement, a property seller and buyer may disagree on whether rentals should be considered prepaid expenses. Rentals are not expressly viewed as prepaid expenses under successful efforts or full cost accounting. If sales agreements call for adjusting the nominal sales price for prepaid expenses including rentals, buyers should be cautious that the nominal sales price does not already reflect such amounts.

Contrary to commentary in FAS 19, paragraph 195, delay rentals can enhance the future benefits of the lease. Postponing drilling operations for several months could significantly reduce drilling costs, or increase potential production, by allowing additional time to assess the outcome of drilling and production on nearby properties. Valuable additional information could become available on whether to drill and, if so, how best to accomplish it.

By commencing drilling on or before the rental due date and continuing drilling operations, a company eliminates the need for paying a delay rental. From year to year, accrual-based accounting for recurring, relatively small prepaid expenses (such as a typical E&P company's delay rentals as a group) is immaterial to the company's annual income. Thus, the error in FAS 19, paragraph 195, as to the nature and economic substance of delay rentals does not significantly affect financial reporting practices.

PROPERTY TAXES ON UNPROVED LEASES

Many state and local government units levy property taxes on mineral interests as well as on surface rights. Property taxes on mineral rights owned by a lessee are merely another carrying cost of the property and are charged to expense. Taxes involved in this situation are incurred after the lessee has acquired the mineral rights, and are not to be confused with any delinquent taxes assumed by the lessee at the time of acquiring the lease. If property taxes assessed on the Landers lease are $500, the entry to record the expense is:

802.002	Ad Valorem Taxes, Lease No. 24078	500	
301	Vouchers Payable		500
To record property taxes on the Landers lease.			

OTHER CARRYING COSTS

Other types of lease maintenance and carrying costs, such as clerical and recordkeeping costs and legal fees for title defense, are charged to expense under the successful efforts method in the same manner as delay rentals and property taxes; these same expenditures are capitalized under full cost.

ACCOUNTING FOR IMPAIRMENT
AND ABANDONMENT OF UNPROVED LEASES

Generally, a substantial portion of the unproved acreage acquired by an operator is later surrendered or abandoned without production having been obtained. A number of methods have traditionally been used to provide for these known or reasonably anticipated losses. Oi5 and Reg. S-X Rule 4-10 provide general guidance to be used by successful efforts companies (and in certain cases by full cost companies as explained in Chapter 19) to account for the decrease in value of unproved properties. Rules for handling the impairment of unproved properties were not changed by FAS 144, *Accounting for the Impairment or Disposal of Long-Lived Assets*.

Under Oi5, unproved properties must be assessed periodically, at least annually, to determine whether their book values have been impaired. If impairment has occurred, a valuation allowance is established to reflect the reduction in value. Although Oi5 does not define impairment, Oi5.119 does suggest that:

[a] property would likely be impaired, for example, if a dry hole had been drilled on it and the enterprise has no firm plans to continue drilling. Also, the likelihood of partial or total impairment of a property increases as the expiration of the lease term approaches if drilling activity has not commenced on the property or on nearby properties.

The SEC's Codification of Financial Reporting Releases,§406.01.c.i, reprinted in Appendix 1, adds that ". . .unevaluated properties are required to be assessed periodically for impairment and to have value at least equal to their carrying costs (including any capitalized interest). . ."; however, the term *value* is not defined.

Impairment of value can be recognized in two ways. It is done on an individual property basis or a group basis, depending on whether the cost of an individual property is significant. The method chosen also determines how costs of abandoned leases and leases transferred to proved properties should be handled.

RECORDING IMPAIRMENT OF INDIVIDUAL PROPERTIES

If costs associated with an individual property are significant, impairment is assessed on a property-by-property basis. Individual impairment may also be recorded on leases that are not individually significant (although there is no requirement to do so). For successful efforts, the definition of an individually significant property is unclear; however, under full cost accounting, the SEC has stated that it generally means a property with capitalized costs exceeding 10 percent of the net capitalized costs of the country-wide cost center.

Responses to the *2001 PricewaterhouseCoopers Survey of U.S. Petroleum Accounting Practices* indicated that companies typically use various criteria for determining significance. Some companies have established a specific dollar amount as a minimum cost for a property to be deemed significant. Presumably, a company has arrived at a floor after considering the size of its enterprise, total assets, total investments in oil and gas properties, net income, and similar factors. Each year acquired leases are examined in light of the factors previously listed.

The concept of impairment of unproved property introduced in FAS 19 is somewhat unusual in authoritative accounting literature. Neither the FASB nor the SEC has defined the term, nor has either clearly indicated how impairment of an individual unproved property is to be measured. The aforementioned survey found that companies considered various factors in assessing impairment. Over 90 percent of the respondents considered whether the company still intended to drill on the lease. The majority of respondents also considered: (1) other wells drilled in the area, (2) the geologist's valuation of the lease, and (3) remaining months in the lease's primary term. Only three of 14 respondents considered the market value of similar acreage in the area.

Consideration for impairment assessment can include:

- If the company has definite plans to drill on a lease, its assessed value might be equal to net book value, and no impairment is recognized.

- If drilling is somewhat likely, the company's assessed value of the lease may be significantly less than original cost.

- If the company has no plans to drill on a lease due to recent dry holes on or adjacent to the company lease, then that lease may have little or no assessed value and be substantially impaired.

- A company's impairment policy might recognize partial impairment as time elapses on the primary term of each lease.

To illustrate impairment of significant leases, assume that a company has five significant leases for which no impairment has previously been recorded. Costs and assessed values on December 31, 2005, are:

	Cost	Assessed Value	Impairment
Lease *A*	$100,000	$ 85,000	$ 15,000
Lease *B*	110,000	100,000	10,000
Lease *C*	400,000	300,000	100,000
Lease *D*	125,000	190,000	0
Lease *E*	45,000	500,000	0
	$780,000	$1,175,000	$125,000

Since each lease is deemed to be significant, assessments must be made on a lease-by-lease basis. Even though the total value exceeds total cost, impairment of any single lease is still recognized. The entry to record the impairment of value at December 31 is:

806	Impairment, Amortization, and Abandonment of Unproved Properties	125,000	
	219 Allowance for Impairment of Unproved Properties		125,000
	To record loss on impairment of individual leases for the period.		

After impairment is recorded, the net book value of unproved properties is:

Unproved Properties	$780,000
Less: Allowance for Impairment, Unproved Properties	(125,000)
Net	$655,000

Surrender of Impaired Significant Unproved Property. When an impaired significant property is surrendered, the net carrying value (capitalized cost minus valuation allowance) of that lease is charged to expense under successful efforts, or to Account 227, Abandoned Properties, under the full cost method. Assume in 2006, leases *A* and *D* in the preceding example are abandoned.

219	Allowance for Impairment of Unproved Properties	15,000	
806	Impairment, Amortization, and Abandonment of Unproved Properties	85,000	
	211 Unproved Property Acquisition Costs		100,000
	To record surrender of lease A.		
806	Impairment, Amortization, and Abandonment of Unproved Properties	125,000	
	211 Unproved Property Acquisition Costs		125,000
	To record surrender of lease D.		

Subsequent Evaluation. After recording impairment, a company cannot record any recovery in value. For example, assume that on December 31, 2006, the company in the preceding illustration prepares the following schedule of unproved properties:

	Net Cost	Value	Calculated Impairment
Lease *C*	$ 300,000	$680,000	$ 0
Lease *E*	45,000	500,000	0
Lease *F* (new)	1,000,000	800,000	200,000

An impairment of $200,000 would be recorded on lease *F* acquired in early 2006 by the usual entry. Even though the value of lease *C* now exceeds its cost, the allowance for impairment of $100,000 set up on December 31, 2005, would not change. No gains on increases in value of such properties are recorded.

RECORDING IMPAIRMENT ON A GROUP BASIS

For companies using the successful efforts method, Oi5.119 provides that:

When an enterprise has a relatively large number of unproved properties whose acquisition costs are not individually significant, it may not be practical to assess impairment on a property-by-property basis, in which case the amount of loss to be recognized and the amount of the valuation allowance needed to provide for impairment of those properties shall be determined by amortizing those properties, either in the aggregate or by groups, on the basis of experience of the entity in similar situations and other information about such factors as the primary lease terms of those properties, the average holding period of unproved properties, and the relative proportion of such properties on which proved reserves have been found in the past.

In computing amortization to reflect impairment, all of an entity's unproved properties may be placed in a single group, or multiple groups may be used. If multiple groups are used, the aggregation may be based on geographic location (such as onshore, offshore, Gulf Coast); dollar cost ($500,000 or less; $500,000 to $1,000,000; $1,000,000 to $10,000,000); geologic area (Tuscaloosa Trend, Permian Basin); year of acquisition (2004, 2005, 2006); or another logical basis. The purpose is to derive an overall estimate of impairment that would reflect impairments if assessed on individual properties.

Several approaches are used to estimate the annual impairment provision on a group basis. They fall into two categories depending on what is emphasized in the calculations:

- Expense computations based on the average holding period for properties in each group

- Balance sheet valuation by maintaining the valuation account at some predetermined percentage of the unproved properties account

Impairment Procedures Emphasizing Amortization Expense. The basic notion underlying group amortization is this: properties that will not become productive over time should be considered impaired, while properties that will become productive should not. Using this methodology, the portions of properties that will not be productive are estimated based on the company's past experience. If activities or strategies of exploration have changed, or if the company has little history, it may utilize industry-wide experience.

Straight-Line Amortization. If a company carried out drilling on a relatively even basis over the terms of its leases, it might be appropriate to record impairment of the expected worthless leases on a straight-line basis over the lease terms.

Some companies using straight-line amortization apply the rate to the balance of the unproved property account (which reflects additions, surrenders, and transfers to proved properties). Others apply the rate to the net book value of unproved properties (balance of unproved properties minus the total allowance for impairment). However, since the amortization rate is usually based on original acquisitions, that amount should be the basis for the computation. If a group includes properties acquired in more than one year, the amortization rate is applied separately to the leases acquired each year.

To illustrate a basic application of the group method of recording impairment using a straight-line rate, assume that a company includes all of its unproved properties in a single group and records amortization on that basis.

The company keeps a record of leases acquired each year and makes a separate computation of amortization for each year's acquisitions. An analysis of leases acquired in only one year, 2005, shows that acquired unproved property acquisition costs of $1,200,000 were charged, along with leases acquired in other years, to the Unproved Property Acquisition Costs account. As of December 31, 2005, the balances of the Unproved Property Acquisition Costs account and Allowance for Impairment account were $4,000,000 debit and $1,980,000 credit, respectively.

Experience indicates that ultimately 20 percent of the leases will become productive and that the average holding period of the remaining leases is four years. Thus, $960,000 ($1,200,000 x 80%) of the leases acquired in 2005 will ultimately be abandoned over an average period of four years (beginning in 2006). Note that in this calculation the beginning balance in the Allowance for Impairment of Unproved Properties account is ignored. Amortization of $240,000 may be recorded for 2006 as shown in the following entry:

806	*Impairments and Abandonments of Unproved Properties*	240,000	
	219 *Allowance for Impairment of Unproved Properties*		240,000
	To record amortization of unproved properties.		

Similar calculations are made for leases acquired in each year, and the amortization is recorded in the same way. Assume amortization on other leases totaled $560,000 for 2006, so that the total amortization for 2006 was $800,000 ($240,000 + $560,000).

When impairment of individually insignificant properties is measured and recorded on a group basis, accounting for the surrender of unproved properties and transfers to proved properties is simplified. The original capitalized cost of a surrendered lease is charged to the Allowance for Impairment account and removed from the Unproved Property Acquisition Costs account at the time of surrender. The Proved Leaseholds account is charged and the Unproved Property Acquisition Costs account is credited for the cost of a property that is proved during the period. For example, continuing the above illustration, assume that the following occurred in 2006:

- Additional unproved properties were leased for $1,600,000.

- Leases that cost $750,000 were surrendered.

- Leases that cost $320,000 were proved.

211	*Unproved Property Acquisition Costs*	1,600,000	
	306 *Vouchers Payable*		1,600,000
	To record cost of leases acquired during year.		
219	*Allowance for Impairment of Unproved Properties*	750,000	
	211 *Unproved Property Acquisition Costs*		750,000
	To record cost of surrendered leases.		
221	*Proved Leaseholds*	320,000	
	211 *Unproved Property Acquisition Costs*		320,000
	To record cost of properties proved during the year.		

After these transactions have been entered, the Unproved Property Acquisition Costs account and the Allowance for Impairment account would appear as follows:

Account 211	**Unproved Property Acquisition Costs**		
12/31/05 Balance	$4,000,000	2006 Surrenders	$750,000
2006 Additions	1,600,000	2006 Proved	320,000
12/31/06 Balance	$4,530,000		

Account 219	**Allowance for Impairment of Unproved Properties**		
		12/31/05 Balance	$1,980,000
2006 Surrenders	$750,000	2006 Amortization	800,000
		12/31/06 Balance	$2,030,000

The amortization for 2007 on leases acquired in 2005 would again be $240,000, and assuming that the company's estimate of surrenders has not changed, amortization on leases acquired in 2006 would be $320,000 (1/4 x 80% x $1,600,000). Those amounts, along with amortization on acquisitions of other years, would be charged to Account 806, Impairments and Abandonments of Unproved Properties, and credited to Account 219, Allowance for Impairment of Unproved Properties. If the allowance previously provided is inadequate to absorb the cost of a surrendered lease, a loss equal to the difference between the cost of the property surrendered and the balance in the Allowance for Impairment account should be recognized upon the surrender of a property.

Amortization Based on Analysis of Yearly Surrenders. Another approach for computing amortization is to use annual rates based on past experience. In developing its experience pattern, a company should use at least one complete cycle of lease acquisition and exploration. All leases acquired during the base period should be included; if not feasible, a representative sample of leases is permissible. Calculations can be based on monetary amounts or on acreage (when leasehold costs per acre fluctuate widely). Assume a company has analyzed its cycle for leases with primary terms of four years. A three-year recurring analysis as of early 2006, based on acreage, is shown below.

Year Acquired	Total Cost	Ultimate Cost Allocation				Ultimately Productive Property
		Property Found to be Nonproductive in Year:				
		1	2	3	4	
2001	$ 45,000	*	*	*	$16,000	$ 4,000
2002	60,000	*	*	$21,000	20,000	6,000
2003	50,000	*	$ 8,500	17,000	10,000	6,000
2004	100,000	$ 7,000	14,500	31,000	**	**
2005	70,000	6,800	15,500	**	**	**
2006	80,000	7,500	**	**	**	**
Totals		$21,300	$38,500	$69,000	$46,000	$16,000
3 yr avg %***		9%	18%	33%	30%	10%

*   Known but not part of the latest three-year average.
**   Unknown at the time of analysis in early 2006.
*** For example, 21,300/(100,000 +70,000 + 80,000) = 9%.

History suggests that 90 percent of the costs relate to leases that are ultimately nonproductive, and become partially impaired as time passes, until the leases are found to be worthless. Three different methods can be used to calculate annual amortization rates for the 90 percent of costs expected to be found worthless. First, the petroleum accountant can use a straight-line calculation over the four-year primary term; annual amortization is one-fourth of 90 percent or 22.5 percent as shown in the following Table 1. Second, annual amortization rates can be calculated by allocating costs over the properties' expected lives; e.g., for the 18 percent of costs related to properties expected to be found worthless and abandoned in Year 2, assume half is impaired and expensed in

Year 1 and half in Year 2 as shown in Table 2. Third, calculate amortization by allocating a specific portion (say 20 percent) in each year prior to the expected year of abandonment; e.g., for the 18 percent of costs related to properties expected to be abandoned in Year 2, assume 20 percent of 18 percent, or 3.6 percent, is impaired and expensed in Year 1 and 14.4 percent in Year 2 as shown in Table 3. The third approach should reflect management's judgment and experience that leases retain much of their value until the year when they are found to be nonproductive.

Table 1

| | Aban. % | Allocated Straight-Line over Four Years | | | |
		1	2	3	4
	90.0%	22.5%	22.5%	22.5%	22.5%

Table 2

| Year After Acquisition | Aban. % | Allocated Straight-Line over Expected Life | | | |
		1	2	3	4
1	9.0%	9.0%			
2	18.0	9.0	9.0%		
3	33.0	11.0	11.0	11.0%	
4	30.0	7.5	7.5	7.5	7.5%
	90.0%	36.5%	27.5%	18.5%	7.5%

Table 3

| Year After Acquisition | Aban. % | Allocated at 20%/yr until Worthless | | | |
		1	2	3	4
1	9.0%	9.0%			
2	18.0	3.6	14.4%		
3	33.0	6.6	6.6	19.8%	
4	30.0	6.0	6.0	6.0	12.0%
	90.0%	25.2%	27.0%	25.8%	12.0%

Notice in the tables that first-year amortization varies from 22.5 percent to 36.5 percent, but always exceeds the nine percent of costs that is attributable to leases expected to be found worthless in Year 1.

For this example, one should not calculate first-year amortization as simply nine percent of costs; otherwise, the accounting is merely expensing the estimated costs of worthless property in the year found worthless. Amortization is intended to reflect lease impairment, including partial impairment after one year for leases expected to be found worthless in years two, three, and four. First-year amortization needs to reflect both: (1) the nine percent of costs, and (2) a portion of the 81 percent of total lease acquisition costs that will be found worthless in the primary term.

Impairment Procedure Emphasizing Asset Valuation. A simple approach to measure the impairment of a group of unproved properties is to adjust the Allowance for Impairment account to some predetermined percentage of Unproved Property Acquisition Costs. Lease acquisitions, abandonments, and transfers to unproved properties are handled in the way described earlier.

For example, assume that past experience indicates that approximately 80 percent of its unproved leases are abandoned. The company has adopted a policy of maintaining the Allowance for Impairment account at 80 percent of the Unproved Property Acquisition Costs account. This approach is conservative in that $80 is immediately considered impaired for every $100 of new lease acquisition costs. Some companies adjust the allowance account to only 40 percent of the Unproved Property Acquisition Costs account on the theory that, on average, only one half of the leases that will ultimately be worthless are impaired at any balance sheet date. For example, assume that as of December 31, 2006, the two balance sheet accounts involved are as follows before annual impairment is recorded:

Account 211	Unproved Property Acquisition Costs	
11/30/06 Balance	$10,000,000	
12/06/06 Acquisitions	5,000,000	
12/31/06 Balance	$15,000,000	

Account 219	Allowance for Impairment of Unproved Properties	
	12/31/06 Balance	$4,000,000

Since the allowance account balance on December 31, 2006, is only $4,000,000 and a balance of $6,000,000 (40% of $15,000,000) is needed, the following entry adjusts it:

806	Impairment and Abandonment of Unproved Properties	200,000	
219	Allowance for Impairment of Unproved Properties		200,000
	To adjust allowance account to desired balance.		

This simplified procedure is appropriate only if acquisitions and surrenders are relatively stable from year to year and the company has many unproved properties which are not individually significant.

MEASURING IMPAIRMENT OF INDIVIDUAL PROPERTIES UNDER FULL COST ACCOUNTING

Under full cost, companies may (but are not required to) exclude from the amortization pool the acquisition costs of unevaluated properties and unevaluated exploration costs. If this procedure is followed, the entity is required to begin immediate amortization of any amount of impairment. Similar to successful efforts accounting, impairment of unproved properties must be on a property-by-property basis for individually significant properties.

As mentioned previously, the SEC has stated that for full cost companies the term individually significant identifies a property or project where costs exceed 10 percent of the net capitalized costs of the cost center. Individual impairment is allowed for insignificant properties. Impairment for full cost companies is discussed further in Chapter 19. Note that impairment of unproved properties does not give rise to an expense or loss for a full cost company; it merely accelerates the costs subject to amortization.

UTILIZING POST-BALANCE-SHEET EVENTS IN ASSESSING IMPAIRMENT

Oi5. 130 provides that:

> information that becomes available after the end of the period covered by the financial statements but before those financial statements are issued shall be taken into account in evaluating conditions that existed at the balance sheet date, for example in assessing unproved properties [for impairment]. . . .

Suppose ABC Oil Company owns a leasehold that is individually significant (cost $500,000), and has an estimated value on December 31, 2006, of $1,200,000. No impairment recognition seemed necessary on December 31, 2006. However, in February 2007, before the financial statements for 2006 are issued, another company abandoned as a dry hole a well drilled on a contiguous lease. An assessment reveals that the lease is now worth only $100,000. This post-balance-sheet-date information requires recognition of an impairment loss of $400,000 in the 2006 income statement, and establishment of an impairment allowance of $400,000 in the balance sheet as of December 31, 2006.

TRANSFERS TO PROVED PROPERTY

Transfers of unproved property acquisition costs to proved property acquisition costs take three forms:

- An unproved property individually impaired has its net book value (NBV) transferred to proved property costs:

219	*Allowance for Impairment*	10,000	
221	*Proved Property Acquisition Costs*	90,000	
	(also called Proved Leasehold Costs)		
	211 *Unproved Property Acquisition Costs*		100,000

- An unproved property subject to a group impairment allowance has its gross acquisition cost reclassified:

221	*Proved Property Acquisition Costs*	100,000	
	211 *Unproved Property Acquisition Costs*		100,000

- A vast single property, such as a foreign concession, has reclassified only that portion of its costs (or NBV) deemed related to the proved reserves. For example, for a 50,000-acre concession including a 1,000-acre proved field, only two percent of an assumed $10,000,000 in unproved property acquisition costs are reclassified:

221	*Proved Property Acquisition Costs*	200,000	
	211 *Unproved Property Acquisition Costs*		200,000

TOP LEASES AND LEASE RENEWALS

In some cases the operator may be unable to or unwilling to drill on an unproved property before expiration of its primary term; however, it may wish to retain the property for possible future drilling. In this event, the operator can negotiate with the mineral owner to extend the primary term of the original lease or sign a new lease contract. Under both full cost and successful efforts accounting, the bonus for signing a new lease is capitalized.

A new lease signed before expiration of the original contract is called a **top lease**. Under the successful efforts method, the book value of the original lease may be treated as a part of the capitalized cost of the top lease. If, however, the original lease expires and the lessee gives up all rights before obtaining a new lease, the expiration of the old lease should be treated as an abandonment.

Under full cost, the cost of the original lease remains capitalized as part of the cost pool.

TAX TREATMENT OF UNPROVED PROPERTY ACQUISITION, MAINTENANCE, AND ABANDONMENT COSTS

For federal income tax purposes, the bonus payment and incidental acquisition costs, such as recording fees and broker's commissions, must be capitalized as depletable mineral costs. Historically, the operator has had a year-by-year and property-by-property election to either charge carrying costs, including delay rentals, to expense as they are paid or incurred, or to capitalize them as depletable leasehold costs. Almost universally, taxpayers have elected to charge carrying costs to expense. However, the current IRS position is that delay rentals must be capitalized as depletable leasehold costs.

Costs of unproved properties must be charged off in the year they become worthless, which may be either at the same time or before the time they are abandoned or surrendered. For tax purposes, there is no deduction for partial worthlessness or impairment or for amortization of unproved property costs. When a property becomes productive, its costs become subject to depletion as the reserves are produced.

• • •

8

DRILLING AND DEVELOPMENT

Key Concepts:

- Overview of regulatory requirements for well drilling and development

- Drilling preparations

- Footage-rate, day rate, and turnkey drilling contracts

- The drilling process

- Offshore drilling techniques

- Completing the well

- Development of the reservoir

When subsurface formations point to the presence of hydrocarbons and related leases are executed, significant hurdles remain for an operator. Complex regulatory issues must be navigated with various agencies. Detailed planning is conducted including decisions on a drilling method and choice of a contractor. Once the well is drilled, it is either completed and production begins, or the site is abandoned.

REGULATORY REQUIREMENTS

ONSHORE REGULATORY REQUIREMENTS

A **drilling permit** must be secured from the appropriate state or federal regulatory agency before an oil or gas well may be drilled. At the state level, many jurisdictions require permits and specific minimum **spacing** for wells. Operators must provide certain information to government agencies up-front, including:

- Proof of financial assurance supported by either a bond from an insurance company or a letter of credit from a bank.

- An Application to Drill form, which requires the exact legal location (staked location) of the well, planned **TD (total depth)**, spacing, target geological formation (reservoir), well type (oil or gas), distance to the nearest completed well in the reservoir, and lease name.

- A plat, which is a scaled diagram of the lease showing the proposed drilling location, spacing unit boundaries, distance to the nearest well in the same reservoir, northerly direction, scale of diagram, and legal name of the surveyed acreage.

- Payment of the applicable regulatory drilling fee, which usually varies by depth.

While there are exceptions to the rule, spacing in the continental U.S. is commonly no more than one oil well per 40 acres and no more than one gas well per 640 acres. Greater spacing for gas wells is required because gas moves through a formation more easily than oil, and fewer wells are needed to physically deplete it economically. It should be noted that offshore well spacing is normally driven by either the constraints of the installation or the seabed infrastructure.

The total amount of oil and gas recovered from a reservoir, known as the ultimate recovery, may be only moderately affected by the number of wells drilled into the reservoir. However, the speed at which the reservoir is physically depleted can be very important. If production is accelerated beyond certain technical limits, ultimate recovery is reduced. Uneven flow from different portions of the reservoir can isolate pockets of hydrocarbons with possible early water breakthrough or loss of reservoir drive mechanism. Secondary recovery methods can be utilized, but the potential ultimate recovery is usually never achieved following poor initial reservoir management. More wells may be drilled to ensure even depletion of the reservoir to maximize recovery and to accelerate cash flow from production. The high cost of drilling, however, serves to impede overdevelopment unless it is critical to optimize the reservoir development plan.

DRILLING ON FEDERAL LANDS

In the U.S., drilling activities on federally-owned land are governed by the Bureau of Land Management (BLM). It was granted oversight by the Mineral Leasing Act of 1920, as amended, and the Mineral Leasing Act for Acquired Lands of 1947, as amended. The

BLM has responsibility for oil and gas leasing on about 570 million acres of BLM, National Forest, and other federal lands, as well as private lands where mineral rights have been retained by the federal government.

The BLM issues two types of leases for oil and gas exploration and development: competitive and non-competitive. In 1987, Congress passed the Federal Onshore Oil and Gas Leasing Reform Act that requires all public lands available for oil and gas leasing be offered first by competitive leasing. Only after the land has been offered competitively at an oral auction, and no bid has been received, can a non-competitive lease be offered.

The maximum competitive lease size on federal property is 2,560 acres in the lower 48 states and 5,760 acres in Alaska. The maximum non-competitive lease size in all states is 10,240 acres. Both competitive and non-competitive leases are issued for a 10-year period, and may continue as long as oil or gas is produced in paying quantities.

OFFSHORE REGULATORY REQUIREMENTS

According to the Minerals Management Service (MMS) of the U.S. Department of the Interior, approximately 20 percent of U.S. natural gas production and 30 percent of U.S. oil production come from offshore well sites on the Outer Continental Shelf (OCS). The OCS is comprised of federal lands submerged off the U.S. coasts. The MMS conducts all leasing and resource management functions for the Gulf of Mexico OCS Region and Atlantic OCS area.

Offshore drilling is expected to increase as a percentage of total production. Extensive information is required before a permit to drill offshore is granted by the MMS, including a description of the drilling vessels and platforms or other structures, various details about the equipment, pollution control and prevention items, location of each well, targeted locations for directionally drilled wells, and structural interpretations of exploration data.

ENVIRONMENTAL AND SAFETY REQUIREMENTS

Good business principles dictate that drilling companies operate in a safe and prudent manner toward their workers and the environment. Such practices are part of a company's overall risk management program. The U.S. Environmental Protection Agency, Occupational Safety and Health Administration, and various state agencies regulate the energy industry. Rules have been developed to promote safety and environmental protection for drilling activities; some regulations go so far as to prohibit drilling in certain areas, such as off the coast of Florida. Organizations such as the American Petroleum Institute (www.api.org) provide guidelines and updates regarding industry-specific regulations.

The oil and gas industry has made great strides in recent years to improve its environmental and safety performance. For example, the U.S. oil and natural gas industry's investment in the environment approached $10.3 billion in 2004 (latest figures), according to API.

The following section outlines the significant federal regulations and oversight agencies.

The Environmental Protection Agency (EPA) is the federal agency that oversees protection of the environment.

- The Comprehensive Environmental Response, Compensation and Liability Act of 1980 (CERCLA) established the Superfund that provides for liability, compensation, cleanup, and emergency response for hazardous substances released into the environment and cleanup of inactive hazardous waste disposal sites.

- The Superfund Amendments Reauthorization Act (SARA Title III), including a free-standing law known as the Emergency Planning and Community Right-to-Know Act of 1986 (EPCRA), exists to encourage and support emergency planning efforts at state and local levels. It provides government officials with information concerning potential chemical hazards present in their communities.

- The Oil Pollution Act of 1990 (OPA '90) set up a trust fund to help clean up oil spills and provide prevention and response resources.

- The Resource Conservation and Recovery Act (RCRA) is the primary federal law governing municipal and industrial waste management. Waste recycling and reduction are the two main objectives of the RCRA.

- The Clean Air Act of 1990 is a federal law that is also enforced at the state level. It sets limits on how much of particular pollutants can be present in the air.

- The Clean Water Act was adopted in 1972 to protect surface water quality. Amendments to the Act have changed the focus from providing municipal grants to partnering with states to address specific water quality needs. The most recent amendment was the Great Lakes Legacy Act of 2002 which authorized $270 million to clean up contaminated sediments in the Great Lakes.

- The Safe Drinking Water Act (SDWA) was passed in 1974, and amended in 1986 and 1996. It requires specific actions to protect drinking water and its sources in rivers, lakes, reservoirs, springs, and groundwater wells.

The Occupational Safety and Health Administration (OSHA) is housed under the U.S. Department of Labor, and is charged with protecting the safety and health of U.S. workers. Its Hazardous Communication Standard empowers the agency to set safety and health standards and conduct inspections to ensure that employers are providing safe and healthful workplaces.

A division of the Department of the Interior, the U.S. Fish and Wildlife Service is the only federal agency in the country charged with conserving fish, wildlife and plants. The Migratory Bird Treaty Act of 1918 gave the U.S. Fish and Wildlife Service authority to establish reservations for migratory birds and protect them from contamination or injury.

Individual states oversee state radiation regulations and the licensing of what is known as Naturally Occurring Radioactive Material (NORM). NORM is encountered in oil and gas operations when certain subsurface formations contain radioactive materials, such as uranium. Each state regulates the disposal of these materials in order to protect public health and the environment.

Ongoing regulatory issues and legislative changes continue to impact the oil and gas industry. Critical topics currently being debated include greenhouse gases and climate change. While carbon dioxide and methane gases naturally blanket the earth, evidence shows their levels are increasing, and fossil fuels are largely blamed. Concern about atmospheric warming is worldwide, and in 1997 leaders met in Kyoto, Japan, to discuss ways to reduce greenhouse emissions. The Kyoto Protocol was adopted, but to-date, its terms have not been ratified by the U.S. government.

Complying with numerous regulations can be complicated for E&P companies in that the rules continually evolve. Environmental and safety studies should be performed (and regularly updated) on all oil and gas properties in order to stay in compliance. Larger companies dedicate employees solely to environmental and safety issues, while smaller ones hire consultants for the same purpose.

Noncompliance can carry a hefty price tag. For instance, the Clean Air, Clean Water, and Toxic Substances Control acts all provide fines up to $25,000, up to one year in jail, or both, for each day of violation. Under the Safe Drinking Water Act, fines range from $5,000 to $10,000 with no imprisonment. The Resource Conservation and Recovery Act assesses penalties up to $50,000 and up to two years in jail for most violations. If an RCRA violation places another person in danger of death or serious bodily injury, penalties can be levied for up to $25,000 ($1 million for companies) and up to five years' imprisonment.

U.S. ENERGY POLICY ACT OF 2005

In late July 2005, the U.S. Congress passed the Energy Policy Act of 2005, a comprehensive legislative package that addresses policies on oil and gas, ethanol, hydrogen, nuclear, coal, conservation, efficiency, and R&D. Taxes and incentives were also included in the federal program. President Bush signed the bill into law on August 8, 2005. Selected provisions of the Act relating to oil and gas companies include:

- Permanent authorization of the Strategic Petroleum Reserve and authorization to fill the reserve to one billion barrels.

- An inventory of oil and gas resources on the U.S. Outer Continental Shelf (OCS) by the Department of the Interior to enable the federal government to assess the extent of offshore resources.

- Ways to streamline the permitting and siting processes for pipelines with FERC as the lead agency for consolidating records.

- Coastal impact assistance of $1 billion over four years.

- Clarification of FERC's exclusive authority to site LNG facilities.

- Establishment of a task force on a national oil shale and tar sands leasing program.

- Conducting an oil shale R&D program.

DRILLING CONTRACTS

Oil and gas well drilling is generally carried out by independent drilling contractors. Due to their specialized skills, they can normally drill more economically and efficiently than oil and gas operators. Three basic types of contracts exist between the parties: **footage-rate**, **day rate**, and **turnkey**. The type used depends on the category of drilling to be done, location of the well, and environmental factors.

In the early 1980s, the demand for rigs exceeded supply and almost all contracts were day rate arrangements. A typical day rate (or day work) drilling contract is illustrated in CD Reference Exhibit D. Although day rates are still the most common contracts offshore, footage contracts dominate the onshore arena.

All drilling operations start with an Authorization for Expenditure (AFE) prepared by the operator. An AFE is a summation of the expected drilling and completion costs for a particular well (see Chapter 6). In 2004, API reported the average cost of drilling an onshore oil well was $1,054,000 and about $16.3 million was the average cost per offshore oil well. (See Figure 8-12 for additional cost data.) Wells drilled in deep and ultra-deep water can cost significantly more, especially when exploring for new reservoirs.

FOOTAGE-RATE CONTRACTS

Under a typical footage-rate contract, the drilling contractor is paid a specified amount per foot of hole drilled. Costs increase significantly as the depth of the well increases. Offshore drilling is more expensive than onshore drilling. Footage drilling rates are tracked by API and in its 2004 Joint Association Survey on Drilling Costs (Figure 8-12), the average costs for U.S. onshore and offshore wells were:

- $247.51 per foot for oil wells

- $269.04 per foot for gas wells

- $285.14 per foot for dry holes

A footage-rate contract usually calls for drilling to a specified depth or a predetermined number of feet below a specific geological **horizon**, whichever comes first. The footage-rate is determined by taking the total estimated costs to drill to that depth (including **bit** and rig costs), adding a risk factor and profit, and then dividing the total by the targeted depth. The contractor furnishes the rig, crew, services, and certain materials and supplies. The operator normally furnishes the well equipment and may provide drilling **mud**. Several activities are not included in a footage-rate arrangement, such as taking **core** samples, running certain tests, and **logging**. These are usually considered extraneous to drilling and are separately charged to the operator on a day rate basis.

Each drilling contract contains payment terms for work performed. Payments under the contract, including amounts owed for day work, may be required at specified time intervals or when drilling reaches a certain depth. A drilling contractor may require that a portion of estimated total costs be prepaid. Except for factors outside the contractor's control, payment is usually contingent upon reaching the contract depth.

DAY RATE CONTRACTS

Day rate, or daywork, contracts are conceptually simple. The drilling contractor provides drilling rigs and rig crews and receives a fixed amount per day for drilling wells, regardless of the number of feet drilled. The operator bears most of the ancillary costs of well construction and supporting drilling operations, as well as the economic risk for the wells. Usually, the contract specifies two daily rates: one for time when the contractor is actually engaged in drilling operations and a lesser figure for standby time when the operator is running tests or having other services performed.

Day rate contracts are used for virtually all offshore work. Like footage-rates, onshore day rate charges vary depending on the location, environmental issues, and demand for rigs in the area. Offshore day rates are priced by the type of equipment (jack-up rig or semi-submersible rig), drilling conditions, and water depth. An online source for up-to-date offshore day rates is Rigzone (www.rigzone.com). In September 2006, Rigzone reported offshore day rates for jack-up rigs averaged nearly $90,000.

TURNKEY CONTRACTS

Turnkey contracts have been used in the industry for many years and originate from real property law in the U.K. The basic feature of a turnkey contract is performance by the drilling contractor of specified services for a set price. The operator merely has to "turn the key" when the project is completed. No liability is assumed by the operator until contract requirements are met. In some cases, partners of an operator may require a turnkey contract in order to have greater confidence in the project.

Turnkey contracts have advantages and disadvantages for both contractors and operators. Contractors often have greater latitude in the way drilling is done and in the selection of drilling mud and drill bits. Operators benefit because no matter what problems are encountered, the total cost of the well is limited to the contract price. In addition, the operator is assured that appropriately skilled employees will be available to handle peak workloads.

A disadvantage for drilling contractors is that they must complete the well within established cost parameters. Many events can occur in the drilling process to make turnkey contracts a costly risk to the contractor. However, these uncertainties can be addressed through the use of contractual loss caps and walk-away rights.

OTHER ARRANGEMENTS

Alternative approaches can be used to arrive at the payment amounts for drilling and equipping a well. These arrangements usually involve modifications to or combinations of the contracts previously discussed. Transferring an operating or non-operating interest in a lease is an alternative form of compensation. Drilling contractors can be given an overriding royalty interest in the drill spacing unit (versus the well) in return for providing services and supplies.

DRILLING PREPARATIONS

STAKING THE WELL

While exploration activities for a new production area may point to a certain property, additional geological work is performed to locate the well site and stake the well mark. Scientific data, including seismic, magnetic, or gravity surveys, are analyzed to determine the exact drilling point in the structure.

While subsurface structure is the most important consideration, surface conditions become significant when they impose constraints on drilling. These can result from natural phenomena, such as bodies of water, marsh areas, hostile terrain, or other obstructions. Drilling constraints may also derive from the lease itself. Examples are clauses that preclude drilling within a specified distance of existing structures or within a municipality. When surface constraints are present, the well site is staked in a satisfactory area, and a directional well is drilled so as to bottom out at the target.

Particular attention must be given to lease and property boundaries to ensure that the well is drilled on property for which the operator holds a working interest. Cases have occurred in which wells were drilled on acreage owned by others; thus, the importance of carefully locating the well cannot be overemphasized.

WELL SYMBOLS

Symbols are used to depict the status of wells on location maps, including:

1. An open circle for a proposed well location or well in progress

2. A simple black circle to indicate an oil well

3. An open circle with eight spokes to indicate a gas well

4. An open circle with four spokes to indicate a dry hole

5. A circle encircling a cross to indicate a salt water **disposal well**

6. A half-black circle with spokes symbolizes wells producing both oil and gas

Figure 8-1 illustrates the use of well symbols for a rectangular 320-acre lease having eight 40-acre drill sites and three producing oil wells. The three wells plus three others on different leases are producing from an oblong reservoir. A seventh oil well produced, but was later abandoned.

Figure 8-1
Field Map Using Common Symbols for Wells

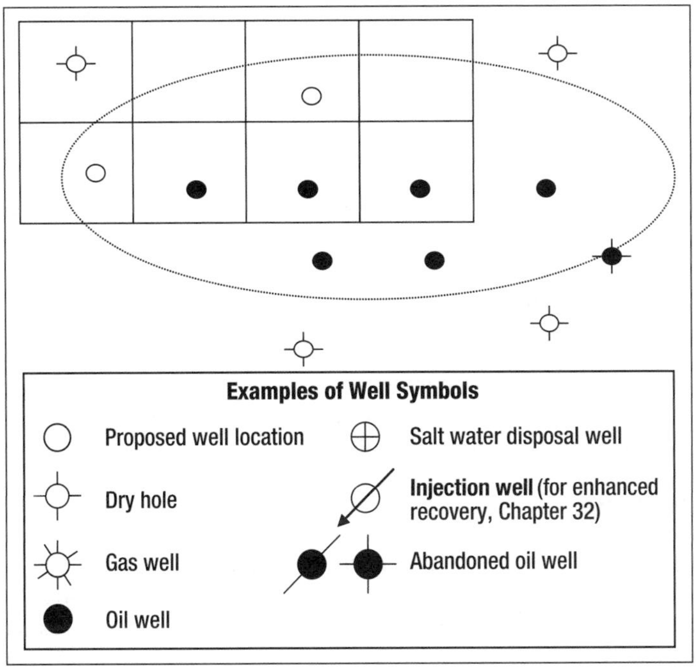

PREPARING THE LOCATION

At this stage in a project, the well has been staked, or at least the location is pinpointed. Once permits to drill have been arranged, the well site is ready to be prepared. Often, drillers create a Well Proposal that outlines the objectives and type of well to be drilled. Studies are made of the surface location, downhole targets, and depths/descriptions of strata. Information to be gathered from the well is identified, along with any post-completion issues.

Several additional steps are taken before drilling commences on an onshore property. First, access to the location must be established. In many areas, it is a simple matter of grading an access road to the location. However, transportation can be a major problem in other locations. Roads and bridges rated for extreme loads may be necessary. In swampy areas, such as portions of southern Louisiana, temporary roads are built using heavy timbers. Uneven terrain may require the use of bulldozers and roads may have to be blasted through the sides of mountains. When access is secured and the site is leveled, heavy equipment is brought in.

Occasionally, a drilling structure is so complex that it is equivalent to offshore construction. Platforms are called for in marshy areas and regions in Alaska or the Arctic where permafrost must be protected from the heat generated by the drilling rig.

Offshore locations present their own challenges. Required navigational warnings must be installed. Environmental requirements must also be addressed. Most of the problems relate to transportation, installation, and positioning of the drilling rig, rather than well site preparations. Once the rig is on location, however, continuously supplying drilling materials and consumables to the site can pose the most daunting set of problems.

Damages. Although oil and gas leases give operators the right to explore for and produce oil and gas, and include the right of ingress and egress, operators may have to pay for use of the surface—and will almost certainly pay for any damages to it. Most leases now include requirements to restore the surface to its original condition. **Damage payments** represent another cost of locating and preparing the well site prior to commencement of drilling operations.

THE DRILLING PROCESS

For many years, the cable-tool method was used for drilling into the earth's surface. A cable-tool rig drilled the Drake well in Titusville, Pennsylvania, in 1859 and marked the beginning of the oil industry as it is known today. It used a walking beam mounted to the derrick. A cable with a bit attached was lowered and raised by the beam. Each time the bit was lowered, it hit against rock to drill a hole.

While cable-tool drills were suitable for shallow wells in hard rock formations, wells located in softer formations required a different technology. The rotary method came into significant use just prior to 1900 and is used extensively to drill oil and gas wells.

ROTARY RIG DRILLING

Rotary drilling is the most widely used method of drilling for oil and gas today, both onshore and offshore. In rotary operations, a hole is drilled with a powerful motor that rotates a drill bit downward through the formations. The drill bit, with its rows of teeth, is attached to the bottom of a jointed drill string or hollow pipe. The drill bit is rotated using a rotary table, top drive, or downhole motor. The drill floor is located at the top of the substructure, which straddles the well and supports the drilling mast or derrick. Similar to a turntable, the rotary table at the center of the drill floor has a master bushing. In the master bushing, drive holes are fitted with a special hexagonal pipe known as a **kelly**. The kelly connects to the top of the drill string, and down to steel rollers on the rotary table, allowing a turning motion that creates torque.

Power is transmitted to turn the rotary table, which in turn rotates the kelly, drill pipe, drill collar(s), and drill bit. As the drill bit rotates, it cuts or chips away pieces of the formation. As drilling proceeds downward, additional lengths of drill pipe are added to the string as needed. To keep cuttings clear of the hole, fluid is circulated under pressure down through the drill pipe, and out small holes in the drill bit at the bottom of the hole into the wellbore. Next, the fluid circulates outside the pipe—it returns to the surface carrying the cuttings from the formation with it. This fluid is called drilling mud.

The need to drill deeper and directionally has driven a number of design improvements for rotary drilling. Topdrive or overhead rotary drilling systems have improved upon the kelly system. A kelly can be up to 54-feet tall, but a topdrive system stands at 90-feet or greater. Added height reduces the number of pipe connections that need to be made. These overhead systems efficiently rotate in and out of the hole. Safety is also improved due to the decrease in handling pipe and making pipe connections.

Downhole motors have also improved drilling capabilities. A downhole motor looks like a piece of pipe. For directional work, it is usually attached to a bent sub with one to three degrees of angle. Using drilling fluid to power the motor, these units do not turn the entire drill string. Instead, the mud pumped down the drill string powers the motor which then turns the drill bit. The advantages of using such a device include less wear on the equipment, such as the casing and drill string, and improved control in the direction of the drilling. Using measurement while drilling (MWD) techniques, the crew can monitor the drilling progress and determine the direction of the hole on a computer.

Components of a typical onshore **drilling rig** (see Figure 8-2) fall into five major groupings: the derrick or mast, power system, hoisting equipment, rotary system, and mud system.

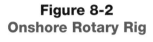

Figure 8-2
Onshore Rotary Rig

Courtesy of University of Texas Petroleum Extension Service

In rotary drilling, operations normally continue around the clock by using two or three drilling crews. The person in charge of rig equipment is referred to as the toolpusher or rig manager, and has overall responsibility for operations. Normally, the toolpusher is on call 24 hours each day. A driller leads each crew and operates the drilling controls. Crew members include: (1) a derrick man (if automated pipe-handling equipment is not used) who works in the derrick when pipe is being placed into or being removed from the hole (normally referred to as tripping), and (2) two or more rotary helpers, or roughnecks, who work on the rig floor. A motor man may also be included in the crew to take care of the engines and power equipment, although this additional responsibility is sometimes given to the derrick man to perform.

In onshore drilling, it is normal for each of three crews to work an eight-hour shift (or tour, pronounced tower); because of the logistics of offshore operations, crews work 12 hours and are off duty for the next 12 hours. Even when not on duty, offshore crews remain on the drilling platform for at least seven days and then return to shore for the same number of days. Since most drilling is now performed by independent drilling contractors, an engineer or geologist employed by the operator will also be present on location at all necessary times.

Offshore crews are usually larger than land crews because of their remote locations. The offshore installation manager (OIM) is responsible for the overall rig operations. Crane operators load and unload supplies using the rig's deck cranes. Additional workers, known as roustabouts, are the general labor force onboard and perform various daily tasks that keep the main deck operating efficiently. Engineers, marine crew, maintenance technicians, catering crew, radio operators and emergency medical staff are among the other personnel found on offshore rigs.

PARTS OF A RIG

Derrick or Mast. The derrick or mast is the structure placed over an intended drilling location. Although the terms are used interchangeably, a derrick is a structure assembled piece by piece, whereas a mast is a single structure that is portable. The rig floor, located at the base of the derrick, houses much of the equipment needed for the drilling operation and serves as a base for the derrick itself. Loads from the derrick are transmitted through the rig floor to the substructure of the rig.

For shallow well drilling and for some **workover** operations, a self-contained rig mounted on a large truck may be used. For most onshore work, however, a jackknife mast is used. It consists of a series of modules that can be erected at the well site.

Derrick and mast structures range in height from 65 to over 200 feet. By design, they must be capable of withstanding extremely heavy loads of up to 1.5 million pounds or more in vertical capacity. The structures must be also designed for wind loading due to their size and variable operating locations.

Power Supply System. The power system furnishes power for rotating the drill string and bit, hoisting operations, fluid circulation, compressed air, lighting, and other functions. Land rigs capable of drilling to shallow or moderate depths may require only 1,000 horsepower, while those capable of drilling over 20,000 feet may require more than 3,500 horsepower. Diesel, diesel-electric, gasoline, and other types of power sources are used.

Hoisting Equipment. Hoisting equipment must bear heavy loads in supporting the drill string and the movement of strings in and out of the hole. The hoist (or drawworks), mast, crown block, traveling block and wire rope drilling line comprise the hoisting system. Drilling line looks like steel rope, and can be up to two inches in diameter. Depending on the hook loads anticipated, the line can be strung multiple times (up to 16 lines). An illustration of a hoisting system is shown in Figure 8-3.

> ### "Upstream oil and gas expenditures in the US this year will climb nearly 4%. Total spending for exploration, drilling, and production activity will total almost $162 billion, OGJ forecasts."
>
> – *Marilyn Radler*, "Oil and gas capital spending to rise in US, fall in Canada,"
> Oil & Gas Journal, Volume 105: Issue 13, April 2, 2007

Figure 8-3
Hoisting System

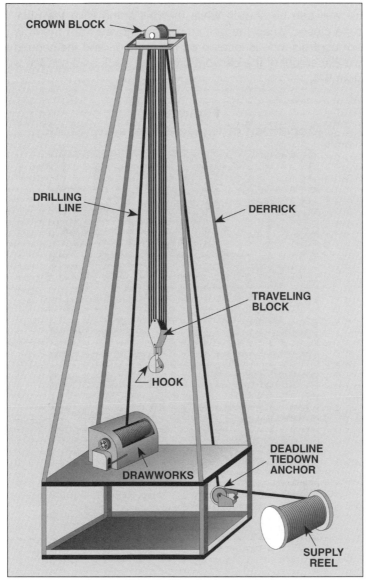

Courtesy of University of Texas Petroleum Extension Service

Rotary System. A simple rotary system begins with the rotating swivel at the top of the kelly and ends with the drill bit at the bottom of the hole. The swivel allows the entire system to rotate while being held by the hoisting system. Power is applied to the rotary table, and when the kelly bushing is engaged, the drill string, collars, and bit rotate so that the bit cuts into the formation. Advances in technology, including implementation of the topdrive and the use of downhole motors, have been necessary to meet the increasing demands placed on the modern drilling rig. These demands include the need to drill much deeper and more efficiently. Most of the larger and more modern drilling rigs are now fitted with topdrives, which improve the safety and productivity of drilling operations.

Blowout Preventers (BOPs). A **blowout** can occur when **formation pressure** exceeds the pressure being maintained by the drilling mud in the wellbore. To protect the wellsite from this danger, **blowout preventers** are installed on the wellhead and provide essential secondary well control protection. They usually comprise two or more stacks, or large **valve** packages, capable of withstanding high pressures. One set of valves is installed so the well can be shut-in while the drill string is in the hole, and the other is designed to be closed when the drill string is removed from the hole. BOPs usually have two sets of controls: one is located on the rig floor, and the second is housed at a remote location. Placement of the blowout preventer stack on a surface wellhead system is shown in Figure 8-4.

<h2 style="text-align:center">Figure 8-4
Placement of Blowout Preventer Stack</h2>

Courtesy of University of Texas Petroleum Extension Service

BOPs vary in size according to the wellhead bore used and are typically rated to contain pressures up to 15,000psi. In some extreme cases, equipment has been used to withstand 20,000psi wellbore pressures.

Mud System. In rotary drilling, the fluid or drilling mud plays several important roles. The circulating drilling mud suspends the cuttings of the formation and brings them to the surface. These cuttings are analyzed to identify the formation and determine if hydrocarbons are present. Drilling mud lubricates and cools the drill bit and coats the walls of the well. This seals off the formations and makes the well walls more stable. The weight of the drilling mud offsets the underground or reservoir pressure, which helps prevent blowouts. Fluid mixtures and specific gravity are constantly monitored to provide optimal drilling conditions and control of the well. The mixture of materials used in the mud determines the weight of the fluid column.

To achieve specific objectives, different types of drilling muds are used. A commonly used mud is a mixture of special clay, water weighting material, and chemicals. The mineral barite is used to add weight to the drilling fluid; it is about 4.2 times as heavy as water. Certain types of formations could be damaged by water; in these cases, an oil-based fluid is used for the drilling mud. Even in drilling a single well, several changes in the drilling mud may be made.

Figure 8-5 shows the path taken by the drilling mud in circulating through the well. From the mud pumps, the fluid goes through the discharge line to a standpipe. Mud flows out of the standpipe into a rotary hose connected to the swivel (on rotary table) or the top drive. Mud goes down through the kelly (or through a passage inside the top drive), and through the drill pipe to the bit. At the bit, the drilling mud washes the cuttings from the bit and the bottom of the hole and carries them back to the surface through a U-shaped **annulus**. At the surface, a pipe carries the cuttings in suspension to a shale shaker that removes cuttings from the mud. From the shaker, the mud flows to a tank and the whole cycle starts again.

Mud can be sent through additional cleaning systems, including desanders, desilters, mud cleaners and mud centrifuges to remove finer particles and keep out contaminants. A degasser is used to remove any gas that might enter the drilling mud as it circulates through the system.

Figure 8-5
The Mud System of a Rotary Rig

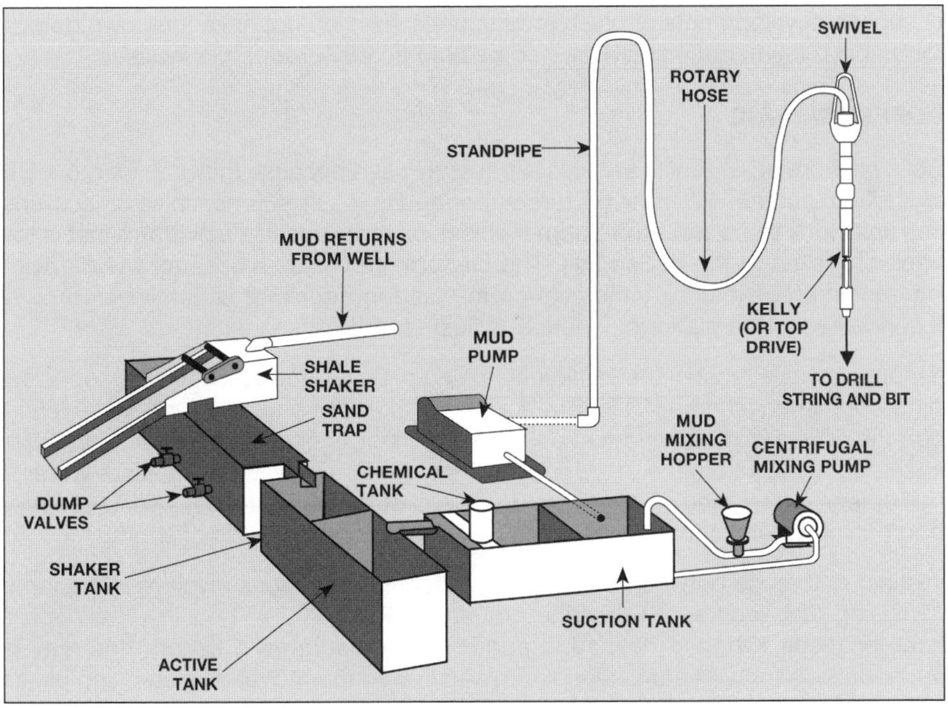

Courtesy of University of Texas Petroleum Extension Service

OFFSHORE DRILLING TECHNIQUES

The first offshore platform was erected in 1947 in the Gulf of Mexico. Offshore drilling has steadily increased since then. The most dramatic advances in offshore drilling involve the ability to reach extraordinary depths; some wells have surpassed 25,000 feet.

Four main types of offshore rigs are used:

- Submersibles are drilling structures that are floated into shallow locations, usually 80 feet or less, and then ballasted down to rest on the seabed.

- Jack-up rigs are towed or transported to the drilling location. While floating over the well location, their legs are lowered. As the legs touch the seabed and continue to be jacked down, the hull rises up above the water by about 50 feet. Jack-up rigs can be used in waters up to 600 feet deep depending on leg length and environmental conditions.

- Semi-submersibles are mobile structures that are towed or self-propelled to the location. The rig structure is steadied on hulls or pontoons, which are often ballasted below the water surface. Semi-submersible rigs are frequently used in deeper waters or in locations where inclement weather frequently occurs. The good motion response of these rigs maximizes drilling up-time during less favorable conditions.

- Drill ships are more commonly used in deeper waters where they are dynamically positioned over the well location using satellites or acoustic beacons. Large capacities make them ideal for working in remote locations during exploratory drilling operations.

Once exploration wells are drilled and field development commences, a more permanent structure known as a production platform is erected at the well site. This mode of development depends on the water depth, number of wells, and type of reservoir. Many subsea developments or clusters of subsea wells do not have their own dedicated platform above them, but instead are tied back to nearby production facilities.

THE OFFSHORE RIG

Mobile offshore drilling units are most frequently used because they can be moved from one drill site to another. Whether bottom-supported (such as submersibles or jack-ups) or floating units (drill ships and semi-submersibles), offshore rigs use a platform that is towed or is self-propelled to the drilling site. The platform serves as a base for the derrick and drilling equipment. A derrick either sits on the platform deck, or is cantilevered on steel arms connected to the platform. Figure 8-6 illustrates an offshore rig.

Offshore rigs have most of the same functioning parts as landrigs, but with modifications to suit an ocean environment. Bottom-supported rigs, such as jack-ups, have legs that support the drilling platform and rest on the ocean floor or on a special mat. Floating units are anchored to the seafloor and are raised or lowered in the water using air or water to fill the hull or legs (depending upon the model). Semi-submersibles work well in deeper and more turbulent waters, and are one of the more common rigs found offshore.

A distinct difference between onshore and offshore operations involves transportation and housing for workers. Personnel must be carried by boat or helicopter to offshore locations. Often, a helipad is added to rig platforms. Offshore rigs may have accommodations for workers to sleep, eat, and live on them. Waste, water, and electrical systems are maintained on the units.

Figure 8-6
Offshore Rig

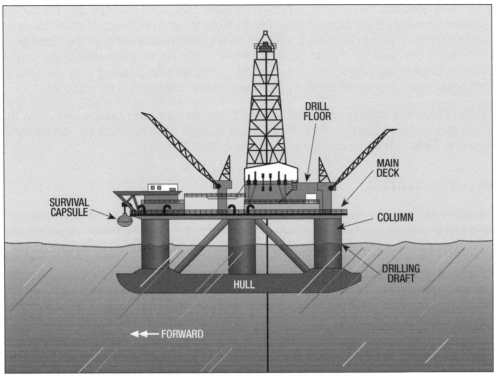

Courtesy of University of Texas Petroleum Extension Service

Derrick. Derricks on offshore drilling units are essentially the same as those on land or platform rigs, except when they are located on floating vessels. In this case, vessel motion adds dynamic loading to the structure. Some ultra deepwater drilling vessels have derrick structures rated for as much as three million pounds and can be over 200 feet tall.

Power Supply System. In addition to drilling equipment system loads, the power system on an offshore drilling rig may also be used for the vessel's main propulsion. On ultra deepwater/harsh environment units, the main engines can deliver over 60,000 horsepower.

Hoisting Equipment. Hoisting systems on offshore drilling rigs are essentially the same as those on land or platform rigs. However, two differences should be noted: (1) the size increases quite dramatically on deepwater floating units, and (2) the hoisting system has to account for vessel motion. Movement can be addressed by either passive or active motion compensators.

Rotary System. Most offshore drilling rigs are now fitted with topdrives to improve their drilling performance and may also use downhole motors to improve **directional drilling** through the reservoir.

Blowout Preventers (BOPs). Offshore rigs use a blowout preventer stack that consists of BOPs placed on top of one another. Floating units (drill ships and semi-submersibles) normally use a subsea BOP stack, which is clamped to a wellhead cemented in the seafloor.

In deepwater operations, these 15,000psi-rated BOP stacks can contain up to six ram and two annular preventers, which reach heights up to sixty feet tall and weigh around 350 tons. Multiplexed control systems are required for the BOP stack, enabling rapid shut-in of the well prior to disconnecting the marine riser and moving off location.

The Mud System. Depending on the mud type used, drill cuttings can be dumped overboard after they have passed over the shakers to recover returned mud. Increased shaker retention time improves the amount of drilling mud recovered from the cuttings and can eliminate the need to dry the cuttings before dumping. In some cases, the cuttings cannot be discharged overboard and must be collected after passing over the shakers. Cuttings are then transferred as slurry onto barges and transported for disposal.

Larger deepwater drilling units can have as many as four mud pumps and more than eight shakers. Active and reserve drilling mud storage volumes can be significant for deepwater wells with some capacities exceeding 20,000 barrels.

DRILLING ACTIVITIES

For onshore locations, work crews remove the first 10 feet of dirt to create a rectangular-shaped pit known as a cellar. This is where the base of the rig is installed. Rigs that use a kelly require a rathole, which is a shallow hole drilled to the side of the main **borehole**.

Spudding-in is the industry term for the commencement of drilling operations. A special bit is used for the initial drilling of the main hole. This section of the hole is relatively large to allow the installation of any casing required by the drilling plan. Large conductor casing (often 20 inches in diameter) may be installed at the surface to prevent cave-ins of the hole and provide a foundation for subsequent casing strings. Surface casing (perhaps 13 3/8 inches in diameter) is installed and **cemented** to a point below all fresh water formations to prevent contamination. Additional casing strings are installed as needed. The types of casing and pipe typically used in a land well are shown in Figure 8-7.

Depending on the rig and well type, offshore conductor casing ranges from a standard 48 feet to more than 80 feet. It is designed to handle high wellhead bending loads. **Joints** range in diameter from 20 to 48 inches. Using high pressure water streams, the rig crew creates a hole for the conductor casing. Floating operations call the initial casing a foundation pile; it is usually 36 inches in diameter and is jetted to an appropriate depth.

Although drilling progresses rapidly near the surface, continuous attention is given to the drilling mud indicators: (1) cuttings from the bottom of the hole, and (2) drilling speed. These observations provide crucial information on the condition of the drill bit. More importantly, they indicate the type of formations being drilled. When formation material changes significantly, or the drill bit becomes worn, it must be changed. Depending on the hardness of the formations, a bit may be used for only a few hundred feet or for several thousand feet. Bits are available in a variety of sizes and materials, and are designed to drill in formations that range from soft to very hard and abrasive. Tungsten carbide and synthetic or natural diamonds are common materials used in manufacturing these bits.

Bits come in two main categories: roller cone bits and fixed head bits. Roller cone bits have steel teeth that roll over the bottom of the hole crushing the rock or soil as they go. Fixed head bits use jets that move cuttings out of the way as the fixed head rotates. Additional weight is normally needed to help the bit work more effectively. Drill collars are placed on the bottom portion of the drill string to enable more weight to be put on the bit. These drill collars are usually 30 feet long, and can weigh about 6,000 pounds. Multiple drill collars are used to handle the thousands of pounds of weight on the bit.

Figure 8-7
Casing & Pipe in a Typical Land Well

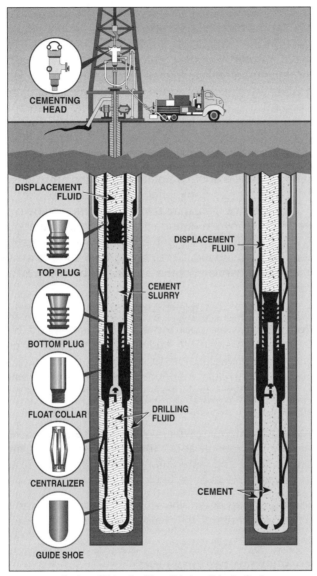

Courtesy of University of Texas Petroleum Extension Service

As the hole is drilled, additional pieces of drill pipe in 30-foot lengths are added to the string. When changing the drill bit, all of the drill pipe is pulled from the hole, the old bit is removed, a new bit is attached, and all drill pipe is reinserted in the hole. This process is referred to as **making a trip** (tripping-out and tripping-in), and the entire process is called making a round trip. In making a round trip, the drill string is disconnected and reconnected in strands consisting of one, two, three, or even four 30-foot sections of drill pipe depending on the size of the rig. Because a round trip at a depth of 14,000 feet can take as much as twelve or as little as five hours, depending on the type of rig, a considerable amount of time can be spent merely changing bits when drilling a well. Good planning and careful selection of drill bits is essential to ensure efficient drilling progress is made.

Throughout the drilling process, several tests are performed regarding drilling fluids, pressures, and cuttings from the well. Once the target depth is achieved, additional tests evaluate the formations for sufficient hydrocarbons to justify completion of the well.

When cuttings indicate the presence of hydrocarbons, further information is sought. A larger sample is taken from the formation by means of coring. The drill string is taken out of the hole, and in place of the drill bit a core barrel is attached; the drill string is then lowered back into the hole. The core barrel is a specially designed, long bit with a hollow center. The size of the core varies from about one inch to slightly over four inches in diameter, but can be over a hundred feet long. Core barrels permit capture of a sample which is brought to the surface for evaluation (**core analysis**). A sidewall sampler can also be lowered into the borehole to penetrate the rock and cut a small core. Cores are evaluated for reservoir characteristics such as **porosity**, permeability, saturation, and fluid content.

Additional information is gained about a potential formation by running a drill-stem test. This test is essentially a temporary completion of the well. A packer is inserted into the hole and expanded to seal off the drilling mud from the formation being tested. Formation fluids are then allowed to flow upward through the drill string. Data about the fluid content, formation pressure, and other factors are gathered. As drill stem testing is performed on offshore wells, oil and gas may surface. If they do, special burners are used to safely flare these substances into the atmosphere, or the liquids can be captured and stored in tanks while the gas is flared.

Certain tests, referred to as well logging, can be run at virtually any point during drilling, but are usually performed when the approximate target is reached. By using a sonde, a specialized tool that measures electrical, radioactive and acoustic properties of rocks, experts can evaluate the transmitted log to determine whether or not hydrocarbons exist. Each formation and each fluid respond differently to tests made by the logging instruments. Proper interpretation of well logs indicates the type of formation and fluids present at various depths.

Newer technologies, such as logging while drilling (LWD) and measurement while drilling (MWD), provide real-time information about the well, even from a remote location. The need to provide more accurate and faster information about the well as it is being drilled will continue to drive advancements of technology.

Tests performed during drilling determine whether the well has the potential for being economically productive. At all depths, they help geologists make more accurate decisions about the future of the well.

DIRECTIONAL AND HORIZONTAL DRILLING

In the early days of the industry, wells drilled with cable tool equipment were assumed to be vertical. The advent of rotary drilling revealed that it is nearly impossible to drill a truly vertical well. Changes in the angles of rock formation layers (known as dip angles), differing rock strength, and drilling practices cause the drill bit to drift away from true vertical. Drillers learned how to purposely drill in a certain direction; this allowed them to access oil and gas in areas where the surface location didn't allow a rig to be set up, such as offshore Huntington Beach, California, and under the state capitol building in Oklahoma City, Oklahoma.

When offshore platforms were set in the Gulf of Mexico, even more emphasis was placed on directional drilling. The wells on a typical offshore platform branch out in all directions, allowing each platform to drain a much greater area than would be possible with one well. When drilling a directional well, a vertical hole is drilled and then deflected in a particular direction.

Subsequent holes, or sidetracks, can be drilled from the same original vertical hole. The distance away from the platform that a directional well can reach depends on many factors, particularly the depth of the target formation, but a reach of one mile is not uncommon.

One of the main factors governing the rate of oil or gas flow into the wellbore is the length of section exposed to the wellbore. The industry has long recognized that if this section could be lengthened by drilling horizontally, instead of vertically, along the strata in the formation, production rates and recoverable reserves could be greatly increased. With advances in areas such as downhole rotating motors and bits, metallurgy, downhole gyroscopic steering tools, mud systems, and logging tools, horizontal drilling has become a technical and economic reality. Figure 8-8 illustrates a directional well.

Figure 8-8
Directional Drilling Diagram

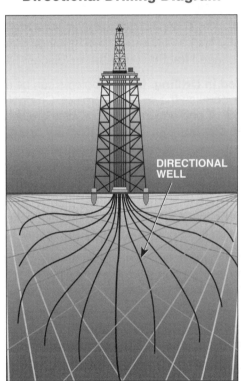

Courtesy of University of Texas Petroleum Extension Service

Directional and horizontal drilling use a more flexible drill pipe that allows the drill string to bend. Other specialized equipment is often used, such as a downhole motor. The motor is paired with a technique mentioned earlier that is known as measurement while drilling or MWD. An MWD tool attached to the drill string sends information to a computer control at the surface. A directional operator monitors the information in order to steer the direction of the drilling.

On a smaller scale than conventional drilling, coiled tubing drilling can be a very effective way of directional drilling. Coiled **tubing** is a continuous length of coiled pipe (usually 2" diameter or less) that is wrapped around a reel. The tubing is reeled into the well with a mud motor attached to its end. Drilling fluid is pumped down the tubing which rotates the motor and causes the drill bit to spin. Coiled tubing drilling can be very cost effective for the right application, particularly small wellbore sidetracks.

A typical horizontal well starts out much the same as a vertical one. At a predetermined point above the target formation known as the kickoff point, a special directional drill string is run to start the turn from vertical to horizontal. The radius of curvature between vertical and horizontal depends on many factors, but can be from a few feet to several hundred feet depending on the design of the tools and the requirements of the situation. In a typical well, the wellbore path is designed to be horizontal at the time the target formation is encountered, and the wellbore is continued so that it remains within the target formation during the horizontal segment.

To further increase the flow from a reservoir, multiple wellbores or branches can be drilled from a single wellbore through the producing formation. These multilaterals range from a single well with one branch to three or four branches radiating from the main borehole. They can reach different depths and assist with even drainage of fragmented reservoirs. Such wells can be more cost effective than traditional drilling, although they add further complexity to the drilling process.

Improved horizontal drilling techniques have aided in unlocking hydrocarbons previously bound up in tight formations, such as in shale. These methods allow for greater contact with the reservoir rock and enhanced fracture **stimulation** (discussed later in this chapter).

Problems Encountered in Drilling. Many problems can be experienced when drilling wells, and they inevitably increase the cost of a project. One potential problem is the risk of a high-pressure blowout. If one occurs, workers' lives are endangered, and economic and environmental losses can be high. The well must be brought under control, even if "**killing**" it is required.

Losing equipment in the hole is another hazard often encountered. Part of the drill string may twist off and normally must be retrieved before drilling can continue. The driller must attempt to remove the obstruction by **fishing** for the pipe or other equipment stuck in the hole. If the material cannot be retrieved, the hole can be sidetracked around the lost pipe. In some cases, the only solution is to move the rig and start a new hole known as a twin well.

When a hole partially collapses or sharp bends occur, the pipe can become stuck. If the drill string cannot be removed, the only alternative is to cut off the string at the stuck point and proceed in the same way as when a pipe is lost in the hole.

While drill pipe in 30-foot sections appears to be rigid, it becomes quite flexible when several joints of pipe are on a string. Deviations from a true vertical axis are normal, but the deviations must be controlled so that the hole is not drilled in an unacceptable direction.

Another problem encountered is lost circulation of the mud. This occurs when a drill bit breaks through into caverns or formations with large openings. Drilling mud escapes into the formation. In this event, the formation must be plugged before drilling can continue.

COMPLETING THE WELL

After drilling a well to final depth and evaluating tests from each stage, an operator faces the decision of whether to abandon the well or attempt completion. There is no clear answer to this question; it depends on whether the operator thinks there are enough hydrocarbons present to economically justify the additional expenditures for completing, equipping, and producing the well.

DRY HOLES

If an operator judges that there are no reserves, or an insufficient quantity of reserves to justify completion, the well is plugged and abandoned (P&A'd). Cement plugs are normally used to seal it. Equipment in the hole is salvaged and either sold or returned to a warehouse if suitable for future use. However, very little of the equipment installed in the hole, such as casing, can be salvaged because of physical constraints or regulatory requirements. Potentially high formation pressures or other factors can call for the entire casing string to be encased in cement.

In any event, the surface casing usually cannot be removed because almost all governmental regulatory bodies require it to be cemented in the hole, along with a cement plug at the surface. If the well is never to be re-entered, the protruding section of the wellhead is normally severed to complete the abandonment process.

ONSHORE WELL COMPLETION

An operator may think there is enough evidence to justify the additional costs of well completion. However, completion of a well does not necessarily mean that it will be profitable. Many wells are completed that will never recover all drilling, completion, and production costs. A well is completed if anticipated revenues from production are expected to significantly exceed anticipated completion and production costs. Therefore, even if the overall operation is not profitable, in the sense that all costs (including drilling costs) will not be recovered, completion of a well can be economically justified.

In completing a well, the identified formation must be closed off. Often, production casing is set and cemented into the hole, perhaps cemented only at the bottom of the well and at the surface. The next step is to make perforations in the casing to allow produced fluids to flow into the well bore. A perforating gun is lowered into the hole on either wire line or drill pipe. At the proper depth, the gun is fired and perforations are made through the casing and into the formation. Perforations are normally made using a jet or rocket charge that cuts the hole using a jet of energy. While other techniques are being invented for perforating casing, the purpose is to create a hole to allow hydrocarbons to flow through any localized formation damage, through the cement and casing into the wellbore before flowing to the surface. Offshore wells can also use perforating to open the well for production.

In some cases, the formation's permeability is low and oil or gas cannot readily flow into the wellbore. Steps must be taken to increase the localized permeability, which include **acidizing** and **fracturing**. If the formation is made of calcium carbonate material, acid can be pumped through the perforations (acidizing) to dissolve portions of the formation. In this way, channels are created through which formation contents can flow.

However, the usual process in sandstone formations is called fracturing. Coarse sands or synthetic beads, called proppant, are mixed in a fluid and pumped down the well bore through the perforations and into the formation under very high pressure. This causes the formation to split or fracture. When pressure is released, the fluid comes back into the well bore. The coarse sand grains continue to prop open the fractures and allow the hydrocarbons to flow into the well bore with greater ease.

As an example, fracturing has been used successfully in an area near Fort Worth, Texas, known as the Barnett Shale. After nearly 20 years of modest production, new technologies have significantly changed the outcome. Operators began employing advanced water fracturing techniques to unlock the vast reservoir of gas bound up in the tight formations. When pumped into a well, water-based fluids create hydraulic pressure that cracks the shale and keeps it open over a period of time as the gas is produced. Barnett is now a blockbuster field producing about 1.4 billion cubic feet of gas each day.

Lastly, when there is fluid in a well (such as drilling mud) and reservoir pressure is low, it may be necessary to **swab** the well to remove the fluid. Swabbing is a relatively simple process: a small expandable packer is lowered into the well, and by swiftly pulling it back out of the hole, the fluid is removed. Alternatively, a lighter fluid or even gas can be circulated into the wellbore to underbalance the well and promote flow. Many other methods exist for completing wells and are selected specifically to meet the needs of the various reservoirs being developed.

EQUIPMENT REQUIRED TO COMPLETE A WELL

The equipment used in completing a producing well depends in part on whether the well produces oil, gas, or both. Additionally, it depends on whether the well is flowing or being produced by a form of artificial lift. In either case, casing is run into the well and wellhead connections are attached in order to control production.

As previously discussed, surface casing is cemented through all fresh water formations to prevent contamination and cave-ins. Usually, casing is not used for producing the well. Small-diameter pipe known as tubing (ranging from a diameter of one-inch to over seven-inches) is run into the cased well using a packer. Coiled tubing can also be used for production. Oil and gas could be produced through casing, but a string (or strings) of production tubing is normally run into the well. If repairs are later required, it is easier to remove the production tubing than a cemented casing. In addition, the tubing to casing annulus can be monitored for pressure to determine whether tubing integrity has been lost.

Multiple completions, including **dual completion**, occur when two or more formations are produced through the same well. Procedures for preparing each formation are identical to those used in single completions. Cement and/or packers are generally used above and below each of the producing formations so that the producing formations are sealed off to produce into the **production strings**. As shown in Figure 8-9, a simple **Christmas tree** is used when a well is **flowing** from its own reservoir pressure. Likewise, a simple Christmas tree is used for a well produced by pumping. Various gauges and meters are attached to the Christmas tree to measure pressure and the flow of liquids. In an offshore environment, Christmas trees can be wet or dry. A wet tree is installed on the seabed with electrohydraulic controls to operate the valves remotely. Dry Christmas trees are those installed on a floating vessel or platform.

Figure 8-9
A Christmas Tree Valve to Control Production in a Flowing Well

Courtesy of University of Texas Petroleum Extension Service

Onshore, if a well is not capable of flowing as the result of formation pressure, a form of artificial lift or pumping unit is employed. The most common form of pumping unit on land wells is a walking beam unit depicted in Figure 8-10. Sucker rods are attached to the beam unit at the surface. The up-and-down movement of the beam unit activates a simple lift pump located at the formation. The most common forms of artificial lift used on offshore wells are **gas lifts** and electric submersible pumps (ESPs).

Figure 8-10
A Walking Beam Artificial Lift Installation

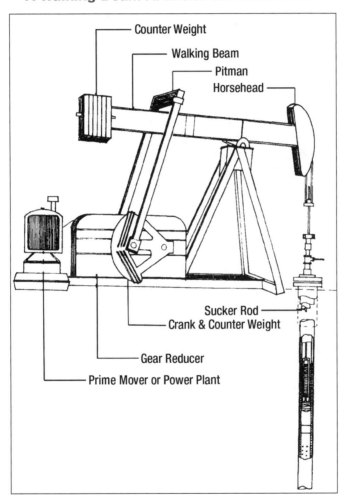

Lifting hydrocarbons to the surface is only one of the operations necessary for producing oil and gas. Other types of equipment required on a lease depend on whether the well produces oil and/or gas and the amount of treatment needed to process the hydrocarbons for sale or use. Treatment of the oil or gas is not a manufacturing process, but rather involves the removal of impurities.

Offshore, the drilling platform becomes the production platform. The derrick can be used to lift and lower tools into the wells. If a well is subsea, oil and gas flow from the wells either through a pipeline to a nearby platform or to a production riser into a buoy that connects to a tanker. The liquids are then separated, treated, and either pumped down the pipeline to shore or stored in the ship's tanks until they can be moved to an onshore terminal.

If a well is classified as oil only, it means the well produces no gas or only insignificant quantities. When oil is predominant, but a significant quantity of gas is present, it is classified as an oil/casinghead gas well.

Casinghead gas (also called **dissolved gas** or solution gas) is dissolved in the reservoir's crude oil, but bubbles out at the surface at normal atmospheric pressure. Gas in the **gas cap** overlying the oil is called **associated gas**. A gas reservoir with little or no oil is said to produce **non-associated gas**. These terms are explained further in the Glossary.

To be classified as gas only, production from the well must have only insignificant amounts of liquid present. A gas/condensate well produces both natural gas and condensate. In the reservoir, gas and liquids are part of homogeneous hydrocarbons. When gas is withdrawn from the reservoir and pressure drops sufficiently, lighter fluid fractions condense as discussed in Chapter 1.

DEVELOPMENT OF THE RESERVOIR

Normally, a single well does not constitute the complete development of a reservoir. As discussed previously, even though additional wells may not significantly affect the quantity of hydrocarbons ultimately recovered, the number of wells does affect the rate of extraction of the hydrocarbons, and thus the present value of the income stream. Figure 8-11 illustrates the development process for a simple anticlinal structure.

Figure 8-11
Reservoir Development

Site	Well	
D	1	Discovery, field exploratory well establishes offset sites C and E as proved.*
E	2	Offset, development, producing well. Well 2 proves Site F.*
F	3	Offset, development producing well. Assume data does not prove Site G.*
B	4	Step-out, exploratory producing well on an unproved drill site. Assume data proves Site A.
C	5	Offset, development, producing well.
A	6	Offset, development dry hole. Costs remain capitalized as development costs. Well is plugged.
G	7	Offset, exploratory dry hole. Costs are expensed. Well is plugged.

*Proving a site means that geological and engineering data indicate with reasonable certainty that the site has sufficient reserves to economically justify (at current prices) drilling the site. Usually a successful well and G&G data prove only sites offsetting the successful well's site (as further discussed in Chapter 16). The data may or may not prove all offset locations. See the Glossary for definitions of **discovery well**, **offset well**, and **step-out well**.

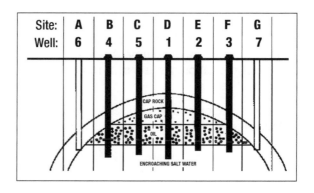

Ultimate development of a reservoir is contingent on various factors. Even though production has been established by drilling a discovery well, the property may or may not have sufficient potential reserves to warrant further expenditures for complete development. Volumetric estimates of hydrocarbons in place can be prepared on an initial basis when the first well is tested. However, the samples are quite small. If a 4-1/2 inch core (which is a rather large core) is taken in a 40-acre spacing tract, the sample size is only one in over 13,000,000. Yet this sample, along with pressure tests, flow tests and rates, fluid analyses, and geological data, is used to decide whether the reservoir is viable or not.

In spite of advanced technology, drilling provides the only final answer concerning the existence of hydrocarbons. Assuming a successful well has been drilled, drilling and development continues until the boundaries of the reservoir are delineated by dry holes or marginally economic wells.

Placing wells on production. Various types of surface equipment are required to place the wells in production by collecting and gathering the oil and gas, treating each product for the market, briefly storing the produced oil, measuring the volumes produced and sold, and removing the oil and gas from the lease. This process and its associated equipment are described in Chapter 11.

WELL COSTS

The cost to drill and equip a well varies by such factors as the depth of the well, its general location, and industry economics that drive demand for drilling rigs in the immediate area of the well site. Figure 8-12 provides general statistics on the cost of wells in the U.S.

Figure 8-12
Costs to Drill and Equip U.S. Wells

For 2004	# of Wells Drilled	PER WELL AVERAGES Depth (feet)	Cost (U.S. $)	Average Cost/Foot
U.S. Total (excluding sidetrack wells)				
Onshore - Oil Wells	7,650	4,852	$ 1,054,000	$ 217.23
Onshore - Gas Wells	20,642	5,965	1,479,000	247.95
Onshore - Dry Holes	3,236	5,725	1,111,000	194.06
Total Onshore	31,528	5,670	1,338,000	235.98
Offshore - Oil Wells	84	11,969	16,265,000	1,358.93
Offshore - Gas Wells	220	10,661	14,696,000	1,378.48
Offshore - Dry Holes	122	13,198	17,589,000	1,332.70
Total Offshore	426	11,645	15,834,000	1,359.73
All Wells (excluding sidetrack wells)				
Oil Wells	7,734	4,929	1,220,000	247.51
Gas Wells	20,862	6,014	1,618,000	269.04
Dry Holes	3,358	5,997	1,710,000	285.14
Total	31,954	5,750	1,531,000	266.26

Source: API Joint Association Survey on Drilling Costs, 2004

• • •

ACCOUNTING FOR COSTS INCURRED IN DRILLING AND EQUIPPING OIL AND GAS PROPERTIES

Glossary Terms

casing point

lease and well equipment

nonoperators

outpost wells

plugs back

Key Concepts:

- Methods for recording drilling in progress and outcomes of exploratory wells

- Guidelines on post-balance-sheet events

- Cost deferral when well success is undetermined

- Development well costs under successful efforts

- Special problems areas in accounting for drilling and development

- Authorization for Expenditure system and procedures

Successful efforts accounting for drilling and equipping wells can be summarized as follows:

Exploratory drilling costs are deferred until the outcome of the well is known. If an exploratory well finds proved reserves, the deferred costs are transferred to the company's Wells and Related Equipment and Facilities accounts. Absent proved reserves, the deferred costs of the well, net of salvage, are charged to expense. All costs of wells drilled to develop proved reserves, along with all costs of equipment necessary to produce and handle the hydrocarbons, are capitalized—even if a development well proves dry.

Under full cost accounting, all drilling and equipment costs are capitalized and become part of the full cost pool at the time they are incurred.

For income tax accounting, well costs are categorized as either intangible or tangible. The distinction is irrelevant for financial accounting, but very important for income tax accounting. Often, this is reflected in a company's chart of accounts. For determining taxable income, intangible drilling costs (IDC) are generally expensed as incurred, but tangible costs are capitalized and depreciated as described in Chapter 26.

SUCCESSFUL EFFORTS ACCOUNTING FOR EXPLORATORY WELL COSTS

Under Oi5, the drilling of exploratory wells is considered an exploration activity. Under successful efforts, exploration costs generally are expensed as incurred. However, costs of an exploratory well in progress are capitalized. If proved reserves are found, the costs of the well remain capitalized, and they become subject to amortization. When an exploratory well is considered a dry hole, capitalized costs are charged to expense. A detailed discussion of the classification of reserves is found in Chapter 16.

INITIAL RECORDING OF DRILLING IN PROGRESS

Oi5.110 specifies that costs of drilling an exploratory well are to be deferred until the outcome of the drilling is known:

> The costs of drilling exploratory wells and the costs of drilling exploratory-type stratigraphic test wells shall be capitalized as part of the reporting entity's uncompleted wells, equipment, and facilities pending determination of whether the well has found proved reserves.

Using the Chart of Accounts of ABC Oil Company in Appendix 3, intangible drilling costs incurred on an exploratory well are charged to Account 241, Work in Progress—Intangible Costs, while the costs of tangible assets, such as casing installed in an exploratory well, are charged to Account 243, Work in Progress—Tangible Costs. Many companies use only one general ledger account for Work in Progress, with separate subsidiary ledger accounts for intangible and tangible cost categories.

For example, assume that ABC receives a statement for $98,000 from a drilling contractor for work performed on the first well on the Dorothy DiTirro lease. The effects on the general ledger accounts are shown by the following entry.

241	Work in Progress—Intangible Costs	98,000	
301	Vouchers Payable		98,000
	To record drilling costs on the DiTirro #1 exploratory well.		

In ABC's books, the costs of equipment, such as casing installed in an exploratory well, are accumulated in Account 243, Work in Progress—Tangible Costs. A $45,000 invoice received by ABC for casing used in the exploratory well is recorded as follows:

243	Work in Progress—Tangible Costs	45,000	
301	Vouchers Payable		45,000
	To record cost of casing installed in the DiTirro #1 exploratory well.		

RECORDING THE OUTCOME OF EXPLORATORY WELLS

Oi5.110 requires that when the successful efforts method is used, the accumulated costs of an exploratory well are disposed of as follows:

> If the well has found proved reserves (refer to paragraphs .122 through .125), the capitalized costs of drilling the well shall become part of the enterprise's wells and related equipment and facilities (even though the well may not be completed as a producing well); if, however, the well has not found proved reserves, the capitalized costs of drilling the well, net of any salvage, shall be charged to expense.

When a well finds proved reserves, the appropriate accumulated costs are removed from the Work in Progress accounts, and are charged to accounts and subaccounts for Proved Property Well and Development Costs. Assume that DiTirro #1 in the previous example finds proved reserves. The effects on general ledger accounts are as follows:

231	Intangible Costs of Wells and Development	98,000	
233	Tangible Costs of Wells and Development	45,000	
241	Work in Progress—Intangible Costs		98,000
243	Work in Progress—Tangible Costs		45,000
	To reclassify the costs of the successful DiTirro #1 exploratory well.		

When an exploratory well drilled by ABC is determined to be dry, the accumulated costs, less salvage value, applicable to the well are charged to Account 804, Unsuccessful Exploratory Wells, and removed from Work in Progress—Intangible Costs and from Work in Progress—Tangible Costs, as shown in the following entry for a second exploratory well on the DiTirro lease:

804.001	Unsuccessful Expl. Wells—Intangibles	100,000	
804.002	Unsuccessful Expl. Wells—Tangibles	40,000	
241	Work in Progress—Intangible Costs		100,000
243	Work in Progress—Tangible Costs		40,000
	To expense costs of the unsuccessful DiTirro #2 exploratory well.		

If any tangible equipment is removed from the hole and saved, the net salvage value is credited to the Unsuccessful Exploratory Wells—Tangibles account.

A major accounting problem facing companies using the successful efforts method is determining how long to defer costs applicable to an exploratory well that has been drilled, but whose outcome is not certain. This challenge is examined in the next section.

DEFERRAL OF COSTS OF AN EXPLORATORY WELL WHERE THE OUTCOME IS NOT IMMEDIATELY ASCERTAINED

Paragraphs 31-34 of FASB Statement No. 19, *Financial Accounting and Reporting by Oil and Gas Producing Companies*, (Oi5.122 and 125) provides guidance on whether to expense or defer exploratory well costs or exploratory-type stratigraphic test wells when the well's success cannot be determined at the time drilling has been completed. Due to changes in today's exploration environment, questions have arisen regarding the application of Oi5.122 and Oi5.125. In response, the FASB issued FASB Staff Position (FSP) No. FAS 19-1, *Accounting for Suspended Well Costs*, in April 2005, which amended and replaced paragraphs 31-34 of FASB Statement No. 19 (Oi5.122-Oi5.125).

FSP FAS 19-1 provides clarification and guidance in two areas: (1) accounting when drilling of an exploratory well or an exploratory-type stratigraphic well is completed, and (2) progress on assessing reserves. The FSP also requires disclosures designed to provide information about management's evaluation of capitalized exploratory well costs.

Occasionally, an exploratory well or exploratory-type stratigraphic well finds oil and gas reserves, but the classification as proved reserves cannot be made when drilling is completed. In these cases, the capitalized drilling costs continue to be capitalized when the well has found a sufficient quantity of reserves to justify its completion as a producing well, and sufficient progress is being made in assessing the reserves and operating viability of the project. If either criteria is not met, or substantial doubt exists about the economic or operational viability of the project, the exploratory well or exploratory-type stratigraphic well costs are considered impaired, and such costs (net of salvage) are charged to expense.

FSP FAS 19-1 further clarifies the issue of capitalizing exploratory well and exploratory-type stratigraphic well costs. Such costs should not continue to be capitalized on the chance that current market conditions will change or technology will be developed in the future to make the project economically and operationally viable.

When addressing whether sufficient progress has been made on assessing the reserves and the economic and operational viability of the project, the FSP provides certain indicators to consider, including:

- Commitment of project personnel who are at the appropriate levels and who have the appropriate skills.

- Costs are being incurred to assess the reserves and their potential development.

- An assessment process covering the economic, legal, political, and environmental aspects of the potential development is in progress.

- Existence (or active negotiations) of sales contracts with customers for the oil and gas.

- Existence (or active negotiations) of agreements with governments, lenders, and venture partners.

- Outstanding requests for proposals for development of any required facilities.

- Existence of firm plans, established timetables, or contractual commitments that may include seismic testing and drilling of additional exploratory wells.

- Progress is being made on contractual arrangements that will permit future development.

- Identification of existing transportation and other infrastructure that is or will be available for the project (subject to negotiations for use).

Long delays in assessment or development plans may raise doubts about whether sufficient progress is being made to justify the continued capitalization of exploratory well and exploratory-type stratigraphic well costs after the completion of drilling.

As noted above, FSP FAS 19-1 requires certain annual and interim disclosures related to exploratory well and exploratory-type stratigraphic well costs pending the determination of proved reserves. These disclosures are required for each annual period an income statement is presented, as follows:

- Capitalized exploratory well costs including: (1) additions to capitalized exploratory well costs that are pending the determination of proved reserves; (2) capitalized exploratory well costs that were reclassified to well, equipment and facilities (e.g., wells determined to have proved); and (3) capitalized exploratory well costs that were charged to expense. This disclosure should not include amounts capitalized and subsequently expensed in the same period.

- Exploratory well costs that have been capitalized for a period greater than one year after the completion of drilling, including the number of projects associated with such costs and an aging of each project using a range of years.

- A description of the project and activities undertaken in order to evaluate the reserves and projects, including the remaining activities necessary to make the determination of proved reserves for each exploratory well or project that continues to be capitalized for a period greater than one year.

POST-BALANCE-SHEET EVENTS

Oi5.130 provides that post-balance-sheet events should be considered in determining the proper disposition of costs accumulated on exploratory wells in progress at the balance sheet date.

> Information that becomes available after the end of the period covered by the financial statements but before those financial statements are issued shall be taken into account in evaluating conditions that existed at the balance sheet date, for example, . . . in determining whether an exploratory well or exploratory-type stratigraphic test well has found proved reserves . . .

For example, assume that costs of $248,000 are accumulated for an exploratory well on which drilling is completed prior to the balance sheet date of December 31, 2006. At year-end, the results of the well are uncertain. However, on February 10, 2007 (before the 2006 financial statements are issued), it is decided that the well does not have proved reserves. With these facts, the costs of $248,000 accumulated at December 31, 2006, should be charged to expense in 2006.

A different situation occurs when drilling is in progress at year-end for an exploratory well. If found to be a dry hole prior to issuance of the financial statements, a question arises not only as to proper treatment of the costs incurred during the period, but also the treatment of any costs incurred after the balance sheet date. FAS Interpretation No. 36 (see Oi5.130 in Appendix 2) requires that the costs incurred after the balance sheet date must be charged to expense in the period following the balance sheet date, while costs accumulated through the balance sheet date must be charged to expense in the period ending with the balance sheet date. Equipment salvage value should be considered in the calculations.

For example, suppose ABC begins drilling an exploratory well in November 2006. During November and December, drilling costs totaling $260,000 are incurred. During January and early February 2007, additional drilling costs of $108,000 are incurred. On February 13, 2007, the well is evaluated to be dry. Financial statements for 2006 are issued on March 10, 2007. Under the requirements of FAS Interpretation No. 36, $260,000 of costs incurred and accumulated through December 31, 2006, less expected salvage value, are charged to expense in 2006, and costs of $108,000 incurred in January and February, net of salvage value, are charged to expense in 2007.

FULL COST ACCOUNTING FOR EXPLORATORY WELL COSTS

Under full cost, all expenditures for an exploratory well are capitalized, whether it is successful or dry. The Work in Progress account is used to accumulate the costs of wells being drilled, just as it is used for successful efforts companies. All accumulated costs may be closed into the Wells and Related Facilities accounts at the end of each period. Alternatively, the costs can be left in Work in Progress until the outcome of the well is known, at which time they are transferred to Wells and Related Facilities, which is part of the full cost pool.

The Work in Progress account may be included in the amortization calculation, or it may be omitted from the calculation. In any event, as soon as the outcome of the well is known, its costs must be included in the amortization computation (see Chapter 17).

SUCCESSFUL EFFORTS ACCOUNTING FOR DEVELOPMENT WELL COSTS

For companies using the successful efforts method of accounting, all development costs are capitalized [Oi5.103(b)]. Development costs are defined in Oi5.112 as follows:

Development costs are incurred to obtain access to proved reserves and to provide facilities (refer to paragraph .117) for extracting, treating, gathering and storing the oil and gas. More specifically, development costs, including depreciation and applicable operating costs of support equipment and facilities and other costs of development activities, are costs incurred to:

a) Gain access to and prepare well locations for drilling, including surveying well locations for the purpose of determining specific development drilling sites, clearing ground, draining, road building, and relocating public roads, gas lines, and power lines, to the extent necessary in developing the proved reserves.

b) Drill and equip development wells, development-type stratigraphic test wells, and service wells, including the costs of platforms and of well equipment such as casing, tubing, pumping equipment, and the wellhead assembly.

c) Acquire, construct, and install production facilities such as lease flow lines, separators, treaters, heaters, manifolds, measuring devices, and production storage tanks, natural gas cycling and processing plants, and central utility and waste disposal systems.

d) Provide improved recovery systems.

Reg. S-X Rule 4-10(a)(16) provides a similar definition of development costs.

Obviously, if the costs of exploratory dry holes and stratigraphic test wells that do not find proved reserves are expensed, while costs of development dry holes and all costs of development-type stratigraphic test wells that are not completed as producers are capitalized, the distinction between development wells (including development-type stratigraphic test wells) and exploratory wells (including exploratory-type stratigraphic test wells) becomes important. Reg. S-X Rule 4-10 provides guidance in making this distinction by defining the terms exploratory well, development well, and stratigraphic test well. The definitions that follow are similar to the definitions in Oi5; specific section references are provided.

Exploratory well. A well drilled to find and produce oil or gas in an unproved area, to find a new reservoir in a field previously found to be productive or oil or gas in another reservoir, or to extend a known reservoir. Generally, an exploratory well is any well that is not a development well, a service well, or a stratigraphic test well, as those items are defined below. (Oi5.402)

Development well. A well drilled within the proved area of an oil or gas reservoir to the depth of a stratigraphic horizon known to be productive. (Oi5.401)

Stratigraphic test well. A drilling effort, geologically directed, to obtain information pertaining to a specific geologic condition. Such wells customarily are drilled without the intention of being completed for hydrocarbon production. This classification also includes tests identified as core tests and all types of expendable holes related to hydrocarbon exploration. Stratigraphic test wells are classified as (a) *exploratory-type*, if not drilled in a proved area, or (b) *development-type*, if drilled in a proved area. (Oi5.408)

These definitions severely limit the types of wells that can be considered development wells. For example, wells drilled to define the perimeters of a reservoir are labeled exploratory wells, not development wells. A well drilled to a formation (horizon) in which no proved reserves have been found is classified as an exploratory well, even if production has been secured from another horizon on the lease. Only if the well is drilled within a proved area and to the depth of a stratigraphic horizon known to be productive is it classified as a development well; thus, **outpost wells** or step-out wells are categorized as exploratory. There should be very few development dry holes; those that do occur are likely to result from faulting of the strata or mechanical problems while drilling.

Assume that a third well is drilled within the confines of a proved area on the DiTirro lease with the intent to extract minerals from a currently producing formation. Casing costs of $6,000 and drilling costs of $96,000 are charged to Work in Progress as incurred:

241	Work in Progress—Intangible Costs	96,000	
243	Work in Progress—Tangible Costs	6,000	
	301 Vouchers Payable		102,000
	To record costs incurred for drilling and casing the DiTirro #3 development well.		

Before the well reaches completion, a structure is encountered that makes it impossible to continue drilling. The well is abandoned, and none of the casing is salvageable. Abandonment is recorded as follows:

231	Intangible Costs of Wells and Development	96,000	
233	Tangible Costs of Wells and Development	6,000	
	241 Work in Progress—Intangible Costs		96,000
	243 Work in Progress—Tangible Costs		6,000
	To record abandonment of the DiTirro #3 development well and transfer of costs to Proved Property Well and Development Costs.		

If production had been obtained from the development well, the journal entry would reflect the same amounts.

The seemingly inconsistent treatment of costs of unsuccessful exploratory wells and those of unsuccessful development wells is supported by FAS 19 (Paragraphs 204 through 207). It holds that once proved reserves have been found, development costs result in the creation of a producing system of wells and related facilities much like the production system of a manufacturing company. Paragraphs 204 and 205 state:

> After discovery, all costs incurred to build that producing system, including the costs of drilling unsuccessful development wells and development-type stratigraphic test wells, are capitalized as part of the cost of that system. . . . There is an important difference between exploratory dry holes and development dry holes. The purpose of an exploratory well is to search for oil and gas. The existence of future benefits is not known until the well is drilled. Future benefits depend on whether reserves are found. A development well, on the other hand, is drilled as part of the effort to build a system of wells and related equipment and facilities. Its purpose is to extract previously discovered oil and gas reserves.

Refer back to Figure 8-12 for an illustration that distinguishes development wells from exploratory wells.

FULL COST ACCOUNTING FOR DEVELOPMENT WELL COSTS

The accounting principles and procedures related to capitalization and used for development well costs are the same under full cost as under successful efforts.

SPECIAL PROBLEMS IN ACCOUNTING FOR DRILLING AND DEVELOPMENT

Situations frequently occur in drilling and development that give rise to complicated accounting questions. Some result from the distinction between exploratory wells and development wells. Others arise because of a halt or delay in drilling activities. Full cost companies are not affected because all drilling and development costs are capitalized under that approach. Companies using successful efforts may follow alternative procedures in accounting for the situations described below; however, the practices discussed in this section are accepted within the E&P industry.

DEEPER DRILLING BEYOND PRODUCING HORIZONS

If a well is drilled within the proved area of an oil or gas reservoir to the depth of a stratigraphic horizon known to be productive (a development well) and continues to be drilled deeper into unproven strata, the petroleum accountant must determine whether it is a development well or an exploratory well. In this case, it is reasonable to treat the well (i.e., the single long hole) as two wells for accounting purposes: (1) the costs to drill to the proven horizon are treated as development costs, and (2) the incremental costs to drill deeper for additional reserves are considered exploratory costs.

In drilling an exploratory well, an operator frequently discovers oil in commercially productive quantities and completes the well (or plans to complete the well) at that level. The operator then drills deeper in the same hole to explore another formation found to be noncommercial. Costs of drilling to the producing horizon are capitalized as the costs of a successful exploratory well, but the incremental costs of drilling deeper without finding additional proved reserves should be charged to expense as unsuccessful exploratory drilling costs.

Similarly, if the operator enters a producing well and drills deeper to an unproved horizon, the incremental costs are charged to expense if no production is secured at the greater depth.

PLUG BACK AND COMPLETION AT SHALLOWER DEPTH

The inverse of the situation described in the last section also may occur. For example, suppose that the operator drills an exploratory well with a formation at 9,000 feet as the target. At 6,000 feet, a formation containing hydrocarbons is encountered. Drilling continues to the 9,000-foot test depth, but no hydrocarbons are found at that level. The operator then **plugs back** to the 6,000-foot level and completes a producing well from that formation. Incremental costs applicable to the drilling between 6,000 and 9,000 feet are charged to expense as unsuccessful exploratory drilling costs, and costs of drilling to the producing horizon at 6,000 feet along with the completion costs are capitalized as costs of wells and related facilities. Some companies also charge to expense a portion of the costs of drilling to the upper producing horizon on the basis that these costs were necessary to drill the lower portion of the well that has been abandoned.

Conflict arises as to how drilling costs should be allocated between the portion of the well abandoned and the portion resulting in production. A mere per-foot allocation would not be appropriate. Instead, the incremental costs applicable to the abandoned portion should be the amount charged to expense. When this is impractical, a per-day apportionment may be the best solution.

COSTS OF ABANDONED PORTION OF WELL

In drilling an exploratory well targeted to a specific formation or trap, difficult conditions can be encountered that make it necessary to abandon the hole and start a new well nearby. If the second hole is completed as a producer, a decision must be made on the treatment of the costs of the abandoned hole. Successful efforts companies must determine whether the costs incurred on the abandoned hole should be charged to expense or capitalized as part of the cost of the completed well that found proved reserves.

It is preferable for costs applicable to the abandoned hole to be charged as an exploratory dry hole expense because the abandoned hole added nothing to the utility or value of the completed well. If the well originally being drilled had been classified as a development well under Oi5.401, all costs involved are capitalized. In drilling a well, if it is necessary to abandon the lower portion of the well in order to plug back and side-track to reach the same objective through directional drilling, the cost of the abandoned portion should likewise be charged to expense as a dry hole cost.

Some companies capitalize the costs of an abandoned well if the target of the second well (or the sidetracking) is the same as that of the abandoned well. The second well (or twin well) and the sidetracking are simply unexpected additional costs to get a well drilled to the target.

AFE SYSTEM FOR DRILLING AND DEVELOPMENT

Management should exercise close control over expenditures to realize maximum profit, especially when large sums are involved. The tool commonly used for controlling drilling and development costs is the Authorization (or Authority) for Expenditures (AFE) system, which is described in Chapter 6.

AFEs are part of the capital budgeting process. An E&P company budgets for capital projects by assessing major capital needs and available financing for the coming year. Capital projects are ranked as to expected internal rate of return, overall expected profitability, and other factors. Projects with the highest rankings are financed first, although funds are typically allocated to several projects to spread the risks of an exploratory drilling program. Some discretion is required as project profitability can change during the year. Also, unexpected projects may arise that should be funded, such as major well repairs or development of a significant new discovery. To finance unplanned capital needs, an E&P company maintains lines of credit and borrows funds.

An AFE system uses a form (Figure 9-1) to document: (1) expected costs of a project for review by management and joint venture partners, and (2) approvals to proceed with the project. AFEs are customary for all major projects in drilling and equipping oil and gas properties, purchasing drilling equipment and service units, and constructing field facilities and buildings. It is not practical, however, to obtain specific approval for lesser capital items, such as minor equipment replacement or supplies for routine operations; thus, standing authorizations for small purchases are generally granted to the responsible department head.

In most companies AFEs are not required for operating expenses other than for costs of well workover projects. Even for them, an AFE is necessary only if the total estimated cost is greater than a specified amount, such as $20,000.

SUMMARY OF PROCEDURES USED FOR AN AFE

The following summary outlines AFE system procedures and suggests the forms and records for implementing a system:

- Asset acquisition and construction costs are budgeted at least one year in advance (where possible).

- Even if an E&P company has only a small working interest in a well or project, the AFE system tracks and compares budgeted and actual costs for the full 8/8ths or 100 percent working interest. Full project costs are easier for a petroleum engineer to review, compare, and evaluate than the company's net costs. However, accounting ledgers and subledgers reflect the company's net cost for its share of a working interest.

- Authority for carrying out a specific project is assigned to operating personnel, such as the district superintendent or division superintendent.

- Selected management officials approve each stage of the project. Approval is in the form of an AFE (Figure 9-1). Each AFE is assigned a number, and the project itself is identified by this number. AFE budgets are prepared by project and by subaccount cost category.

- A project's costs are accumulated in Work in Progress accounts.

- For each project, actual costs incurred are periodically compared by subaccount to budgeted costs. Differences are assessed and, depending on acceptable limits of cost overruns, a supplemental AFE may be required.

AN AFE EXAMPLE

ABC Oil Company budgets for drilling operations a year in advance whenever it can. ABC has made plans to drill an exploratory well during the current year on a 200-acre lease obtained from R.L. Jones in Clarke County, Mississippi. The budget calls for drilling one well to 12,000 feet on the property and—if the well is productive—installing necessary **lease and well equipment**. The projected total cost of drilling the well is $616,200 for intangibles and $54,500 for well equipment associated with drilling. To complete and equip the well if it is successful, ABC estimates it will spend $359,600 (Figure 9-1).

AFE forms for drilling activities are multipurpose. They are designed to be used for completing wells, installing production and lease equipment, and handling well workover jobs. Companies typically prepare exploratory well AFEs showing estimated costs to both drill and complete the well. If the exploratory well finds reserves and will be completed, a copy of the original drilling AFE is also used for the completion and equipping AFE. When a well is completed as a producer, the AFE form has two numbers assigned to it: (1) the drilling AFE number covering amounts in the drilling cost money column (costs to **casing point**), and (2) the completion AFE number covering the amounts in the completion cost column. Total drilling and equipping costs are then entered in a third column for completed well costs (see Figure 9-1).

The AFE numbering system used by ABC is a five-digit number: the first two numbers represent the year and the last three are the sequential numbers of the AFE for the period. The AFE in Figure 9-1 contains approval to drill an exploratory well and shows a detailed breakdown of total expected drilling costs of $616,200 for intangibles and $54,500 for casing and other subsurface equipment. Authorization is complete when proper signatures have been affixed to the request.

A time limit should be set for the commencement of a project, after which a new appropriation would have to be made to start the project. This requirement also allows the project's financial needs to be more accurately estimated and controlled.

A request for approval of expenditures is usually accompanied by statements showing in detail how the estimated costs were determined. In many companies, supporting analysis indicates which costs require cash outlays and which will use items already on hand. In this way, cash requirements can be more readily ascertained.

Figure 9-1
Illustrative AFE for Drilling

Authorization for Expenditure for drilling wells		AFE #	06-017

Well Description:

Operator:	ABC Oil Company	Well No. 1	Target Depth: **12,000'**
State:	**Miss.**		Target Formation(s): **Smackover**
County:	**Clark**		Well Type: **Oil**
Prospect/Field:	**Wildcat**		
Well Location:	500' FWL & 1250' FNL of Sec. 33-T2N-R17E		

	Budgeted Costs:	Cost to Casing Pt.	Complete	Total Well Costs
	INTANGIBLE			
001	Footage (or Turnkey) Ft @ $ /Ft			
002	Day Rate: 37 and 12 days @ $5,200/day	$192,400	$62,400	$254,800
003	Site Preparation, roads, pits	89,800	3,500	93,300
004	Bits, Reamers, Tools	42,000	2,500	44,500
005	Labor – Company			
006	Labor – Other	1,500	1,500	3,000
007	Fuel, Power, Water	17,000	5,500	22,500
008	Drilling Supplies	1,000		1,000
009	Mud and Chemicals	50,000	5,000	55,000
010	Drill Stem Tests			
011	Coring, Analysis	4,000		4,000
012	Electric Surveys, Logs	40,000		40,000
013	Geological and Engineering	2,000	1,000	3,000
014	Cementing : Surface	21,000		21,000
015	Intermediate			
016	Oil String		20,000	20,000
017	Float Equipment, Centralizers, Etc.	4,000	2,500	6,500
018	Completion, Frac., Acidizing, Perforating		13,500	13,500
019	Rig Transportation, Erection, Removal, Other Transp.	54,500	10,000	64,500
020	Other Services	70,000	15,000	85,000
021	Overhead	2,000	800	2,800
022	Miscellaneous	25,000		25,000
	TOTAL INTANGIBLE COSTS	616,200	143,200	759,400
	TANGIBLE			
030	Casing			
031	Surface Ft 16" OD@ $/Ft	3,500		3,500
032	Intermed. 3,000 Ft 9 5/8" OD@ 16.00 $/Ft	48,000		48,000
033	Production 12,550 Ft 5 1/2" OD@ 10.75 $/Ft		135,000	135,000
034	Liner Ft OD@ 10.75 $/Ft			
035	Tubing 12,300 Ft 2 3/8" OD@ 2.75 $/Ft		33,800	33,800
036	Rods Ft OD@ $/Ft			
037	Well Head and Subsurface	3,000	17,000	20,000
038	Pumping Units			
039	Tanks		5,300	5,300
040	Separators		20,000	20,000
041	Heaters – Treaters		3,000	3,000
042	Engines and Motive Power			
043	Flow Lines			
044	Miscellaneous Equipment		2,300	2,300
045	Installation Costs of Surface Equipment			
	TOTAL TANGIBLE COSTS	54,500	216,400	270,900
	TOTAL WELL COSTS	**$670,700**	**$359,600**	**$1,030,300**

APPROVALS		Name	Date
	Prepared by	E.N. Gineer	4/10/06
Operator's internal approvals:	**Division**	T. Boss	4/10/06
	Corporate	T. Rex	4/12/06

Approvals of Working Interest Owners:

		Costs to			
Owner	WI%	Casing Pt.	Complete	Approved By	Date
Operator	60%	$402,420	$215,760	See above	See above
ABC Oil Co.	40%	268,280	143,840	A.B. Cloud	4/16/06
Total	**100%**	**$670,700**	**$359,600**		

SUPPLEMENTAL AFE

As the project progresses, expenditures incurred to date are periodically compared with estimated costs. It may become evident that the amounts authorized for certain costs are insufficient. Company policy, the initial AFE, or the joint venture operating agreement may require a supplemental AFE for actual costs exceeding a stated percentage of the original budget.

Operating agreements do not normally require joint venture operators to issue a supplemental AFE to joint venture **nonoperators**. Thus, the AFE may reflect the operator's preference that no supplemental AFE is required for budget overruns. Conversely, an AFE may contain language beneficial to nonoperators by requiring a supplemental AFE for approval on expenditures exceeding 10 or 15 percent of the original budget.

Detailed analyses should be made of over-expenditures by category of costs, rather than simply examining AFE totals. Comparisons of authorized costs and actual costs help identify errors in accounting, vendor billing, and AFE budgeting.

INTEREST CAPITALIZATION

FAS 34 requires that a portion of interest costs incurred during the construction period of assets should be capitalized:

> .06 The historical cost of acquiring an asset includes the costs necessarily incurred to bring it to the condition and location necessary for its intended use. If an asset requires a period of time in which to carry out the activities necessary to bring it to that condition and location, the interest cost incurred during that period as a result of expenditures for the asset is a part of the historical cost of acquiring the asset. The term *intended use* embraces both readiness for use and readiness for sale depending on the purpose of acquisition.

Assets qualifying for interest capitalization are the assets produced for a company's own use, including oil and gas properties and facilities. Conceptually, the interest to be capitalized is the amount of interest that would not have been incurred if the project had not been undertaken. The appropriate interest rate (detailed in FAS 34) is applied to the average amount of capitalized costs of the project during the year. The total interest cost capitalized in an accounting period should not exceed the total interest cost incurred by the enterprise in that period.

Interest costs are capitalized during a period when three conditions are met:

- Capital expenditures have been made.
- Activities necessary to ready the asset for its intended use are in progress.
- Interest costs are being incurred.

For oil and gas companies using the successful efforts method, the major questions related to interest capitalization center around the applicable time period. For example, assume the following activities take place on the dates indicated.

January 2, 2006	*Leases acquired on a prospect.*
July 1 - August 31, 2006	*Seismic and other exploration work carried out on leases.*
June 1, 2007	*Exploratory drilling begun.*
August 15, 2007	*Exploratory well completed as a producer.*

It might be argued that FAS 34 permits capitalization of interest on the project only during the periods July 1-August 31, 2006, and June 1-August 15, 2007, because during these periods physical activities are occurring. However, Paragraph 17 of FAS 34 provides:

> . . . The term *activities* is to be construed broadly. It encompasses more than physical construction; it includes all the steps required to prepare the asset for its intended use. For example, it includes administrative and technical activities during the preconstruction stage, such as the development of plans for the process of obtaining permits from governmental authorities; it includes activities undertaken after construction has begun in order to overcome unforeseen obstacles, such as technical problems, labor disputes, or litigation. If the enterprise suspends substantially all activities related to acquisition of the asset, interest capitalization shall cease until activities are resumed. However, brief interruptions in activities, interruptions that are externally imposed, and delays that are inherent in the asset acquisition process shall not require cessation of interest capitalization.

Because of broad interpretation of the term *activities*, a variety of practices exist for successful efforts companies to choose starting and ending dates for interest capitalization. Analyzing seismic charts, obtaining financing, arranging for drilling rigs, and other nonphysical activities are considered qualifying activities by some companies. These organizations capitalize interest on the average balance of unproved properties as well as on costs applicable to drilling and development in progress. The *2001 PricewaterhouseCoopers Survey of U.S. Petroleum Accounting Practices* found that three of 15 respondents using successful efforts capitalized interest on unproved leasehold costs during ongoing activities.

The following assets have been identified for interest capitalization in light of FAS No. 34:

> **Undeveloped leases.** Undeveloped leases qualify for interest capitalization as long as exploration activities necessary to get a lease ready for its intended use are in progress. Interest capitalization begins with the first expenditure to explore the lease and continues (assuming exploration activities are continuous) until the property is ultimately written off or produces oil or gas. Qualifying activities can include pre-field administrative and technical work such as:
>
> - Work performed by internal or external geologists and engineers to identify areas that may warrant further examination and examine specific areas that are believed to contain oil and gas
>
> - Title opinion curative work
>
> - Obtaining work permits from regulatory agencies
>
> Payments of delay rentals are inadequate evidence that exploration activities are under way. In the case of an undeveloped lease that covers a large number of acres, the situation must be carefully reviewed to determine whether the work done on a portion of the acreage allows interest capitalization on the entire block of acreage.
>
> **Shut-in properties.** As suggested by Oi5.122 and Oi5.125, occasionally an exploratory well may find oil and gas reserves, but those reserves cannot be classified

as proved until additional testing and evaluation are performed. Oi5.122-.125 provides guidance on indicators that support continued capitalization of the exploratory well's cost. If continued capitalization is appropriate, interest capitalization can continue as long as exploration activities are continuous.

Wells that are capable of production, but are awaiting the construction of additional facilities (e.g., gas wells awaiting construction of a pipeline), are considered qualifying assets. Interest capitalization continues as long as development activities on the pipeline are continuous. However, wells that are shut-in because of lack of a market or because of depressed gas prices do not qualify for interest capitalization.

Drilling and development costs. Costs of drilling and developing proved properties, including costs of unsuccessful development wells, are capitalized as part of the cost of oil and gas properties. Assuming that development activities are continuous, development costs qualify for interest capitalization until the related property is capable of producing and delivering oil or gas.

Significant development costs (e.g., costs of an offshore production platform) are often incurred in connection with a planned group of development wells before all the planned wells have been drilled. Oi5.126 allows exclusion of a portion of those development costs in determining the unit-of-production amortization rate until additional development wells are drilled. In these circumstances, interest capitalization continues on the portion of development costs deferred as long as development activities are continuous.

Oil and gas leases held for resale or contribution to a partnership. In many cases, leases held for resale or for contribution to a partnership do not qualify for interest capitalization because qualifying activities are not being performed on the property. If the company performs activities (e.g., geological and geophysical work) to prepare the lease for resale or contribution, the property should qualify for interest capitalization as long as the activities are continuous.

FAS 34 does not require specific identification of interest expense with an expenditure for an asset. However, Paragraph 16 of FAS 34 specifies that interest capitalization may be applied only to "capitalized expenditures (net of progress payment collections) for the qualifying asset that have required the payment of cash, the transfer of other assets, or the incurring of a liability on which interest is recognized (in contrast to liabilities such as trade payables . . .)."

For example, assume Company A normally pays its vendors on 90-day terms and vendors do not charge interest on the outstanding balance. Also, assume Company A drills, tests, and completes a well in 60 days. Company A is not able to capitalize any interest as part of the acquisition cost of the well because the well was completed and ready for its intended use before any net capitalized expenditures were made.

FAS 34 also indicates that reasonable approximations of net capitalized expenditures may be used. It is not necessary to prepare detailed analyses of payment dates to determine the point in time that capitalized costs become capitalized expenditures.

The Capitalization Period. To qualify for interest capitalization, activity does not have to be performed on each asset every day. Brief interruptions in activities, interruptions that are externally imposed, and delays inherent in the asset acquisition process do not require cessation of interest capitalization. However, if substantially all activities related to acquisition of an asset are suspended, interest capitalization ceases until activities are resumed. For example, if a company determines that an exploration project is too expensive or risky to pursue without joint venture partners and suspends all activities on the project until partners are located, interest capitalization should cease. When activities resume, the project again qualifies for interest capitalization.

FAS 34 provides that interest capitalization must end when an asset is substantially complete and ready for its intended use. Generally, this is when proved reserves have been discovered through drilling a successful exploratory well. At this time, the lease becomes part of a producing asset system under the successful efforts accounting rules. However, Paragraph 18 of FAS 34 refers specifically to an exception to this rule for companies using successful efforts accounting:

> . . . Some assets cannot be used effectively until a separate facility has been completed. Examples are the oil wells drilled in Alaska before completion of the pipeline. For such assets, interest capitalization shall continue until the separate facility is substantially complete and ready for use.

Similarly, interest is capitalized for a well until it has reached completion since the well cannot be used effectively until that time.

Immaterial Activity. Paragraph 8 of FAS 34 provides that interest capitalization is not required in circumstances where the effect would be immaterial. Most larger companies (and some smaller ones) establish a policy that interest is not capitalized unless an individual project or program has a total cost expected to exceed a specified threshold. The *2001 PricewaterhouseCoopers Survey of U.S. Petroleum Accounting Practices* found that all three of the three major companies responding to the survey had such policies. Two of the companies had established thresholds of at least $100 million. Approximately 32 percent of the responding independent companies had capitalization thresholds. All but two used thresholds of at least $1 million.

Another convention is the minimum required length of a project or program before interest on expenditures is capitalized. Minimum time periods required for capitalization are often six months to one year. These conventions eliminate the administrative costs of capitalizing insignificant interest costs for numerous small capital construction projects and short construction periods.

Interest Capitalization Under Full Cost Accounting. *FAS Interpretation No. 33* clarifies the interest capitalization rules for oil and gas producers using the full cost method. It states that full cost companies should capitalize interest only on assets that have been excluded from the amortization pool. Assets being amortized relate to reserves being produced and, thus, constitute assets being used in the earning process. Hence, interest related to those assets cannot be capitalized.

Once the properties or projects that have been excluded previously from the amortization pool are transferred to the amortization pool, capitalization of interest ceases. Interest previously capitalized becomes a part of the cost of the related assets and will be subject to amortization when the costs of the related properties or projects are transferred to the amortization pool.

• • •

10

ACCOUNTING FOR JOINT OPERATIONS

Key Concepts:

- **Legal forms of joint activities**

- **Joint venture agreements and joint operating agreements**

- **Accounting procedures of joint operating agreements**

- **Recording joint interest transactions**

- **Transfer of materials**

- **Joint interest audits**

- **Electronic data interchange**

Previous chapters have emphasized the high risk nature of oil and gas exploration and development activities. As further evidence of the risk involved in E&P, the Energy Information Administration has reported more than half of the U.S. exploratory wells were classified as dry holes in 2005. Not only is the industry inherently risky, it frequently requires enormous up-front investments. For example, leasing an offshore block can be a $25 million expense and exploration, drilling, and development could cost hundreds of millions of dollars.

Most costs are incurred prior to knowing if reserves exist and, if so, in what quantities. It is not surprising that otherwise fierce competitors choose to routinely combine their capital and expertise in joint operations. Cost- and risk-sharing arrangements allow companies to acquire, explore for, develop, and produce oil and gas under costly and hazardous conditions such as in offshore areas.

In regions that are not especially hazardous or costly, cooperation can make good economic sense, or it may be dictated by social concerns. If several operators own working interests in small leases in an area of interest, it is wasteful for every operator to drill wells on every property. Not only is it unnecessary for producing the reservoir, state spacing laws might actually prohibit it. In addition, the administrative and supervisory efforts required by each operator in carrying out a drilling project involving only one or two wells, and then producing the reserves from those wells, may be greater than any potential benefits.

In some instances, development and production activities are almost impossible to carry out unless the mineral owners are willing to join together. For example, it is not economical for secondary or tertiary recovery techniques to be employed on only part of a reservoir underlying a single lease. Instead, these processes must be applied to the reservoir as a whole.

Finally, good conservation practices dictate that production of minerals in the reservoir must be carefully planned and controlled. This requires cooperation among mineral owners in the reservoir. Thus, jointly conducted operations are routine throughout the petroleum industry.

LEGAL FORMS OF JOINT ACTIVITIES

Three types of legal forms are generally used for joint operations.

- **Joint ventures of undivided interests.** By far, the most important and most common form of joint venture in the oil and gas industry is a joint venture of undivided interests, or unitized interests. In this arrangement, working interest owners join together for drilling, development, and operation of a jointly owned or unitized property (or properties) according to a written agreement executed by the parties. The term joint venture usually refers to a project in which the parties own an undivided interest (including divided interests that through unitization effectively become undivided interests) referred to as a joint interest.[1]

- **Legal partnerships.** Oil and gas entities may join together to explore and develop a project by forming a partnership under state law. The partnership is a legal entity; it holds title to assets, incurs debts in its own name, and otherwise carries on business activities.

  Limited partnerships managed by an E&P company as general partner and substantially funded by individual investors as limited partners were popular in the 1970s and early 1980s. Limited partnership investments in exploration and development were called drilling funds. Other limited partnerships acquired producing oil and gas properties and were called income funds. In recent years, master limited partnerships have been formed to own oil and gas activities.

Today E&P company joint ventures are not generally structured as legal partnerships for carrying on exploration, development, and production operations. Accounting for partnership interests is discussed in Chapter 24.

- **Jointly owned corporations.** Certain legal, political, or economic reasons may encourage oil and gas companies to undertake cooperative ventures by forming a separate corporation. For example, three domestic oil companies may wish to undertake exploration and production activities in a foreign country. A new corporation is formed in the foreign country with each domestic enterprise owning one-third of the stock. Frequently, these enterprises own stock in the foreign corporation along with either the government of the foreign country or a native corporation. Similarly, corporations may join together to form a new corporation to build a pipeline, explore a new area, or construct secondary recovery facilities.

JOINT VENTURES

This chapter focuses on how joint interest owners account for joint venture activities, particularly the sharing and recording of joint venture costs.

Formation of a joint venture reflects either a pooling of capital or an exchange of like-kind assets. In either case, no gain or loss is generally recognized by the parties at the inception of the joint venture, as further addressed in Chapters 21 and 23.

Each joint venture has a purpose that involves one or more of the activities of lease acquisition, exploration, development, or production. In order to carry out this purpose, definitions and guidelines are established under which all parties in the joint venture must operate. Fortunately, the U.S. oil and gas industry has a long history of cooperative enterprises from which to draw various model forms for agreements and joint operating agreements.

PROPERTIES INCLUDED IN JOINT OPERATIONS

To conduct a joint operation, one or more mineral interests has been identified as the subject of the venture. The joint venture may cover a single well or project, or a single lease. Typically, it covers a group of jointly owned leases of mineral interests and takes one of three forms:

- **Jointly owned leases within an area of mutual interest specified in a joint venture agreement.** Working interests in oil, gas, or other mineral leases are acquired and held as undivided ownership interests by two or more E&P companies.

- **A pooled drilling and production unit.** Relatively small leases or portions of leases, which are separately owned by E&P companies, are pooled or combined into a single drilling and production unit. Not all the leases in a field choose to participate in the enterprise.

  A pool or unit is created under several types of scenarios. Working interest owners can invoke the express pooling provisions contained in their separate oil and gas leases that grant the rights to pool working and royalty interests. Another type of pool can be created by a separate voluntary agreement that joins working interest owners and royalty interests in separate tracts. In other cases, royalty owners may not be involved in the pooling arrangement.

Drilling and production units frequently do not involve all owners in a field and may be either purely voluntary or forced by government controls. For example, state spacing requirements may decree a minimum of 40 acres is required for an oil well or a minimum of 640 acres is required for a gas well. The owner of a 20-acre lease must join with other owners to pool their leases in order to establish a drilling block.

- **Field-wide unitization.** All separately owned tracts in a field are unitized into a single unit or property. As discussed in Chapter 23, all working interest owners and all royalty owners in the field contribute their separate properties to the unit; in return, they receive smaller fractional interests in the combined properties (and sometimes pay or receive money under equalization settlements). Field-wide or reservoir-wide unitization is especially common when operations such as secondary or tertiary recovery, pressure maintenance, or gas cycling are planned. Field-wide unitization agreements are more complex than those found in simple drilling and production unit pooling operations.

Two types of agreements guide participants in joint operations: (1) the Joint Venture Agreement establishes the joint venture, and (2) the Joint Operating Agreement governs how the joint venture is to be operated.

JOINT VENTURE AGREEMENTS

Exploration agreement, pooling agreement, and unitization agreement are industry terms referring to specific types of pooling arrangements. The more general term—joint venture agreement—refers to an agreement of E&P companies to own undivided interests in specific leases, or any leases within a specified land area such as a large portion of a county.

A joint venture agreement identifies the E&P companies, the leases within the joint venture, and the parties' respective working interests in the leases. Normally, such leases cover adjoining acreage or acreage within a small area.

The agreement designates an area surrounding the leases as an **area of mutual interest (AMI)**. Any joint venture owner acquiring leases in the AMI must acquire them on behalf of the joint venture. This provision is intended to preclude an owner from unfairly profiting from joint venture information such as a new discovery on venture leases.

Whether involving a single tract of land, a block of leases jointly owned, or a field-wide unitization, formation of a joint interest is a matter of negotiation by management representatives. Company specialists in geology, land, engineering, legal, tax, and accounting departments may offer input. Outside expertise may be sought depending on the size of the company, available resources, and project scope and size. The agreement should be carefully reviewed by qualified representatives of each party as to its form and terms prior to execution. When executed, the written joint venture agreement becomes effective on the date specified.

One of the working interest owners is designated as the operator to manage the development and operation of the joint venture's properties in an efficient manner. Joint operation of a single property or block of properties is carried out under a joint operating agreement (JOA), which is separate from the joint venture agreement. The JOA sets out the duties, obligations, rights, and responsibilities of the working interest owners to the joint venture operations and specifies how costs and benefits are to be shared. Because the JOA is crucial to accounting procedures and principles for joint operations, it is examined in detail in the following pages.

THE JOINT OPERATING AGREEMENT (JOA)

Operating agreements for smaller pooled drilling and production units or single tracts of land are not as complex as field-wide unitizations. However, the general principles, purposes, and certain provisions of operating agreements are the same in all situations and may address the following:

1. **Definitions.** Defines terms used in the agreement such as operator and nonoperator. Also, in the case of a pooled unit or field-wide unit, this section defines unitized substances, unitized formation, working interest owner, royalty interest owner, and other terms.

2. **Creation and effect of joint operation or unit.** Describes oil and gas leases and property involved for a single tract of land. In the case of a pooled unit or field-wide unit, it describes the mineral leases, interests, separate properties, mineral or minerals unitized, and producing zones that make up the unitized area.

3. **Interests of parties.** Sets out the participating interest of each working interest owner in the costs and production of the unit. In field-wide units, the agreement may set out participation factors by individual tracts.

4. **Plan of operations.** Provides for a drilling or development program, workover operations, abandonment, and similar activities. This section may be separated into several articles. In the case of a single tract or drilling unit, drilling of the first well is expressly agreed on, and the mechanics of obtaining an agreement for drilling additional wells are provided. Also, if not all working interest owners agree to participate in drilling a subsequent well or wells (referred to as **nonconsent** or going nonconsent), provisions are included to permit independent operations. In this case, the party desiring to drill, complete, rework, and recomplete can do so without the consent of the other parties. The consenting parties absorb all costs of the operation, including a dry hole. When such a well produces, the driller is permitted to recoup a percentage of the drilling and equipping costs out of production attributable to the nonconsenting parties' interests. This percentage is specified in the JOA and can range from 100 percent to 800 percent; however, in practice, it generally ranges from 300 percent to 500 percent.

5. **Operator.** Identifies the party with operational control over and supervision of the joint operation.

6. **Duties and obligations of operator.** Sets out the powers and duties of the operator to develop and operate the joint operation area in an efficient manner; requires lands and leases in the covered area to be kept free from third-party statutory liens; describes records and reports to be provided to nonoperators and governmental authorities; explains the procedure for resignation or removal of the operator, and sets out other similar requirements.

7. **Relationship of parties.** Provides the duties, obligations, and liabilities of the parties are intended to be several—not joint or collective. Also, it provides nothing contained in the JOA creates an association or trust or imposes a partnership duty, obligation, or liability with regard to any one or more of the parties. Each party is individually responsible for its obligations as therein provided. Related to this provision is an agreement the parties do not intend to operate or be taxed under federal income tax laws as a partnership. The operator agrees to file appropriate forms with the IRS to elect out of Subchapter K partnership provisions.

8. **Effective date and term.** Provides the timeframe for the agreement to be in effect. In field-wide units, this section requires a specified percentage of all working interest ownerships and a specified percentage of royalty interest owners to execute the agreement before it becomes effective. It specifies the term or period of time the agreement remains in effect after its **effective date** (e.g., so long as the leases continue in effect, operations are conducted, or production continues).

9. **Allocation of production.** Provides each party has the right to take in-kind or separately dispose of its proportionate share of the oil or gas produced from the joint operation area. (The right to take oil and gas in-kind is a defense against an IRS assertion that the joint venture is really a taxable corporation.) This section may state each party is responsible for royalties on its share of production and holds other parties free from such liability. Alternatively, the duty to keep the records and handle the payment of royalties may be delegated to the operator.

10. **Taxes.** May provide for the operator to render—for ad valorem tax purposes—all jointly owned property and to pay property taxes for the benefit of the parties in accordance with the applicable provisions of the Accounting Procedure (discussed in the next section). It may specify each party separately pays its individual proportionate tax obligation. Also, this provision may state each party is responsible for the payment of production, severance, excise, gathering, and all other taxes on its proportionate share of the oil and gas produced.

11. **Insurance.** Requires the operator to carry specified types of insurance such as workers' compensation, employer's liability, comprehensive public liability, and comprehensive automobile liability. The limits of coverage may be prescribed. Wording may provide that if the operator does not comply, then it assumes all risks and sole liability. This section establishes premium payments will be made in accordance with applicable provisions of the Accounting Procedure.

12. **Development and operating costs.** Other than for named exceptions, provides the operator must promptly pay and discharge all costs and expenses incurred in the development and operation of the joint interest area, and charge all parties with their proportionate shares on the basis provided in the Accounting Procedure. The operator is granted the right to demand and receive payment from other parties of their shares of the estimated costs to be incurred during the next succeeding month (known as cash calls). The operator may be required to avoid any single project that is reasonably estimated to require an expenditure in excess of a stipulated amount without consent from nonoperators.

13. **Claims and litigation.** Provides if any party to the agreement is sued on an alleged cause of action arising out of operations in the joint interest area involving titles of any single tract subject to the agreement, the party shall give prompt written notice to the operator and all other parties. It specifies suits may be settled only with the consent of all parties. This section of the JOA states no charges are to be made for the services of staff attorneys of the parties. Outside attorneys are to be employed only with the consent of all parties and costs so incurred, along with other costs related to the defense of suits when properly authorized, are considered costs of operation. These will be charged to and paid by all parties in proportion to their interests in the joint interest operation.

14. **Force majeure.** Provides all obligations of each party, except payment of money, are suspended while that party is prevented from complying by strikes, fire, war, civil disturbances, acts of God, laws, regulations, inability to secure material, or other causes beyond the reasonable control of the party.

15. **Notices.** Provides all notices authorized or required between the parties and required by any of the provisions of the agreement are furnished in writing by mail or other specified means and addressed to the party to whom the notice is given at the address listed.

16. **Other provisions.** Adds any other provisions deemed necessary to set out the rights, duties, and obligations of the parties and efficiently and economically carry on the operations.

The JOA provisions noted in this book represent a sampling of terms found commonly in operating agreements. Petroleum accountants should be aware additional provisions exist and may add layers of complexity to the parties' understanding. In the case of single tract units and small pooled units, operating agreements are usually prepared by one of the parties to fit that particular situation.

Several standard operating and unit agreement forms have been published. One of these was developed by the American Association of Professional Landmen (AAPL) and is reproduced with permission in CD Reference Exhibit E.

Operating agreements typically include an exhibit on joint venture accounting procedures. The exhibit addresses topics such as the basis of direct charges and credits to the joint account, overhead charges, disposal of equipment, basis of materials transferred on and off the property, inventories, billings, and advance payments.

Over the years, the Council of Petroleum Accountants Societies (COPAS) has developed several model *Accounting Procedure Joint Operations* exhibits. (It should be noted when a new exhibit is issued, it does not affect an *Accounting Procedure* previously adopted as part of a JOA.) When a joint operation is formed and the operating agreement is entered into, the applicable **COPAS Accounting Procedure Joint Operations** form is adopted— without modification or with agreed-upon changes—as an exhibit to the JOA. Forms used over the past 30 years are found in COPAS' *Model Form Interpretations* (MFI-1 through MFI-4). CD Reference Exhibit F contains the most recent form issued in 2005.

While standardized forms of operating agreements and accounting procedures are widely available to the industry, it is important to note they are not used in every case. Contractual rights and obligations vary in every joint operation, and this can present a challenge to accountants and tax advisors.

ACCOUNTING PROCEDURE PROVISIONS
OF JOINT OPERATING AGREEMENTS

Common provisions of an *Accounting Procedure* exhibit for joint operations are reviewed in this section. Such exhibits have two major parts: (1) the exhibit form, and (2) interpretive guidance on applying the form's provisions.

The form consists of the following five sections:

A. **General Provisions.**

1. **Definitions.** This section defines terms used in the contract, including joint property, joint operations, joint account, operator (the party designated to conduct joint operations), nonoperators (parties to the agreement other than the operator), parties, first-level supervisors, technical employees, personal expenses, materials, and controllable materials.

2. **Statements and billings.** Most agreements provide for the operator to bill nonoperators monthly for their share of charges. Billing is made on or before the last day of the following month and must contain appropriate detail. The lease, facility, AFE, or other project unit is identified. Charges and credits are summarized by appropriate classifications of investment and expense. Additional details are to be provided for controllable materials, unusual charges, and credits.

3. **Advances and payments by nonoperators.** Usually, operators are given the right to make cash calls. According to the *Accounting Procedure*, each nonoperator must pay its bill within 15 days after receipt. Interest is charged at a specified rate on any late payments.

4. **Adjustments.** To take exception to billings and claim adjustments, nonoperators are given 24 months following the end of a calendar year in which a billing was made.

5. **Audits.** Nonoperators generally have the right to audit the operator's records related to the joint account. The audit right typically extends to 24 months following the fiscal year-end. Joint Interest Audits are discussed later in this chapter.

6. **Approval by nonoperators.** An operator must give proper advance notice to nonoperators of items requiring approval or agreement. Agreement or approval of a majority (in interest owned) of nonoperators is binding on all nonoperators.

B. **Direct Charges.** Certain items are charged directly to the joint operation including:

1. **Rents and royalties** on the properties.

2. **Salaries and wages** of the operator's field employees directly employed on the property, first-level field supervisors, and technical employees employed directly on the property (if technical costs are not already included in overhead rates). Charges for salaries and wages include the related costs of holiday, vacation, disability, and other allowances, as well as expenditures or contributions imposed by governmental authority. Related personnel expenses are also direct charges.

3. **Employee benefits** applicable to direct labor costs. Benefits are customarily limited to a percentage of labor costs; amounts are recommended by COPAS on an annual basis.

4. **Materials** purchased or furnished by the operator for use on the joint property. (Detailed provisions related to materials and equipment are discussed later in this chapter.)

5. **Transportation** of employees and materials necessary for joint operations and subject to site conditions.

6. **Services.** Costs of contract services, equipment, and utilities with specified exceptions and limits.

7. **Equipment and facilities furnished by the operator.** An operator has the right to charge the joint account for use of equipment and facilities at rates commensurate with costs of ownership and operations. Detailed suggestions for bases to be used in making charges for such costs are included in Section II-8 of the Explanation part of MFI 17, *Accounting Procedure Joint Operations*. In lieu of charging for actual costs, an operator may charge an amount for services equal to normal commercial rates in the area, less 20 percent.

8. **Damages and losses to joint property**, except those resulting from the operator's gross negligence or willful misconduct.

9. **Legal expenses related to joint property.** Payments to outside firms are chargeable. Special provisions may allow for use of the operator's own legal staff.

10. **Taxes** of all kinds on the joint property, its operations, and production.

11. **Insurance** costs on joint interest property, personnel, and operations.

12. **Other necessary direct costs.**

C. **Overhead.** Misunderstandings can easily arise among joint interest owners over direct costs, overhead charges, and costs that may not rightfully belong to the joint account. As a result, detailed provisions for these items are usually included in the agreement.

Salaries, wages, and personal expenses of technical employees and contract personnel may be charged directly to the joint account or may be included in the overhead rate.

As compensation for administration, supervision, office services, and warehousing costs (and, if applicable, technical personnel), an operator can charge drilling and producing activities on either a fixed-rate basis or a percentage basis. Under the fixed-rate basis, a rate per well per month is set for wells being drilled, and a lower rate per well per month is charged for producing wells. Reference to Section III of the *2005 Model Accounting Procedure Exhibit* found in CD Reference Exhibit F reveals the complexity of such overhead rules. The three major subheadings of the overhead section are:

1. Overhead—Drilling and Producing Operations

2. Overhead—Major Construction and Catastrophe

3. Amendment of Overhead Rates

D. **Pricing of Joint Account Material Purchases, Transfers, and Dispositions.** The operator of a joint interest frequently transfers materials and equipment from its own warehouse (or solely owned property) to the jointly owned property, and vice-versa. Also, operators routinely purchase materials and equipment designated for the joint operation. Later, these items are removed and sold. Since prices of materials change frequently, it is not feasible for joint owners to negotiate each transaction. As a result, the industry has developed widely accepted rules that govern the pricing of materials and equipment purchases, transfers, and dispositions. COPAS has been the guiding force behind these standards. As an example, this chapter will discuss the industry term "condition value" of materials acquired or disposed of as found in Section IV of COPAS MFI-4.

E. **Inventories.** The accounting procedure requires an operator to maintain detailed records of controllable materials and conduct periodic and special physical inventories.

Finally, a basic principle of joint operations is cost sharing. An operator should neither make a profit nor incur a loss merely because of holding the position of operator.

NONOPERATORS HAVE OPERATING INTERESTS

E&P companies may use seemingly conflicting terms to describe aspects of the business. Petroleum accountants should clearly understand the distinctions. For instance, holders of operating interests who do not have responsibility for operating the property are called nonoperators, even though they hold working interests in a property. (Holders of nonoperating interests, such as royalty owners, are not referred to as nonoperators.) Likewise, *Accounting Procedure* exhibits refer to any owner of an operating interest that is not the operator of the property as a nonoperator.

RECORDING JOINT INTEREST TRANSACTIONS

Joint interest owners commonly use the proportionate consolidation method of accounting. Proportionate consolidation provides for each owner to pick up its proportionate share of assets, liabilities, revenues, and expense items according to its own account classifications. The joint venture is not regarded as a unique accounting entity; thus, separate financial statements are not prepared for that venture. If a joint venture uses a corporate structure, which would be rare in the U.S., proportionate consolidation may not be appropriate.

RECORDS OF NONOPERATOR

Joint interest billing procedures. Nonoperators are billed monthly by the operator for their shares of charges and credits. Amounts typically include costs and cost adjustments related to the joint operation. The joint interest billing (JIB) is the principal source document provided to nonoperators each month. Prepared by the operator, the JIB contains sufficient detail to enable nonoperators to debit or credit appropriate accounts in their own records.

COPAS MFI-26, *Classifications for Use in Summary Form Billing* (revised October 1994), suggests categories and classifications to be used in JIBs. These listings are designed to identify various types of costs, but do not necessarily coincide with GAAP or income tax accounting. As a result, nonoperators must exercise judgment in recording such costs. An operator cannot accommodate every nonoperator's chart of accounts. In practice, though, JIBs usually meet the broad financial accounting classifications of successful efforts and full cost companies, as well as their tax reporting requirements.

Monthly billing for a joint account contains: (1) a summary statement and invoice showing total charges and amounts due from every working interest owner, along with an individual invoice to the nonoperator receiving the statement; and (2) supporting schedules that help identify the expenditures and properly account for them according to the project's Authorization for Expenditure (AFE).

When a JIB is received from the operator, it is routed for approval to the engineer or department responsible for monitoring the operations. Approval should entail a review for reasonableness of amounts and cost description of the stated classifications, property, well, AFE, and month of occurrence. Next, the billing is routed to the joint interest billing department where it is checked for evidence of approvals, coded, and entered into the accounting system.

From the JIB, nonoperators make entries in their detailed subsidiary records. This step may require professional judgment in classifying billed items using the nonoperator's chart of accounts.

Account titles used to record charges from the billing are the same as if the properties involved belonged solely to the nonoperator. Only the subsidiary accounts reflect the fact the properties are jointly owned and operated.

Payments made to the operator to are charged to Vouchers Payable. Advances may be charged either to the payable account or to a prepayment account.

Illustration of Joint Interest Billing. To see a nonoperator's accounting treatment of the monthly billing from an operator, refer to Figure 10-1(A-D). Country Service Company, a nonoperator, owns a .0547563 interest in the N. Moore Lease. Venture costs incurred from the prior month include certain costs of a new well known as N. Moore #2, and prior month's production costs of the N. Moore #1 well.

Example of Joint Operating Agreement Announcement:

ExxonMobil and Pertamina Sign Joint Operating Agreement for Cepu Block

IRVING, Texas--(BUSINESS WIRE)--March 15, 2006--ExxonMobil Corporation (NYSE:XOM) announced today that its subsidiaries Mobil Cepu Ltd. and Ampolex (Cepu) Pte. Ltd. have signed a Joint Operating Agreement (JOA) with P.T. Pertamina EP Cepu, a subsidiary of P.T. Pertamina, for the Cepu Contract Area located in East and Central Java, Indonesia.

The signing of the JOA follows the execution of the Cepu Cooperation Contract in September of 2005 and enables the parties to begin the activities and make the investments required to develop the discovered resources and further explore the block during the thirty-year contract period. The JOA provides the basis for joint development of the block, which will be managed by the parties under a Joint Operating Committee. Pertamina and ExxonMobil each will provide management oversight, technology and manpower under the agreement.

Ampolex (Cepu) Pte. Ltd. and Mobil Cepu Ltd. acquired their respective interests in the Cepu Contract Area in 1997 and 2000 with the approval of both Pertamina and the Government of Indonesia. In March 2001, Pertamina and ExxonMobil announced the Banyu Urip discovery on the Cepu Contract Area. Banyu Urip is estimated to contain more than 250 million barrels of oil. At peak production, the field is expected to produce up to 165,000 barrels of oil per day. The Area has potential for additional exploration and development opportunities.

Pertamina and ExxonMobil each hold a fifty-percent interest in the Contract, with the parties anticipating entry of a regional entity at the ten-percent level in the future. The ten percent will be provided equally by both parties.

- *http://www.exxonmobil.com*

Figure 10-1A
Joint Interest Billing

BIG OIL USA, INC.
P.O. BOX 12345, DENTON, TX 76201

COUNTRY SERVICE COMPANY   INVOICE NO.: 0623174
15467 EAST 107TH AVENUE   INVOICE DATE: MAY 24, 2006
HOUSTON, TX 77046   TERM: NET 30 UPON RECEIPT
        MONTH: APRIL 2006
        PROPERTY: N. MOORE LEASE

SUMMARY STATEMENT AND INVOICE

OWNER NO.	OWER NAME	WORKING INTEREST	AMOUNT
1123500	ABC OIL	.0447897	$ 24,033.14
1118600	CORONADO HILLS PARTNERS	.0635633	34,106.62
5117300	COUGAR PETROLEUM	.0153747	8,249.72
2954800	WILL B. SMITH	.0226632	12,160.56
1431400	COUNTRY SERVICE COMPANY	.0547563	29,380.99
0488500	J.B. JONES	.0258106	13,849.38
8224400	BDF OIL & GAS	.3833124	205,676.74
0000001	BIG OIL USA, INC.	.3897298	209,120.16
		1.0000000	

Total Current Period Charges to Joint Account		$536,577.31

TO INVOICE YOU FOR:

Drilling and Development Charges	$ 29,102.52
Lease Operating Expenses	278.47
Total Current Period Charges	29,380.99
Previous Balance Carried Forward	0
Total Due	**$ 29,380.99**

REMITTANCE INSTRUCTIONS
Please reference the above invoice number and mail payment to:
Big Oil USA, Inc.
P.O. Box 12345
Denton, TX 76201

Figure 10-1B
continued

BIG OIL USA, INC.

P.O. BOX 12345, DENTON, TX 76201

COUNTRY SERVICE COMPANY

15467 EAST 107TH AVENUE

HOUSTON, TX 77046

PROPERTY: N. Moore Lease

WELL: N. Moore #2

INVOICE NO.: 0623174

INVOICE DATE: MAY 24, 2006

TERM: NET 15 UPON RECEIPT

MONTH: APRIL 2006

AFE No.: 102

Drilling and Development Charges:

S/L	DESCRIPTION	AMOUNT	TOTAL
104	Tubing	$147,780.21*	
105	Wellhead Assembly	764.88	
115	Misc. Non-Cont. Surface Well Material	684.79	
122	Production & Other Lease Facilities	14,111.02*	
133	Installation Cost	4,245.70	
244	Permits, Site Prep & Cleanup	8,638.74	
248	Other Contract Services	116.25	
249	Contract Drilling	301,903.89	
251	Direct Supervision	7,870.42	
255	Bits	(1,297.06)	
267	Equipment Rentals	3,449.50	
268	Small Tools & Supplies	206.90	
269	Transportation Land	6,156.29	
273	Communications	177.66	
275	Testing, Drafting & Inspection	22,083.03	
277	Perforating	8,280.20	
280	Drilling Overhead Charge	5,000.00	
283	Loss & Damage	1,319.23	

Total Drilling and Development Charges   **$531,491.65**

*Controllable material detail is attached.[2]

Figure 10-1C
continued

BIG OIL USA, INC.
P.O. BOX 12345, DENTON, TX 76201

COUNTRY SERVICE COMPANY   INVOICE NO.: 0623174
15467 EAST 107TH AVENUE   INVOICE DATE: MAY 24, 2006
HOUSTON, TX 77046   TERM: NET 15 UPON RECEIPT
PROPERTY: N. Moore Lease   MONTH: APRIL 2006
WELL: N. Moore #2   AFE No.: 102

Controllable Material Detail:

ACCOUNTING CODE	DESCRIPTION	AMOUNT	TOTAL
27-2631-102-104	MT60549		
	13,005.8" (411 Jts.) 2 7/8 6.5# L-80 AB Mod R-2		
	Tubing, Condition A		$147,780,21
27-2631-102-122	M0208		
	30.0 ea.-2150# WN Flange w/std bore	$ 331.68	
	7.0 ea.-21N #143 Rockwell Plug Valve	419.96	
	20.0 ea.-3150# RF WN Flange w/std bore	276.16	
	7.0 ea.-31N #143 Rockwell Plug Valve	690.23	
	4.0 ea.-41N #143 Rockwell Plug Valve	536.98	
	332.0 ea.-5/8 x 3 ½ B07 Ht. Alloy Std. w/2	367.73	
	270.7 ft. – Ft. 3 in sch-40 A-53-B SMLS Pipe PE	1,513.48	
	1.0 ea.-4 std. weld cross	243.28	
	5.0 ea.-3 Fig 100 FE #021027-15-BS-285	1,805.00	
	1.0 ea.-2 Fig 100 FE #031027-F-15-BS	220.00	
	139.0 ft.-2 sch 40 SMLS Line Pipe	625.29	
	3.0 ea-4 PE BLK Pipe x 21'	415.80	
	17.0 ea-2 PE BLK Pipe x 21'	817.08	
	3.0 ea-4 wafer butterfly valve demco	323.97	
	Miscellaneous Non-Controllable Items	2,558.34	
		11,144.98	
	M0266		
	30.0 ea.-2150# WN Flange w/std bore	144.66	
	M0310		
	Miscellaneous Non-Controllable Items	2,631.00	
	M0443		
	Miscellaneous Non-Controllable Items	141.60	
	M0444		
	Miscellaneous Non-Controllable Items	48.78	

Total Production and Other Lease Facilities $14,111.02

Figure 10-1D
continued

BIG OIL USA, INC.

P.O. BOX 12345, DENTON, TX 76201

COUNTRY SERVICE COMPANY   INVOICE NO.: 0623174

15467 EAST 107TH AVENUE   INVOICE DATE: MAY 24, 2006

HOUSTON, TX 77046   TERM: NET 15 UPON RECEIPT

PROPERTY: N. Moore Lease   MONTH: APRIL 2006

WELL: N. Moore #1   AFE No.: N/A

Lease Operating Expense:

S/L	DESCRIPTION	AMOUNT	TOTAL
120	Contract Labor	$2,903.61	
121	Rig Services	406.71	
125	Gas Handling	6.81	
128	Salt Water Disposal	375.75	
140	Chemicals	44.72	
141	Small Tools & Supplies	55.34	
143	Automotive Expense	198.36	
170	Telephone & Telegraph	53.50	
180	Employee Travel & Gen Exp	68.13	
800	General Services	112.08	
824	Area Expense	510.65	
880	Production Overhead	350.00	
	Total Lease Operating Expense		$5,085.66

The journal entry made by Country Service Company to record the April billing is:

241	Work In Progress—Intangible Costs of Wells and Related Development—N. Moore #2 [.0547563 x (Items 133-283)]	20,158.58	
243	Work In Progress—Tangible Costs of Wells and Related Development—N. Moore #2 [.0547563 x (Items 104-122)]	8,943.94	
710	Lease Operating Expenses—N. Moore #1 (.0547563 x $5,085.66)	278.47	
	301 Vouchers Payable		29,380.99
	To record receipt of joint interest billing for April for N. Moore wells.		

RECORDS OF THE OPERATOR

Most operating agreements require an operator to pay all costs and expenses incurred and charge each nonoperator its proportionate share. The operator's accounting system must properly accumulate and classify expenditures for preparation of monthly billings. Also, the system should support the accounting procedure adopted in the joint operating agreement. Oil and gas companies use software to facilitate these processes.

Operator Overhead Cost Reimbursements. Accounting for operator overhead cost reimbursements has been the subject of scrutiny in recent years. Many operators treat overhead cost reimbursements by nonoperators as reductions of lease operating expense (i.e., netted with both operator and nonoperator overhead charges recorded in lease operating expense). The initial cost was recorded in the operator's records as a debit to lease operating expense. Many view this approach as consistent with proportional consolidation to reflect the provisions of the joint operating agreement. Further, it is referred to in the AICPA *Oil and Gas Guide*. If this approach is taken, it would not be appropriate to record the overhead cost reimbursement in a separate account from the initial debit.

Emerging Issues Task Force (EITF) 01-14 addresses the income statement characterization of reimbursements received for out-of-pocket expenses incurred. Following this approach, amounts being reimbursed for overhead costs would be reported as revenue by an operator, not as a reduction of production costs or lease operating expense.

The SEC has indicated either method is acceptable since both approaches are referred to in the AICPA *Oil and Gas Guide*.

Charging Costs to Joint Interest Accounts. Typically, operators identify each charge or credit with an individual joint operating agreement, classify the item by account number, and record it to the property by way of an identifying number at the 100 percent gross (8/8ths) amount of a vendor invoice. Subsidiary records by account number are maintained for each joint operation; customarily, these records agree with the operator's Work In Progress, Wells and Related Facilities, Revenue, and Lease Operating Expense subsidiary ledgers. The property's identifying number contains allocation information for billing each working interest owner.

For example, if Big Oil USA, operator of the N. Moore #2, received a statement for $301,903.89 from the contract driller of N. Moore #2, the entry made by Big Oil would be:

241	*Work In Progress—Intangible Costs of Wells and Related Development, N. Moore #2*	301,903.89	
	301 *Vouchers Payable*		301,903.89
	To record receipt of statement from drilling contractor on N. Moore #2.		

The operator's proportionate share of each cost is netted in the appropriate account in its financial records, while the nonoperators share of total charges is charged to Accounts Receivable (or a similarly titled account).

Based on the joint interest billing percentages shown in Figure 10-1, the operator's joint interest billing system would make the following entry at the end of April relating to the contract drilling costs on N. Moore #2.

123	*Accounts Receivable—Joint Interest Billings*	184,242.95	
	241 *Work In Progress, N. Moore #2*		184,242.95
	To record receivable from nonoperators for shares of N. Moore #2 drilling costs. [(1.0 - .3897298) x $301,903.89]		

Since the joint interest billing system is processed at the end of each month, only the operator's interest and a receivable from the other working interest owners appear in the monthly financial statements. During the month when costs are accumulated for each joint activity, the detailed records form a Joint Interest Ledger.

Some companies use a variation of the method noted where joint interest entries are processed on a daily basis; however, JIBs continue to be sent out at the end of the month.

Allocating Each Transaction to each Joint Interest's Accounts. Another approach used by many operators to record joint venture transactions is to analyze each individual transaction prior to recording it. The portion applicable to nonoperators is immediately charged to Accounts Receivable—Joint Interest, while the operator's share is charged to its usual asset and liability accounts.

For example, if this method had been used by Big Oil USA on a statement for $301,903.89 from the drilling contractor on Well # 2, the entry would be:

241	Work In Progress—Intangible Costs of Wells and Related Development	117,660.94	
123	Accounts Receivable—Joint Interest Billings (and detailed accounts for nonoperators)	184,242.95	
	301 Vouchers Payable		301,903.89
	To record receipt of statement from drilling contractor on N. Moore #2.		

MATERIAL TRANSFERS

Under the proportionate consolidation method, each owner records its share of equipment included in Tangible Costs of Wells and Related Development. Items moved between the joint venture's well sites, and the operator's warehouses and equipment yards, must be recorded properly. COPAS developed special rules to help petroleum accountants address these issues.

When an operator transfers used material or equipment to a joint property, the transfer price should reflect an approximate current market value. The *1995 COPAS Accounting Procedure MFI-30* lists several pricing methodologies to assist operators in obtaining generic prices for recording transfers. One method uses a database developed by COPAS and known as the Computerized Equipment Pricing System (CEPS). It calculates a generic price for each piece of material or equipment from a published base price list. Amounts are updated annually by using a historical price multiplier (HPM).

In addition to CEPS, the *Accounting Procedure* states the following methods can be used as long as the pricing is equivalent to current market value:

- manually applying the HPM to published material and equipment price listings

- vendors' quotes

- historical purchase prices

- mutual agreement of the transfer prices by the parties involved

TRANSFER FROM WAREHOUSE TO JOINT ACCOUNT

When equipment is transferred from the operator's wholly owned warehouse inventory to a jointly owned property, the transaction is considered a sale. The *Accounting Procedure* in the venture's joint operating agreement specifies "condition values" should be used.

For example, assume an item of equipment is carried in the operator's warehouse inventory account at an original cost of $20,000. The current price of a new asset is $32,000. The equipment is considered to be in Condition Value B (see CD Reference Exhibit F), which means it will be valued at 75 percent of current new cost. The equipment is transferred to joint interest property No. 12103J. Because the operator owns three-fourths of the working interest, the nonoperator owner is charged $6,000 ($32,000 x .75 x 1/4) for its new one-fourth interest in the property.

Since the operator's original cost for the one-fourth interest was $5,000 (1/4 x $20,000), a gain is realized on the portion of the asset sold. (No gain is realized on the three-fourths interest belonging to the operator because a sale to an outsider did not take place.) After ignoring transportation expenses, the transfer is recorded as follows:

123	Accounts Receivable—Joint Interest Billings (1/4 x .75 x $32,000)		6,000	
233	Tangible Costs of Wells and Related Development (3/4 x $20,000)		15,000	
	132	Warehouse Inventory		20,000
	630	Other Income		1,000
	To record transfer of equipment to jointly owned property.			

Other procedures can be used to recognize profit or loss on the share of equipment sold to the nonoperator; however, profit is never recorded on the share retained by the operator. Freight and installation costs are charged directly to the joint interest and treated as part of the equipment's cost by all parties.

Transfer from Wholly Owned to Jointly Owned Lease. Equipment transfers between leases during drilling and production phases require a slightly different treatment. Assume an item of equipment with an original cost of $20,000 is transferred from wholly owned Lease 18610 to Lease 18205, in which the operator owns a one-fourth working interest. The equipment is categorized as Condition Value B and is charged to the joint lease at $24,000. In this transaction, three-fourths of the asset is sold for $18,000 (3/4 x $24,000).

However, in accordance with Reg. S-X Rule 4-10 and Oi5, no gain or loss is recognized on the sale or retirement of wells or equipment under the full cost or successful efforts method until the last well is abandoned. Until then, all proceeds are credited to the asset account rather than recording a gain on sale. If the asset's original cost is known, it should be removed from the asset cost account and the accumulated amortization account should be adjusted to defer the gain or loss, if needed. The entry to be recorded is:

123	Accounts Receivable—Joint Interest Billings		18,000	
233	Tangible Costs of Wells and Development— Lease 18205		6,000	
	234	Accumulated Amortization of Tangible Costs of Wells and Development—Lease 18610		4,000
	233	Tangible Costs of Wells and Development— Lease 18610		20,000
	To record transfer of equipment from wholly owned lease to jointly owned lease.			

Alternatively, the entry could debit Account 233 for $5,000 and credit Account 234 for $4,000 so as to record Lease 18205 equipment cost at 25 percent of the $20,000 original cost, rather than 25 percent of the price at transfer.

REMOVAL OF ASSETS FROM JOINTLY OWNED PROPERTY

A third example illustrates an entry for assets that are removed from jointly owned properties and transferred to the operator's warehouse. Assume the operator removes an asset originally installed new at a cost of $20,000 from Lease 06203J. The operator owns one-fourth of the working interest in the lease. The asset is transferred to the operator's warehouse where it is to be reconditioned for use on the operator's wholly owned Lease 17304. At the time of removal, a new identical asset would cost $32,000. The removed asset's Condition Value is C, which establishes a value of 50 percent of current new cost.

In effect, the operator purchased three-fourths of the equipment from the nonoperator for $12,000, and removed one-fourth of the equipment (cost $5,000). Salvage value is $4,000 (1/4 x $16,000). The transfer is recorded as follows:

132	*Warehouse Inventory (.50 x $32,000)*		16,000	
234	*Accumulated Amortization of Tangible Costs of Wells and Development—Lease 06203J*		1,000	
	123	*Accounts Receivable—Joint Interest Billings*		12,000
	233	*Tangible Costs of Wells and Development— Lease 06203J*		5,000
	To record transfer of equipment from jointly owned lease to operator's warehouse.			

Note the Accumulated Amortization account absorbs the residual amount from the entry since no gain or loss is recognized currently.

TRANSFER BETWEEN TWO JOINTLY OWNED LEASES

Equipment may also be transferred by the operator between two jointly owned leases. For example, assume a piece of equipment with an original cost of $20,000 is transferred to Lease 10723J, in which the operator and Little Oil Company each own one-half shares. The equipment previously belonged to Lease 10792J, which is three-fourths owned by the operator and one-fourth owned by Danielson Oil Company. The equipment is transferred at a condition value that applies a factor of 75 percent to the new equipment price of $21,333, resulting in a transaction value of $16,000.

This transfer scenario creates a challenging problem, and one without a fully satisfactory solution. A common approach is to assume one-fourth of the equipment is being purchased for $4,000 from the joint owners of the lease where the asset was originally located. The remaining three-fourths of the equipment with a condition value of $12,000 is removed from the lease with no gain or loss recognized. In effect, one-half of the equipment has been sold to the joint owners on the new lease for condition value and one-half has been transferred to the operator's accounts relating to the new location. The entry to record this approach follows:

123	Accounts Receivable—Joint Interest Billings, Little Oil (1/2 x $16,000)	8,000	
233	Tangible Costs of Wells and Development— Lease 10723J (1/2 x $16,000)	8,000	
234	Accumulated Amortization of Tangible Costs of Wells and Development—Lease 10792J ($20,000 - $16,000) x 75%	3,000	
	123 Accounts Receivable—Joint Interest Billings, Danielson Oil (1/4 x $16,000)		4,000
	233 Tangible Costs of Wells and Development— Lease 10792J (3/4 x $20,000)		15,000
	To record transfer of assets between joint interest properties.		

JOINT INTEREST AUDITS

After joint interest billings are received, approved, and processed, nonoperators can gain further assurance on the accuracy of billed charges by examining the operator's internal records. These examinations are called joint interest audits and are authorized by the *Accounting Procedure* exhibit of the JOA. Most JOAs define the audit period as the current year and prior two years. Additional guidance on joint interest audit protocol and procedures is provided by the COPAS Accounting Guideline No. 19 (AG 19).

Generally, the nonoperator with the largest working interest initiates the audit, contacts the operator, and plans and executes the work. An experienced person within or outside the company is appointed by the nonoperator as the lead auditor. He or she alerts the operator of the desire to audit the records, requests the necessary documents, and decides on the timing of the audit. The lead auditor prepares a confirmation letter to the operator providing: (1) names and addresses of all working interest owners, (2) properties to be covered in the audit, (3) on-site visitation dates and estimated number of auditors who will be present, (4) time period of activities that will be audited, (5) arrangements to access pertinent original records, and (6) a description of records requested in advance. The operator's original records generally include the company's chart of accounts and organization charts; field schematic; drilling contracts and permits; daily drilling, tour, cementing, completion, mud, chemical, bit usage, and plug and abandon reports; casing specifications; journal vouchers with backup; material transfers; and all pertinent records from the operations department.

The lead auditor prepares a ballot letter which is sent to the nonoperators informing them of the operator's consent to the audit. Pertinent information is provided, including the date of the audit, properties, estimated cost, and completion time for the audit. Nonoperators are requested to agree to the audit and either share in costs or send their own auditors. The letter should also include a date it should be returned to the lead auditor.

In planning an audit, the lead auditor does a risk assessment. Questions such as:

- Have there been previous associations with the operator? If not, what is the reputation of the operator?
- Has a previous audit been completed? What were the results?
- How many properties should be audited?
- What types of expenditures should be examined?
- What amount of billed expenditure is too small to evaluate?
- Has the lead auditor's management requested specific wells for the audit?

The lead auditor prepares the audit program, coordinates the work and supervises staff. He or she communicates with all parties on audit findings, the operator's response, follow-up, billing audit costs, and any other issues.

The lead auditor should ensure as much work as possible is done up-front before reaching the operator's office. These procedures can include reading the daily drilling reports to get a history of the properties, reviewing the information contained in any previous audit reports and files, and preparing any lead schedules with information from the operations department or Joint Audit Data Exchange (JADE) data, an electronic file of the cost detail transactions related to all the requested properties to be audited.

When the audit is completed, the lead auditor presents the findings to the operator; prepares an audit report; identifies the exceptions (either for or against the operator); distributes the audit report to members of the audit team, nonoperators and the operator; follows up on resolution of open issues; and writes a final closure letter.

General steps for a joint interest audit are summarized in Figure 10-2. COPAS AG 19 provides example forms of the required letters and reports.

Figure 10-2
General Steps for a Joint Interest Audit

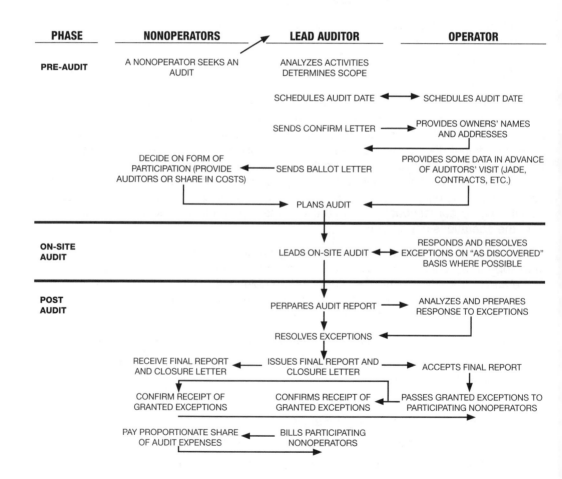

ELECTRONIC DATA INTERCHANGE (EDI)

Joint interest operations require oil and gas companies to exchange huge quantities of operating and accounting data. In its early years, the industry compiled, classified, and disseminated this information using manual methods. Computer technology later allowed individual companies to develop software programs for accumulating data and preparing reports. However, companies receiving the data would have to enter the information in their own accounting and data systems. Later, some companies adopted the practice of providing computer tapes to interested parties.

Recently, electronic data interchange (EDI) has simplified the problem of information transmittal and receipt in joint operations and in accounting for other transactions between companies such as the exchange of petroleum products.

Through the initiative of COPAS members and others, computer programs now facilitate the accumulation, transmittal, and receipt of data. The General Electric Information Services electronic data exchange systems may be the best known of these programs. Participating companies retain their in-house coding systems. Data to be transferred to other companies is converted to standard codes and formats for transmission. At the receiving end, the information is converted from the standard format and coding to the company's own in-house codes and formats.

Among the most important parts of this data exchange program are the following:

- **CODE (Crude Oil Data Exchange).** Furnishes run ticket and run statement information on the receipt and delivery of crude oil through carrier pipelines.

- **CDEX (Check Stub Data Exchange).** Automates the collection and distribution of check detail information on jointly-owned oil and gas properties.

- **GRADE (Gas Revenue Accounting Data Exchange).** Records information on natural gas/NGL metered volumes, allocated volumes, test data, and plant settlement data.

- **PETROEX (Petroleum Product Exchange System).** Provides bills of lading and bulk custody information on furnished product exchange transactions.

- **RECON (The Exchange Reconciliation System).** Produces a record of unmatched exchange transactions on a contract and a product basis.

- **TABS (Terminal Administration and Billing System).** Provides credit and product authorization at exchange terminals and captures bill of lading information.

- **JADE (Joint Audit Data Exchange).** Compiles information needed for review and verification of a joint venture operator's source documents. The system helps reduce the audit time required by auditors and the operator's support staff.

- **JIBE (Joint Interest Billing Exchange).** Enables the electronic transmission of monthly joint interest billing statements and invoices to other working interest owners.

$$\bullet \ \bullet \ \bullet$$

---

1   An undivided interest owner has a share in the entire lease or property. For example, a joint owner might own a 50 percent interest in a tract of 640 acres. Alternatively, an owner might own a divided interest of 100 percent of the interest in 320 acres included in a 640 lease.

2   Controllable material refers to items that can be reasonably controlled and accounted for by periodically taking a physical inventory of the items. COPAS MFI-28 provides a list of such material.

11

PRODUCTION AND VOLUME MEASUREMENT

Key Concepts:

- Equipment and processes used to produce, move, treat, and handle oil and gas

- Contractual arrangements for processing gas

- Reinjected gas

- Storage in above ground and underground facilities

- Measurement of crude oil, nonprocessed natural gas, natural gas liquids, and residue gas

The ultimate objectives of oil and gas operations are to produce and sell hydrocarbons for a profit. Procedures used to measure, process, market, deliver, and finally account for these products are important to understand. Many industry terms related to production and volume measurement are introduced in this chapter. Readers should keep in mind that the use of terms can vary slightly among petroleum accountants, engineers, and other industry groups.

Related topics dovetail with this chapter: Chapter 12 discusses marketing issues for crude oil and natural gas, while Chapter 13 describes accounting issues for recording oil and gas sales.

PLACING THE WELL ON PRODUCTION

After a well is completed, it is placed on production by installing surface equipment. Figure 11-1 illustrates typical surface equipment used for oil and gas production. The equipment performs the following:

- Collects and gathers the produced emulsion of natural gas, oil, and water from the well

- Separates the gas, oil, and water

- Treats the gas and oil to minimize remaining impurities and bring them to marketable condition

- Stores the oil briefly prior to sale (which further removes impurities)

- Measures the volumes produced and sold

- Facilitates the removal of gas, oil, and water

Several transportation modes are used when a well begins producing. Natural gas is typically transported by gas pipelines; oil is carried by crude pipelines, barges, or trucks. Produced water from the site is treated and injected into underground reservoirs using commercial salt water disposal wells. In the case of some offshore wells, salt water is released into the ocean.

Natural gas is typically transported by gas pipelines; oil is carried by crude pipelines, barges, or trucks.

Figure 11-1
Schematic of Lease Production Facilities

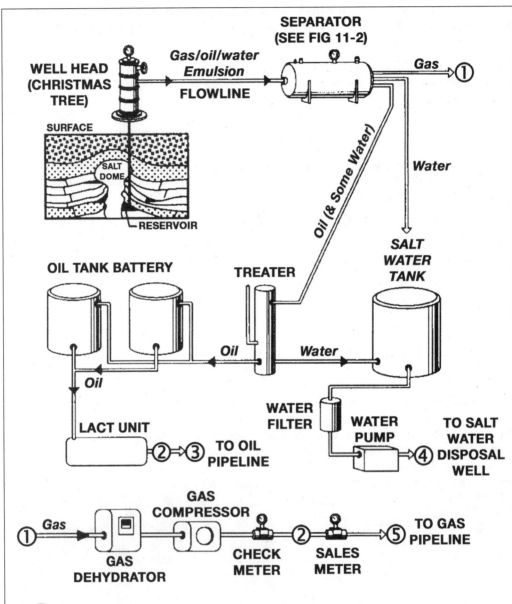

② = The point of movement when title transfers at the lease as the oil or gas is sold.

③ = Oil is removed by pipeline, barge, or tanker. It may also be removed by truck without the use of a Lease Automatic Custody Transfer unit.

④ = Water is pumped underground using a salt water disposal well.

⑤ = Gas is sent into a gas gathering system or gas pipeline (and perhaps on to a gas processing plant for removal of NGL).

To collect and gather gas, oil, and water produced in a field, an E&P company connects wellheads to pipes called **flow lines**, which are usually buried beneath the surface. Often called a **gathering system** or network, this collection of flow lines leads to various surface equipment. (The term gathering system refers to any system of pipes over a wide area that gathers gas from wells and fields for **delivery** to a major gas pipeline or processing plant.)

Even though a well may be classified as a gas well or an oil well, few reservoirs produce only one product. Individual products may need to be separated and treated to remove impurities (such as sediment, water, or water vapor) before the product is removed from the field. Most pipelines and refineries require: (1) the content of crude oil contains less than one percent of basic sediment and water (BS&W), and (2) natural gas has no more than seven pounds of water vapor per MMcf.

The oil and gas mixture is directed through an enclosed steel cylindrical or spherical piece of equipment called a separator. Gravity, and sometimes centrifugal force, separates the gas from any liquids. Oil and gas flow through the separator in a one to six minute process, depending on the oil density. Gas, which is lighter than liquids, travels through an outlet at the top of the separator, and liquids escape through lower outlets.

Two-phase separators are designed to separate gas from liquids, while three-phase separators separate gas, water, and oil. A horizontal separator is illustrated in Figure 11-2.

Figure 11-2
A Horizontal Two-Phase Separator

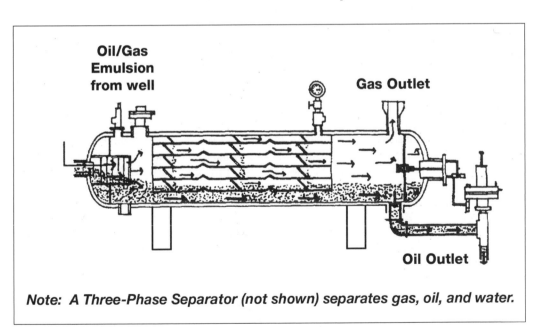

Note: A Three-Phase Separator (not shown) separates gas, oil, and water.

Oil droplets that are trapped and suspended in water are called oil-in-water emulsion. Water-in-oil is known as reverse emulsion. Either type of mixture is treated with demulsifing chemicals and heat to assist gravity in separating the products. A more sophisticated separator known as a heater treater is used with these emulsions. Another type of treater employs an electrostatic process that uses an electrical charge instead of heat to cause water to settle out of the oil. Treaters also serve to separate any gas trapped in the emulsion.

Stage separation refers to the process of running the mixture through separators before selling the products. Three-stage and four-stage separation refers to the number of times the mixture is run through at decreasing levels of pressure to maximize product recovery.

Crude oil moves through the flowline and is stored in large steel storage tanks (stock tanks or flow tanks) until sold. The stock tank is counted as one of the stages in three-stage and four-stage separation because any remaining BS&W will settle to the bottom of the tank.

Depending on the crude oil produced, a significant amount of natural gas can separate from the oil in the stock tanks, despite several stages of prior separation. Stock tanks may be connected to a vapor recovery system that collects the gas either for sale, lease use, or flaring. If there is sufficient quantity to justify the cost of compressing the gas for movement to a gas pipeline, the gas will be sold. **Lease use** gas refers to the portion of gas used on a lease as fuel for heater treaters, **dehydration** units, or gas compressors. Typically, the last stage of separation yields a small quantity of gas that is not economical to compress and sell. It may be **flared** if there is enough volume to maintain a constant flame. If not, the gas is vented into the atmosphere when government regulations allow it.

Water and impurities are removed from natural gas before it is accepted by a pipeline. **Field processing** techniques used are dependent on the composition of the gas. Dehydration removes water vapor by several methods: heating, adding drying agents, adding antifreeze agents, expanding the gas and refrigerating it with heat exchangers, or using a glycol dehydrator that works on the principle of absorption and pressure. Gas conditioning (or sweetening) is the process of removing impurities, such as CO_2 and H_2S, by using additives, heat, and filtering methods.

Each lease normally has two or more stock tanks that can hold several days of oil production. The tanks are connected by flow lines (referred to as a **tank battery**) and are equipped with inlets and valves for controlling the flow of the oil into and between the tanks. Oil processed through the separators fills one stock tank while a valve is closed to isolate the other tank. This allows the oil to be measured and drained into a truck, barge, or a pipeline.

Oil is transferred from the stock tanks through an outlet called a sales line, which is approximately one-foot from the bottom of the tank. Sediment and water settle to the bottom of the tank. Placing a sales line near the bottom of the tank ensures that the purchaser or transporter receives only sales-quality oil. Occasionally, residue below the sales line, referred to as tank bottoms or bottom oil, is drained and reprocessed through the separators, or it may be sold separately. Metal seals with recorded serial numbers are used to close the outlet valve on the sales line and are tracked by the lease operator and oil purchaser to safeguard against unauthorized movement of oil from the stock tanks.

OIL STORAGE

The U.S. demand for crude oil substantially exceeds U.S. production **capacity** throughout the year and minimizes the need for field storage. As a result, crude oil inventories for most companies consist of insignificant amounts of unsold oil in field tank batteries. Tank capacities vary according to a field's early production rates and remoteness from pipelines. The change in inventory volume from quarter to quarter does not vary significantly. For this reason, many companies do not reflect crude oil inventory on their balance sheets.

In the U.S., the only substantial underground crude oil storage is the Strategic Petroleum Reserve (SPR). As mentioned in Chapter 1, the U.S. government began storing crude oil in underground leached salt caverns in the Gulf Coast area, Michigan, and New York in

1977 to prevent a major supply disruption, such as an abrupt decrease in foreign imports. Approximately 689 million barrels of crude oil were in storage as of April 2007 according to the SPR website.

REMOVING THE PRODUCTS FROM THE LEASE

Crude oil is transferred from a lease by pipeline, truck, barge, or rail tank car to a refinery or an intermediate oil purchaser. For oil delivered into a pipeline, the product is likely measured by a lease automatic custody transfer unit (**LACT unit**). This equipment automatically measures, samples, and tests the oil and either returns it for additional treatment or sends it into the pipeline. If a LACT unit is not used, then operators manually gauge stock tanks, test and measure samples, and calculate volumes delivered.

Natural gas is transferred from a lease through a gas meter that is used for measurement. The product moves to a regional gas gathering system or may go directly into an intrastate or interstate gas pipeline.

Gas meters are typically owned by gas purchasers and are referred to as sales meters. Not as accurate or dependable as those used for crude oil, the meters must be recalibrated frequently. Lease operators often install another unit, called a check meter, on the pipeline immediately in front of the sales meter. Volumes are compared and gas contracts usually specify that differences greater than two to five percent are cause for recalibration.

If necessary or economical, gas in the gathering system or pipeline is sent to a gas processing plant for removal of natural gas liquids (NGL) such as ethane, propane, butane, and natural gasolines. Gas processing is described in more detail later in the chapter.

Gas Compression. Gas moves through a pipeline because it is under pressure. Gas compressors can be installed to further compress the gas and push it through the pipeline more effectively. Compressors are powered by gas turbines, steam turbines, electric motors, or gasoline engines, and compressor stations may be located every 40 to 50 miles along the pipeline system.

When reservoir pressure is sufficiently high, it pushes produced gas into the gas gathering or pipeline system. In the later stages of a field's productive life, pressure will decline. Gas compressors are added at the lease site, as needed, to enhance delivery of the product.

GAS INJECTION

Gas produced from a reservoir is reinjected into the reservoir when: (1) it will increase the ultimate recovery of oil or condensate, or (2) there is no economic market for such gas sales. (Regulatory authorities do not generally permit excess gas to be flared.) Reinjection typically improves production of the more valuable oil or condensate. Also, the reinjected gas may be produced and sold at a future time if economics allow.[1]

For example, the substantial volumes of gas produced on the North Slope of Alaska cannot be economically transported to markets outside the state. Instead, they are classified as unproved gas reserves, and are reinjected into the producing reservoir after processing to remove marketable condensate and NGL.

Gas Injection for Pressure Maintenance in Oil Reservoirs. In some situations, the ultimate recovery of oil is increased by maintaining the reservoir pressure above the bubble point—the pressure at (or below) which gas bubbles out of the liquid. At pressures above the bubble point, all gas molecules stay dissolved and in solution with the crude oil. However, at pressures below the bubble point, gas bubbles begin to break out of the solution and rise to the highest part of the reservoir to form a secondary gas cap. As the gas escapes, **viscosity** of the crude oil increases and mobility of the oil decreases, causing ultimate oil recovery to decrease.

Large capital expenditures are required to install equipment necessary for reinjection of gas. Further, revenues from sale of the gas are delayed until most of the recoverable oil reserves are produced. Data from geologists, engineers, and financial analysts helps determine the merits of a gas injection project to increase ultimate oil recovery.

Gas Injection for Pressure Maintenance in Gas Condensate Reservoirs. In most cases, the ultimate recovery of condensate can be increased by maintaining reservoir pressure above the dew point. At this pressure, all gas and condensate exist as a single solution. At pressures below dew point, liquid drops of condensate begin to form and fall out of the solution. Some drops wet the rock surface and stick to the surface, while others fill the pore space around each wellbore. Liquid condensate does not flow through the reservoir rock as easily as gas; thus, a drop in reservoir pressure below the dew point decreases the amount of condensate that can flow to the wellbore and restricts the flow of gas through the reservoir. Reservoirs producing with these characteristics are often called retrograde condensate reservoirs.

In a gas **cycling** operation, lean gas (the resulting gas stream after it has passed through separators and condensate has been removed) is reinjected into the reservoir where it maintains pressure, absorbs condensate, and is ultimately produced, processed, and reinjected. Cycling operations are illustrated in Figure 11-3.

When injection of lean gas no longer contributes to increased liquid recovery from a reservoir, gas injection is discontinued, and future produced gas is sold after processing. At that point, the reservoir is said to be in a blowdown phase.

For **pressure maintenance** of either oil reservoirs or retrograde condensate reservoirs, the injected gas may be part or all of a field's production, or it may be purchased for use from other sources.

Figure 11-3
Gas Cycling Operations

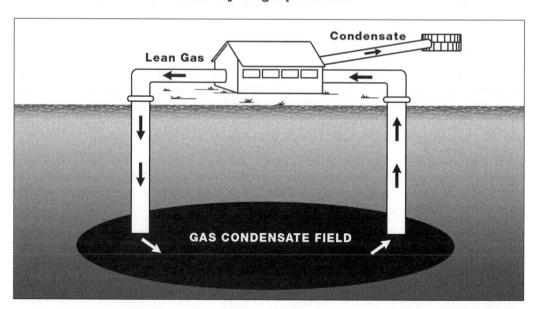

Artificial Gas Lift. In an artificial gas lift, gas is injected into an oil well (not the reservoir) between the tubing and casing. Pressure from the injected gas opens a valve in the tubing string near the bottom of the well that allows the gas to combine with the crude oil in the tubing. This action lifts oil from the bottom of the well to the surface. Similar pressure-sensitive valves may be installed at selected points along the tubing string to help start the artificial gas lift.

MEASURING VOLUMES OF OIL AND GAS

An important step in revenue accounting is determining the volume and quality of the oil, condensate, and natural gas that are produced and sold. The physical activities of taking readings, testing, and measuring are performed by the purchaser and company field personnel. However, revenue accountants must know and understand these procedures to ensure that they are being followed correctly.

Appropriate internal controls are necessary because inaccurate measurements of volume or quality can result in lost revenue. The American Petroleum Institute (API) has issued numerous production and measurement standards. A revenue accountant should apply these procedures and ensure compliance by field personnel and purchaser representatives.

MEASURING OIL VOLUMES PRODUCED AND SOLD

As mentioned, oil is measured by one of two methods: (1) manually by gauged tank levels where the product is moved by truck, barge, tank car, or pipeline to a purchaser or refinery, or (2) automatically by a LACT unit where the product flows into the purchaser's pipeline.

Manual Measurement—Gauging A Tank. Manually measuring the oil volume sold from a stock tank involves several steps:

1. Obtaining volume measurements of an empty stock tank to determine the amount of oil that can be held at various tank levels

2. Measuring the levels of oil in the tank before and after the oil is removed

3. Converting measured oil levels to oil volumes to compute the reduction of oil volume in the tank

Before a new tank battery is put into operation, each empty tank is strapped. Strapping means the tank dimensions are measured to determine the fluid volume for any given fluid level. The tank is normally measured by an employee of the tank vendor (**tank strapper**) at four or five key points according to industry standards. Measurements are witnessed by a representative of the producer and are recorded on a tank strapping report, which is signed by the tank company employee and producer's representative. The strapping report is then sent to an independent tank engineer who computes the volume of oil to be contained in each interval (usually one-quarter inch) of height of the tank. Although tanks are manufactured to uniform dimensions, they tend to bulge outward at the middle. In a large tank, a slight bulge can account for several barrels of oil. The standard unit of measurement of crude oil–known as a stock tank barrel, or STB–is a barrel of 42 gallons of marketable crude oil held at a temperature of 60 degrees Fahrenheit (60°F) and at atmospheric pressure. Tank capacity is recorded on a table where each one-quarter inch from the bottom to the top is associated with a volume of oil.

A portion of a typical **tank table** is shown in Figure 11-4. Volumes for each one-fourth inch from 1' to 1'10 3/4" and from 6' to 6'10 3/4" are illustrated. (Other table readings have been omitted to simplify its use later in the chapter.)

The table indicates that if the level of liquid is 6'10", the liquid volume is 442.92 barrels; at 1'4", the volume is 86.48 barrels. If the tank level is 6'10" and liquid is removed, lowering the level to 1'4", the volume of the removed liquid is 442.92 less 86.48, or 356.44 barrels unadjusted for temperature or **gravity**.

A tank table or its equivalent table of tank increment factors is a basic reference source for calculating the volume of oil produced into or delivered from a lease tank. Tank tables are stored as computer files for fast accurate conversion of tank levels into volumes produced or sold.

A gauger is a person, usually the oil purchaser's representative, who measures the quantity and quality of lease products. The term pumper refers to the producing company's employee (or contractor) responsible for operating and maintaining equipment on the lease.

The pumper is responsible for an E&P company's testing, gauging, and initial recording of volumes produced and sold. Visiting the lease site daily, the pumper gauges the tank and records the results on a pumper's report (sometimes called a gauge sheet). This operational report acts as a check against the purchaser's **run ticket**–a term used for the receipt generated at the point of delivery. The pumper has the right and responsibility to witness the gauger's testing and measuring of the oil. An E&P company does not expect the pumper to witness all of the gauger's activity, but rather to reconcile the run ticket data to crude oil levels noted on the pumper's report.

Immediately before running a tank of oil (i.e., moving the oil) into the pipeline or truck, the oil purchaser's representative (observed by the oil producer's representative) measures the top level of the oil, or opening gauge. This is performed with a steel measuring tape (gauge tape), which is weighted by a brass weight called a plumb bob or gauge bob.

Using a device known as a **thief** that permits extraction of oil from any desired level in the tank, samples of oil are secured for several intervals just above and below the pipeline connection in order to determine whether the BS&W content of the oil is less than one percent. This test is referred to as a shakeout. If the tank contains too much BS&W, the measurements will indicate how much BS&W must be drained from the tank in order to lower the salable oil to the pipeline connection. The samples obtained are placed in glass tubes and spun in a **centrifuge**. Centrifugal force causes BS&W to settle to the bottom of the glass tube and the BS&W content can be read from graduations on the tube. The amount of BS&W in the oil actually sold is also determined by this method.

Calculating Volumes Using Computers. If purchasers of oil use computer equipment to calculate the volume of oil, a tank table is supplemented by a table of tank increment factors. It lists the barrels of oil per one-quarter inch between various levels of the tank. A table of tank increment factors (increment factor sheet) is shown in Figure 11-5.

Figure 11-4
Illustrative Tank Table
[Values for all but two columns have been omitted.]

BARRELS (42 Gallons)
FEET PER ONE-QUARTER INCH
STRAPPED

BY: J. SMITH   FOR: KT OIL
BY: FOR:

P.L.
OLD No.   CONN.

DISTRICT: COVINGTON
OWNER: KT OIL
LEASE: KNIGHT
TANK No. 41-2

1	64	86	6	388	95
¼	66	21	¼	390	30
½	67	56	½	391	65
¾	68	91	¾	393	00
1	70	26	1	394	35
¼	71	61	¼	395	70
½	72	97	½	397	05
¾	74	32	¾	398	40
2	75	67	2	399	75
¼	77	02	¼	401	09
½	78	37	½	402	44
¾	79	72	¾	403	79
3	81	07	3	405	14
¼	82	42	¼	406	49
½	83	78	½	407	84
¾	85	13	¾	409	19
4	86	48	4	410	54
¼	87	83	¼	411	89
½	89	18	½	413	24
¾	90	53	¾	414	59
5	91	88	5	415	94
¼	93	23	¼	417	29
½	94	58	½	418	64
¾	95	94	¾	419	99
6	97	29	6	421	33
¼	98	64	¼	422	68
½	99	99	½	424	03
¾	101	34	¾	425	38
7	102	69	7	426	73
¼	104	04	¼	428	08
½	105	39	½	429	43
¾	106	75	¾	430	78
8	108	10	8	432	13
¼	109	45	¼	433	48
½	110	80	½	434	83
¾	112	15	¾	436	18
9	113	50	9	437	53
¼	114	85	¼	438	88
½	116	20	½	440	22
¾	117	56	¾	441	57
10	118	91	10	442	92
¼	120	26	¼	444	27
½	121	61	½	445	62
¾	122	96	¾	446	97

Columns 2, 3, 4, 5, 7, and 8 are present but empty.

Figure 11-5
Illustrative Table of Tank Increment Factors

13-350-S

ABC PETROLEUM COMPANY
INCREMENT FACTOR SHEET

District _____Newgulf_____

Tank   Date of
Number _____19127_____   Table _____May 12, 2006_____

Operator Name _____ABC Petroleum Co._____   Pipe Line
                                                          Company _____

Lease Name _____

Lease No. _17-583_   Pipe Line Code _____   Gauger District _____

Truck Code _____   State Code _____   Tax Code _____   Price Code ____

Tank Strapped By: _____

No.	INCREMENT		VERTICAL COMPONENTS				Volume in	No. of QTR. INCHES	
	(Use 5 Decimals)	From	To				Barrels Per		
	Barrels per ¼ inch	Feet					Vertical Component	From	To
1	.34600	0	0	0	8		43.07200		
1	.15791	0	8	0	10		9.26328		
1	.34891	0	10	3	0		140.28664		
1	.34605	3	0	6	0		193.83120		
1	.34106	6	0	7	9		112.64904		

Unadjusted Tank Capacity	499.10216
Correction Factor and Cone Capacity	0.00931
Total Adjusted Tank Capacity	499.11147

Factors Determining Oil Price and Volume. In the U.S., crude oil sells at a price per barrel based on a posted **price bulletin** and tank barrel volume.[2] Prices vary according to:

- General geographic location, such as West Texas, identified on the posted price bulletin

- General degree of sulfur in the crude oil

- Date of sale

- Oil density (measured in degrees of API gravity) at 60°F [3]

The first two factors—location and general sulfur content—do not change for a given oil reservoir. Sulfur is a contaminant not typically removed from oil at a lease and is expensive to remove at the refinery. Thus, crude oil higher in sulfur content sells for less. Sulfur content is expressed in three degrees or classes: (1) sweet crude having little sulfur, generally less than 0.6 percent by weight, (2) intermediate having a sulfur content generally between 0.6 and 1.7 percent, and (3) sour crude with a sulfur content generally above 1.7 percent.[4] Geographic location and sulfur factors are expressed in the price bulletin as a type or name of crude oil, such as West Texas Intermediate or Louisiana Sweet.

Posted prices vary by date of sale for various reasons, such as changes in the global and national prices of crude oil and refined products. Changes in local supply and demand for crude oil and refined products also play a role in pricing.

The density of crude oil affects the cost for refining it into valuable products such as gasoline. Heavy crude oil has more mass, but less value per barrel. Light crude oils with high API gravities command higher selling prices because a greater proportion of gasoline is obtained without employing expensive refining techniques to break the long, heavy hydrocarbon molecules into smaller, lighter molecules found in gasoline.

Run Ticket. The run ticket is a legal document on which the gauger, witnessed by the pumper, records information necessary to establish the correct price and STB volume of the oil removed including:

- Specific location or tank, which indicates the first two pricing factors of general geographic location and type of oil

- Date of removal or sale, which is the third pricing factor

- Observed API gravity and the corresponding observed temperature of the oil sample (so they can be corrected to API gravity at 60°F, the fourth pricing factor and a secondary factor in determining STB volume)

- Tank level of oil just prior to oil removal and corresponding crude oil temperature

- Tank level of oil just after oil removal and corresponding crude oil temperature

- BS&W content of the crude oil removed

Tank levels determine gross oil volumes at the corresponding oil temperatures. Gross volumes are corrected to stock tank barrels at 60°F for the calculated API gravity at 60°F. Full correction includes volume reduction to exclude BS&W content.

The gauger measures the oil's API gravity with a hydrometer. Oil temperature is taken by lowering a thermometer into the oil in the tank.

Information recorded on the run ticket also includes the purchaser's name, lease owner or operator's name, run ticket number, and signatures of the gauger and pumper.

Run tickets also have spaces for recording gravity adjusted to 60°F and the result of volume calculations. These calculations are not completed on the copy of the run ticket supplied for accounting purposes, but are made by employees of the production department for use in control of operations and compliance with regulations. In most large companies, calculations are made with electronic data processing equipment. Figure 11-6 illustrates a run ticket reflecting delivery of oil from the tank used to illustrate Figure 11-4.

A run ticket generated by a LACT unit is called a meter ticket. It contains the meter readings for volumes, observed gravity and temperature, average line temperature (if the meter is not temperature compensated), and the BS&W.

Determining API Gravity at 60°F. API gravity at the observed temperature is corrected to API gravity at 60°F (also called true gravity or corrected gravity) by the use of a gravity correction table. A gravity correction table, partially reproduced in Figure 11-7, shows true gravity for each one-tenth degree of observed gravity. For example, if observed gravity is 23.2° API and observed temperature is 100°F, then the true or corrected gravity is 20.9° API at 60°F.

Determining the Volume Correction Factor. The amount of observed volume at an observed temperature is multiplied by a volume correction factor to calculate volume at 60°F. Volume correction is a function of the observed temperature and the oil's API gravity at 60°F. The appropriate factor is determined from a volume correction table. Figure 11-8 illustrates a volume correction table for various temperatures from 50°F to 104°F and API gravities of 20° to 29°.

Figure 11-6
Pipeline Run Ticket

OPERATOR (OR FIELD LOCATION)	*ABC Oil Company*			
LEASE OR COMPANY NAME	*24001*		Delivery	Receipt
			☐	X
FOR ACCOUNT OF			Crude Grade or Product	
CONSIGNEE (if delivered to connecting carrier)			Reid Vapor Pressure	
CREDIT				

MOVED BY				TO (line or station)
Pump	Gravity	Truck		*XYZ Pipeline Co.*
☐	☐	X		

TANK SIZE	*500*	POWER FURNISHED BY OR TRUCKED BY		
MO. *7*	DAY *15*	YR. *2006*	DISTRICT NO.	TICKET NO. *1442*
TANK OR METER NO. *2401*		OFFICE CODES		LEASE NO.

		OIL LEVEL				CALCULATIONS OR REMARKS
GUAGE	FT.	IN.	FRACT.	TEMP		
1st	*6*	*0*	*1/2*	*102*		
2nd	*1*	*9*	*1/2*	*86*		
OBS. GTY. & TEMP.		TRUE GRAVITY				
23.2	*100 F*					
CODES		BS & W				
POWER	TRUCK	*0.4%*				

	METER				
TRANSACTION NO.	PRINTING HEAD NO.	☐ Barrels		☐ Gallons	10ths
OFF					
ON					
AVG. METER PRESS	METER FACTOR	METERED BARRELS			
psi					
TEMPERATURE COMPENSATED?		AVG. LINE TEMP	COMPRESSIBILITY FACTOR	NET BARRELS	
☐ Yes ☐ No		° F			

	GAUGER *Ernest Hobbs*	TIME *8:00 AM*
ON	OPERATOR'S WITNESS OR WAIVER NO. *Terry Roundtree*	SEAL OFF *83661*
OFF	GAUGER *Ernest Hobbs*	TIME *9:10 AM* / DATE *7/15/2006*
	OPERATOR'S WITNESS OR WAIVER NO. *Terry Roundtree*	SEAL ON *84471*

INSERT FACE DOWN   ⏚   THIS END FIRST

Figure 11-7
Gravity Correction Table

For Observed Temperature of 100 to 114°F	API Gravity at 60°F								
	23.0	23.1	23.2	23.3	23.4	23.5	23.6	23.7	23.8
	Factor for API Observed Gravity of 23.0-23.8°								
100	20.7	20.8	20.9	21.0	21.1	21.2	21.2	21.3	21.4
101	20.6	20.7	20.8	20.9	21.0	21.1	21.2	21.3	21.4
102	20.5	20.6	20.7	20.8	20.9	21.0	21.1	21.2	21.3
103	20.5	20.6	20.7	20.8	20.9	21.0	21.1	21.2	21.3
104	20.4	20.5	20.6	20.7	20.8	20.9	21.0	21.1	21.2
105	20.4	20.5	20.6	20.7	20.8	20.9	20.9	21.0	21.1
106	20.3	20.4	20.5	20.6	20.7	20.8	20.9	21.0	21.1
107	20.3	20.4	20.5	20.6	20.7	20.8	20.8	20.9	21.0
108	20.2	20.3	20.4	20.5	20.6	20.7	20.8	20.9	21.0
109	20.2	20.3	20.4	20.5	20.6	20.7	20.7	20.8	20.9
110	20.1	20.2	20.3	20.4	20.5	20.6	20.7	20.8	20.9
111	20.0	20.1	20.2	20.3	20.4	20.5	20.6	20.7	20.8
112	20.0	20.1	20.2	20.3	20.4	20.5	20.5	20.6	20.7
113	19.9	20.0	20.1	20.2	20.3	20.4	20.5	20.6	20.7
114	19.9	20.0	20.1	20.2	20.3	20.4	20.4	20.5	20.6

Figure 11-8
Volume Correction Table

ASTM-IP

20-29 ° API
50-104 °F

Observed Temperature, °F	API Gravity at 60°F									
	20	21	22	23	24	25	26	27	28	29
	Factor for Correcting Volume at 60°F									
50	1.0039	1.0040	1.0040	1.0040	1.0040	1.0041	1.0041	1.0041	1.0042	1.0042
51	1.0035	1.0036	1.0036	1.0036	1.0036	1.0037	1.0037	1.0037	1.0038	1.0038
52	1.0031	1.0032	1.0032	1.0032	1.0032	1.0033	1.0033	1.0033	1.0033	1.0034
53	1.0028	1.0028	1.0028	1.0028	1.0028	1.0029	1.0029	1.0029	1.0029	1.0029
54	1.0024	1.0024	1.0024	1.0024	1.0024	1.0024	1.0025	1.0025	1.0025	1.0025
85	0.9902	0.9902	0.9901	0.9900	0.9899	0.9899	0.9898	0.9897	0.9896	0.9895
86	0.9898	0.9898	0.9897	0.9896	0.9895	0.9895	0.9894	0.9893	0.9892	0.9891
87	0.9895	0.9894	0.9893	0.9892	0.9891	0.9891	0.9890	0.9889	0.9888	0.9887
88	0.9891	0.9890	0.9889	0.9888	0.9887	0.9887	0.9886	0.9885	0.9884	0.9883
89	0.9887	0.9886	0.9885	0.9884	0.9883	0.9883	0.9882	0.9881	0.9879	0.9878
100	0.9844	0.9843	0.9842	0.9841	0.9839	0.9838	0.9837	0.9835	0.9834	0.9832
101	0.9840	0.9839	0.9838	0.9837	0.9835	0.9834	0.9833	0.9831	0.9830	0.9828
102	0.9836	0.9835	0.9834	0.9833	0.9831	0.9830	0.9829	0.9827	0.9826	0.9824
103	0.9833	0.9831	0.9830	0.9829	0.9827	0.9826	0.9825	0.9823	0.9822	0.9820
104	0.9829	0.9827	0.9826	0.9825	0.9823	0.9822	0.9821	0.9819	0.9817	0.9816

Computing the Volume Run. Steps for computing the standard barrels at 60°F of oil run from a tank are summarized in Figure 11-9.

Figure 11-9
Computing the Volume Run

	Example	
	Amount	Source
Per Run Ticket from the Field:		
Observed gravity of sample	23.2	Fig. 11-6, Run Ticket
Observed temperature of sample	100°F	Fig. 11-6
1st gauge height	6' 0.5"	Fig. 11-6
1st gauge temperature	102°F	Fig. 11-6
2nd gauge height	1' 9.5"	Fig. 11-6
2nd gauge temperature	86°F	Fig. 11-6
BS&W content	0.4%	Fig. 11-6
Production Department's Calculations:		
Step 1: Correct to "true gravity" at 60°F	20.9	Fig. 11-7, Gravity Correction Table
Step 2: Determine "opening" fluid volume	391.65	Fig. 11-4, Tank Table
Step 3: Correct to bbls at 60°F	385.19	Fig. 11-8, Volume Correction Table
Step 4: Determine fluid volume left in tank	116.20	Fig. 11-8
Step 5: Correct to bbls at 60°F	115.01	Fig. 11-8
Step 6: Determine net fluid bbls removed	270.18	[385.19 - 115.01]
Step 7: Adjust bbls to exclude BS&W	269.10	[270.18 x 99.6%]
		i.e., 269.10 bbls of 20.9 API gravity crude sold

Related monthly processes:

a)   Accumulate adjusted volumes by tank.

b)   Compare accumulated total to purchaser's run statement.

c)   Allocate sales volumes to wells.

d)   Prepare production and sales reports for government agencies and internal records.

Step No. 1.   Correct the observed gravity at the observed temperature to the true gravity at 60°F. Observed gravity indicated on the Figure 11-6 run ticket is 23.2° API at 100°F. By referring to the gravity temperature correction table in Figure 11-7, true gravity is determined to be 20.9° API.

Step No. 2.   Determine the gross amount of fluid (oil and BS&W) in the tank before the run by applying the first measurement to the proper tank table (Figure 11-4). The first measurement of oil level indicated on the run ticket is 6' 1/2" at 102°F. By referring to the tank table (Figure 11-4), a gross volume of 391.65 barrels is obtained.

Step No. 3.   Correct the volume obtained in Step 2 to the volume at 60°F. Use the volume correction table (Figure 11-8) to find the factor to apply to observed volume.

ABC Oil Company rounds off the true gravity reading of 20.9° API to the nearest whole number to arrive at an adjusted true gravity of 21° API.[5] The volume correction table shown in Figure 11-8 shows that for gravity of 21° API and an observed temperature of 102°F (the temperature for the first measurement of oil level from the run ticket), the volume correction factor to adjust the volume to 60°F is 0.9835. Multiplying this factor by the volume of 391.65 barrels on the first observed reading yields a corrected volume of 385.19 barrels.

Step No. 4.   Determine the gross amount of fluid remaining in the tank after the run by applying the second measurement to the proper tank table. The second measurement indicated on the specimen run ticket is 1' 9-1/2" at a temperature of 86°F. By referring to the specimen tank table (Figure 11-4), the gross volume of 116.20 barrels is obtained.

Step No. 5.   Correct the volume obtained in Step 4 to the volume at 60°F as in Step No. 3. The true gravity is 20.9° API, rounded to 21°. The volume correction table (Figure 11-8) shows that for API gravity of 21° at temperature of 86°F, the reduction factor is 0.9898. Applying this factor to the volume of 116.20 barrels at the second measurement yields a corrected volume of 115.01 barrels.

Step No. 6.   Determine the net volume of fluid (oil and BS&W) run by subtracting the result obtained in Step 5 from that obtained in Step 3: 385.19 – 115.01 = 270.18 barrels.

Step No. 7.   Adjust the volume of liquid run for the BS&W content. Since BS&W content indicated on the run ticket is 0.4 percent, oil content of the volume run is 99.6 percent. Thus, the corrected net volume of oil sold is 270.18 barrels x .996 = 269.10 stock tank barrels at 20.9° API gravity at 60°F. For revenue determination, oil volume is measured to the hundredth barrel.

For volume measurement, crude volume at the observed temperature is sometimes called the "gross volume," while the volume of stock tank barrels (at the standard temperature) is the "net volume." In accounting for an owner's share of 8/8ths production, the terms gross volume and net volume are used to refer to 8/8ths production and an owner's net share of the 8/8ths production, respectively.

When crude oil is used for fuel or other operating or development purposes (either on the lease where produced or on another lease), the amount withdrawn from the tanks is recorded on a standard company run ticket. In this way, proper accounting for lease revenue, expense, and taxes can be made. If the crude oil is subsequently recovered, such as when it is used complete a new well, affidavits to that effect are supplied by production department personnel so that taxes are not paid twice.

Automatic Measurement—LACT Unit. The LACT unit has been a significant development in automating oil field functions. It meters oil, records temperatures, takes and stores oil samples at predetermined intervals for later gravity determination, measures BS&W content, diverts the oil back through the treating system if BS&W is too high, turns the oil into the pipeline, and cuts off the valves when the oil has been run into the pipeline. If the unit malfunctions, it shuts down and an alarm sounds in the field office so that personnel can investigate and correct the malfunction.

When a LACT unit is used to record the sale of oil into a pipeline, a meter measures the volume of oil that enters from the LACT unit's dump tank (also called the metering tank or surge tank). The dump tank is not strapped; therefore, there are no tank tables or increment factor sheets. Instead, the LACT meter must be proved on a regular basis to verify its accuracy. The meter proving report supplies a meter accuracy factor. The meter factor is then applied to the difference between the opening meter reading and closing meter reading to obtain the true gross barrels that entered the pipeline.

All measurements and other data are recorded on a meter ticket for the production and accounting records. Depending on the software used, gravity and temperature adjustments may be calculated automatically by the unit, eliminating production staff time.

DETERMINING VOLUMES OF NATURAL GAS SOLD

Natural gas is an energy resource that is increasingly important to the U.S. economy. Wellhead revenue for natural gas exceeded crude oil revenue for the first time in 1993.[6] The U.S. Energy Information Administration forecasts that natural gas demand will grow by more than 50 percent by 2025. Yet, storage levels are near record lows.

In order to determine the quantity of gas that changes ownership when a sale is made, the unit of measurement must be specified and the volume calculated according to terms in the gas sales contract.

Measuring Nonprocessed Gas Volumes Produced and Sold. As mentioned in Chapter 1, natural gas is measured in two ways—by volume and by heat content. The standard volume unit of measure in the U.S. is Mcf, which is the amount of gas expressed in thousand cubic feet at standard atmospheric pressure and temperature. Standard pressure bases used by the industry for gas volume reporting are approximately sea-level atmospheric pressures of 14.65, 14.73, and 15.025 pounds per square inch absolute (psia). When arriving at contract settlements or filing state and federal production reports, an accountant must determine which pressure base is required. Most federal governmental reporting is done at the 14.73 psia pressure base. Some state reporting requires the pressure base to be 14.65 psia (Texas, Oklahoma) or 15.025 psia (Louisiana). The standard temperature used is 60°F.

The heat content measurement called a British thermal unit (Btu) is defined as the heat necessary to raise the temperature of one pound of water by 1°F.

Historically, many gas sales contracts were priced on a Mcf basis. Most contracts now express prices in terms of one million British thermal units, or MMBtus. Prices are independent of gas temperature or pressure. Some contracts, particularly with utility companies, are expressed in decatherms, which equal one MMBtu. The Btu content (energy) in a volume of gas does not change with a pressure base change. Thus, the total Btu determined at one pressure base is equal to the total Btu determined or reported at another pressure base. From a production standpoint, most companies record gas produced in Mcf—this makes it easier when analyzing reserves. Most state and federal regulatory agencies require reporting to be expressed in Mcf. The U.S. is the only market not using the metric system for volume measurements.

When gas quantities are expressed in volume, but price is initially expressed in terms of heat content or MMBtu, the price per MMBtu must be converted to price per Mcf. To accomplish this, the price per MMBtu is multiplied by the heating value (Btu) of a unit of gas volume (Mcf). For example, if the price is $6.00 per MMBtu and the Btu content is 1.1000 MMBtu/Mcf at 14.73 psia, then the price per Mcf at 14.73 psia is $6.60 ($6.00 x 1.1000). For proper comparison, both the Btu content of the gas and the Mcf must be measured using the same pressure base.

Gas volumes can be converted to MMBtu by multiplying the volumes expressed in Mcf by the Btu content per Mcf to arrive at the number of MMBtus purchased, and adjusting for any differences in pressure base. For example, if one Bcf measured at 14.65 psia is sold, then the equivalent volumes sold at the higher pressure of 14.73 psia are smaller, specifically, one Bcf x 14.65 /14.73, i.e., 0.9946 Bcf. If the Btu content per Mcf at 14.73 psia were 1.1 MMBtu, then the MMBtu sold would be 994,600 Mcf x 1.1 MMBtu/Mcf, or 1,094,060 MMBtu.

Gas volume measurement is accomplished when gas flows through a meter that records temperature, pressure, or other specific information needed to calculate the volume. The petroleum industry uses four types of meters: (1) orifice, (2) turbine, (3) diaphragm positive displacement (the type used to measure most residential use), and (4) rotary gas displacement. However, metering technology is developing more sophisticated electronic or ultrasonic metering systems, especially for offshore development where gas quantities are larger and the accessibility of the meter is more difficult. Until these systems are competitively available to the market, most companies will continue to use one of the four meter types in combination with electronic communication systems. The subsection below briefly explains the use of a common **orifice meter** and illustrates the unique difficulties in measuring natural gas. Calculations are complex and rely on accurate readings from the meters and correct application of formulas.

As discussed earlier, gas flows from wells through pipelines to a central facility where separation and processing take place. Sufficient residues are removed so the gas can continue on to the purchaser, transporter, or gas processing plant. For proper accounting records, volume readings are taken at the wellhead and central delivery facility. Measurements are also recorded at the points where gas leaves or re-enters the pipeline or gathering system, such as to (1) run lease equipment, (2) flare into the air, (3) process for NGL removal, (4) return from the processing plant, or (5) be injected into a reservoir. As with crude oil, a gas producer may have a check meter installed on the line downstream of the purchaser's or transporter's sales meter to verify and prove the accuracy of the sales meter. Alternatively, E&P company representatives may regularly witness the sales meter calibration by outside specialists.

Because of the complex nature of gas, readings rarely agree, and gas sales contracts specify an allowable percentage difference. If a gas measurement audit finds the difference larger than allowable, adjustments are made.

Measuring Natural Gas with an Orifice Meter. In general, natural gas volume is measured based on the relationship of the space occupied by a given weight of gas to conditions of temperature and pressure. An orifice meter is an important tool for calculating gas volumes. It consists of small pipe, about two or three inches in diameter, that is divided by a doughnut-shaped flat plate barrier with a hole in the middle. The hole is approximately 0.75 inches in diameter. Mounted to and alongside the gas pipeline, the meter allows gas to flow through it and then back into the pipeline. Gas pressure drops just downstream of the orifice—this is called differential pressure. The pressure of the gas before it meets the orifice is known as static pressure.

Higher volumes of gas moving through a pipe in a given time period result in greater differential pressure and/or greater static pressure. The orifice meter continually measures both pressure readings to enable volume to be calculated. The circular paper chart records each 24 hour or each one week period. Two pens (one for differential pressure and one for static pressure) move to and from the outside of the paper circle as it slowly turns. When the cycle is completed, the chart is removed and integrated, which means it is read for recorded pressures.

The pressure readings are entered into equations that calculate the gas volume flowing through the meter for the given time period. An overly simplistic equation is:

$$\textbf{Mcf/day} = \sqrt{\text{differential pressure} \times \text{static pressure}} \times \textit{special factor,}$$

where the *special factor* is a function of data such as the meter's pipe diameter, orifice size, gas specific gravity, and gas temperature.

Formulas for calculating gas volumes from orifice meter readings have been established by research organizations and appear in numerous technical reports. Application of basic formulas would result in reasonably accurate metered volumes of *ideal* gas. However, natural gas is composed of infinite combinations of true gases and light hydrocarbon vapors. In order to determine correct volume, formula adjustments are made for base pressure, flowing temperature, specific gravity, and supercompressibility. The extent of these adjustments is influenced by company policy, contractual stipulations, regulations, and tariffs.

Prior to chart integration, the company's production department receives orifice meter charts from the field. They are logged in a chart register by data sequence to ensure that all charts from a location have been received. An employee trained to recognize erratic registrations in the field—such as freeze-ups, over-ranging, or possible malfunctioning of metering devices—reviews the charts. The source of the gas and basic metering conditions are noted on the chart by field personnel and verified with records compiled from various field measurement and attest reports.

If all information is correct, the charts are processed by an integrator machine that uses the temperature of the gas flow and pressure readings on the orifice plate to compute gas volume. Integrators are calibrated daily to a very close tolerance, and operators keep records of the calibration to attest the accuracy of chart readings.

Pertinent flow data and computed gas volumes for each chart are posted to the gas statement so that a cumulative volume can be reported for each meter station each month.

Internal integration is rarely used in the industry today. Most producers outsource the calculations to companies skilled in integration. Manual paper charts or electronic readings from the lease site are shipped directly to an outside company, which delivers the volumes and other readings to the production accounting department of the producer. The production accounting department generates internal statements, such as run tickets, sales tickets, inventory statements, production statements, and governmental volumetric reporting. In turn, these statements are used by the producer's revenue accounting department for verifying and recording sales, determining take-in-kind allocations, and governmental sales reporting.

Measuring NGL Volumes Produced and Sold. NGL are liquids recovered from a wet (or rich) natural gas stream. The constituents of the gas are determined by tests or analyses of gas streams delivered from each lease (or combination of leases) serving a gas processing plant. **Gas chromatographs** and spectrometers are devices used for such analysis.

NGL volumes are measured with turbine meters or similar meters used to measure natural gas. Flowing NGL spin the turbine in the meter and the rotation speed is recorded. This indicates flow rate for a given type of fluid flowing through the meter. Alternatively, the meter may be a mass measurement meter that weighs the volume of gas to indicate the NGL portion of the measured gas volume.

NGL portions are expressed in terms of **gpm** or gal/Mcf (gallons per thousand cubic feet). For example, gas having a 1.0 gpm contains one gallon of NGL in each Mcf.

Allocating Gas Sales. The allocation of sales from multiple leases served by a central delivery facility is a complex procedure requiring several calculations. The following example of an allocation is used with permission from Section 6 of COPAS Accounting Guideline No. 15.[7]

Figure 11-10 is a gas flow schematic (also called a gas **flow chart**) for the example. Leases A, B, and C all have wells classified as oil wells that also produce gas. The gas emerges from oil production at lease separators. During the month, gas production was 11,000 Mcf, 13,000 Mcf, and 17,000 Mcf from the three oil leases, respectively. Leases D, E, and F have gas wells. Production measured at the wellhead was 25,000 Mcf, 22,000 Mcf, and 28,000 Mcf, respectively. Based on tests of gas from each well, the theoretical dry gas should be 96.0 percent, 93.2 percent, and 91.1 percent of the production volume from the three leases, respectively. Thus, the total theoretical volume of dry gas is 70,000 Mcf (24,000 + 20,500 + 25,500 Mcf) from Leases D, E, and F. The gas well gas is passed through a central LTX (low temperature extraction) unit where condensate liquids are removed. The LTX output was 650 barrels of condensate and 70,500 Mcf of lean, high pressure gas. The condensate was piped to storage tanks where 2,000 Mcf of vapors (**flash gas**) from the storage tank went to low pressure gathering lines to be commingled with the **oil-well gas.**

The low pressure oil-well gas (measured at Meter No. 1 to be 40,500 Mcf) and the flash gas (measured at Meter No. 2 to be 2,000 Mcf) pass through a compressor where they are boosted into the high pressure sales line. A portion of the gas is burned as fuel for the compressor. Total output from the compressor (measured at Meter No. 3 to be 40,800 Mcf) and the output of high-pressure gas well gas from the LTX unit (measured at Meter No. 4 to be 70,500 Mcf) were combined and sold. Meter No. 5 on the high pressure gas line indicated that 110,000 Mcf were sold. Volumes sold are allocated back to leases in five steps.

Step 1. Allocate Meter No. 5's total sales volume of 110,000 Mcf to Meters No. 4 and No. 3 in proportion to each meter's throughput into Meter 5.

Meter	Metered Throughput				Allocated Sales
No. 4	70,500 Mcf	x	110,000/111,300	=	69,677 Mcf
No. 3	40,800 Mcf	x	110,000/111,300	=	40,323 Mcf
Total	111,300 Mcf				110,000 Mcf

Figure 11-10
Gas Flow Schematic for the Sales Allocation Example

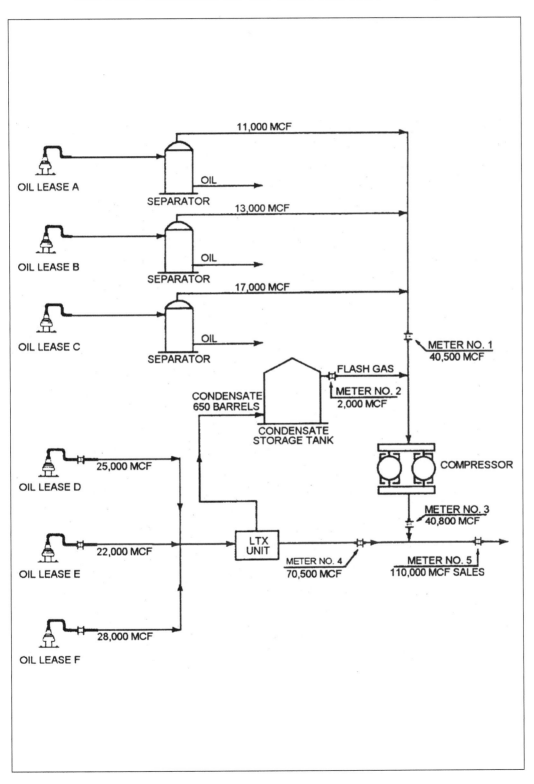

Step 2. Allocate the 69,677 Mcf of sales attributed to Meter No. 4 to the three gas leases on the basis of theoretical lean gas remaining after extraction of condensate.

Lease	Theoretical				Allocated Sales
D	24,000 Mcf	X	69,677/70,000	=	23,889 Mcf
E	20,500 Mcf	X	69,677/70,000	=	20,405 Mcf
F	25,500 Mcf	X	69,677/70,000	=	25,383 Mcf
Total	70,000 Mcf				69,677 Mcf

Step 3. Allocate the 40,323 Mcf of sales attributed to Meter No. 3 to Meters No. 1 and No. 2 on the basis of metered throughput. This charges fuel gas used by the compressor to oil-well gas and flash gas.

Meter	Metered Throughput				Allocated Sales
No. 1	40,500 Mcf	X	40,323/42,500	=	38,425 Mcf
No. 2	2,000 Mcf	X	40,323/42,500	=	1,898 Mcf
Total	42,500 Mcf				40,323 Mcf

Step 4. Allocate the 38,425 Mcf attributed to Meter No. 1 to the oil leases on the basis of oil-well gas production.

Oil Lease	Gas Production				Allocated Sales
A	11,000 Mcf	X	38,425/41,000	=	10,309 Mcf
B	13,000 Mcf	X	38,425/41,000	=	12,184 Mcf
C	17,000 Mcf	X	38,425/41,000	=	15,932 Mcf
Total	41,000 Mcf				38,425 Mcf

Step 5. Allocate the adjusted 1,898 Mcf of flash gas attributed to Meter No. 2 to gas leases on the basis of condensate produced. Condensate produced by well is determined by use of well tests of condensate-gas ratios.[8]

Gas Lease	Condensate				Flash Gas
D	210 bbls	X	1,898 Mcf/650 bbl	=	613 Mcf
E	190 bbls	X	1,898 Mcf/650 bbl	=	555 Mcf
F	250 bbls	X	1,898 Mcf/650 bbl	=	730 Mcf
Total	650 bbls				1,898 Mcf

Summary of Gas Sales Allocations

Lease	Production (Mcf)	Sales (Mcf)			
		Oil-Well Gas	Gas Well Gas	Flash Gas	Total
A	11,000	10,309	0	0	10,309
B	13,000	12,184	0	0	12,184
C	17,000	15,932	0	0	15,932
D	25,000	0	23,889	613	24,502
E	22,000	0	20,405	555	20,960
F	28,000	0	25,383	730	26,113
Total	116,000	38,425	69,677	1,898	110,000

GAS PROCESSING

Often, natural gas contains excessive natural gas liquids and impurities (sulphur, water, and carbon dioxide) that must be removed before it can enter downstream pipeline systems. Field equipment is frequently used at lease facilities to remove the heaviest liquids and some impurities.

Gas transported from the lease with significant NGL content (called wet gas) or impurities is sent by pipeline to a gas processing plant. Larger, more sophisticated, and far more expensive than field equipment, these plants remove the NGL and impurities and produce merchantable dry gas known as residue gas, which consists mostly of methane and is sold at the tailgates of gas plants.

Although gas processing is expensive and reduces the energy content and value of the processed gas, recovered NGL have many uses in manufacturing and petrochemicals. The U.S. market for NGL is priced high enough to make it profitable. During 2006, U.S. gas processing plants extracted an average of 1.74 million barrels of NGL each day; in comparison, crude oil production averaged about 5.14 million barrels daily in 2006.[9]

GAS PROCESSING CONTRACTUAL ARRANGEMENTS

Petroleum accountants should have general knowledge of the purpose and functions of processing plants and the types of processing contracts and arrangements in use.

A gas producer often does not own the plant that processes the produced gas. In such cases, the producer contracts with the gas plant owner or plant operator—which may be a joint venture of several companies. Plant owners may or may not have working interests in nearby gas fields.

It should be noted that if a producer does not contractually reserve processing rights prior to the passing of title, such rights are lost. Subsequent downstream gas processing will not cost the producer anything, but neither will a direct benefit be derived by the producer from processing and product sales done by others.

Two types of contracts address gas processing: (1) gas purchase agreements, and (2) gas processing agreements.

In gas purchase contracts, title to a supply of gas is transferred from the producer to a plant owner at the sales meter on the lease. Payments are based on formulas involving the liquid content of the gas and sale prices received by the plant owner for the resulting products and residue gas.

Gas processing contracts treat ownership of the gas differently. Title does not pass to the owner; instead, the plant owner agrees to process the producer's gas for a fee or take a percentage of the gas or liquids in-kind. Fees are calculated at: (1) a percentage of the products extracted, (2) a portion of the revenue received from the sale of the products, or (3) a rate per Mcf processed per MMBtu, or per gallon extracted.

Processing agreements take one of two forms. In the first, the producer arranges for processing the gas, retains title to it, and receives back the liquids and residue gas from the plant for injection, lease use, or sale under other marketing agreements. A fee is paid to the processor for services rendered.

Under the second type of processing agreement, a producer sells gas before it is processed, but retains the right to the liquids after the gas enters the purchaser's custody. A plant owner takes possession of the gas, extracts the liquids, and then directs the residue gas to a pipeline for delivery to a purchaser.

Assuming a purchaser allows a third-party to process its gas, several types of agreements enable the producer to derive a special economic benefit. One type provides for the processor to purchase gas liquids from the producer. In return, the producer bears any financial obligation to the gas purchaser for plant volume reduction (PVR) or plant thermal reduction (PTR) volumes (i.e., the residue gas having less volume and less energy than the wet gas). The producer forfeits the right to take its liquids in-kind. Compensation to a producer in this case takes the form of: (1) a percentage of net profits from the sale of the liquids, often figured on a sliding scale, or (2) a straight cents per gallon of NGL sold.

Keep-whole agreements are another type of processing arrangement. The total payment to a producer for residue gas and liquids from a processor is equal to or greater than the compensation the producer would have received under its gas sales arrangements.

Finally, some producers elect to more closely control the gas processing function. Plant capacity may be leased for a fixed amount each month by a producer. Others find it most economical to buy moveable (or skid-mounted) processing equipment and perform their own processing and that of other nearby gas producers.

TYPES OF PROCESSING

Processing plants consist of a combination of separation, purification, compression, extraction, liquids handling, and measurement equipment that ranges from small capacities to over one Bcf per day. Since the mid-1970s, processing technologies have lent themselves to modular plant units that fit onto trucks for ready mobility. The opportunity to readily move to new sources of gas extends a processor's lines of business.

Two technologies are generally employed in the processing of natural gas—lean oil absorption and cryogenics. Both produce liquids and can be applied to most gas streams. However, important differences exist relating to capital and operating costs.

Lean oil absorption is an older technology that utilizes chemical processes to extract NGL from a gas stream as it passes through a series of special oil-bearing contactor towers. Lean oil plants are usually block mounted; thus, they are not easily moved. These plants are inefficient in extracting the lighter ends of NGL components such as ethane. The advantages of lean oil absorption are its minimal use of fuel for compression and a high degree of flexibility in the volume of gas it can efficiently process.

Cryogenic plants have become the preferred plant technology over the last two decades. A cryogenic process causes condensation of NGL from the gas stream by chilling through one or a combination of two basic methods or cycles—refrigeration and expansion. A refrigeration cycle uses various working fluids to chill the wet gas stream. Expansion cycles use a large drop in pressure through valves and/or turbines to achieve very cold temperatures, sometimes with a refrigeration cycle to chill the feed gas. Cryogenic processes require large amounts of gas and refrigerant compression making fuel expense significant to the operation. They are efficient at extracting the available liquids, often achieving extraction of 95 percent of the ethane and virtually 100 percent of the heavier components including butane and natural gasoline.

A drawback to cryogenic plants is that efficiency falls rapidly at levels of throughput below 50 percent of the plant's rated capacity. However, they can often be moved to new locations. In nearly all instances, cryogenic plants are modular in design, and the primary pieces of equipment fit onto a semitrailer for transportation.

TYPES OF PLANTS

Gas processing plants are categorized according to the type and extent of processing, use of the residue gas, a plant's location relative to transmission pipelines, and local or company traditions. They are called gas plants or gas-liquids extraction plants.

The name given to plants—such as lean oil or cryogenic (or refrigeration)— reflects the type of process used to remove the NGL. For example, a refrigeration plant may refer to a plant that cools the gas to a range of +15°F to -40°F and, at the lower temperature, recovers about 70 percent of ethane, 90 percent of propane, and virtually all of the heavier NGL. A true cryogenic refrigeration plant cools gas to a range of -150°F to -225°F to recover 95 percent of the ethane contained.

Bob-tail plant is an old term referring to a gas plant that removes the NGL as a single stream which is then sent to a fractionation plant (discussed in the next section) to separate the NGL into its components. A cycling plant is a facility for handling residue gas that is to be reinjected into a reservoir. The term straddle plant generally refers to a plant located on a transmission pipeline system as opposed to one plant located between the field gas gathering system and the pipeline. Gasoline plant is a confusing, perhaps archaic, term for a gas plant and refers to the natural gasolines typically removed from the gas.

FRACTIONATION

A fractionation plant receives an NGL stream from one or more gas processing plants and fractionates the stream into separate products. A single fractionation plant may handle the output of several true gas processing plants, thereby reducing the need for fractionation facilities at each gas processing site. This approach also provides a more economical means of transporting NGL from the gas plant to a shipping point because only one pipeline is needed for moving the mixed liquids.

Fractionation is accomplished by heating and cooling the NGL mix in tall towers where components can be drawn off at the height at which they settle. Fractionation facilities operate continuously and have consumers and/or storage for the finished products in close proximity. NGL market prices are established at these sites. Expenses of transportation and fractionation are then subtracted to arrive at plant tailgate prices for NGL.

NATURAL GAS LIQUIDS

Dry natural gas is over 90 percent methane, which is the simplest and smallest hydrocarbon molecule, consisting of one carbon atom bonded with four hydrogen molecules (CH_4). NGL are the slightly larger natural hydrocarbon molecules of ethane (C_2H_6), propane (C_3H_8), butane (C_4H_{10}), and natural gasolines (which have five to ten carbon atoms per molecule, the C5s to C10s for short). Liquefied natural gas (LNG) is a popular term for propane or a propane-butane mixture that has been compressed into a liquid for use in backyard gas barbecue grills, rural home heating and cooking, and other applications.

Like gas and oil from a lease, NGL produced from a plant must meet minimum quality requirements to be accepted by a carrier or purchaser. The plant operator draws NGL samples to identify gross impurities that might require a shutdown or diversion of plant production until cured. Testing procedures involve using corrosion sensitive test strips (commonly copper) and color charts (Saybolt colorimeter test).

NGL delivered into a pipeline are spot-sampled by the plant operator or automatically sampled on a continuous basis, depending on contract terms with the purchaser or carrier. In the case of truck or rail deliveries, samples of each load are taken. These are analyzed using a chromatograph similar to natural gas measurement. Constituents, including any impurities, are reported on a volume percent basis. Chromatograph analyses often report a number of chemically distinct constituents to a far greater level than is recognized in field market arrangements. In such a case, constituents of the liquids simply are grouped to their market designation and totaled for settlement purposes. For example, the analysis may report hexanes plus, or C6+, in addition to the pentanes, or C5s, where a processing agreement only provides for settlement to pentanes plus. The accountant simply adds the reported percentages attributable to hexanes and pentanes together to arrive at the settlement quantity of pentanes plus, or C5+.

Upon carrier acceptance, the liquids are transported to a user or market center. Market centers have facilities for NGL receipt, storage, and fractionation and provide standard exchange and delivery procedures to facilitate the trading of liquids (see Chapter 12).

RESIDUE GAS

Residue gas or dry gas is over 90 percent methane and has a heat content approximating one MMBtu per Mcf at atmospheric pressure. Residue gas volume and heat content are significantly less than the volume and heat content of corresponding wet gas put into the plant. Shrinkage (or plant volume reduction, PVR, and plant thermal reduction, PTR, in processing) results primarily from: (1) using gas as fuel to operate the plant, (2) extracting the NGL and impurities, and (3) plant losses and meter differences arising from gas volumes not being measured in normal operations with complete accuracy. Extraction loss is greater for a gas stream having a high liquid content than for a stream containing less liquid. Thus, this shrinkage factor is taken into consideration when determining each lease's share of NGL and residue gas produced by the plant.

The total volume of residue gas remaining after processing is the sum of residue gas volumes actually delivered from the plant to producers and gas purchasers. This volume, when multiplied by the Btu content of the residue gas, is allocated between the leases or wells on the basis of respective volumes of theoretical residue gas using a factor that represents the liquids and extraction loss.

Plant operations personnel keep records of products delivered to the plant through the plant's inlet metering systems, and products delivered out of the plant through its outlet metering systems. Also, operations reports are maintained for volumes produced and sold. If any inventories of NGL or the combined products in the gas stream are kept at the plant, then inventory records must be maintained. Metering systems and various records should be accurate and available for audits by producers and purchasers.

Residue Gas Allocation. In making lease settlements for residue gas collectively sold by the plant operator, a reasonable allocation is made to each lease or field that supplied the original gas. First, the total amount due all leases is determined. That amount is allocated between the leases or wells on the basis of theoretical residue gas available for sale as calculated for each lease. The gas sales proceeds—to which the appropriate percentage is applied—are usually the amounts received from gas purchasers. Some gas contracts provide that the plant owner can reduce the gross sales revenue by specified charges per Mcf to cover dehydration or other services performed to make the gas salable.

Determining the volume of residue gas attributable to a lease or well involves several factors. The quantity is calculated as the volume of gas received at the plant from the lease or well, less an allocated portion of gas consumed in the plant, less extraction loss, and less the volume of any residue gas returned to the producer for lease or well operations.

Using volumes computed in an earlier example for a gas sales allocation from a central delivery facility, assume the gas streams from Leases D, E, and F enter a processing plant. Sales allocations are the allocated volumes measured at the plant inlet meter (24,502; 20,960; and 26,113 Mcf, respectively). Assume the actual residue gas sold by the plant operator is 50,000 Mcf after delivering 4,000 Mcf taken in-kind by Lease F owners.

				Residue Gas Allocation	
Lease	Inlet Volume	Theoretical Shrinkage	Theoretical Residue	Taken in-Kind	Gas Sold
D	24,502	(5,289)	19,213	0	18,753*
E	20,960	(4,345)	16,615	0	16,217
F	26,113	(6,616)	19,497	4,000	15,030
Total	71,575	(16,250)	55,325	4,000	50,000

* Computed as:

$$\frac{\text{Lease D's theoretical residue of 19,213}}{\text{Total theoretical residue of 55,325}} \quad \text{X} \quad 54,000 \quad = \quad 18,753 \text{ Mcf}$$

It is possible that the volume of residue gas returned to the lease or well will exceed that lease's or well's theoretical residue gas. If this occurs, the lease or well has no residue gas available for sale and the excess volume is treated as a sale of residue gas by the plant owner to the producer. Payment for the gas must be made by the producer. Revenue from the sale is included with revenue from the other sales by the plant owner in settling the other leases.

If a producer is selling gas from two or more leases to the plant owner under a single contract, the contract may contain a residue pooling provision where all leases covered by the contract are considered a single lease for determining the volume of residue gas that the producer is entitled to have returned, regardless of the lease to which the gas is returned. If more gas is returned to a lease than the actual residue gas remaining for that lease, the excess is charged against the actual residue gas remaining for one or more of the producer's other leases.

When residue volumes are pooled, the plant owner should inform the producer of the volumes of *actual residue gas remaining* that were transferred between leases in making the lease settlement calculation. The transfer of such volumes from a lease reduces the amount of settlement to that lease for residue gas. Therefore, the producer must make appropriate adjustments for royalty and tax purposes, as well as for the purpose of recording lease revenues and expenses.

GAS PLANT SETTLEMENT

As described, gas processing can be a complex activity. Detailed calculations are used to determine volumes and proceeds of products sold, as well as products taken in-kind. The **gas settlement statement** is a required schedule prepared by a gas plant accountant. The settlement statement verifies amounts for producers or other buyers, in-kind volumes, and volumes and prices of products sold for each lease or well.

Gas settlement statements provide detail for the gas producers' and buyers' accounting departments to record the sale of products. They include the property name, actual residue gas and NGL, theoretical residue gas and NGL, volume of extraction and processing loss, volumes sold, gpm of each product, Btu of the gas, prices paid per product, deductions taken by the plant owner, and the total settlement amount for the property. A settlement statement is illustrated in Chapter 13. (Figure 13-2)

GAS STORAGE

In the U.S., natural gas demand is seasonal with regions having different seasons of peak and off-peak demand. In northern states, higher demands occur in winter for space heating, while in the south more demand exists in summer to generate electricity for air conditioners. Overall, natural gas demand is higher in the winter than in the summer. Gas production during seasons of low demand is stored in underground reservoirs for use in months when demand peaks. These gas storage facilities are typically downstream on the pipeline system and temporarily store gas that comes from numerous fields.

Gas storage has been traditionally defined as a series of operations whereby a quantity of production is injected into an underground depository to meet later demand. Depleted oil/gas reservoirs were historically utilized for gas storage. However, leached salt dome structures, including those holding the Strategic Petroleum Reserve, have been used in recent years in areas with underground salt domes such as the Gulf Coast.

Storage capacity in a salt dome is increased by pumping in fresh water that dissolves the salt walls. This technique for storage is easier and less expensive than the use of depleted reservoirs, which take a long time to fill. (It may take much of a year to fill a depleted reservoir for a winter withdrawal.) Salt dome storage facilities are usually capable of more rapid filling, and commonly provide a cycling period of one month or less.

Limited pipeline capacity from a producing area to a market acts to restrict delivery capacity during peak demand periods. Restricted ability to move gas provides an incentive to produce it at a relatively constant rate throughout the year.

Historically, gas storage was performed primarily by pipeline companies. They charged one inclusive fee that paid the cost of transportation and other pipeline company functions, such as compression charges, withdrawal charges, matching buyers and sellers, intrahub transfer fees, temporary storage (called banking or parking), and long-term storage. As the natural gas market has grown in national importance, the market structure and rules have changed, especially as the result of FERC Order No. 636 (issued on April 8, 1992) and subsequent amendments. The Order requires pipelines to unbundle transportation services from other functions and charge fees for specific services performed. Under new market rules, pipeline companies are primarily transporters of gas, while producers and others sell gas predominantly to end-users or local distribution companies (LDC). In turn, this has encouraged producers, major end-users, and LDCs to seek storage rights, as needed, in order to meet their new sales commitments.

NGL STORAGE

A gas processing plant owner accumulates NGL inventories that must be stored on-site. The most common liquids storage is a one to three day supply of NGL stored in above ground bullet tanks (an industry term which is descriptive of the tank shape). Liquids are transported from storage facilities by a connection to an NGL pipeline or by trucks or rail cars loading at plant terminals. Underground storage is also used for NGL, either as a mix of products or a purity product (which refers to the pure product or the liquids that meet the specifications of the purchaser).

Many underground storage facilities are located near fractionation plants and wholesale market delivery or consumption points. In these circumstances, one method frequently used in determining the price paid to a producer is to pay or make settlement in the month the NGL are produced and stored, based on prices received from actual sales during the current month or during the last preceding month in which sales were made. Depending on company policy and contract terms, adjustments may or may not be made at a later date for the difference between the price initially used for settlement purposes and the price received at the time the NGL are withdrawn from storage and sold.

Another method used to determine the amount due is to defer settlement until the NGL are withdrawn from storage and sold. These settlements are based on the prices actually received from the sales. Plant owners must maintain monthly records of the products placed in storage in order to ensure a proper allocation between leases at the time of withdrawal. Sales from storage are usually allocated on a first-in-first-out basis.

• • •

---

1 Oil recovery methods are grouped into two broad classifications: primary recovery and enhanced recovery, as discussed in Chapter 32.

2 Posted price bulletins are further explained and illustrated in Chapter 12.

3 The relation between API gravity and specific gravity is purely mathematical. API gravity varies inversely with specific gravity. For example, oil with specific gravity of 0.90 has an API gravity of 25.7, while oil with a specific gravity of 0.80 has an API gravity of 45.4. See API gravity in the glossary for further explanation and the conversion formula.

4 Source: *Dictionary of Petroleum Exploration, Drilling & Production*, PennWell Publishing Co., 1991. The *Dictionary* added that sweet crude may refer to crude with a sulfur content below one percent while sour may refer to crude with a sulfur content above one percent. *Oil Markets and Prices*, Oxford University Press, 1993, notes that West Texas Intermediate (WTI) is actually a sweet crude with a sulfur content of 0.4 percent and a 40° API gravity. The NYMEX crude oil futures contract is not strictly for WTI but for a sweet crude oil with a sulfur content less than 0.5 percent and an API gravity between 34° and 45°. Several U.S. and foreign sweet crudes meet those specifications.

5 Such rounding has little effect on revenues. Even a full one degree difference in API gravity changes the volume by only 0.01 percent, or about $2.31 for the 385.19 barrels valued at $60 per barrel.

6 DeGolyer and MacNaughton, *Twentieth Century Petroleum Statistics*, Dallas, 1994.

7 COPAS Accounting Guideline No. 15 (AG 15), *Gas Accounting Manual* (revised April 1993). For the example and Figure 11-10, meter numbers are revised from the presentation in AG 15.

8 Using the condensate volumes given in AG 15.

9 Petroleum production statistics provided by the U.S. Energy Information Administration, April 2007.

12

MARKETING CRUDE OIL, NATURAL GAS, AND NGL

Glossary Terms

EDQ

make up gas

nomination

Key Concepts:

- Marketing issues of quality, customers, location, and demand for crude oil and natural gas in the U.S.

- Evergreen, spot, and exchange sales contracts

- Components of oil pricing

- Posted price bulletins

- History of natural gas regulation and pricing deregulation

- Roles of producers, marketers, and end-users

- Types of gas contracts and major terms

- NGL marketing

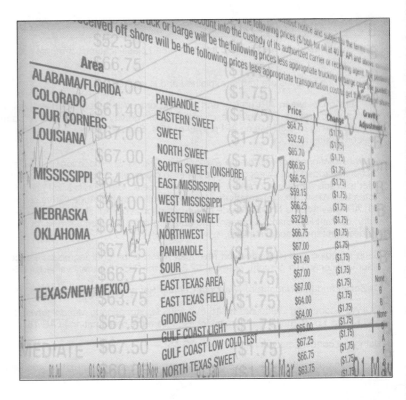

After oil and gas are discovered, many processes take place to bring them to a marketable state. Oil, natural gas, and NGL are fungible commodities; thus, sales values are not enhanced by product differentiation strategies such as packaging or advertising. Instead, marketing and pricing are influenced by: (1) a product's physical quality, (2) potential customers, (3) location of product and customer, and (4) supply and demand for the commodity.

In the U.S., federal price controls were in effect for the industry until the 1980s. Since that time, the price of oil and gas has experienced much volatility.

CRUDE OIL MARKETING

OIL MARKETING FACTORS

Several general factors apply to the marketing of crude oil in the U.S.

Physical Quality. Crude oil varies in density (measured in degrees of API gravity) and in sulphur content. As a general rule, the greater the density or sulphur content, the lower the value of the crude and its resulting price.

Potential Customers. Crude oil is ultimately sold to refiners who separate and process it into refined products such as gasoline and diesel fuel. The U.S. refinery business is competitive—about three dozen companies own 90 percent of the country's refining capacity. Some refiners process only certain types of crude oil or are more profitable refining a selected type. Generally, refineries are most profitable if the quality and type of crude oil are relatively constant for several months or years. Given the variations in crude oil gravity and sulphur content, versus the needs of individual refineries, crude oil is not as fungible as dry natural gas.

Crude oil is transported from a well to the refinery via truck, barge, rail car, tanker, or pipeline. Consequently, crude oil is sold at the lease site to either: (1) refiners that arrange for transportation to refineries, or (2) other companies in the business of purchasing crude at well sites and transporting it for resale to refiners.

Location. Transportation costs and local supply versus local demand create price differences based on general locations. For example, the wellhead value of crude oil produced on the North Slope of Alaska and transported to market via the Trans Alaska Pipeline System and ocean tanker is far less than the wellhead value of similar quality crude oil produced near the large and more accessible refineries on the Texas/Louisiana Gulf Coast.

Supply Versus Demand. The U.S. produces approximately 44 percent of the crude oil it consumes. As a result, oil produced in the U.S. has a ready market. Unlike natural gas, crude oil production is not curtailed by seasonal drops in demand.

TYPES OF MARKETING ARRANGEMENTS

Several arrangements are commonly used to market crude oil:

- Royalty owners allow the working interest owners to: (1) market the lease's entire production, and (2) arrange for royalty owners to receive their share of sales proceeds (rather than take their royalty interest share of oil in-kind and market it themselves).

- Joint venture nonoperators also have the right to take their share of oil in-kind and market it. Typically, they allow the operator to market the venture's gross production from year-to-year.[1]

- E&P companies, particularly large operators, may employ crude oil marketers (or crude oil traders) to sell the oil produced. The marketer's goal is to negotiate the best possible contract price. (It should be noted that some companies have separate divisions or subsidiaries to market their own oil production, along with oil from other producers.)

- At times the best price for crude oil is not obtained by selling the product. Exchanging the produced crude oil for other crude may be the better option. For example, assume Company A produces California crude and owns a Texas refinery. Company B produces Texas crude and owns a California refinery. A and B may agree that A's oil production will be given to B for its California refinery. In exchange, a similar volume of B's Texas oil production will be given to A for its Texas refinery. Any exchange differential due to variances in crude oil quality, local market price, or transportation costs is paid by the liable party.

- In addition to selling to refineries, E&P companies may market crude oil to nonrefiners known as crude oil trading companies. These trading companies can be a producer's subsidiary, but are often marketing agents independent of producers and refiners. Key employees who negotiate the purchases, sales, and exchanges of crude oil are called crude oil traders.

Sales arrangements are expressed in written, negotiated agreements containing the names of the parties to the contract, date of the agreement, property name and location, transporter, sales volume or production time period, delivery point, price, and geographic, physical, or chemical characteristics of the oil. The oil producer or operator is referred to as the seller, and the refiner or oil trader is the purchaser. A set of general terms and conditions (GTC) in the agreement specifies remedies if the contract is not followed. Parties often adhere to the GTC written by one of the major oil companies, and any modifications to those terms are noted in the contract.

Three basic types of crude oil sales arrangements exist:

- Evergreen sales contracts

- Spot sales contracts

- Exchange contracts

Month-to-month sales contracts, called evergreen sales contracts, are negotiated for an initial 30-day period and renewed monthly thereafter until either party cancels. During times of oil price volatility, evergreen contracts reflect a negotiated price per barrel based either on a fluctuating market price, indexed price, or fixed price plus adjustments or escalations. (Crude oil pricing structures are discussed in the next section of this chapter.)

A spot sales contract is a second type of sales arrangement. It involves the short-term sale of a stated volume of production for a brief period, such as a few days or a couple of months. Spot sales contracts provide for the sale of crude oil based on a negotiated price between the buyer and seller. For example, parties may agree to buy/sell 100 barrels per day of South Texas Light crude oil from the Ralph #1 well, located in Hidalgo County, Texas, for each day of March 2006 at $62.00 per barrel. Once the time period ends or the sale occurs, the contract is fulfilled.

Evergreen and spot sale contracts allow producers to change oil purchasers on short notice, but most producers rarely do so.

The third type of sales arrangement is the exchange (sometimes referred to as a buy/sell arrangement). In this case, producers exchange crude oil production for another stream of oil production. An exchange contract was demonstrated in the previous example of the two companies exchanging Texas crude oil for California crude.

> *"Generally, crude oil and petroleum products flow to the markets that provide the highest value to the supplier. Everything else being equal, oil moves to the nearest market first, because that has the lowest transportation cost and therefore provides the supplier with the highest net revenue, or in oil market terminology, the highest netback. If this market cannot absorb all the oil, the balance moves to the next closest one, and the next and so on, incurring progressively higher transportation costs, until all the oil is placed."*
>
> **Office of Oil and Gas, Energy Information Administration** *"Oil Market Basics,"*
> http://www.eia.doe.gov/pub/oil_gas/petroleum/analysis_publications/oil_market_basics/default.htm

U.S. OIL PRICING

Each delivery (referred to as a run of oil) from a lease storage tank has the volume and date of withdrawal recorded on either a run ticket or a report from the LACT unit (discussed in Chapter 11). Crude oil is priced separately based on the date of removal from the tank. Sales contracts specify the price to be used for the indicated time period. The values of all the runs during the month are accumulated, and settlement is made monthly by the purchaser.

As mentioned, prices may be based on a fixed, stated price at the beginning of the contract. However, most crude oil contracts are negotiated at least a month before any transactions take place. Oil prices may derive from fluctuating reference prices (such as published posted prices or index prices) to approximate current market prices as the oil is delivered. Certain contracts state a minimum floor or maximum ceiling in conjunction with a fluctuating reference price for added protection in negotiating the transaction price.

Price adjustments in sales contracts are called differentials, bonuses, deducts, premiums, or discounts. They range from a few cents to a few dollars per barrel from the fluctuating reference price. A premium might be negotiated for crude oil in large volumes or for supplies that are favorably located for the purchaser. Producers or brokers who agree to sell all of their oil production, or all of their production from a geographical area, may also command a premium. Alternatively, discounts may be negotiated to compensate buyers for oil in a remote location that requires higher transportation expenses. Discounts may also be imposed to compensate for impurities such as sulphur content.

In exchange contracts, price adjustments are commonly used for the difference in location or when a less valuable crude oil is exchanged for a higher value product.

Gravity adjustments are the most common type of premium or discount for crude oil. As discussed in Chapters 1 and 11, heavy crude oils (typically with an API gravity below 20°) have less value than light crude oils (typically above 35° API), which yield more gasoline and other valuable products. Adjustments based on the gravity of the oil are discussed in the next section on calculating prices from posted price bulletins.

During contract negotiations in a volatile market, oil marketers attempt to make the most favorable settlements for their companies. To this end, they may recommend their companies purchase or sell various financial instruments (such as futures contracts) in an attempt to protect against pricing risks. However, most holders of futures contracts close out their position by taking an opposite position rather than having to receive or deliver physical barrels when a contract expires.

For example, assume an E&P company has a futures contract to sell 1,000 barrels of crude oil during one month in 2006 at $60 per barrel. The company obtains a futures contract to receive 1,000 barrels of crude oil, thereby netting the two contracts to close out the position.

Crude oil futures contracts are referred to as "paper barrels," as distinguished from physical barrels that are known as "wet barrels." Futures contracts generally provide for oil to be delivered at a specified tank farm or refining facility at a future date and price. Oil producers, refiners, and third-party traders as well as other investors who speculate on oil prices comprise the futures crude oil market.

Assume a buyer of sweet crude oil futures on the New York Mercantile Exchange (NYMEX or MERC) is committed to buy West Texas Intermediate crude oil (or similar sweet crude) at Cushing, Oklahoma, at a stated price when the futures contract expires. This buyer can arrange to receive (or a futures seller can arrange to deliver) a different crude oil at a different location by an exchange of futures for physicals (EFP). An EFP is an agreement whereby a futures obligation is exchanged for a physical obligation. The futures buyer gives its futures contract to another party (with NYMEX recording the change in ownership) and commits to buy other crude from that party at an agreed-upon price. Futures contracts and price hedging are discussed further in Chapter 33.

Posted Price Bulletins. Posted price bulletins (also referred to as crude oil price bulletins, price bulletins, or posted prices) are publications that list the prices a particular purchaser may pay for various types of oil. The documents contain adjustment factors for crude oil that range above and below an API gravity of 40°. Posted prices originated from the early days of the industry when purchasers posted their offers to buy on fence posts in the oil fields. Today's posted price bulletins serve primarily as indicators of prices rather than solicitations to buy. Posted prices are tied to many factors including the physical quality of the oil, other prices in the same geographical area, location of products to buyers, cost and risk of transport and ownership enroute, supply versus demand, pricing history, and NYMEX's oil futures market.

While price bulletins vary in format, most contain the following information:

- A listing of crude types[2] by geographical area, state, county, or even a particular field. Includes distinguishing chemical or physical characteristics (sour, intermediate, and sweet refer to the sulphur content; light and heavy refer to the API gravity).

- Posted prices for each type of crude at a stated benchmark API gravity (generally 40°).

- The bulletin number and effective date of change to the posted price contained in the column headings.

- A gravity adjustment scale of price decrements (occasionally increments) for crude with an API gravity below or above 40°.

Premiums or discounts may be added to or subtracted from the posted price. These amounts depend on the difference between the bulletin's stated benchmark API gravity and the actual API gravity of the oil delivered. Lower-gravity oil which is below 40° and extremely high-gravity oil—over 45°—generally receive a deduct adjustment. In some instances, oil with gravity in excess of 40° API and up to a stated maximum acceptable receives a premium adjustment.

Figure 12-1 illustrates a posted price bulletin example from Big Oil, Inc.

Figure 12-1
Big Oil, Inc. Posted Price Bulletin

Big Oil, Inc.
P.O. Box 2842
Houston, TX 77002

MEMORANDUM – June 5, 2006

Bulletin 06-F198
Big Oil, Inc. has changed its posted prices as shown below:

Effective 7:00 a.m. on the date(s) indicated, and subject to change without notice and subject to the terms and conditions of its division orders or other contracts, Big Oil, Inc. will pay the following prices ($/bbl) for oil at 40.0° API and above, except as noted below, delivered into pipelines for its account into the custody of its authorized carrier or receiving agent. The posted prices for crude oil transported by truck or barge will be the following prices less appropriate trucking or barge cost. The posted prices for crude oil received offshore will be the following prices less appropriate transportation cost to get the crude onshore.

Area		Price	Change	Gravity Adjustment
ALABAMA/FLORIDA	PANHANDLE	$64.75	($1.75)	D
COLORADO	EASTERN SWEET	$52.50	($1.75)	B
FOUR CORNERS	SWEET	$65.70	($1.75)	D
LOUISIANA	NORTH SWEET	$66.85	($1.75)	B
	SOUTH SWEET (ONSHORE)	$66.25	($1.75)	D
MISSISSIPPI	EAST MISSISSIPPI	$59.15	($1.75)	H
	WEST MISSISSIPPI	$66.25	($1.75)	B
NEBRASKA	WESTERN SWEET	$52.50	($1.75)	B
OKLAHOMA	NORTHWEST	$66.75	($1.75)	D
	PANHANDLE	$67.00	($1.75)	A
	SOUR	$61.40	($1.75)	C
TEXAS/NEW MEXICO	EAST TEXAS AREA	$67.00	($1.75)	B
	EAST TEXAS FIELD	$67.00	($1.75)	None
	GIDDINGS	$64.00	($1.75)	B
	GULF COAST LIGHT	$64.00	($1.75)	B
	GULF COAST LOW COLD TEST	$65.00	($1.75)	None
	NORTH TEXAS SWEET	$67.25	($1.75)	B
	PANHANDLE	$66.75	($1.75)	A
	SOUTH TEXAS HEAVY	$63.75	($1.75)	F
	WEST CENTRAL TEXAS	$67.50	($1.75)	B
	WEST TEXAS/NEW MEXICO INTERMEDIATE	$67.50	($1.75)	B
	WEST TEXAS/NEW MEXICO SOUR	$60.05	($1.75)	G
WILLISTON BASIN	NORTH	$53.50	($1.75)	B
WYOMING	ASPHALT SOUR	$51.75	($1.75)	E
	GENERAL SOUR	$52.50	($1.75)	E
	HEAVY SOUR	$48.05	($1.75)	G
	MEDIUM SOUR	$51.80	($1.75)	G
	SOUTHWEST	$69.25	($1.75)	C
	SWEET (OTHER)	$54.50	($1.75)	B

Gravity Adjustment for Crude Oils
Prices are subject to the following gravity adjustments:

Scale A:	Deduct $0.020/bbl per full degree below 40 degrees API gravity
Scale B:	Deduct $0.015/bbl per 1/10 degree above 45 degrees API gravity
	Deduct $0.020/bbl per full degree below 40 degrees API gravity
Scale C:	Deduct $0.015/bbl per 1/10 degree above 45 degrees API gravity
	Deduct $0.015/bbl per 1/10 degree below 40 degrees API gravity
Scale D:	Deduct $0.015/bbl per 1/10 degree above 45 degrees API gravity
	Deduct $0.020/bbl per full degree from 35 to 40 degrees API gravity
	Deduct $0.015/bbl per 1/10 degree below 35 degrees API gravity
Scale E:	Deduct $0.015/bbl per 1/10 degree above 45 degrees API gravity
	Deduct $0.020/bbl per full degree from 36 to 39 degrees API gravity
	Deduct $0.040/bbl per full degree from 34 to 35 degrees API gravity
	Deduct $0.020/bbl per 1/10 degree below 34 degrees API gravity
Scale F:	Deduct $0.015/bbl per 1/10 degree above 45 degrees API gravity
	Deduct $0.020/bbl per full degree from 19 to 29 degrees API gravity
	Deduct $0.000/bbl per full degree below 19 degrees API gravity
Scale G:	Deduct $0.015/bbl per 1/10 degree above 45 degrees API gravity
Scale H:	Deduct $0.05/bbl per 1/10 degree below 27 degrees API gravity

Donald James Refining Company negotiates to purchase on June 5, 2006, Louisiana South Sweet (Onshore) production from the Douglas #2 lease using the Big Oil, Inc. average monthly posted price plus $.25/bbl. Assume the oil delivered to the company has a 32.5° API gravity. The gravity adjustment column refers to the gravity adjustments located on the lower portion of Big Oil, Inc.'s bulletin. The deduction subtracted from the posted price would be $0.48/bbl, calculated using Scale D in Figure 12-1 as follows:

1st Step:	Deduction for the difference between			
	35.0° and 40.0° (5.0° @ $.02 per degree):			$0.10
2nd Step:	Additional deduction for below 35°:			
	35.0° - 32.5°	=	2.5 whole degrees	
	2.5° x 10	=	25 tenth degrees	
	25 x $.015	=		0.38
	Total deduction per barrel			**$0.48**

In most cases, the oil is purchased at the average price for the month adjusted for the gravity. Assuming the contract for the Douglas #2 production states the oil is to be sold at the monthly average price, the price is calculated as follows:

June 5, 2006 price	$66.25
Less the gravity adjustment	(0.48)
Plus the bonus	0.25
Total price per barrel	**$66.02**

If the contract states production is sold as equal daily quantities (**EDQ**), the crude oil is considered to be delivered in equal quantities during each day of the month. EDQ can be specified on a contract even though the crude is picked up by truck, which is normally priced at that day's posting. LACT units always use the EDQ method. If June 2006 production for Douglas #2 is 3,000 barrels, then EDQ is 100/bpd. The price is calculated using the appropriate daily price from the price bulletin, as adjusted for gravity and bonus. To calculate total sales for the month, multiply each daily-adjusted price by the EDQ.

Other Reference Prices. Other prices referenced in the sales contract may incorporate the daily closing NYMEX crude oil futures prices plus a premium or discount. To determine the sales price of the oil, contracting parties may agree to use the average of each closing futures price for every day in the month the NYMEX is open and trading. Clear disclosure of reference pricing is important, including the averaging formula or dates to be used and the name of the source in quoting NYMEX prices (such as *The Wall Street Journal*, *Bloomberg's Business News*, or *Reuters America Inc.*). Certain sources may include or exclude the final one or two prices of the day in arriving at their closing prices.

Various publications poll oil traders or other sources for the prices of recent oil transactions. These publications cull out the highest and lowest prices quoted, compile the data, and publish an index of crude oil prices.

In summary, an oil sales contract must clearly state the index used and include any premium or discount adjustments added to the index price.

NATURAL GAS MARKETING

Natural gas has been a fuel supply in the U.S. for over 180 years. In 1816, the Gas Light Company of Baltimore, forerunner of Baltimore Gas & Electric Company, was formed. It received a franchise to light Baltimore's streets. Service to the first gas street lamp occurred in 1817. Gas cooking originated in England in 1840, and exhibitions in the United States introduced gas stoves to consumers.

Local distribution companies (LDCs) arose during the early days of gas marketing. Owned by local governments, trusts, or investor groups, these utilities built a basic infrastructure by laying gas distribution systems within certain service areas. LDCs also manufactured gas from bituminous coal or wood. In the first half of the 20th century, long-distance pipelines were constructed to move gas from production areas to end-users. Many pipelines were developed as an outgrowth of the war effort in the 1940s.

As mentioned in Chapter 1, natural gas has many uses including home heating, cooking, air conditioning, chemical feedstock, and electric power generation. It has gained more uses as a result of compliance standards of the Clean Air Act of 1990. Some cars and trucks now run on compressed natural gas. Selected city buses can run on LNG (gas liquified by chilling). Demand for natural gas as a fuel for generating electricity is growing. Various companies have built or are now building gas-to-liquids (GTL) plants to convert natural gas to liquid fuels, such as gasoline and diesel, that have little or no sulfur contaminants.

Understanding the history of natural gas regulation and the deregulation of pricing provides insight into the current natural gas marketing arena.

HISTORY OF NATURAL GAS REGULATION

Today natural gas is considered a premium, clean-burning fuel. Yet, a hundred years ago it was an unwanted commodity. Producers were disappointed when wells turned out to deliver gas rather than oil. At times, night skies over Texas were lit up by producers flaring unwanted gas. This was done to prevent an explosion of volatile unburned gas. While it may have been considered a waste product to early producers, gas eventually became a necessity in heating millions of U.S. homes and providing energy and feedstock for various industrial and manufacturing companies. The expanding natural gas markets for local gas utilities served by relatively few interstate pipelines created fears of monopolistic power that warranted government oversight and regulation.

States enacted laws to form public service commissions for the oversight of local gas and electric utilities. An example was the Public Service Commission of Maryland formed in 1910. The federal government began regulating interstate gas pipelines after passing the Natural Gas Act of 1938. However, recent federal deregulation of the interstate transport and commerce of natural gas has left state level regulators as the more active participants in today's gas market.

Natural Gas Act of 1938. The Natural Gas Act of 1938 sought to protect the public from the possibility of monopolistic pricing and service practices by the few large interstate gas pipelines. It also regulated pipelines that extended from federal leases in the Outer Continental Shelf to shore or inland facilities. The Federal Power Commission (FPC) was created in the legislation to regulate the construction, operations, and rates of interstate commerce in order to ensure that public convenience and needs were being served. Permission from the FPC had to be sought in advance to construct and operate new pipeline facilities, add sales arrangements, and charge rates for various sales, transportation, and storage services. The Act did not seek to regulate the price of natural gas at the wellhead.

Phillips Decision. A 1954 U.S. Supreme Court decision contradicted certain provisions of the Natural Gas Act of 1938. Known as the Phillips decision, it expanded regulations and price controls to include natural gas wellhead sales by producers to interstate pipelines. However, the case did not extend regulations to the intrastate gas market. As a result, producers shifted their sales to the unregulated intrastate sector during the 1970s when booming oil prices raised the value of natural gas as an alternative energy source.

Shortages. After the court ruling, producers could sell the same volume of natural gas in the intrastate market as in the regulated interstate market. In general, they received higher prices and eliminated the regulatory burdens of interstate gas commerce. With producers avoiding the interstate market and flooding the intrastate markets, supply problems began to develop. Demand was booming for artificially cheap interstate gas, especially in the nonproducing states of the industrial belt.

Recognizing the real shortages of supplies to the interstate market, the FPC (renamed the Federal Energy Regulatory Commission, or FERC, in 1978[3]) started approving "just and reasonable" sales rates which reflected higher wellhead prices. Area-wide rates for gas produced from specific regions were approved; then nationwide rates were established using the same rate structure regardless of the geographic region. These area and national rates replaced the practice of approving rates for each individual contract. Still, the regulated prices of interstate gas averaged well below gas prices in the intrastate market.

Beginning in the early 1970s, industrial customers outside of producer states began to experience gas curtailments. Shortages during the winter of 1976-77 created emergency situations in the Ohio Valley and other parts of the northern U.S. Legislation to temporarily alleviate gas supply shortages in the interstate market was passed by Congress.

Natural Gas Policy Act. Recognizing some of the problems caused by having dual markets, Congress passed the Natural Gas Policy Act (NGPA) in 1978. The NGPA was complex legislation that deregulated price controls on 29 categories of gas, which were defined by aspects such as well spud date, interstate or intrastate, and onshore or offshore. It immediately raised the prescribed price on other types of gas, and phased out price controls and governmental approvals for sales on a variety of categories of gas over time.

Substantial portions of gas continued to be sold to interstate pipelines at federally mandated maximum lawful prices (MLP), which were well below intrastate free market prices. Consequently, the interstate gas market bid up the price of some unregulated gas as high as $10/MMBtu. Priced above its true market value, this gas could be averaged with less expensive gas by interstate pipelines and the LDCs served by them. Artificially high prices, coupled with high prices for deregulated gas, caused a tremendous drilling boom. Within a short time, drilling activity created a much larger reserve and delivery base of natural gas than previously existed. The price of unregulated gas climbed in the interstate market, but demand did not. As a result of higher gas prices, alternate fuels such as residual fuel oil began to displace gas. The gas supply in both the interstate and intrastate markets increased at the same time that demand for natural gas decreased. This led to a gas bubble, or surplus. Natural gas for the next decade was produced below capacity at various times of the year and from various wells within the U.S.

Interstate and intrastate pipelines tried to keep their markets by lowering the price of natural gas to their suppliers. Often, they refused to honor previously negotiated higher-priced contracts. This led to the price of gas falling for the producer, but not necessarily the user. It became apparent that the price to the users of natural gas would have to be competitive with that of alternate fuels in order for the user to remain a gas customer.

Federal Deregulation. Through a variety of FERC orders starting in 1983, including FERC Orders 436 and 500, pipelines became less involved in the business of purchasing gas from suppliers and reselling to customers (i.e., performing the merchant function). Instead, pipelines became more engaged in transporting gas for a fee, and producers or other entities began to sell gas directly to customers. Maximum lawful prices and regulations applicable to producer sales gradually came to an end.

Currently, any willing buyer and seller can make a deal for the purchase and sale of natural gas without prior federal governmental approval on service or rates. Since the LDC market segment continues to be regulated at the state level, LDCs must justify rates paid for gas purchased in connection with transportation.

Interstate pipelines historically performed the functions of transporting, marketing, and storing natural gas. These duties were bundled in a single rate charged by the pipeline. FERC Order 636, issued in 1992, ordered the services to be unbundled; each pipeline user would now contract only for the services required. Thus, cross-subsidization of pipeline services was no longer permitted. It should be noted that interstate pipelines continue to be regulated by FERC for rate approvals, operating tariff approvals, and construction of facilities.

Today it is acknowledged that the supply and demand of natural gas are balanced out by free market prices. Deregulation has enabled more efficient use of pipeline and storage services. This sea change in the natural gas industry has caused a multitude of problems that are still being addressed. Some are regulatory in nature, while others concern market dislocations. Many of the issues resolved at the federal level by Order 636 have been shifted to the states. One of these problem areas is the subsidization of residential user rates. Historically, LDCs used industrial customer rates to partially subsidize the true cost of serving residential customers. The evolving gas market is now moving to eliminate cross-subsidies. Thus, LDCs and state regulatory commissions will need to resolve the differentials.

GAS MARKETING FACTORS

General factors in marketing natural gas are noted in the following section.

Physical Quality. Produced natural gas can be processed to extract NGL and remove impurities. This results in a dry residue natural gas that is over 90 percent methane. Dry natural gas is more fungible than crude oil; such gas is more readily combined and transported in a pipeline system that delivers dry gas from the well or processing plant to millions of end-users such as individual residences.

Potential Customers. FERC has allowed pipelines to act as transporters, not as gas purchasers or resellers. This has enabled producers to sell gas to local gas utilities and even the utilities' former customers. Thousands, if not millions, of potential customers have become available to producers. In response, several large gas marketing companies have emerged to perform the merchant function of buying and selling gas.

Location. Since gas is transported almost exclusively by pipeline in the U.S., location plays a greater role in gas marketing than in crude oil marketing.

Supply Versus Demand. Annual U.S. gas productive capacity approximates annual demand, which is substantially less in the summer than in the winter due to home heating use. A small percentage of demand is met with imported Canadian gas. Supply and demand are drivers that cause many U.S. gas wells to produce below their capacities; for this reason, wells may be shut-in at times during a year. Wells may then produce at capacity in the summer when the gas is transported to underground gas storage facilities.

Futures Contracts. As with crude oil, buyers and sellers of natural gas can hedge the price of gas using futures, options, or another derivative product as discussed in Chapter 33.

GAS MARKETING STRUCTURE

The sale of natural gas has changed dramatically in recent years. Until the early 1980s, volumes were sold primarily under long-term contracts to pipelines that resold the gas to an LDC. In today's structure, producers and third-party marketing companies sell gas directly to end-users.

Producers. In order to realize revenue, a producer takes one of two paths. It can sell some or all of its natural gas production to a third-party gas marketer, or it may contract with a gatherer, processing plant, or pipeline to transport the gas to downstream customers. Some of the natural gas may be used in producer facilities, such as field equipment or company-owned refineries. A producer may even purchase additional gas from other sources to add to its own supplies.

Royalty owners and joint venture nonoperators typically have the right to take their share of produced oil and natural gas in-kind. Often, they choose to have the joint venture operator sell the gas on their behalf. This practice is less common among working interest owners for gas than oil, and can give rise to the problem of gas imbalances discussed in Chapter 14.

The marketing process involves selling next month's gas, negotiating prices, and determining sales and delivery points. This cycle is completed prior to the close of the NYMEX futures contracts sales, which is generally five working days before the end of the month. The majority of sales are arranged either the week before a closing date, or more commonly, in the two days before a closing date. This timing is known as the bid cycle (or bid week).

If a producer has not sold the gas at the wellhead, any pipeline transportation needed to sell the gas downstream must be scheduled (referred to as the **nomination** process) with a pipeline company. Parties to the transportation process are called the shipper and transporter.

A producer, marketer, processing plant, LDC, pipeline, or other party that retains title to the gas or contracts with a producer to oversee shipment is called a shipper. The gatherer, pipeline, processing plant, LDC, or any other transportation party responsible for physically moving the gas is called a transporter. A shipper notifies a transporter of the quantity of gas to be shipped (i.e., generally the MMBtu of gas per day), dates when the gas will be shipped, receipt point (i.e., meter) into the pipeline, delivery point where gas will be taken by a customer, and volume to be delivered to the customer.

Transporters confirm the respective nominated quantities and terms with producers and their customers. While nominations are estimates of gas flow for a given day and month, actual gas flow is likely to be different. This can be due to pipeline pressures, fuel usage, pipeline loss, or other conditions. Each party should maintain accurate volumetric records of transactions, and any volume variances are recorded and resolved at a delivery point (where the title transfers from the producer to the transporter/purchaser) determined by contract.

Marketers and Marketing Companies. Marketers and marketing companies are middlemen in the disposition of natural gas. A true gas marketer is neither a physical producer nor a user of natural gas; it purchases gas for resale much like a crude oil trading company does for crude oil. Value is added by aggregating supplies and markets, and by creatively using available transportation services and storage.

Historically, LDCs purchased gas from pipeline companies, transported it, and resold it locally to various retail classes of customers. LDCs now buy gas directly from producers and other third-party marketers, and resell it to residential, commercial, and industrial users including electric power generators. In many areas, there is a trend toward limiting the LDC merchant function to small commercial and residential customers who do not purchase directly from producers because of their low volumes.

End-Users. End-users of gas have been categorized three ways: residential, commercial, and industrial. A new fourth category encompasses electric power generation, which was previously included in the industrial sector.

Residential usage, consisting primarily of home heating, is largely weather-dependent. Households also use small amounts of gas in stoves, clothes dryers, water heaters, and other appliances. Residential users continue to purchase gas from LDCs, although in the future some residential users may be able to purchase gas from other third-party (non-LDC) marketers.

Shopping centers, office buildings, restaurants, and small stores are all examples of commercial users. These customers have traditionally purchased gas service from LDC suppliers. Now, they are actively moving to new gas marketing suppliers, such as third-party marketing companies, to supply their gas service.

Industrial users comprise the largest segment of the natural gas market. Gas can serve as a feedstock or can be used directly to fuel on-site boilers and other machinery. Industrial customers have created the most competitive price structures due to their newfound sophistication in the gas market. In addition, they are the segment of users most likely to have alternate fuel capability.

GAS CONTRACTS AND AGREEMENTS

Several types of agreements are used in connection with gas marketing. They include:

- Gas purchase and sales agreements

- Gas gathering agreements

- Gas transportation agreements

- Gas processing agreements

- Management services contracts

Each type of agreement is discussed in this section (gas processing is discussed in Chapter 11) and commonly used variations are identified.

Purchase and Sales Agreements. Spot sales contracts are used for gas sales as well as for crude oil. A spot contract for gas sales is a brief document that covers sales for a period of up to one month, although longer periods of time may also be covered. Most contracts have an evergreen clause that allows automatic renewal beyond the primary term. Shell forms may be used that leave the price, volume, delivery point, and term open for negotiations. Spot contracts historically contain no penalty for nonperformance by either party. They call for a best efforts performance (of an "up to" quantity), which is a phrase with little meaning. Alternatively, such contracts may specify liquidated damages for nonperformance.

Term contracts are generally longer-term contracts such as for periods of one month or more. They contain negotiated, detailed contract provisions in the body of the agreement. Price, volume, delivery point, contract term, and additional elements are specified. Term and spot contracts typically differ in how performance obligations are covered.

A term contract may establish a maximum daily quantity to be provided; this is an amount the seller must be willing to make available each day during the contract term. The buyer's requirement to take gas (if not 100 percent) may be specified prior to each month by a notice given to the seller. While the quantity is normally a set daily amount throughout the month, it can vary. In an extreme case, the seller may be required to have the maximum daily quantity available on any day the buyer wishes to purchase it. Yet, the buyer may be obligated to take only minimal amounts throughout any month during the contract term. While the subject of substantial negotiations, these provisions are reflective of the buyer's need to serve specific target markets and uses.

A brief description of some of the more important contract terms and provisions are provided in the following sections.

Delivery Point. The delivery point is the location immediately after a specified gas meter (either at the lease, on a gathering system, on a pipeline, or at a hub) where the gas is considered delivered to the buyer. Title, ownership responsibilities, and risks transfer at this point.

Pricing. Pricing provisions contained in spot sales contracts are usually very simple. There is a specific price set forth for the sale of a certain gas quantity during a specified limited time, usually no more than one month.

Some long-term contracts, particularly older ones, provide for fixed or specified prices. Fixed pricing has been used to lock-in gas supply economics on projects, such as co-generation plants or power generation projects. Pricing provisions allow for price re-determination: the parties can renegotiate the price at specified points in time. Frequently, parties negotiate a fixed price that changes according to either an escalation factor (a scheduled percentage change), a government inflation indicator (such as the Consumer Price Index), or the price of alternate fuels.

Absent a specified price, the spot contract should clearly provide a fluctuating reference price, or index price, along with any premium or discount to the index chosen. Currently, there are around 150 different index prices found in periodicals such as *Inside F.E.R.C.'s Gas Market Report*, *Natural Gas Week*, and *Natural Gas Intelligence Gas Price Index*.

Term. The term of a gas contract is the length of time the agreement is in effect. A spot contract generally terminates after a fixed period; however, an evergreen clause provides that a contract remains in effect until one of the parties cancels by giving written notice within a prescribed time period.

Payment. Payment provisions contain the timing and manner in which a seller is paid for the gas. Payment is made by check or wire transfer. Sales data and pipeline data (measurement and transportation statements) are not available until the following month. Invoices are generated in the middle of the month following actual sales unless an estimate using nominations is utilized. The most common provision states the buyer will pay the seller within 10 days of invoice date or on the 25th day of the month, whichever is later.

Many contracts provide that the buyer pays the seller interest for payments made after the contractual due date. Late interest charges take many forms; calculations can be based on the current prime rate or an agreed-upon fixed percentage.

Letter of Credit and Corporate Guaranty. When a buyer is deemed by a seller to be a credit risk, the seller may demand the buyer secures its purchases through a Letter of Credit issued by a reputable bank. While the Letter of Credit ties up the buyer's credit line, it serves as a guaranty that the seller will get paid for any gas sold.

Frequently, buyers or sellers are simply corporate shells with insufficient assets to pay damages for lack of contract performance. A contract may call for the shell company's parent or affiliate to guarantee performance.

Gas Committed. Historically, sales contracts provided for certain gas reserves of the seller to be committed to ensure delivery of specified gas volumes. Such provisions are uncommon in today's gas sales contracts. Instead, they provide that an agreed-upon deliverability volume be available. Sometimes, the deliverability commitment is subject to a best efforts requirement or volumes deliverable up to a specified maximum amount. While best efforts once meant the same as a non-firm gas supply, it now has legal significance and carries with it a performance obligation.

Take or Pay Contract. This provision refers to a certain volume of gas that must be taken by the buyer in a time period (e.g., a month or year). If the buyer does not take the agreed-upon volume of gas within the time frame, the buyer must pay as if it took the gas. After payment, there may be an opportunity for the buyer to take an equivalent gas quantity at a later date (**make up gas**). In today's market, what had been the take-or-pay provision is now more normally called a reservation charge. Without this provision, liquidated damages provisions may apply to encourage contract performance.

Gathering Agreements. Gathering agreements are used when wells are not connected directly to an interstate or intrastate pipeline. Gas from the field is aggregated by a third-party gatherer and eventually moved into a pipeline system or processing plant. Gatherers often provide a service where gas is centrally compressed on their system; this alleviates the need for producers to set compressors at their wells to increase gas flow against prevailing pipeline pressures. At times, plant operators may act as gatherers.

Transportation Agreements. Historically, gas was shipped by and for pipeline companies. As the new gas market evolved, gas users acquired their own supplies of gas through purchase arrangements and arranged shipping for it on one or more pipeline systems.

The two major types of transportation agreements are: (1) firm, and (2) interruptible. In a firm transportation agreement, the pipeline guarantees a specific volume of available capacity for the shipper to use each month—regardless of actual usage. Firm contracts can be compared to the terms for renting a home. There is no refund for nonuse of pipeline volume, just as there is no reduction in rent for nights spent away from home.

A firm transportation agreement requires each shipper to pay a specified monthly fee to reserve a set amount of capacity. This is known as a reservation charge. It is calculated by multiplying the maximum daily quantity contained in the transportation agreement by the reservation charge per MMBtu for that service. The reservation charge is paid whether or not a shipper moves its maximum daily quantity.

Firm service has historically been purchased from pipelines. However, as a result of FERC Order 636, if a purchaser of firm service determines that its allotted capacity is not needed, it may be released to another party in a secondary market. This is done by posting the released firm capacity on an electronic bulletin board, and FERC regulations stipulate how the released capacity must be posted, bid upon, and awarded to ensure open access to all market services. Capacity released to the secondary market may be relinquished for less than what the original firm transporter pays to the pipeline. The original firm transporter retains a binding contract with the pipeline, which must be paid whether or not a loss exists on any released capacity. This secondary market has become an important price driver in the transportation services market.

Another transportation service option allows a shipper to exceed the maximum delivery volume of gas for a specified time, such as 24 hours, without incurring additional penalties. If a pipeline provides this service (known as firm transportation with overrun capability) and the shipper and pipeline have stipulated this term in the contract, there is usually a fee involved.

Other charges to shippers are based on actual volumes of gas transported and must conform to prices governed by pipeline tariffs. One of these is a commodity charge, which is a variable cost based on the actual volume of gas shipped. It is paid in addition to the reservation charge. Pipelines also collect other volumetric charges such as FERC surcharges. These are specified in each pipeline's tariff. Generally, the amount of such charges increases with the distance gas is transported.

An interruptible transportation contract allows a transporter to interrupt or reduce its service to a shipper. In this case, the shipper pays only the actual transportation charges on a volumetric basis (commodity charges) incurred in transporting gas when pipeline capacity is available (after accommodating the transportation needs of shippers under firm transportation agreements). Any applicable FERC surcharges are added to the commodity charge.

Rate and Term Provisions. Interstate and many intrastate pipelines fall under the regulatory authority of FERC. Terms and conditions of pipeline transportation and rates are regulated through FERC-approved pipeline tariffs. Tariff and rate case negotiations between pipelines, their customers, and FERC are complex and lengthy affairs.

Pipeline tariffs filed with FERC appear in a common format. A map of the pipeline system is followed by a listing of rates for various pipeline services, which include not only transportation, but also ancillary services such as storage. Next, the tariff contains a lengthy description of the various services (called rate schedules) the pipeline is willing to perform, along with the unique details of that service. The rate schedule section is followed by a list of general terms and conditions (GTC) common to all of the pipeline's rate schedules. The GTC section lists such items as definitions, payment provisions, ways in which service may be interrupted or emergency conditions declared, and information about a pipeline electronic bulletin board. Finally, a standard form of agreement for each rate schedule appears in the tariff.

Pipelines subject to FERC regulation show maximum and minimum rates to be charged for service under each tariff rate schedule. Shippers and pipelines negotiate their rates within a specified range for services to be provided.

The length or term of a transportation or storage contract is also negotiated. While the term is something a prospective shipper provides in its notice, the pipeline advises whether or not the service requested is available for that term.

Fuel Charges. Pipelines usually issue a fuel charge for running compressors and other equipment. Fuel charges are specified in the pipeline tariff, generally as a percentage of the shipper's gas. Fuel charges and gas supplies lost or consumed in the gathering and transportation process are sometimes referred to as shrinkage.

Market Centers. The concept of market centers, or hubs, has been widely embraced by the gas industry. A market center is a location where pipeline systems come together and specific services are provided to facilitate the trading of natural gas (envision a bicycle wheel where the spokes represent numerous pipeline systems transporting gas to and from a central hub where the pipelines interconnect). Market centers help promote competition (especially for smaller customers), provide service reliability, and increase access to multiple pipelines.

As an example, Henry Hub in southern Louisiana is a market center that provides both physical and transactional services for customers. It is also a point for gas delivery under NYMEX gas futures contracts.

The hub administrator (or operator) has unique knowledge of the activities taking place at the hub; this enables the administrator to offer a wide variety of physical services, such as transportation, storage, compression, and processing. Transactional services are also available, including title transfer, price swaps, and imbalance trading. Many services are identical to those offered by pipelines, although they may be called by different names. Some of the more common market center services are:

- **Transportation Services.** A hub may facilitate wheeling, which is the movement of gas from one pipeline system to another interconnecting pipeline by opening valves at the interconnects of the various pipelines in the hub or by a paper transfer that nets corresponding receipts and deliveries of the gas. A hub might also provide nomination assistance, track released firm capacity, and provide other agreed-upon services.

- **Storage/Lending Services.** A market center operator may offer: (1) traditional storage services over several months, or (2) short-term storage within a given month. Short-term storage includes parking (i.e., storing gas until needed to meet a customer's peak demand during the month) and banking (i.e., having the hub store gas that was not taken by the customer, such as by an industrial customer on a slow weekend). Short-term borrowing of gas from the hub may also occur when a shipper sells more gas at the market center than the shipper delivers. Whether lending or storing gas, the hub operator charges a fee for services rendered, and imbalances must be cleared eventually.

- **Buy/Sell Transactions.** A hub may facilitate tracking custody and title of the gas among sellers, buyers, shippers, and transporters and provide appropriate accounting documentation for intra-hub transfers.

The operator of the market center may match buyers and sellers of natural gas at the market center and issue invoices for these services to the parties involved.

It may also allow shippers to trade gas imbalances to minimize a shipper's exposure to imbalance charges in the market center. On an electronic bulletin board, the market center administrator provides a list of shippers willing to trade imbalances or those requesting the hub's assistance in finding another shipper willing to trade. A fee is charged for providing the match. Parties willing to trade then determine a settlement value between themselves.

Allocating Gas on the Pipeline. If gas deliveries into a pipeline are either less than or exceed nominations for the period, then the transporting pipeline company must allocate actual deliveries among its shippers' customers. If a shipper does not specify how a differential should be handled, the pipeline company makes the allocation. Generally, the default is to a pro-rata allocation based on the percentage nominated to each contract. Since nominated gas volumes and actual gas flow never match exactly, it is to the shipper's advantage to direct in advance where the gas should be allocated. Proper planning allows a shipper to avoid the penalties and negative economic impacts of arbitrary allocations of gas. A schedule furnished to the pipeline, called a predetermined allocation (PDA), details how a shipper's actual delivered gas should be allocated to its customers. The shipper ranks the priority of each customer's contract on the PDA. The pipeline then completely delivers to the first contract on the ranked list before proceeding to the second name on the list.

Simple examples of both the PDA and pro-rata allocation methods are shown in Figure 12-2 using a nominated volume of 100,000 MMBtu scheduled for shipment and actual pipeline deliveries of 90,000 and 120,000 MMBtu.

Figure 12-2
Examples of Predetermined and Pro-Rata Allocation

Predetermined Allocation (PDA):

Shipper Contract	Nominated MMBtu	Rank	Allocation of Actuals	
			Under Delivery Scenario	Over Delivery Scenario
A	50,000	1	50,000	50,000
B	30,000	2	30,000	30,000
C	20,000	3	10,000	40,000
	100,000		90,000	120,000

Pro-rata Allocation:

Shipper Contract	Nominated MMBtu	%	Allocation of Actuals	
			Under Delivery Scenario	Over Delivery Scenario
A	50,000	50%	45,000	60,000
B	30,000	30	27,000	36,000
C	20,000	20	18,000	24,000
	100,000	100%	90,000	120,000

In the PDA example in Figure 12-2, the actual volume deliveries are ranked via instructions from the shipper. Contract C becomes the swing volume contract. If the shipper delivers only 80,000 MMBtu to the transporter, then the transporter delivers no gas under contract C.

Allocation methodology is more difficult to apply when a shipper attempts to allocate volumes to meet both daily and monthly required deliveries for numerous contracts. For example, if a shipper has contracted to deliver 10,000 MMBtu every day on Contract X, then the shipper may rank that customer as number one every day or give the producer a keep-whole provision. The shipper also has Contract Y that requires a 15,000 MMBtu minimum daily delivery. Contract Z has a minimum monthly delivery. The shipper must allocate the gas so that Contract X receives the 10,000 MMBtu per day, Contract Y receives 15,000 MMBtu per day, and Contract Z receives the contracted minimum deliveries of gas by the end of the month. Ensuring that allocations are completed as indicated by the PDA is critical for avoiding nonperformance penalties on the contracts or additional expenses in trading or buying additional gas to meet contract volumes.

Imbalance and Scheduling Penalties. As discussed in Chapter 11, it is important for gas to be measured, dispatched, and allocated properly. Increased numbers of transportation transactions have made the nomination and allocation of gas volumes more difficult. Failure to properly nominate and allocate volumes can lead to large gas imbalances over a pipeline's stated tolerances, and result in substantial penalties charged by the pipeline.

Producer imbalances can exist between producers at a lease or gathering facility when one uses or sells more or less gas than its working interest share. Pipeline imbalances occur during the transporting of gas between the lease and a gatherer, the gatherer and a transporter, or the transporter and a marketer. The term pipeline imbalance refers to an imbalance between a purchaser and seller when the amount of gas delivered to the point of sale does not agree with the amount of gas the buyer makes payment on and receives.

Scheduling penalties occur when there is a variance between the gas nominated by a producer and the actual gas volume sent into the pipeline.

Imbalance penalties occur when the amount of gas received from a producer and delivered to the customer falls over or under the pipeline's designated tolerance.

Shippers are constantly faced with tough decisions in choosing the most economical, practical method of transporting the gas. Firm transportation, interruptible transportation, and firm transportation with overrun capability are considered in the equation. Fuel usage and pipeline loss must be taken into account when determining the gas volumes delivered. Additionally, a shipper can pull gas out of storage or place gas in storage to balance pipeline receipts and deliveries.

Penalties can be offset by purchasing or selling gas with third parties to round out shortages and overages. One way to reduce the effects of imbalances between a shipper's nominated volumes and actual gas shipped is through operational balancing and pooling agreements with other parties. Operational balancing agreements attribute gas imbalances to the producer and customers, and leave the shipper out of the picture. Pooling agreements allow a producer to net gas volumes at several different receipt and delivery points, and state how any imbalances will be resolved at a later date.

Pipeline accountants have the responsibility to pass through any penalties to producers, sales customers, or shippers depending on the source of the penalties. Daily and monthly penalties may be incurred for imbalances over or under the pipeline tolerances. Accurate records are critical for reconciling volume discrepancies because pinpointing the cause of pipeline penalties is a tedious process.

Management Services Contracts. A management services contract provides one party the right to transport, purchase, or sell gas on another party's behalf. The management services company receives payment of a specified amount per MMBtu of gas purchased or sold. Frequently, the fee is calculated as a percentage of either the price or the savings generated.

NATURAL GAS LIQUIDS MARKETING

U.S. NGL MARKETING

Several factors affect the marketing of NGL at natural gas plants in the U.S. They include the following:

Physical Quality. NGL consist of distinct types of hydrocarbons with different markets and competitive products. Relative U.S. production in 2005 is summarized in Figure 12-3:

Figure 12-3
2005 U.S. NGL Production

Hydrocarbon	Annual Production (Ending Stocks) 2005 _thousand barrels_	Percent
Ethane (C_2H_6)	24,671	21
Propane (C_3H_8)	57,377	49
Normal Butane (C_4H_{10})	20,876	18
Isobutane (C_4H_{10})	6,587	5
Natural Gasolines or Pentanes Plus (C_5H_{12} to $C_{10}H_{22}$)	8,070	7
Total NGL	117,581	100

Source: Energy Information Administration website (www.eia.doe.gov)

Potential Customers. A major NGL end-user market in the U.S. is the petrochemical industry concentrated on the Gulf Coast. Olefin plants use ethane and propane as major feedstocks for making basic petrochemicals such as ethylene and propylene. Alternative major feedstocks for many plants are naphtha and gas oil, which are products from crude oil refining. Variations in the price of crude oil can affect the cost of naphtha and gas oil and, indirectly, the price of ethane and propane as petrochemical plants seek the best, most economical, feedstocks available.

Another major U.S. market is rural home heating and cooking and agricultural use of liquefied petroleum gas (LPG or bottled gas) consisting of propane or primarily propane.

A third major market is crude oil refining that can use butanes and natural gasolines as blendstocks for making refined products such as gasoline.

Major oil and gas companies with gas production facilities, refineries, and petrochemical plants market NGL to downstream intercompany facilities. However, the typical independent producer's potential customer is generally either: (1) a gas plant owner who simply buys the wet gas, or (2) a gas plant NGL customer in transactions arranged by the gas plant owner.

Location. Extraction of NGL in downstream gas processing plants serving several producers leads many producers to market to or through gas plant owners. In a broad geographical sense, the location of NGL production compared with primary markets can also affect the pricing and marketing of NGL components.

Supply Versus Demand. The U.S. NGL supply depends on the production of U.S. natural gas, which has grown in recent years, but is still below productive capacity. U.S. imports of NGL and liquid refinery gases reached 374,000 barrels per day in 2005, up from 305,000 barrels per day in 2004, according to the Energy Information Administration.

The strong demand for NGL is aided by a system of NGL pipelines to move the products to major markets. However, just as crude oil can be sold at the lease into trucks, NGL may be temporarily stored at processing plants to be sold and delivered into special trucks largely to meet regional demands, instead of being delivered into an NGL pipeline to major petrochemical plants.

DESCRIPTION OF MARKETING OPERATION

As discussed in Chapter 11, in addition to separating the dry gas to meet downstream pipeline specifications and make it merchantable, another reason for processing natural gas is to extract the NGL stream. Sale of the products after fractionation of the NGL stream commands a high enough price to make processing profitable and provide valuable products to end-users. A sophisticated marketing system with primary and secondary market centers for the transportation, purification, storage, and marketing of NGL has developed in recent years to meet numerous NGL market requirements.

Natural gas is generally processed at plants located in the field. The wet stream is then sent through the pipeline to either: (1) a fractionation facility in close proximity depending on location and economic factors, or (2) a fractionation facility located closer to the market such as a major pipeline connection or a market center.

NGL sellers may be plant owners or operators who previously purchased natural gas streams from producers through gas purchase contracts. The operators now hold title to the NGL and the gas. Producers of the natural gas stream receive a price for the wet gas based on the value of all the products in the stream: residue gas, any by-products (such as sulphur), and the NGL. Each plant owner negotiates a contract to sell the NGL to a marketer, market center, or a large industrial user or refiner.

If a lease operator or producer has a gas processing agreement, the producer retains title to the NGL and has the same options to sell NGL to a marketer, market center, or large-end user.

Typical contracts in the field provide a producer with an allocation of liquid revenues or in-kind products attributable to a well's production. Preprinted industry forms allow delivery dates, quantities, location, delivery method, special product specifications, and price to be inserted when negotiated. Industry standards and specifications for measurement are usually referenced in the measurement sections of the contract. Penalties are stated for any quantities of product delivered from the plant that fail to meet purchaser specifications. It is common to find provisions for small losses of the product. Exchanges of one product for another with a specified price differential, other price adjustments, or monthly fees for storage services should be clearly stated in the contract. In addition, most agreements provide for an audit of the settlement price.

NGL PRICING

Pricing is determined by industry postings provided at the main market centers of Conway, Kansas, and Mont Belvieu, Texas. These postings cover defined pure products with net-back provisions for transactions at the processing plant. Storage or pipeline facilities within these locations are specified. The Oil Price Information Service (OPIS), a division of United Communications Group, provides PetroScan, an on-line petroleum price database of NGL, gas, and petroleum product prices. PetroScan or the weekly *Oil Price Information Service* newsletter often serves as a pricing reference in contracts for settlement purposes. OPIS definitions and specifications are available from the publisher upon request and should be documented in any payment calculation or audit procedure.

Marketing fees are deducted as: (1) a percentage of the posted prices or actual resale prices, or (2) a fixed number of cents or even fractions of a cent per gallon sold. Pipeline and/or truck transportation and fractionation charges (sometimes called T&F charges) are established with the facilities or equipment owners in the form of fixed amounts per gallon. A market price may be severely discounted in the case of products that fail to meet the purchaser's specifications. In some cases, a seller may incur a cost for proper disposal of contaminated products.

• • •

---

1 Each joint venture owner's right to take oil in-kind is an important joint venture characteristic that helps avoid classification of the venture as a corporation subject to corporate income taxes and venture owners as corporate shareholders receiving taxable dividends.

2 The words type, area, grade, and quality are interchangeable and may be defined differently according to who is using the term. This chapter refers to the geographical location and physical or chemical characteristics that define crude oil.

3 The Federal Energy Regulatory Commission (FERC) is a five-member commission within the Department of Energy that regulates and determines tariffs for the interstate transportation and sale of natural gas, construction of pipeline facilities, pipeline transportation of oil, and transmission and sale of electricity.

CHAPTER

13

ACCOUNTING FOR OIL, GAS, AND NGL SALES

Key Concepts:

- **Complexity of revenue accounting for oil and gas sales**

- **Role of division orders in revenue accounting**

- **Calculation of production taxes**

- **Cash receipts and accounts receivable approaches to revenue recognition**

- **Conversion of natural gas in order to record sales**

- **Residue gas and NGL sales**

- **Shut-in and minimum royalties**

- **Accounting for reinjected gas**

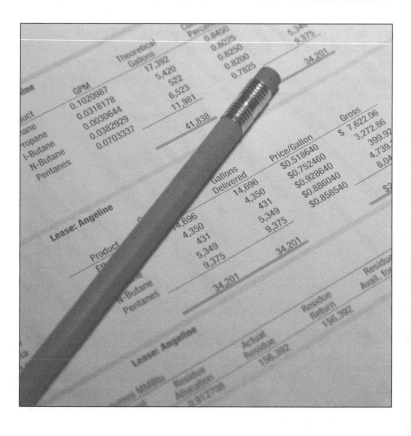

THE COMPLEXITY OF REVENUE ACCOUNTING

Accounting for petroleum revenues can be a complex matter. Numerous factors–such as multiple owners, changes in purchasers, varying production tax rates by property, varying royalty rates by property, purchaser/operator/pipeline accounting errors, gas imbalances, fluctuating prices, and changes in ownership interests–make the proper recording of sales information a challenge.

The following example illustrates the effects of multiple owners and multiple forms of distribution. ABC Oil Company (ABC) has a 30 percent net revenue interest in a property burdened with a 25 percent royalty. Production taxes are five percent. During one month, $100,000 of petroleum is sold from the lease. ABC's revenues are $30,000, and its production tax expenses are $1,500 for each lease. The purchaser's practice of distributing proceeds may be any one of the following:

- Pay ABC $28,500, net of royalty and production taxes. This method is common for sales of U.S. oil production where the purchaser pays the royalty owner and local government directly.

- Pay ABC the entire $100,000 and let ABC distribute the revenues and pay the royalties and severance taxes. This type of entry is common for sales of U.S. natural gas production.

- Pay ABC $95,000 (withhold only production taxes for payment directly to the local government) and let ABC distribute the payment to the royalty holder and working interest owners.

- Pay ABC some other amount between $95,000 and $28,000, e.g., $57,000 for ABC and the group of working interest owners with a combined 30 percent NRI who affiliate with ABC for revenue distributions.

An E&P company must use an accounting system that accurately and efficiently records oil and gas proceeds and properly redistributes proceeds rightfully due to others. One key element in such a system is the division of interest file (also called DOI file or D of I file). This master file contains the revenue-sharing percentages for each unique distribution based on the lease identity, the month of sale, and the petroleum purchaser.

GENERAL ISSUES

Revenue accounting is affected by six general matters:

- Division orders

- Distribution accounting

- Royalty reporting

- Revenue accounting organization

- Revenue accounting centers

- Production and ad valorem taxes

DIVISION ORDERS

As discussed in Chapter 7, the contractual agreements between parties determine ownership interests, and, usually, no two contracts are exactly the same. These agreements can create many different owners of a single mineral property. Proceeds from petroleum sales on the property must be disbursed to each eligible party.

Oil purchasers generally send separate checks to each owner. Conversely, purchasers of natural gas prefer to pay all net revenues to the operator. As a result, the operator becomes responsible for distributing gas revenues to the various owners of the working interests, royalty interests (and any overriding royalty interests), net profit interests, and production payments.[1] If the working interest owners do not sell their gas collectively, each working interest owner may take its gas in-kind, sell it to the party of its choice, and receive a net revenue check from its gas purchaser. For these reasons, the parties must reach agreement as to who distributes gas revenues to whom.

A division of interest order is the agreement between the purchaser of production and all the owners indicating how the purchaser should distribute the production proceeds. If the operator or other working interest owner is receiving revenue on behalf of itself and others, it should have a division order for its distributions to the other parties.

Division orders include the legal description of the property, names of owners of interests in the property, and interest owned by each. Sometimes a division order includes the terms of purchase, including provisions dealing with passage of title to the products, price, measurement, production taxes, and related items.[2] By signing the division order, each owner represents that its ownership stake is correctly listed. In addition, the owner authorizes the purchaser to receive the products from the property, make payments to the owners in proportion to their respective interests, and agrees to all other provisions of the division order.

Copies of division orders are retained by the operator and by the purchaser. These records constitute the accounting department's authorization to make payments to the various owners of interest, credit revenues to related income accounts, and credit revenues from certain other interests to suspense accounts. New division orders or changes in division orders are reported on a Notice of Division Order Changes form. This document contains the lease identification, names and addresses of all interest owners, fractional interest belonging to each, fractional interest or interests to be held in suspense, and for a transfer of interest, fractional interests of the grantor and grantee before and after the transfer or change in interests held in suspense. Figure 13-1 illustrates a division order.

Division orders may have special clauses in the body of the division order or as attachments that contain the legal language and agreements between the interest owner and the operator or payor. These may include definitions of terms, identification of quantity measurement methods, quantity determination, inclusions and exclusions in payment proceeds calculations, circumstances that dictate when proceed amounts may be withheld, dates of payment, methods of payment, confirmation of valid title, and any other special arrangements.

Certified Division Order Analysts *supervise the proper distribution of revenues obtained from oil and gas production or other mineral deposits. This includes ongoing maintenance of the mineral ownership of those wells. A division order analyst can be employed on a contract or permanent basis by a small independent, major corporation, oil and/or gas purchaser, mineral owner, or trust department. Such analysts may specialize in a particular geographic area or department.*

Source: National Association of Division Order Analysts, http://www.nadoa.org, April 2007

Figure 13-1
Oil and Gas Division Order [3]

NADOA Model Form Division Order (Adopted 9/95)
DIVISION ORDER

To: **Date:**   February 5, 2006

Property Number:	094-730-8820-1800	**Effective Date:**	Commencing at
Property Name:	Bell Heirs "A"		7:00 a.m.
Operator:	Big Oil USA, Inc.		Date of First Purchase
County and State:	Montague County, TX		
Property Description:	[Legal Description]		

Production: **X** Oil   **X** Gas _____ Other

Owner Name and Address	Owner Number	Decimal Interests	Type of Interest
Big Oil USA, Inc.	197954	.50000000	WI
KT Oil, Inc.	287643	.21375000	WI
Amber Bell	634322	.06250000	RI
Frederick Bell	725873	.03125000	RI
Micah Bell	725874	.03125000	RI
Walter Johnson	697389	.00672550	ORRI
Phyllis Johnson	697390	.00672550	ORRI
Raymond Skinner	487653	.00345490	ORRI
Melvin Kirkland	567839	.00962500	ORRI
Lois Kirkland	567895	.00962500	ORRI

The undersigned certifies the ownership of their decimal interest in production or proceeds as described above payable by __Big Oil USA, Inc.__ (Payor).
                                 (Company Name)

Payor shall be notified, in writing, of any change in ownership, decimal interest, or payment address. All such changes shall be effective the first day of the month following receipt of such notice.

Payor is authorized to withhold payment pending resolution of a title dispute or adverse claim asserted regarding the interest in production claimed herein by the undersigned. The undersigned agrees to indemnify and reimburse Payor any amount attributable to an interest to which the undersigned is not entitled.

Payor may accrue proceeds until the total amount equals __$25.00__, or pay on December 31, whichever occurs first, or as required by applicable state statute.

This Division Order does not amend any lease or operating agreement between the undersigned and the lessee or operator or any other contracts for the purchase of oil or gas.

In addition to the terms and conditions of this Division Order, the undersigned and Payor may have certain statutory rights under the laws of the state in which the property is located.

Special Clauses:

Owner(s) Signature(s):
Owner(s) Tax I.D. Number(s):
Owner Daytime Telephone #:
Owner FAX Telephone #:

Federal Law requires you to furnish your Social Security or Taypayer Identification Number.
Failure to comply will result in 31% tax withholding and will not be refundable by Payor.

DISTRIBUTION ACCOUNTING

An E&P company's revenues are its share of revenues net of royalties and overriding royalties, and excluding revenue interests owned by others. For example, if a well's gross revenue from gas production is $100,000 before a 10 percent state production tax and the E&P company's net revenue interest is 30 percent, then its revenues are $30,000, and its share of production tax expense is $3,000. If the E&P company receives the full $90,000 of revenue proceeds (net of production taxes withheld and paid to the state), it keeps $27,000 and must distribute $63,000 to other interest owners, including the state tax agency. In such a case, it is common to record the full receivable and full distribution payable while recording net revenue and net production tax expense as follows:

120	Accounts Receivable—Oil & Gas Sales		90,000	
710.011	LOE—Production Taxes		3,000	
	302	Revenue Distributions Payable		63,000
	602	Gas Revenue		30,000
	To record gas revenue for well [name] for [month, year].			

Exceptions to this rule are: (1) accounting for minimum royalties recorded as a production expense (discussed at the end of this chapter), and (2) recognizing revenues for gas quantities taken and sold that give rise to gas imbalances (discussed in Chapter 14). Occasionally in foreign lands, the E&P company's local subsidiary will record royalties as an expense and revenues gross of royalties pursuant to a production agreement with the host country's government. For the E&P company's consolidated financial statements, the royalty expense is eliminated and production revenues are recorded net of the expense.

REVENUES HELD IN SUSPENSE

Revenues may be held in suspense and not distributed for various reasons:

- Awaiting an executed division order.

- Awaiting an executed change in ownership of a working interest or royalty interest.

- Awaiting proof of title or title opinion.

- Awaiting resolution of dispute as to ownership interest.

- An interest owner's signature cannot be obtained on the division order or transfer order.

- The distribution is minimal in size.

- Prior distributions to a particular owner have not been cashed; this could mean the owner cannot be found or has abandoned the property.

When awaiting an executed division order, all revenues may be held in suspense. If one interest owner's information is in doubt, that portion of revenues alone is held in suspense.

The division order typically provides that if a particular distribution is minimal (below a stated amount such as the $25 figure illustrated in Figure 13-1), then the amount need not be distributed until the cumulative distribution payable exceeds the stated amount.

However, it is customary to distribute all amounts owed at the end of each year, even if the total is less than the stated minimum. State or local regulations or the lease agreement itself may set the distribution threshold.

When owners are not known or cannot be located, amounts due are customarily paid into an escrow account. Whether held in escrow or not, unclaimed distributions fall under state escheat laws for handling unclaimed property. Outside companies may be engaged to find the owners; their fees are charged against owner proceeds. After around five to seven years, unclaimed revenues held in suspense accounts must be distributed to the appropriate state agency.

ROYALTY REPORTING

Depending on contract provisions, either the operator or the purchaser makes periodic (usually monthly) payments to royalty owners. Reporting is usually in the form of a settlement statement or check stub, which is also called a revenue remittance advice. This document should identify the lease(s) involved, month covered, number of barrels of oil or condensate or Mcf of gas sold, sales price, royalty owner's percentage of production ownership, state production or severance tax withheld, and net amount paid the royalty owner. Contracts or state regulations sometimes call for other data to be shown or for copies of supporting documents such as pipeline run tickets to be enclosed.

The U.S. Department of the Interior Minerals Management Service (MMS) has the responsibility to collect and account for the royalty interests that are owned by the federal government in onshore and offshore properties. MMS requires that detailed, specific reports on production, sales, and other dispositions of products be filed on a monthly and annual basis along with a check for royalties due. From these reports, MMS compiles information to determine if it is receiving correct amounts. MMS regulations change frequently and are beyond the scope of this book. Official manuals that explain how to file required forms are available for operators. Revenue accountants should remain informed of current regulations because heavy penalties can be incurred.

REVENUE ACCOUNTING ORGANIZATION

Because of differences in individual oil company operations, size, and structure, there is no standard organizational pattern that dictates how the revenue accounting function should be accomplished.

Companies with only a few producing properties may employ one accountant to perform all the functions of a revenue department, or even the functions of the entire accounting department. As in any small company with a job position that involves financial transactions, accountability and segregation of duties should be structured to achieve a workable system of internal controls.

Larger companies may incorporate numerous specialized positions (such as gas accountant or production tax accountant) or units (production accounting, gas control, or royalty owner accounting) to achieve the revenue accounting function. They are more likely to have sophisticated information, accounting systems, and internal controls.

REVENUE ACCOUNTING CENTERS

One of the primary responsibilities of a revenue accountant is to assign and record revenue to the correct property, measurement point, tank, or well. Therefore, one of the first issues is to identify revenue accounting centers to be used to accumulate and group recorded revenue. Generally, the revenue accounting center is by well, but it may also be by field, lease, prospect, or other defined aggregation of activity for grouping volume, cost, and revenue information. Whichever method is chosen, a distinct accounting center reference, such as a combined alpha and numeric code, is assigned. The centers are needed to set up receivables, record production, make proper distribution of proceeds to the working interest and royalty interest owners, record accruals, and calculate taxes.

In many E&P companies, the revenue accounting center is not determined solely by the accounting department, but rather is selected by considering the needs of the whole organization. Revenue centers may be used as areas of responsibility in production, land, and marketing activities, as well as in the accounting department. Hence, centers are commonly referred to as accounting cost centers, even within revenue accounting functions. The amortization cost center for full cost accounting is on a countrywide basis; for successful efforts, it is the lease or reasonable aggregation of leases. However, the accounting cost center often needs to be figured on a well-by-well basis for purposes of management oversight or by lease for income tax reporting.[4]

PRODUCTION TAXES

Most states levy one or more types of tax on oil and gas produced in the state. Production taxes, also called severance taxes, are computed on the basis of volumes and/or values of oil, condensate, gas, NGL, and sulfur produced and sold or consumed. Taxes are usually levied at the time and place that minerals are severed from the producing reservoir.

Another tax imposed by some states is a conservation tax used to fund energy conservation, oversight, and research programs.

Many Indian tribes assess a production tax, which is usually credited against amounts otherwise due the state in which the well is located. Each tribe and state varies as to the assessment method and rates.

Revenue accountants must be familiar with the current tax laws of the states where producing properties are located. Governmental regulations mandating different types of taxes and rates are subject to constant change. The Council of Petroleum Accountants Societies (COPAS) *Oil and Gas Severance Tax Guide*, the Commerce Clearing House, Inc. *State Tax Reporter*, and other sources provide periodic updated information on current taxes related to oil, gas, and NGL production and sales. The Society of Petroleum Evaluation Engineers website at www.spee.org provides information by state to assist petroleum engineers in economic modeling and reserve estimation.

Calculation of Production Taxes. As stated above, the basis for determining the amount of tax due is the value or the volume of the oil or gas produced and sold during a predetermined period of time. The accountant should be aware of whether the taxing entity bases the tax rates on production from the property or sales. It is also important to be aware of whether the purchaser or the producer is responsible for payment and remittance of the appropriate tax.

State laws specify the tax rate and basis of assessment of the particular product. A common tax method specifies a fixed percentage to be applied to the total gross value of the product sold in a month. Other states base their tax on the volume of petroleum sold. A few states combine the two bases of value and volume in assessing taxes due. In this case, either volume or value is used—whichever generates greater revenue to the state. Several special provisions currently being used by taxing entities are listed below:

- Before applying the tax rate, the gross value of oil may be reduced by a designated cents-per-barrel amount to reflect the barge, pipeline, and/or trucking charges necessary to transport oil produced and sold.

- With approval from the state, the value of natural gas may be reduced by documented marketing deductions (e.g., costs incurred beyond the separator, such as dehydration, that may be required to make the gas saleable to a purchaser).

- Different rates can be levied based on the producing property's location within counties, school districts, or municipalities; in some states, rates vary with the date that the lease commenced commercial production.

- Other states have different rates for a special classification of wells, such as wells incapable of producing more than 25 barrels of oil per day.

Payment of Production Taxes. Oil and gas purchasers may deduct taxes from the sales proceeds and pay the producer a net amount. Taxes due, along with tax forms or schedules, are remitted by the purchaser to appropriate state collection agencies. Alternatively, a purchaser may pay producers the gross value of production, and then remit taxes to the designated state agency.

Some production and certain ownership interests can be exempt from taxation. For example, injection gas, vented or flared gas, and gas-lift gas are exempt in some states. Interests owned by the federal government, state government, or Indian tribes are exempt from taxes in most states. Sometimes, contractual agreements between the parties result in tax-free interests. In this situation, other owners must bear the non-tax-paying owner's share. In general, however, production taxes are borne proportionately by all interest owners, including royalty interest owners.

States typically require monthly payment and reporting. Usually, both the producer and purchaser file a monthly tax report due one to two months following production. Reports submitted by the purchaser and producer are compared by state personnel to determine that taxes due were reported and paid correctly. Production reports generated by the operations department and filed with the state may also be compared with the tax reports. Many states also require quarterly and annual reports.

The amount of detail included on the tax reports varies from state to state. Typically, production volume, production value, and tax for each production unit or lease are shown with a summary for each county or parish.

Penalties. The tax-assessing agency may impose penalties and interest for failure to file timely reports and failure to fully pay taxes when due. In many states, penalties may be waived if the delinquency is not attributable to taxpayer negligence. Failure to file tax reports can be classified as a misdemeanor with possible fines and/or jail terms. Some penalties for late filing are set at specific dollar amounts, while others use a specific percentage applied to production volume or value.

Refunds of Production and Other State Taxes. For various reasons, an overpayment of state taxes can occur. Refund procedures vary: some states require filing an official claim for a refund along with supporting evidence, while others have rules that amended tax reports be filed. Certain states allow a reduction in the amount of taxes due in the current month for all refund requests and then notify the taxpayer if the claim is later disallowed.

AD VALOREM TAXES

Ad valorem (a Latin term meaning "according to the value") taxes and property taxes are generally levied by counties, school districts, and other local taxing entities based on where the production occurs. Ad valorem taxes can be based on either: (1) the level of production occurring in the previous calendar year, or (2) the estimated fair market value of well equipment or economic interest in the property. Tax rates vary widely among local taxing entities, and a county or parish may encompass many different taxing entities.

While similar to production taxes in terms of calculation (e.g., applying a statutory rate to the gross value of production or to an assessed value), ad valorem taxes are noticeably separate, and thus provide the revenue and joint interest accountant with some unique challenges. For example, states such as Colorado or Wyoming impose ad valorem taxes on both the gross value of production and equipment.

When paying ad valorem taxes based on gross production value, the distributor of revenues may withhold and escrow estimated taxes from distributions to all interests owners (with the exception of any **exempt owners**). Working interest owners pay all ad valorem taxes assessed on equipment value.

As a general rule, the operator of the property is responsible for reporting and paying ad valorem taxes. However, production and severance taxes are often withheld and remitted by the purchaser. Another difference between ad valorem taxes and production taxes is the frequency of reporting. Production taxes are usually paid and reported on a monthly basis, while ad valorem taxes are paid annually.

Many operators withhold estimated ad valorem taxes from monthly revenue distributions to reduce the risk of uncollectible taxes from owners should the well unexpectedly cease production or a joint venture owner becomes insolvent.

Because of the high degree of specialization and varying regulations imposed by states and local taxing jurisdictions, ad valorem taxes may require a significant amount of attention. Failure to emphasize their importance can expose an E&P company to significant losses resulting from uncollectible taxes from nonoperators or from excessively high property tax appraisals that go unchallenged by the E&P company.

ACCOUNTING FOR OIL SALES

INFORMATION FLOW TO THE ACCOUNTING DEPARTMENT

Revenue accountants are responsible for ensuring correct revenue entries are recorded and accurate revenue disbursements are made to owners. This process includes comparison of the settlement statement or revenue remittance advice information from the purchaser to internal company records of volumes sold, contract prices, tax rates, and net revenue interests. Close interaction is required with the production, land, and marketing departments to access appropriate information to verify proper accounting entries are recorded for each property. The process of information verification varies from company to company, and information from other departments may also be needed.

Most smaller and intermediate-sized companies record revenue, and the volumes associated with the revenue, directly from the check receipt and attached documentation from the purchaser. Procedures need to be established to provide a verification of the volumes measured at the lease or central facility to the volumes indicated and paid for by the purchaser. Larger companies, or those with more sophisticated computer systems, may have the capability to allow the production department to enter actual sales volumes directly into a system accessible by the revenue accountant. Methods for volume verification vary, but can include:

- In small companies, a production clerk/accountant may receive the pipeline run tickets, internally calculate or outsource volume calculations, and verify that the statement of pipeline runs and the volume on the purchaser's check agree with the pipeline run tickets.

- Production clerks, or other operations or production accounting department personnel, maintain the meter tickets. Production calculated from the tickets is provided in a report (sometimes called the production ledger) to the revenue department, which has responsibility for verifying that the volumes agree.

- Production clerks maintain the meter tickets, and the revenue department generates a report (such as the Lease Operating Statement found in Chapter 15) that includes sales volumes received from the purchaser. The production department ensures the correct volumes were received.

- Production clerks maintain the meter tickets and enter the volumetric amount, gravity, and other pertinent information into the company's information system. The revenue accounting department accesses this information and verifies that the volumes paid for by the purchaser agree with the volumes entered by the production department during the monthly closing process.

The company also needs a process to verify that the amounts and terms negotiated on sales contracts are followed when revenue is received. Sales contracts are often maintained in the marketing department. A set of procedures needs to be established to provide the revenue accounting department, or other assigned department, a method of verifying that correct contract terms and prices are being used. This is more easily implemented with an integrated computer system that allows direct on-line entry of contract prices by the marketing department and subsequent access by the revenue accounting department to make monthly closing entries.

As stated previously, the revenue accountant is responsible for ensuring that revenues are properly distributed. Division orders and royalty agreements generally reside in the land department, which provides a record (or information to prepare the record) called the revenue deck. The revenue deck contains the correct group of interest owners and their ownership percentages in the property.[5] This ownership record is assigned a unique code that, when referenced with the property's identifying accounting center number, directs the accountant or the computer system to set up payables to the correct owners at their current ownership percentages in the property. If an interest owner assigns or sells its interest or part of its interest, a new revenue deck reflecting the new ownership is set up and assigned a new unique code.

For example, assume ABC Oil Company has an 80 percent working interest and a 68 percent net revenue interest in a well that started production on August 11, 2006. ABC's accountant sets up a revenue deck called R1 that contains the ABC 68 percent net revenue interest and a 32 percent interest to other owners. ABC sells half of its interests to HES Oil Co. effective October 1, 2006. ABC's accountant sets up a second revenue deck called R2 reflecting the new net revenue interests: ABC, 34 percent; HES Oil Co., 34 percent; and other interest owners, 32 percent. The first revenue deck is closed. Any sales occurring after September 30, 2006, are distributed using the second revenue deck.

EFFECTIVE DATE OF OWNERSHIP CHANGE

To facilitate accounting, agreements that call for ownership changes upon **payout** should specify an effective date. Payout provisions are triggered when revenues to a given interest in a well equal all costs (acquisition, drilling, completion, and operations) allocated to that interest. The governing agreement may provide for the ownership change to be effective: (1) the first day immediately after the month when payout actually occurs, or (2) on the day after payout is calculated to occur. If applicable, the second approach requires a special allocation of the joint venture's revenues and costs for the month as noted in COPAS Accounting Guideline No. 13 (AG 13), *Farmouts/Farmins, Net Profits, Carried Interests*.

RECORDING OIL SALES

Cash Receipts Approach. Some companies record revenues directly from information included with the purchaser's check. Revenue checks are generally received at the company's bank lockbox or in the company's finance office responsible for making deposits. Cash is debited and an accounts receivable for oil and gas sales is credited for the amount of cash received.

The statement or voucher receipt attached to the actual check identifies the production volume purchased, related taxes, and revenue received. It is called a remittance advice or settlement statement. An accompanying statement of pipeline runs should also be provided by the purchaser or pipeline.

To illustrate, suppose that ABC Oil Company receives a statement of oil runs from a lease with the data as follows. The purchaser withholds taxes and pays each interest owner the net amount due.

ABC's share of oil sold is 700 barrels	
Oil revenue at $60/bbl	$42,000
Less 5% state severance tax	(2,100)
Net proceeds received	**$39,900**

The treasury department records an entry debiting cash and crediting accounts receivable for $39,900. The revenue accountant records the following entry:

120	*Accounts Receivable—Oil & Gas Sales*	39,900	
710.011	*LOE—Production Taxes*	2,100	
601	*Crude Oil Revenue*		42,000
	To record revenue on receipt of settlement statement.		

These entries under the cash receipts approach reflect cash basis accounting (even though GAAP calls for accrual basis) and provide little control over sales or production. Since a revenue check generally comes one or two months after the sale, the E&P company accrues on the monthly financial statements estimated revenue earned, but not yet received. The basic journal entry debits an accrued receivable and credits oil (or gas) revenue. The accrual estimation process varies by company; it may be based on the previous one or two month's total revenues or involve a more sophisticated analysis of actual production and estimated or actual prices. The production department should be able to supply current volume information on properties operated by the company. On nonoperated properties, the accountant may need to make an estimate of oil volumes based on past production history of the property.

Accrual entries should include the applicable production taxes and the net amount receivable using the same accounts as in the cash basis entry. This adjusting entry would then normally be reversed at the beginning of the next month so that the E&P company can continue to record revenue and taxes in the usual manner at the time settlement in cash is made. If the accrual and reversal are performed on an annual basis, a reversal in the new period could cause material distortions in interim statements.

Accounts Receivable Approach. Under the accounts receivable approach, the E&P company records each cost center's revenue based on internal records of quantities sold, prices, and production tax rates or internal invoices. The revenue accountant debits accounts receivable and records the receivable to an accounts receivable subledger for the particular purchaser, as though the purchaser had been invoiced. When the purchaser's check is received, a treasury accountant records an entry to debit cash and credit accounts receivable for the particular purchaser. Any unusual balance in the accounts receivable subledger is investigated, and any recording errors or purchaser errors are corrected.

For example, assume that ABC's records show more oil sold and at a higher price than the oil purchaser's remittance advice, as illustrated in the following schedule:

	Per ABC	Per Purchaser
ABC's share of oil sold	705 bbls	700 bbls
Oil price	$60.50/bbl	$60.00/bbl
Oil revenue	$42,653	$42,000
Less 5% state severance tax	(2,133)	(2,100)
Net receivable	**$ 40,520**	**$39,900**

When revenues and production taxes are recorded, accounts receivable is debited for $40,520. When the oil purchaser's $39,900 check is deposited, accounts receivable would be credited for $39,900, leaving a $620 accounts receivable balance to be investigated.

Note that neither the cash receipts approach nor the accounts receivable approach as illustrated above recognizes crude oil inventory in lease tanks. As discussed later in this chapter, it is common for E&P companies not to recognize, subject to materiality, such oil inventory in their financial statements.

A record of the earnings for each lease or well is needed to complete the federal income tax return, prepare management reports, and file reports with regulatory agencies. Thus, revenues are commonly recorded in an operating revenue subledger with a separate record for each revenue accounting center (generally by well). The information shown for each accounting center would include at least the following for oil sales:

• Property identification

• Interest owned

• Oil runs (gross barrels, net barrels)

• Net revenue interest share of gross value included in revenue

• Total revenue for the month

• Cumulative revenue for the year

Gas sales might be shown in the same subledger or a separate gas revenue subledger.

Integrated Information and Accounting Systems. In companies with sophisticated information systems, oil volumes and related volume measures are entered directly into on-line databases. This role is performed by a production clerk, operations employee, production accountant, gas control clerk, or other designee.

The marketing department, having responsibility for negotiations and sales contracts, enters agreements on-line by property or measurement point.

DOI owners and their interests are entered into the system with date-sensitive codes. The current revenue deck contains ownership interests to be used by the system to record and make payments to these owners.

Revenue accountants verify that settlement statement information agrees with on-line numbers collected from other departments. Daily or monthly pipeline information is entered into the system to provide monthly accruals. Production and other state tax information are entered and verified periodically by a tax accounting group.

When revenue accountants are confident that correct information resides in the system, they initiate steps for the computer to record entries, make payments, and generate reports for monthly closings.

Recording for the Integrated Company. In an integrated company, several divisions or subsidiaries may be involved in producing and refining oil, and in producing, processing, and marketing natural gas. A crude oil purchasing division may buy from its own production division as the oil is run from the lease storage tank. The purchasing division may sell oil either to the company's own refinery or to another refiner. It also prepares and circulates the appropriate division order and authorizes payments to the various interest owners.

The accounting entries related to oil production and purchase by an integrated company can be classified into three groups:

- Entries for revenue from a lease in which the company owns the working interest and sells production to another company.

- Entries for revenue from a lease in which the company owns the working interest and purchases the production itself.

- Entries for purchases of oil from a lease in which the company owns no interest.

Sales by the production division to the crude oil purchasing division are eliminated in preparing consolidated financial statements.

OIL INVENTORY

Virtually all E&P companies have oil in lease tanks, but the volumes and changes in inventory are typically immaterial to financial statements. This is why most E&P companies do not bother to recognize the inventory of crude oil in lease tanks when preparing financial statements.[6] Some companies have substantial crude oil inventories, such as those in remote foreign locations or on large ocean-going tankers; inventories of these types should be reflected in the financial statements. Oil and gas inventory is recorded at the lower of cost or market (LCM). Any LCM adjustments are often recorded as an adjustment to lease operating expense rather than to revenues.

To illustrate this procedure, assume that an E&P company's share of crude oil inventory in lease tanks at January 31, 2006, was 100 barrels carried at an LCM of $60 per barrel.

The company's share of February 28, 2006, oil inventory was 60 barrels at an LCM of $58 per barrel. The necessary adjustment would decrease the recorded inventory by $2,520:

Beginning inventory (100 bbls @ $60)	$6,000
Less ending inventory (60 bbls @ $58)	(3,480)
Net decrease in inventory	**$2,520**

The entry on February 28 would be:

710.xxx	*LOE, Change in Oil Inventory*	2,520	
130	*Inventory of Crude Oil*		2,520
	To adjust value of inventory of crude oil on a lease.		

EXCHANGES

As mentioned in Chapter 12, occasionally an E&P company will exchange its crude oil for another company's crude oil, rather than sell it. These exchanges arise to meet location, quality, or timing issues (e.g., to reduce transportation costs or to meet an integrated company's need for a different quality of crude for its local refinery).

The exchange may be structured whereby one party receives a differential from the other for an agreed-upon difference in value of the crude barrels exchanged. Alternatively, the exchange may be structured as a sale of the E&P company's crude oil in exchange for the E&P company's purchase of other crude oil. Each company pays the other for the full purchase price of oil received in the exchange. Normally, the acquired oil is sold during the same month the exchange occurs.

Close scrutiny should be given to exchange transactions as they can give rise to accounting issues surrounding the following:

- Does the exchange agreement meet the definition of a derivative as defined by FAS 133 and related interpretations? If so, is the derivative designated as "held for trading" purposes? Will the contract be physically settled? Each of these answers will have an impact on the ultimate accounting (see Chapter 33 for a further discussion on FAS 133 and derivatives).

- Should this exchange transaction be viewed as a single exchange transaction following the guidance of Emerging Issues Task Force (EITF) Issue No. 04-13?

- Has consideration been given regarding gross versus net presentation of resulting gains and losses by utilizing guidance provided by EITF Issue No. 99-19?

- In a non-monetary exchange, has full consideration been given to the guidance set forth in APB No. 29, as amended by FAS 153, *Exchanges of Nonmonetary Assets*, an amendment of APB Opinion 29? Such a transaction can and may result in a deferred gain recognition.

In evaluating exchange contracts, consideration of the facts and circumstances should be made in the context of the various activities of the entity rather than based solely on the terms of the individual contracts. Further guidance on these issues can be found in EITF Issue No. 03-11, *Reporting Realized Gains and Losses on Derivative Instruments That Are Subject to FASB Statement No. 133 and Not "Held for Trading Purposes" as Defined in Issue No. 02-3.*

ACCOUNTING FOR NATURAL GAS SALES

VALUE DETERMINATION

Chapters 11 and 12 introduced the measurement concepts for various hydrocarbons. As mentioned, the volume of gas produced and recorded in the operating revenue subledger is stated in Mcf. However, most gas sales contracts express price in terms of delivered MMBtu, not delivered Mcf. Revenue (or gross value) is the quantity of Mcf sold times the measured heat content per Mcf (i.e., the MMBtu per Mcf for the gas sold, which is also called the Btu factor) times the price per MMBtu. An Mcf of gas with a relatively high heat content has more energy and more value than an Mcf of gas with low heat content. Generally, dry natural gas that is substantially all methane has approximately 1 MMBtu per Mcf.

The heat content can be determined under various conditions, but generally the sales contract will provide that heat content be determined based on dry Btus, i.e., the heating content in an Mcf of gas measured and calculated free of moisture content. Some contracts may define dry Btus as each Mcf having no more than seven pounds of water. If MMBtu/Mcf is measured as though the Mcf were saturated with water (as was required under old gas price controls), the MMBtu content would be approximately one percent less than MMBtu/Mcf on a dry basis. Note that the terms dry Btus and saturated Btus refer to relative water saturation whereas the terms dry gas (or residue gas) and wet gas refer to NGL content.

E&P companies typically track revenue in terms of Mcf sold times a price per Mcf. To calculate sales price per Mcf, the revenues received and recorded (and paid on a price per MMBtu) can simply be divided by the recorded corresponding gas sales volume. The price per MMBtu may also be converted to a price per Mcf given the heat content, i.e., MMBtu content of an Mcf of such gas. The basic conversion formula is (price/MMBtu) x (MMBtu/Mcf) = price/Mcf.

If the measured MMBtu/Mcf reflects an Mcf at a pressure base and water content inconsistent with the measured volume of Mcf, then multiplying measured MMBtu/Mcf by the measured volumes of Mcf will not give the correct quantity of total MMBtu. In such cases, one or both measurements should be restated for consistent pressure base and water content.

Similarly, in converting a price/MMBtu to a price/Mcf, a consistent pressure base and water content must be used. Typically, the heat content is converted for the pressure base and water content of the volumes recorded in the E&P company's records (generally at 14.73 psia for governmental reporting purposes). One Mcf at 14.73 pounds per square inch absolute (psia) will have less density, less molecules, and less energy than an Mcf at the greater pressure of 15.025 psia for the same mix of natural gases.

Pressure base and water content conversion formulas follow.

Expressing the Volume at a Desired Pressure Base:

$$\text{Mcf at original psia} \times \frac{\text{original psia}}{\text{desired psia}} = \text{Mcf at desired psia}$$

Expressing the Btu Factor at a Desired Pressure Base:

$$\text{MMBtu/Mcf at original psia} \times \frac{\text{desired psia}}{\text{original psia}} = \text{MMBtu/Mcf at desired psia}$$

Expressing the Btu Factor at a Desired Water Content Condition (saturated to dry):

> **MMBtu/Mcf at original psia (sat.) x [orig. psia/(orig. psia - 0.2561)] = MMBtu/Mcf at orig. psia (dry)**

Expressing the Volume at a Desired Water Content Condition (saturated to dry):

> **Mcf at original psia (sat.) x [1-(0.2561/orig. psia)] = Mcf at orig. psia (dry)**

Calculating Gross Value:

> **Mcf at desired psia (dry) x MMBtu at desired psia (dry) x price/MMBtu = Gross Value**

In the following example, these formulas are utilized. The Btu factor is converted to the 14.73 psia.[7] The Btu factor is converted from saturated to a dry condition.[8] The Mcf, measured at 14.73 psia in a dry condition, is multiplied by the MMBtu/Mcf at 14.73 psia (dry) and multiplied by the contract price stated in MMBtu to arrive at the gross revenue value. Alternatively, the contract price stated in MMBtu can be multiplied by the MMBtu/Mcf at 14.73 psia (dry) to arrive at the price per Mcf and then multiplied by the Mcf at 14.73 psia (dry). The volumes sold are 20,000 Mcf at 14.73 psia (dry). The BTU factor is 1.079 MMBtu/Mcf at 15.025 psia (saturated or sat.). The contract price is $6.00/MMBtu.[9] Calculations are as follows:

> **Step 1:**   1.079 MMBtu/Mcf @ 15.025 psia (sat.) x 14.73/15.025 =
> **1.058 MMBtu/Mcf @ 14.73 psia (sat.)**

> **Step 2:**   1.058 MMBtu/Mcf @ 14.73 psia (sat.) x [14.73/(14.73-0.2561)] =
> **1.077 MMBtu/Mcf @ 14.73 psia (dry)**

> **Step 3:**   1.077 MMBtu/Mcf @ 14.73 psia (dry) x 20,000 Mcf @ 14.73 psia (dry) x $6.00/MMBtu =
> **$129,240 gross value**

or Step 3 may be expressed by first calculating the price per Mcf @ 14.73 (dry):

> **Alternate**   (a) $6.00/MMBtu x 1.077 MMBtu/Mcf @ 14.73 (dry) = $6.462/Mcf @ 14.73 (dry)
> **Step 3:**   (b) 6.462/Mcf @ 14.73 (dry) x 20,000 Mcf @ 14.73 psia (dry) = **$129,240 gross value**

RECORDING GAS SALES

Recording sales of unprocessed gas involves essentially the same process as recording sales of oil. For example, suppose that ABC operates the Margaret Theresa Lease #1. The royalty interest is 15 percent. All gas production is sold to RK Gas Resources, Inc. at $5.76 per MMBtu assumed to equate to $6.00 per Mcf. Assume that RK Gas Resources, Inc.

will make the tax payment to the state. The appropriate entry on ABC's books to receive payment for 20,000 Mcf sold in June 2006, including the royalty share, less withheld production taxes of five percent, would be:

120	Accounts Receivable—Oil and Gas Sales		114,000	
710.011	LOE—Production Taxes		5,100	
	602	Gas Revenue		102,000
	302	Royalties Payable		17,100
	To record sale of gas production for June 2006.			

Calculations:			
	20,000 Mcf x $6 x 95%	=	$114,000
	20,000 Mcf x $6 x 85% x 5%	=	$5,100
	20,000 Mcf x $6 x 85%	=	$102,000
	20,000 Mcf x $6 x 15% x 95%	=	$17,100

Many automated revenue systems will make a memo entry for the total gross revenue from the property to provide for governmental and internal management reporting, and the system will allocate the amounts attributable to the working interest and royalty interest owners based on the DOI revenue deck.

When sales are made from a central delivery facility rather than the wellhead, the production department must provide the revenue accounting department with the gas sales volumes allocated by lease. The central delivery facility generally provides a gas allocation statement that details the sales applicable to each lease. Gas allocation statements may also provide the sales price, marketing costs (e.g., gas gathering charges and dehydration charges), production taxes withheld, if any, and the net sales proceeds allocated to each lease or well.[10]

GAS DEMAND CHARGES

Now that gas pipeline companies have become transporters rather than purchasers, some gas producers pay demand charges to secure capacity in the pipeline. Such costs are capitalized (charged to Account 280, Pipeline Demand Charges, in Appendix 3) and amortized over the time period the capacity is available.

ACCOUNTING FOR RESIDUE GAS AND NGL SALES

RESIDUE GAS AND NGL SETTLEMENTS

Accounting for residue gas and NGL from a plant involves complex allocations. The revenue accountant must have a clear understanding of processing arrangements and contract provisions. Liquids contracts, as discussed in Chapters 11 and 12, can have innumerable variations such as: the measurement calculation of the products; the location where gas and/or NGL title passes; identification of the party responsible for transportation, processing, fractionation, marketing, and other charges; the method used to charge for processing (e.g., a product retention or fee per Mcf, MMBtu, or gallon); and various other considerations.

Since it is impossible to discuss and account for all situations encountered in gas plant settlements, the next section examines two revenue determination methods used in the industry for making payments on processed residue gas and NGL. A commonly used method provides for payment based on the allocation of actual product extracted and delivered at the plant tailgate. A second method, used less frequently in industry, provides for payment on a specified percentage of the theoretical volumes of residue and NGL.

Two discussions from Chapter 11 are relevant to these examples: (1) the allocation of gas at a particular measurement point (processing plant) back to the individual leases, and (2) theoretical gallons of liquids contained in unprocessed gas based on test results.

Revenue Based on Actual Product Extracted. To illustrate the first revenue determination method, assume that gas streams produced from two properties, Leases A and B, enter a processing plant. Test results taken at the wellhead provide the theoretical amount of gpm (gallons per Mcf) of each liquid that may be produced from the stream of gas at a particular wellhead. The gas is measured again and tested at the plant inlet. Test results taken at the plant inlet yield a total Mcf and a gpm based on the combination of Leases A and B gas streams into the plant. Volumes from the plant inlet are allocated back to the two leases. Additionally, volumetric and quality measurements are taken at the plant's tailgate. The basis for the settlement payment is typically the quantities extracted and delivered for sale during the month. In this example, calculations for ethane are illustrated.

The processing plant was able to extract almost 95 percent of the ethane that was theoretically determined to be in the gas stream. The quantity of salable liquids actually recovered in the plant differs from the theoretical liquid content of the gas volume owing to variations between the test conditions, plant operating conditions, designed operating efficiency of the plant, and processing losses.

The ratio of a plant's actual volumes to theoretical volumes is called the recovery factor. It is calculated for each individual product extracted in the plant. The recovery factor is multiplied by the theoretical gallons of the product for each lease to determine allocated volumes. Generally, contracts provide for separate settlement calculations for each of the individual components extracted.

Assumptions:	Lease A	Lease B	Total
Wet gas (Mcf) processed	24,000	20,000	44,000
Ethane theoretical gpm at lease	0.120	0.100	
Actual ethane sold (gallons)			4,600
Producers' negotiated share of ethane	70 %	65 %	
Processor's share as a processing fee	30 %	35 %	
Actual ethane price per gallon			$ 0.420
Ethane Revenues:	**Lease A**	**Lease B**	**Total**
Wet gas (Mcf)	24,000	20,000	44,000
x ethane theoretical gpm	X 0.120	X 0.100	
= ethane theoretical gallons	2,880	+ 2,000	= 4,880 (a)
Total actual ethane gallons sold			4,600 (b)
Plant's ethane recovery factor, (b)/(a)			0.9426
Applied to each lease	X 0.9426	X 0.9426	
Actual ethane allocated by lease	2,715	+ 1,885	= 4,600
Producers' negotiated share	x 70 %	x 65 %	
Producers' settlement volumes	1,900	1,225	
Ethane price per gallon	x $ 0.420	x $ 0.420	
Allocated ethane revenue	$ 798	$ 515	

A second revenue determination method used in plant processing contracts provides for payment based on a specified percentage of the theoretical gallons of gasoline, rather than the actual gallons extracted from the product. In theory, settlement based on theoretical gallons may result in the producer's negotiated share being lower than if settlement was based on actual gallons extracted. For this second example, the same facts are assumed except that the producers' negotiated shares of ethane sales are 67 percent and 62 percent for Leases A and B, respectively. The producer does not share in the risks of the plant operation, but receives a negotiated straight percentage of theoretical volumes.

Ethane revenues allocated to Leases A and B are:

Ethane Revenues:		Lease A		Lease B
Wet gas (Mcf)		24,000		20,000
x ethane theoretical gpm	x	0.120	x	0.100
= ethane theoretical gallons		2,880	+	2,000
Producers' negotiated share		x 67 %		x 62 %
Producers' settlement volumes		1,930		1,240
Actual ethane price per gallon		x $ 0.420		x $ 0.420
Ethane revenue		$ 811		$ 521

Variations. The producer may be paid on a sliding scale percentage of the price per gallon with the percentage varying according to either, or both, the price and gpm of the gas. The lower the price and/or gpm, the smaller the percentage due the producer; conversely, an increase in the price or gpm increases the percentage due the producer. Contracts may specify that the payment to the producer is based on the processor's gross NGL sales proceeds or based on proceeds after deduction of cash discounts, transportation costs, or marketing costs.

While a sliding scale approach is more complicated, it reduces the range of the processing fee to more closely approximate a plant operator's processing costs. The operation is provided with a source of steady profits. In this scenario, the producer assumes more risk of changes in NGL prices and gas quality.

NGL Inventory. Producer-owned inventory balances at the plant are rare. Most plants are connected by a pipeline system that allows for residue gas and products to be moved as soon as extracted. However, some NGL may be stored in pressurized tanks at the plant and later removed by truck. It is also possible for a producer to be allocated NGL sales in a manner that creates a negative inventory or over-delivery attributable to the producer's account.

GAS PLANT SETTLEMENT STATEMENT

The gas plant settlement statement in Figure 13-2 presents information used to record the sale of residue gas and liquids. Gas plant settlement statements vary widely due to different customs and contract arrangements. However, most contain the following information:

- Mcf, Btu content, and the MMBtu of unprocessed gas received from the producer allocated to the lease or delivery point
- Residue gas returned to the lease (for injection or fuel usage)
- Residue gas available for sale to a purchaser or end-user and residue gas sold by the plant (if provided for in the agreement)
- Inventory of the volumes by NGL product
- Gross value of the separate NGL products
- Processing fee deductions by NGL product in the form of a percent of product or charge per gallon, Mcf, or MMBtu

Settlement statements may also contain:

- Liquid loss volumes by product, production tax amounts, or other charges
- The net value, after deductions, for each separate NGL product

The gas plant settlement statement in Figure 13-2 depicts June 2006 NGL and residue gas sales for the Margaret and Angeline leases paid under different contract settlement terms reflected by separate contract agreement numbers. The following assumptions apply to the Margaret lease:

- The gas processing contract specifies that the processor will sell the residue gas and NGL for the producer. Propane will be taken in-kind by the producer.
- The producer is paid based on an allocation of actual product.
- The contract specifies that the processor will retain 16 percent of the actual volumes produced of each NGL and the residue gas.
- The contract provides for the processor to be paid: (1) a transportation fee of $0.035 per gallon of NGL available for sale and $0.04 per MMBtu of residue gas available for sale, and (2) a marketing fee of $0.0025 per NGL gallon sold and $0.003 per MMBtu of residue gas sold.
- A small negative inventory balance for ethane exists at June 1, 2006.
- The producer is responsible for paying the state production tax.
- The producer distributes sales proceeds to other interest owners.

The assumptions that apply to the Angeline lease in Figure 13-2 are the same as for the Margaret lease except for the following:

- The gas processing contract specifies that the processor will buy NGL. Residue gas will be returned to the producer.
- A processing fee of $0.05 per MMBtu of residue gas will be separately invoiced.
- NGL volumes attributable to the producer's account are based on a contract percentage of theoretical gallons for each product.

When recording accounting entries for Figure 13-2 sales, assume the following for the Margaret and Angeline leases:

- Big Oil records only the NGL volumes and values attributable to its 84 percent contract percent. This is known as the **net-back method.**[11]
- Big Oil has a 50 percent net revenue interest. Processing fees, transportation, and marketing charges from the processing plant are considered marketing costs and are to be shared with other interest owners in proportion to ownership. Big Oil's working interest percentage is not used for this example.
- Big Oil records the volume and value of the delivered (i.e., sold) residue gas and NGL, rather than the produced amounts because the inventory amounts at the processor's plant are immaterial.
- The state production tax rate is 7.5 percent of the value of the residue gas and NGL. No marketing costs or other deductions from the gross value are allowed, and there are no state or federal royalty interests that are exempt from the production tax.[12]

Figure 13-2
Gas Plant Settlement Statement

Settlement Statement for: ABC Company, Inc.

Summary of Product Payment: ABC Company, Inc.   Production Month: June 2006

Lease # and Name		Contract #		Available Volume	Take In-Kind	Volumes Delivered	Gross	(a) Less Transportation	(b) Less Marketing	Net Due
9738293	Margaret	17465-23	NGL (gal)	32,948	5,078	27,870	$ 19,430.94	$ 2,306.36	$ 139.35	$ 16,985.23
9738293	Margaret	17465-23	Gas (MMBtu)	249,762		249,762	661,016.27	19,980.96	1,498.57	639,536.74
9732387	Angeline	16984-45	NGL (gal)	34,200		34,200	24,083.07	2,394.00	171.00	21,518.07
9732387	Angeline	16984-45	Gas (MMBtu)	189,781	189,781		-	-	-	-
										$678,040.04

(a) Transportation = $0.07/gal. and $0.08/MMBtu of available volumes.
(b) Marketing Fee = $0.005/gal. and $0.006/MMBtu of volumes delivered.

Liquids Production

Contract #:	17465-23		
Production Month:	June-06	Alloc. Inlet	
Lease #:	9738293	Mcf:	256,439
Lease Name:	Margaret		
County:	Hidalgo		
State:	Texas	Alloc. Inlet	
Btu Content:	1.1203	MMBtu	287,289
Pressure Base:	14.65		
Contract Btu:	Dry		

Lease: Margaret

Product	GPM	Theoretical Gallons	Recovery Factor	Actual Gallons	Contract Percent	Producer Entitlement
Ethane	0.1020987	23,965	0.72854864	17,460	0.84	14,666
Propane	0.0318178	6,054	0.99854328	6,045	0.84	5,078
I-Butane	0.0030644	565	0.98738554	558	0.84	469
N-Butane	0.0382929	7,099	0.98775937	7,012	0.84	5,890
Pentanes	0.0703337	12,087	0.83302638	10,569	0.84	8,878
		49,770		41,644		34,981

Liquids Gross Value

Lease: Margaret

Product	Producer's Entitlement	Producer's Beginning Inventory	Available For Sale	In-Kind Gallons	Gallons Delivered	Producer Ending Inventory	Gallons Delivered	Contract Percent	Price/Gal.	Gross
Ethane	14,666	(2,032)	12,634	-	12,634	-	12,634	0.84	$0.479760	$ 6,061.29
Propane	5,078	-	5,078	5,078	-	-	-		$0.717380	-
I-Butane	469	-	469	-	469	-	469		$0.893180	418.90
N-Butane	5,890	-	5,890	-	5,694	196	5,694		$0.862240	4,909.59
Pentanes	8,878	-	8,878	-	8,878	-	8,878		$0.905740	8,041.16
	34,981	(2,032)	32,949	5,078	27,675	196	27,675			$19,430.94

Residue Gas Gross Value

Lease: Margaret

	Residue Volumes MMBtu								
Allocated Inlet	Product Shrinkage	Theoretical Remaining	Residue Allocation	Actual Residue	Residue Return	Residue Avail. for Sale	Contract Percent	Residue Gas Price/MMBtu	Residue Gross
287,289	29,343	257,946	0.968274	249,762	0	249,762	0.84	$3.150696	$661,016.27

Figure 13-2
Gas Plant Settlement Statement (cont'd)

Liquids Production

Contract #: 16984-45
Production Month: June-06
Lease #: 9732387   Alloc. Inlet Mcf: 170,345
Lease Name: Angeline
County: Woodward   Alloc. Inlet MMBtu: 189,781
State: Oklahoma
Btu Content: 1.1141
Pressure Base: 14.65
Contract Btu: Dry

Lease: Angeline

Product	GPM	Theoretical Gallons	Contract Percent	Entitlement Gallons	Take In-Kind Gallons	Total Gallons
Ethane	0.1020987	17,392	0.8450	14,696		14,696
Propane	0.0318178	5,420	0.8025	4,350		4,350
I-Butane	0.0030644	522	0.8250	431		431
N-Butane	0.0382929	6,523	0.8200	5,349		5,349
Pentanes	0.0703337	11,981	0.7825	9,375		9,375
		41,838		34,201		34,201

Liquids Gross Value

Contract #: 16984-45
Production Month: June-06
Lease #: 9732387
Lease Name: Angeline
County: Woodward
State: Oklahoma
Btu Content: 1.1141
Pressure Base: 14.65
Contract Btu: Dry

Lease: Angeline

Product	Gallons Avail. for Sale	Gallons Delivered	Price/Gallon	Gross
Ethane	14,696	14,696	$0.518640	$ 7,622.06
Propane	4,350	4,350	$0.752460	3,272.86
I-Butane	431	431	$0.928640	399.92
N-Butane	5,349	5,349	$0.886040	4,739.30
Pentanes	9,375	9,375	$0.858540	8,048.93
	34,201	34,201		$24,083.07

Residue Gas Gross Value

Lease: Angeline

Residue Volumes MMBtu

Allocated Inlet	Product Shrinkage	Theoretical Remaining	Residue Allocation	Actual Residue	Residue Return	Residue Avail. for Sale	Contract Percent	Residue Gas Price/MMBtu	Residue Gross
189,781	18,432	171,349	0.912708	156,392	156,392	0	0	$3.150696	$0.00

Big Oil makes the following calculations related to its 50 percent interest in the sale of residue gas and NGL from the Margaret lease. Transportation expenses are classified as a marketing expense.

	Total	Big Oil USA	Other Owners
Residue gas sales	$661,016	$330,508	$330,508
Marketing expenses	(21,480)	(10,740)	(10,740)
Production taxes	(49,576)	(24,788)	(24,788)
Net gas proceeds	$589,960	$294,980	$294,980
NGL gas sales	$19,431	$9,715	$9,716
Marketing expenses	(2,446)	(1,223)	(1,223)
Production taxes	(1,457)	(728)	(729)
Net NGL proceeds	$15,528	$7,764	$7,764

The corresponding accounting entries for the Margaret lease are:

120	*Accounts Receivable—Oil and Gas Sales*		639,536	
702	*Gas Marketing Expense*		10,740	
710.011	*LOE—Production Taxes*		24,788	
	320	*Production Taxes Payable*		49,576
	302	*Revenue Distributions Payable*		294,980
	602	*Gas Revenue*		330,508
	To record June 2006 residue gas sales, Margaret lease.			

120	*Accounts Receivable—Oil and Gas Sales*		16,985	
703	*NGL Marketing Expense*		1,223	
710.011	*LOE—Production Taxes*		728	
	320	*Production Taxes Payable*		1,457
	302	*Revenue Distributions Payable*		7,764
	603	*NGL Revenue*		9,715
	To record June 2006 NGL sales, Margaret lease.			

The corresponding accounting entry for NGL sales allocated to the Angeline lease is:[13]

120	*Accounts Receivable—Oil and Gas Sales*		21,517	
703	*NGL Marketing Expense*		1,284	
710.011	*LOE—Production Taxes*		903	
	320	*Production Taxes Payable*		1,806
	302	*Revenue Distributions Payable*		9,856
	603	*NGL Revenue*		12,042
	To record June 2006 NGL sales, Angeline lease.			

A company may also choose to record 100 percent of the residue gas and NGL volumes and values as revenue. The difference between 100 percent and the contract percent is categorized as a processing fee. This can be a desirable method when interest owners' lease agreements specify royalty payment on 100 percent of the value of the NGL extracted, not allowing a reduction of the royalty for volumes taken by the processor. Some lease agreements specify minimum royalties on the NGL. Others specify royalties to be based on the actual volumes and prices received by the plant owner rather than a contract percentage on the theoretical volumes, as in the Angeline agreement.

If the processing fee exceeds the state taxing authority's allowable deduction in computing the production tax, the net-back method may create accounting system problems in calculating and paying the correct amounts. Generally, fees charged by processing companies fall within the state's allowable limits. Revenue accountants should know the state's tax regulations to avoid penalties on underpaid production taxes.

Plant statements may also calculate both the value of the unprocessed gas and the combination of the values of the residue gas and NGL. This generally is the result of a keep-whole provision in the contract that places the risk of processing the gas in the hands of the processor. The producer receives the higher value of the two calculations. Accounting entries for the value received are recorded as shown for unprocessed gas in the earlier Accounting for Natural Gas Sales section or as shown in this section for the sales of residue gas and NGL.

Dual accounting (keep-whole provision) is a requirement for gas plant processing with the Mineral Management Service and Indian tribe royalties. When gas is flowing through an operated gas plant, the MMS will be paid the higher of: (1) the total of NGL cumulative sales, plus residue sales, or (2) the unprocessed (wet) gas value. In rare instances, other royalty owners receive similar keep-whole pricing under their lease agreements.

SPECIAL ROYALTY PROVISIONS

In addition to the basic fractional royalty provided in all oil and gas lease contracts, two other royalty provisions are common. The two provisions, introduced in Chapter 7, are shut-in royalties and guaranteed minimum royalties. Special provisions may involve either oil or gas properties, but more often are applicable to gas wells.

SHUT-IN ROYALTIES

Standard lease agreements provide for the payment of shut-in royalties in the event it is necessary to shut-in a well that is capable of production. This situation can occur due to a lack of market or marketing facilities. Shut-in royalty payments in lieu of production must be made to prevent forfeiture of the lease. If such payments are not recoverable from future production, they are similar in nature to ad valorem taxes assessed on proved property fair value (classified as operating expenses) and to delay rentals (classified as carrying costs of undeveloped property charged under successful efforts to exploration expense and under full cost to capitalized lease acquisition costs). However, it should be noted that a shut-in royalty occurs after proved reserves are discovered and is not truly an exploration cost or carrying cost of undeveloped property.

Companies using either successful efforts or full cost typically charge the shut-in royalty to a lease operating expense account. This action is appropriate even when the shut-in royalty amount is the same as the delay rental amount. Nonrecoverable shut-in royalties are generally immaterial to company financial statements.

If the payment is recoverable from future production, it is usually considered a recoverable advance payment and is recorded as an account receivable by both full cost and successful efforts companies. This is done when there is reasonable certainty that recovery will take place. If a receivable account is used, the amount charged to it should be limited to the amount that can reasonably be expected to be recovered from future royalty revenues in excess of the guaranteed amount. Any amount paid in excess of amounts reasonably anticipated to be recovered should be charged to lease operating expense.

The following entries record shut-in royalties under the two different methods. Assume a shut-in payment of $2,000 was made in the first month (in which there was no production), and the second month's sales were 2,000 Mcf at $6.00 per Mcf. The royalty interest is one-eighth and taxes have been ignored.

Payment Not Recoverable from Future Production:

710.19	Shut-in Royalty Expense	2,000	
	302 Revenue Distributions Payable		2,000
	To record a shut-in royalty.		

Payment Recoverable from Future Production:

126	Accounts Receivable—Other	2,000	
	302 Revenue Distributions Payable		2,000
	To record shut-in royalty recoverable from future production.		

120	Accounts Receivable—Oil and Gas Sales (2,000 Mcf @ $6.00)	12,000	
	602 Gas Revenue (7/8)		10,500
	302 Revenue Distributions Payable (1/8)		1,500
	To record sale of gas.		

302	Revenue Distributions Payable	1,500	
	126 Accounts Receivable—Other		1,500
	To apply royalty on current production against recoverable amount (balance recoverable, $1,500).		

GUARANTEED MINIMUM ROYALTIES

The lease agreement may stipulate guaranteed minimum royalties whereby the lessor receives a minimum royalty each year regardless of the amount of production. For example, Section 4(l) of the State of Texas leasing form in CD Reference Exhibit C calls for a minimum annual royalty after the lease's primary term equal to the annual primary term's annual delay rental. Payments made on this guaranteed basis are sometimes called fixed cash royalties and are normally recorded as a lease operating expense if incurred after proved reserves are recognized.

Nonrecoverable Minimum Royalties. When the lessor is guaranteed a nonrecoverable minimum amount of royalty each period and the value of the lessor's portion of the oil or gas produced is less than that minimum amount, then the required deficiency payments to the royalty owner are customarily treated as production expenses by both successful efforts companies and full cost companies.

Assume a nonrecoverable minimum royalty of $1,200 per month is to be paid. The first month's delivery of gas was 1,000 Mcf at $6.00 per Mcf. The 1/8th royalty earned is $750 (1/8 x $6,000). Gas revenue and minimum royalty would be recorded as follows:

120	Accounts Receivable—Oil and Gas Sales (1,000 @ $6.00)	6,000	
710.19	Minimum Royalty Expense ($1,200-$750)	450	
602	Gas Revenue (7/8 x $6,000)		5,250
302	Revenue Distributions Payable		1,200
	To record lease sale of gas. Excess of minimum royalty over 1/8 of production charged to lease operating expense.		

Some producers handle nonrecoverable minimum royalties differently. They reduce their share of revenues by the full amount of the minimum royalty paid to the lessor—regardless of whether the full amount has been earned out of production. This approach has theoretical merit, but distorts revenue-per-unit from the average sales price and hinders management's review of sales activity. The following entry displays the accounting treatment using this method:

120	Accounts Receivable—Oil and Gas Sales	6,000	
602	Gas Revenue (7/8)		5,250
302	Revenue Distributions Payable		750
	To record sale of gas and to record minimum royalty.		

Recoverable Minimum Royalties. Like shut-in royalties, if deficiency amounts of minimum (guaranteed) royalties are recoverable from future production—and it can be reasonably anticipated that future recovery will be made—minimum payments should be charged to an accounts receivable or advance payment account.

Assume a property is burdened with a minimum royalty of $2,500 per month recoverable from future royalties earned in excess of the minimum. Production for the first six months of the contract was: January, February, and March, no production; April, 4,000 Mcf; May, 12,000 Mcf; and June, 80,000 Mcf. The selling price was $6 per Mcf, and production taxes are ignored for the sake of simplicity. A schedule of recoverable minimum royalties follows:

Month	Royalty Paid	Royalty Earned	Excess Paid Over Earned	Cumulative Recoverable Balance
January	$ 2,500	$ 0	$ 2,500	$ 2,500
February	2,500	0	2,500	5,000
March	2,500	0	2,500	7,500
April	2,500	3,000	(500)	7,000
May	2,500	9,000	(6,500)	500
June	59,500	60,000	(500)	0

If recoverable guaranteed amounts are paid, any amounts recorded as a receivable should generally be charged to lease operating expense if and when it becomes likely that the amount would not be recoverable.

ACCOUNTING FOR REINJECTED GAS

Although several types of injection operations exist, accounting procedures for them are often identical. One factor that determines how transactions are recorded is the source of the natural gas.

GAS CYCLING

One Lease. When gas is produced from and reinjected into the same reservoir under a single lease agreement (or unitization agreement discussed in Chapter 23), ownership equity is undisturbed, and no royalty payments are necessary. Additionally, production taxes are generally not payable on gas injected into the same lease.

Reinjection may be done for the purpose of extracting liquids because it otherwise does not enhance the value of the gas or reduce production costs when the gas is ultimately sold. Thus, no economic value should be assigned to the reinjected gas. All income and lifting costs should be assigned to the liquids until the gas is actually sold. Statistical records should be maintained only for the gas reinjection. When it is produced the second time, sales of the reinjected gas are recorded as lease revenue.

Multiple Leases. A similar situation exists when a single reservoir into which gas is being reinjected underlies more than one tract leased by the same group of working interest owners. The treatment of the working interests' shares of gas would be the same as in the single lease situation.

However, a question of royalty payments arises because some of the gas may be produced on one lease and injected on another lease with a different royalty owner. The best solution is to secure the royalty owners' agreement to unitize, which effectively converts several leases to a single property. Injections using one lease's wells may increase production from wells on other leases producing from the same reservoir.

In the absence of such an agreement and assuming that a royalty must be paid each time gas is produced and leaves a lease, these royalty payments should be charged to the lease benefiting from the injection operations. All expenses should be considered lifting costs attributable to any oil and NGL produced from the reservoir, and none of the injected volumes should be included in revenues of the working interest owners.

GAS ACQUIRED FROM OTHER SOURCES (EXTRANEOUS GAS)

Additional accounting challenges occur if the gas used for injection (often as part of a secondary or tertiary recovery program) is either purchased from outsiders (including royalty owners) or transferred from other reservoirs owned by the producer conducting the injection program. Situations of this type are typical of many pressure maintenance operations involving the injection of gas or a combination of gas and products. For this reason, frequent references will be made to pressure maintenance operations in this section. Since the accounting problems applicable to injected gas are identical to those involving injected products, the discussion is applicable to both.

There are three general ways to account for the cost of injected purchased gas:

- Expense as incurred

- Capitalize as cost of wells and development

- Capitalize as a deferred charge to be credited as the injected gas is reproduced

If injectant costs recur over the property's productive life and are not recoverable, they may be expensed as incurred. Reproduction and sale would be recorded as current revenue (or perhaps as a reduction of production expense).

Some accountants favor charging purchases of extraneous gas and products for pressure maintenance to the well and facilities account, especially in the case of full cost companies. In this instance, costs are amortized on the basis of units produced.

Still other companies treat the cost of reinjected gas or products as a deferred charge (without amortization) until the material is recovered. A deferred charge account is similar to an inventory account. The amount recorded as an asset should represent only the recoverable value of the gas or products, and the difference between the purchase price and the amount recoverable should be charged to pressure maintenance expense of the injected reservoir at the time of injection.

If extraneous gas is injected into a reservoir, it is customary for agreements to be made with royalty owners of the leases into which gas is being injected which permit the later recovery of the extraneous gas without royalty payments. An important factor in determining appropriate accounting procedure is whether all the gas and products injected will be recoverable. Generally, some injected products and gas will remain in reservoirs because it is not economically feasible to recover all of them.

A cumulative record of gas injected must be maintained, and the volume of reproduced gas must be determined when sales are subsequently made. Production taxes and royalty payments may not be due on reproduced gas. Accounting methodologies vary:

- Use the method prescribed by the tax authority or lease agreement

- Assume all injected gas is reproduced before any gas reserves

- Assume all injected gas is produced after estimated reserves

- Assume proportionate production

Gas Purchased from Others. The purchase and subsequent reproduction of injected commodities acquired from outsiders, including amounts purchased from royalty owners on leases from which gas is transferred, are illustrated in the examples that follow. In the first instance, injected gas is charged to expense as incurred. Secondly, the injected gas is charged to a deferred charge account. Finally, assume the gas is capitalized as Costs of Wells and Development.

Recorded as an Expense:

710.21	*Operating Expense—Pressure Maint., Lease A*	1,000	
	301　*Vouchers Payable*		1,000
	To record purchased gas injected in Lease A.		

120	*Accounts Receivable—Oil and Gas Sales*	1,200	
	602　*Gas Revenue, Lease A*		1,200
	To record sale of produced natural gas.		

Recorded as a Deferred Charge:

293	Other Deferred Charges	1,000	
	301 Vouchers Payable		1,000
	To record gas purchased for injection in Lease A.		

120	Accounts Receivable—Oil and Gas Sales	1,200	
	293 Other Deferred Charges		1,000
	630 Misc. Operating Income (or Lease Operating Expenses), Lease A		200
	To record sale of natural gas previously injected.		

Recorded as Capitalized Costs of Wells and Development:

231.005	Intangible Costs of Wells and Development, Enhanced Recovery Projects	1,000	
	301 Vouchers Payable		1,000
	To record gas purchased for injection in Lease A.		

120	Accounts Receivable—Oil and Gas Sales	1,200	
	602 Gas Revenue, Lease A		1,200
	To record sale of gas from Lease A.		

Under this last approach, the capitalized cost of $1,000 becomes a part of the basis for amortization of wells and related equipment and facilities. Depreciation expense for the current year includes amortization of the injected gas costs.

Gas Transferred from Another Lease of the E&P Company. Gas production and reinjection by the same company are not generally recorded as revenue and expense items. However, they may be recorded as such to better track each field's performance—and then eliminated in consolidation. The procedure for handling the value of the E&P company's share of production reinjected in another lease follows:

Entry to Record Injection:

710.021	LOE—Pressure Maintenance, Lease A	1,000	
	602 Gas Revenue, Lease B		1,000
	To record transfer of injected gas from Lease B to Lease A.		

Consolidating Entry:

602	Gas Revenue, Lease B	1,000	
	710.021 LOE—Pressure Maintenance, Lease A		1,000
	To eliminate intracompany income on the transfer of gas from Lease B to Lease A.		

120	Accounts Receivable—Oil and Gas Sales	1,200	
	602 Gas Revenue, Lease A		1,200
	To record sale of produced natural gas.		

• • •

---

1   Overriding royalty, net profits, and production payment interests are discussed in Chapters 21 through 23.

2   Each owner's interest is based on a title opinion rendered by the legal department after examination of abstracts of title supplied by the operator of the property.

3   This division order has been developed by the National Association of Division Order Analysts (NADOA) and is the primary form used in the industry. The NADOA also publishes the *National Association of Division Order Analysts Journal* containing guidelines in writing division orders.

4   Creating an accounting cost center by well is necessary when joint venture owners elect to go nonconsent on a well where revenue interests and working interests vary by well, as discussed in Chapter 23.

5   The revenue deck includes all owners: working interest, royalty, overriding royalty, state, federal and Indian royalty owners. This deck should sum to 100 percent (with the exception of some very unique cases). Most revenue accounting systems then will set up a payable for each owner in the deck. Payables are summed by owner for all properties. On a specified date, the system prints and distributes a single revenue check to each owner for the accumulated royalty payable for a given production month.

6   Only 30 percent of respondents to the *2001 PricewaterhouseCoopers Survey of U.S. Petroleum Accounting Practices* recorded oil in lease tanks as inventory.

7   To convert to the same pressure base used in the volume measurement recorded in the accounting system.

8   The water content condition was converted to a dry condition rather than the volume converted to a saturated condition as most gas contracts specify Btu measurement in a dry condition, and most accounting systems will require the volume and Btu measurements recorded at a dry condition.

9   Contract prices stated in MMBtu are independent of gas temperature or pressure. The volume and Btu factor must be stated at the same pressure base to calculate value; however, the price may be adjusted to the pressure base of the volume rather than converting the Btu factor, as long as both the price and the Btu factor are not converted.

10 An illustration of a gas allocation statement can be found in COPAS Accounting Guideline No. 15 (AG 15), *Gas Accounting Manual*, (revised April 1993).

11 Recording the net volume of gas (the actual gross volume of NGL extracted less the volume charged as a processing fee by the processor) seems to be the method used most frequently by industry revenue accountants. Generally, given the small NGL volumes and values compared with total company energy volumes and values, recording NGL revenues net of the processing fee rather than recording the processing fee as an expense becomes a question of materiality for a particular entity to address.

12 In some states there are regulations that apply to certain types of processing plants, and the plants may have responsibility for the calculation of state production taxes, as the processing plant statement may not contain adequate information for the producer to make accurate calculations. Tax calculations and deductions will appear on the plant settlement statement.

13 An entry to record the gas taken in-kind, processing charges, and related production taxes would also need to be made; the entry would be dependent on the disposition of the in-kind gas.

14

GAS IMBALANCES

cash balancing

gas balancing agreement (GBA)

gas imbalances

Key Concepts:

- Major terms of gas balancing agreements (GBAs)

- Sales and entitlement accounting methods for producer imbalances

- Settlement of gas imbalances

- Pipeline nominations and allocations

- Settling pipeline imbalances

INTRODUCTION

Accounting for the sale of unprocessed gas was discussed and illustrated in Chapter 13, along with accounting for the sale of gas recovered from a gas plant. In those discussions, it was assumed the operator sold the product to a single purchaser. All working interest (WI) owners were allocated revenues from the gas sales in the ratio of their contractual ownership shares in the properties involved.

However, in some cases, one or more than one WI owner may be allocated and sell a volume of gas different from that owner's entitled share of production for the period. This means the other owners will have to take less than their entitled shares of production. The first owner is said to have an over-take (or over-lift), and the other owners have an under-take (or under-lift). This situation is called a producer gas imbalance, sometimes referred to as a producer/producer imbalance.

Rights and responsibilities of the joint venture's WI owners regarding producer imbalances should have been provided for in a **gas balancing agreement (GBA)** entered into early in the joint venture. A GBA is often attached as an exhibit to the joint operating agreement. Unfortunately, many operating agreements executed prior to the mid-1980s do not contain GBAs, leaving the parties to work out an acceptable solution for imbalances.

Imbalances are typically settled in this way: owners who have an under-lift in one period take an extra share of the property's future production. Alternatively, the imbalance might be settled when the owner with an over-take pays cash to the other owners in periods that follow the over-lift. Producer gas imbalances will be examined in greater detail subsequently in this chapter.

Another common type of imbalance occurs when a WI owner nominates and sells to a customer (or customers), and the pipeline delivers to that customer an amount of gas different from the WI owner's share of gas put into the pipeline. This scenario is referred to as a pipeline gas imbalance. It can also be called a producer/transporter imbalance or shipper/transporter imbalance.

Pipeline imbalances are generally more complicated and require more complex calculations than producer gas imbalances. For pipeline gas imbalances, the parties' roles and rights are largely established by contract and by pipeline rules subject to the approval of FERC.

Pipeline and producer imbalances require coordination between operators, nonoperators, consumers, and pipeline companies. COPAS Accounting Guideline No. 22 (AG 22), *Producer Gas Imbalances*, and AG 8, *Joint Task Force Guidelines on Natural Gas Administrative Issues*, provide accounting direction for **gas imbalances**. Also, EITF 90-22 provides guidance on the valuation of receivables and payables resulting from producer imbalances.

PRODUCER GAS IMBALANCES

GAS BALANCING AGREEMENTS

Typically, a GBA is an integral part of the joint operating agreement, which is executed prior to drilling a well. (It has been noted that some joint operating agreements entered into before the mid-1980s may not have GBAs attached.) The GBA serves to reduce operational and settlement conflicts and should be negotiated as soon as possible.

Though more fully addressed in COPAS AG 22, major aspects of GBAs include:

- **Balancing unit and area.** The GBA should address the geological formation covered and whether balancing will be computed on a Mcf or MMBtu basis.

- **Rights and obligations of the parties.** The agreement should address rights and obligations of both the operator and nonoperator concerning nominating gas, curtailments, operational issues, limitations on overproduced gas, and rights of parties in the event an overproduced WI owner becomes bankrupt.

- **Statement of gas balancing.** The GBA should specify the content of the statement, party responsible for its preparation, and timing of its preparation. Typically, the operator prepares the statement.

- **Ownership transfers of interest.** The agreement should address whether gas imbalances are settled in cash when a working interest is sold or transferred to a new owner.

- **Royalty and production tax payments.** The GBA should address the responsibility of each producer for paying royalties and taxes.

- **Volumetric balancing methods.** The agreement should determine what balancing alternatives (gas make-up, exchange make-up, offsetting of imbalances) are available to volumetrically settle imbalances.

- **Cash settlement methodology.** The GBA should describe the frequency of cash settlements and the valuation methodology (actual proceeds; last-in, first-out known as LIFO; first-in, first-out known as FIFO; or current market value).

DETERMINING PRODUCER GAS IMBALANCES

Each month, the production volume allocation statement is the primary source for computing producer balancing positions. The statement distributes the total quantity of gas produced based on a predetermined allocation methodology. Multiple allocation statements are prepared if a well is connected to more than one pipeline. The sum of all allocation statements for the well or property should equal the amount of total production.

A producer gas imbalance is calculated as follows:

- WI owner's share of production on the allocation statement, minus

- WI owner's entitled share of production, which is calculated by multiplying: (1) the total volume of gas produced, by (2) the WI owner's gross working interest.

If a royalty interest owner takes its royalty in-kind, the WI owner's entitled share of production is based on net revenue interest.

The operator is responsible for preparing a monthly gas balancing statement which provides each WI owner with a cumulative over- or underproduced position. Nonoperators should test the accuracy of the gas balancing statement by verifying the accuracy of their working interest, total production amounts, and allocated share of production. All discrepancies should be communicated to the operator and resolved.

SETTLING PRODUCER GAS IMBALANCES

The operator settles producer imbalances in accordance with terms of the GBA. In the absence of a GBA, WI owners determine the settlement alternatives prior to fully depleting reserves. Gas make-up, **cash balancing**, and offsetting imbalances represent the three most common methods used to settle producer gas imbalances. Under the *gas make-up* method, the underproduced owner sells gas volumes in excess of their entitled amounts; in turn, the overproduced owner sells gas volumes less than entitled in order to eliminate the imbalance. *Cash balancing* involves paying a cash settlement to the underproduced party for the imbalance volume. WI owners may also agree to *offset imbalances* of two or more wells or properties in which the owners coincidentally have ownership interests.

ACCOUNTING FOR PRODUCER GAS IMBALANCES

The sales and entitlement methods are the two methods used to account for gas sales and gas imbalances. Both are in accordance with GAAP and are permitted by the SEC. The *2001 PricewaterhouseCoopers Survey of U.S. Petroleum Accounting Practices* found that 53 percent and 40 percent of survey respondents used the sales and entitlement methods, respectively. Thirteen percent used the entitlement method for properties with large imbalances, while the sales method was elected for all other properties.

Sales Method. Under the sales method, a WI owner records revenue only when gas is produced and sold on the owner's behalf. For producer gas imbalances, no receivables or payables are recorded; instead, proved reserves are adjusted as illustrated in Figure 14-1.

When a WI owner has overproduced in excess of its share of remaining estimated reserves, the overproduced party recognizes the excessive gas imbalance as a liability on the balance sheet. An underproduced WI owner may determine that an overproduced partner's share of remaining reserves is insufficient to settle an imbalance. In this case, the underproduced party recognizes a receivable, to the extent collectible, from the overproduced owner. It is necessary for companies utilizing the sales method to create schedules that compare the cumulative over- or under-takes to remaining reserves available to settle imbalances.

Entitlement Method. Under the entitlement method, a WI owner records revenue based on its entitled share of total monthly production. When a WI owner is overproduced, the monthly excess of the value taken over the entitled value is recorded as a payable. The underproduced WI owner records a receivable and revenue for the monthly imbalance amount as illustrated in Figure 14-1.

Producer Imbalance Valuation and Disclosure. The SEC's position on producer imbalance valuation and disclosure has not changed in recent years. At a 1990 meeting of the FASB's Emerging Issues Task Force, an SEC observer noted:

- SEC staff has not taken a position on whether the sales method or entitlement method is preferable.

- If the gas imbalance is significant, companies should disclose the accounting method and the imbalance volume and value.

- Companies should disclose the effect of gas imbalances on operations, liquidity, and capital resources (EITF 90-22) in the management's discussion and analysis section of their annual report.

In addition, companies using the sales method should adjust the standardized measure of future cash flows, as well as net revenues used in the ceiling test, for any imbalances impacting proved reserves.

Figure 14-1
Illustration of Sales and Entitlement Methods

A property owned 60 percent by Owner A and 40 percent by Owner B is subject to a 20 percent royalty interest. The property produces 100,000 Mcf of natural gas in a month; 45,000 Mcf is sold by A at $4.80/Mcf and 55,000 Mcf is sold by B at $4.50/Mcf. Severance taxes are five percent. The gas imbalance is 15,000 Mcf. Net revenues for the month and the corresponding balance sheet amounts at month-end are calculated as follows:

	Entitlement Method		Sales Method	
	A	B	A	B
Revenue Calculation				
8/8ths quantities sold	60,000	40,000	45,000	55,000
Less royalty share (20%)	(12,000)	(8,000)	(9,000)	(11,000)
Net quantities sold	48,000	32,000	36,000	44,000
x price	$ 4.80	$ 4.50	$ 4.80	$ 4.50
Revenue	$230,400	$144,000	$172,800	$198,000
Severance tax expense (5%)	(11,520)	(7,200)	(8,640)	(9,900)
Revenue net of tax	$218,880	$136,800	$164,160	$188,100
Balance Sheet Entries, Dr. (Cr.)				
Accounts receivable (8/8ths)	$216,000	$247,500	$216,000	$247,500
Royalties payable (net of tax)*	(41,040)	(47,025)	(41,040)	(47,025)
Severance tax payable (8/8ths)*	(10,800)	(12,375)	(10,800)	(12,375)
Gas imbal. receivable (payable)*	72,000	(67,500)	0	0
Less related royalties (20%)	(14,400)	13,500	0	0
Less related sev. tax (5%)	(2,880)	2,700	0	0
	$218,880	$136,800	$164,160	$188,100
Reserve Calculation				
Assume beginning 8/8ths ultimate reserves are two Bcf.				
Beginning net reserves, Mcf	960,000	640,000	960,000	640,000
Less entitled prod. in month 1	(48,000)	(32,000)	(48,000)	(32,000)
+/- other quantities sold	0	0	12,000	(12,000)
- Net production deemed sold	(48,000)	(32,000)	(36,000)	(44,000)
Net ending reserves	912,000	608,000	924,000	596,000
Net ending reserves if no imbalance	912,000	608,000	912,000	608,000
+/- gas imbalance not recognized as a receivable or payable	0	0	15,000	(15,000)
Less portion for royalty	0	0	(3,000)	3,000
Net ending reserves	912,000	608,000	924,000	596,000

* The *2001 PricewaterhouseCoopers Survey of U.S. Petroleum Accounting Practices* found approximately 83 percent of respondents paid royalties and severance taxes on the sales method, and 79 percent of those using the entitlement method booked the imbalance as a receivable or payable.

Imbalance receivables and payables should be recorded using the amounts expected to be received or paid. The GBA may specify valuing the imbalance using LIFO, FIFO, average value received, or a current market method. Absent a GBA, gas imbalances are frequently recorded at the average value received when the imbalance arose or at the current market value. The SEC observer stated in the discussion of EITF 90-22, "...a receivable or liability recorded using the entitlements method should be valued at the lower of: (1) the price in effect at the time of production, (2) the current market value, or (3) if a contract is in hand, the contract price."

Depreciation, Depletion, and Amortization (DD&A). Production and estimated reserve quantities used to calculate DD&A should be based on the same method used to record revenue. An overproduced party using the sales method has greater historical revenue and production than under the entitlement method, but also has greater DD&A. When the sales method is utilized, the total remaining reserves must be adjusted for imbalance amounts in order to properly calculate a WI owner's share of remaining reserves.

Operating Expenses. Producers must ensure that operating expenses are recorded in a manner consistent with the method for recognizing revenue. Because WI owners are obligated to pay for their entitled share of operating costs on a monthly basis, the entitlement method provides a proper matching of revenues and expenses without any adjustment of expenses.

Severance Taxes. State severance taxes are usually paid based on actual sales. Consequently, the sales method provides for the proper matching of revenue with severance tax expense. Under the entitlement method, additional state severance tax should be accrued or deferred if a company is under- or overproduced. These accruals and deferrals are reversed as the imbalances are settled. In practice, companies seldom record these entries unless they are considered material.

Royalties. Companies must ensure that royalty payments are made in accordance with lease agreements and regulatory guidelines. In order to properly match cash inflow associated with gas sales, most companies pay royalties on a sales method, regardless of the method used to recognize revenue and record producer imbalances.

PIPELINE GAS IMBALANCES

ROLES OF OPERATORS AND NONOPERATORS

Field operators monitor and control the flow of gas production from wells. As part of the nomination process, operators provide estimates of monthly production to nonoperators for determining gas availability. Nonoperators selling their own gas must establish a market for their products, and must provide a nomination to the well operator or pipeline company. During the month following the gas flow, a production volume allocation statement (allocates actual production to each WI owner) is prepared by the pipeline company for review by the nonoperators.

NOMINATION PROCESS

In order for a producer to market its own gas, a nomination is made to the operator or pipeline company, as discussed in Chapter 12. If the pipeline's capacity exceeds total nominated volumes for the month, then the nomination is confirmed. However, if total nominated volumes exceed the capacity, volumes are allocated based on service type (firm versus interruptible transportation). Nominations are revised, and the producers and pipeline agree to a confirmed nomination. The producer's customer also contacts the pipeline company to confirm its nominated receipt volume. Differences between confirmed nominations and actual gas flow are minimized in order to avoid pipeline imbalance penalties. If actual production varies significantly from the confirmed nomination, the operator modifies the physical gas flow, or the nominations are revised.

ALLOCATION PROCESS

Despite the parties' efforts, physical gas flow seldom equals the total of confirmed nominated volumes. Consequently, the parties involved (operators, pipelines, shippers) execute agreements that determine an allocation method prior to physical flow (predetermined allocation methodology). These agreements consider the contractual and regulatory issues related to an allocation method. Common allocation methods include: (1) pro-rata allocation based on confirmed nominations, and (2) allocation based on entitlements. Agreements also specify the party responsible for preparing the monthly production volume allocation statement, timing for the allocation statement preparation, and the format of the statement. It is reviewed by the other WI owners, and any discrepancies are discussed. Overdeliveries or underdeliveries to the pipeline are recorded by the producer as receivables or payables, respectively.

The following example illustrates the confirmed nominations and entitlements methods. Property that is owned 60 percent by Owner A and 40 percent by Owner B is expected to produce 100,000 Mcf of gas in the next month. Owners A and B make confirmed nominations of 70,000 Mcf and 30,000 Mcf, respectively. The mainline pipeline index price is $5.70 MMBtu, which equates to $6/Mcf. If actual production is 80,000 Mcf, allocations based on the confirmed nominations and entitlements methods are:

Confirmed Nomination Allocation:	Owner A	Owner B
Total actual production	80,000 Mcf	80,000 Mcf
Percentage of production nominated	x 70 %	x 30 %
Allocated actual production	56,000 Mcf	24,000 Mcf

Entitlement Allocation:	Owner A	Owner B
Total actual production	80,000 Mcf	80,000 Mcf
Ownership percentage	x 60 %	x 40 %
Allocated actual production	48,000 Mcf	32,000 Mcf

Assuming the pipeline company delivers each owner's confirmed nomination to their customers, Owners A and B record a pipeline imbalance receivable or payable for the overproduced or underproduced volumes as follows:

Confirmed Nomination Allocation:	Owner A	Owner B
Allocated production	56,000 Mcf	24,000 Mcf
Less confirmed nomination	(70,000) Mcf	(30,000) Mcf
Gas imbalance payable to pipeline	(14,000) Mcf	(6,000) Mcf
x Pipeline index price	x $6 /Mcf	x $6 /Mcf
Pipeline imbalance liability	$(84,000)	$(36,000)

Owners A and B record a pipeline imbalance liability of $84,000 and $36,000, respectively. Owner A is allocated 56,000 Mcf and receives sales proceeds on that basis, although its 60 percent net revenue interest (NRI) share is 48,000 Mcf. A producer gas imbalance of 8,000 Mcf is owed by Owner A to Owner B, which gives Owner A imbalances netting to a 22,000 Mcf payable and giving Owner B imbalances netting to a 2,000 Mcf receivable, as follows:

Entitlement Allocation:	Owner A	Owner B
Allocated production	48,000 Mcf	32,000 Mcf
Less confirmed nomination	(70,000) Mcf	(30,000) Mcf
Gas imbalance receivable from (payable to) pipeline	(22,000) Mcf	2,000 Mcf
x Pipeline index price	x $6 /Mcf	x $6 /Mcf
Pipeline imbalance asset (liability)	$(132,000)	$12,000

Owner A records a pipeline imbalance payable of $132,000, and Owner B records a pipeline imbalance receivable of $12,000. Notice that under the entitlement allocation method, Owner A owes no gas to Owner B, i.e., there is no producer gas imbalance. Instead, Owner A owes the entire 22,000 Mcf imbalance to the pipeline.

SETTLEMENT PROCESS

Producers and transporters must agree on how to settle imbalances. After implementation of FERC Order 636, three common methods are used to settle pipeline imbalances. The *imbalance trading method* provides that two different shippers on the same pipeline can trade their under- and overdelivered positions in order to offset any imbalances. *Volumetric imbalance make-ups* occur when a producer separately identifies and nominates additional or lesser volumes in order to settle under- or overdeliveries. Finally, under the *cash in/out method*, a producer pays or receives cash for pipeline imbalance under- or overdeliveries.

In the example of Owners A and B, a mainline index price is used to value the under- and overdeliveries. Imbalances are valued according to the contractual requirements of the pipeline's tariff, which may require that imbalances be valued at: (1) current mainline index prices, (2) the pipeline's weighted average cost of goods sold (WACOG), (3) a weighted average sales price, or another accepted method. Additionally, a pipeline company can assess penalties for imbalance volumes that exceed specific tolerances in the tariff. Producers should assess the carrying value of unsettled pipeline imbalances to ensure that the amounts agree with the pipeline tariff and any penalties have been properly accrued.

Accounting. Pipeline gas imbalances are generally recorded as accounts receivable or payable at values consistent with contractual arrangements with the pipeline company.

Terms of the GBA should be analyzed to determine whether the definition of a derivative under FAS 133 has been met. In particular, the option in the GBA may not meet criteria 6(a) (as further clarified by the guidance in FAS 133 Implementation Issue No. A6, *Notional Amounts of Commodity Contracts*) with respect to a notional amount, even though it may meet criterion 6(c) as discussed in paragraph 9, in part because the gas is readily convertible to cash. Even if the GBA meets the definition of a derivative, the cash price used in settlement may result in the derivative always having a fair value of zero. Nevertheless, the disclosures specified in paragraphs 44 and 45 of FAS 133 are still required. The option feature of the GBA, if it meets the definition of a derivative, could not qualify for the normal purchases and normal sales exception in paragraph 10(b). This is because GBAs are option contracts, and it is not probable at inception and throughout the term of the arrangement that these contracts will not always settle net and always result in physical delivery. See a further discussion of derivatives and FAS 133 in Chapter 33.

Underproduced parties should consider the creditworthiness of overproduced owners to ensure that the carrying value of the receivable is collectible. If a portion of the receivable is uncollectible, the balance should be adjusted to the amount expected to be received.

• • •

15

PRODUCTION COSTS

Glossary Terms

clean-out costs

Key Concepts:

- **Definition of production costs**

- **Exceptions to direct expense of production costs**

- **Accumulating lease operating expenses by well or by area**

- **Types of accounts used for recording production costs**

- **Use of apportionment accounts for indirect production expenses**

PRODUCTION COSTS DEFINED

Reg. S-X Rule 4-10(a)(17) defines production costs as:

(i) Costs incurred to operate and maintain wells and related equipment and facilities, including depreciation and applicable operating costs of support equipment and facilities and other costs of operating and maintaining those wells and related equipment and facilities. They become part of the cost of oil and gas produced. Examples of production costs (sometimes called lifting costs) are:

(A) Costs of labor to operate the wells and related equipment and facilities

(B) Repairs and maintenance

(C) Materials, supplies, fuel consumed and supplies utilized in operating the wells and related equipment and facilities

(D) Property taxes and insurance applicable to proved properties and wells and related equipment and facilities

(E) Severance taxes

(ii) Certain support equipment or facilities may serve two or more oil and gas producing activities, and may also assist in transporting, refining, and marketing. Depreciation and operating costs for producing activities are classified as exploration, development, or production costs. Depreciation, depletion, and amortization of capitalized acquisition, exploration, and development costs are not production costs but also become part of the cost of oil and gas produced along with production costs identified above.

ACCOUNTING FOR PRODUCTION COSTS

Production costs (also referred to as lease operating expenses or lifting costs) are generally expensed as incurred. However, two exceptions exist:

- Recording oil and gas inventory at cost

- Accrual or deferral of production costs associated with gas imbalances using the sales method of accounting

The first exception recognizes that production costs might otherwise be allocable to inventory and cost of goods sold. However, because oil and gas inventories are often insignificant, E&P balance sheets do not always report them. In fact, the *2001 PricewaterhouseCoopers Survey of U.S. Petroleum Accounting Practices* found that only nine (30 percent) of 30 responding companies recorded a financial statement asset for oil inventory in the field.

The sales method of accounting for gas imbalances relates to the second exception mentioned. Application of this method involves an accrual or deferral of production costs in order to more closely match expenses with related revenues. Chapter 14 presents a further discussion of accounting for gas imbalances.

Petroleum accountants should be familiar with the functional accounts that are commonly used by E&P companies to capture production costs. Sufficient detail must be collected in the accounting system to satisfy GAAP requirements and meet the needs of management and partners in evaluating operations. Accounting records should also furnish the necessary data for federal income tax purposes, as addressed in Chapter 26.

THE COST CENTER

For financial reporting, lease operating expenses can be aggregated either country-wide or by large geographical area. Records at the well and lease levels are most important for management control, joint interest billings (Chapter 10), reserve determination (Chapter 16), and income tax reporting (Chapter 26). While some costs are readily identifiable with a well or lease, other costs must be allocated using a reasonable basis.

ACCUMULATION OF COSTS

In ABC Oil Company, lease operating expenses that are closely related to individual leases are charged directly to Account 710—Lease Operating Expenses (see Appendix 3). Indirect costs are accumulated in Accounts 350 through 369 (known as the clearing and apportionment accounts) and are then allocated to the operating expenses of individual leases. Classifications of specific costs vary by company. Some are considered indirect because of the nature of the cost item itself, e.g. depreciation of support facilities and salt water disposal costs. Others are categorized as indirect because of the practical aspects of cost accumulation.

The following list contains the Appendix 3 subaccounts for Lease Operating Expenses:

Subaccount Number	Subaccount Name	Direct/Indirect
001	Salaries and Wages	Direct
002	Employee Benefits	Direct
003	Contract Pumping Services	Direct
004	Well Services and Workovers	Direct or Indirect
005	Repairs and Maintenance of Surface Equipment	Direct
006	Fuel, Water, and Lubrication	Direct
007	Supplies	Direct
008	Auto and Truck Expenses	Direct or Indirect
009	Supervision	Indirect
010	Ad Valorem Taxes	Direct
011	Production and Severance Taxes	Direct
012	Other Taxes	Direct
013	Compressor Rentals	Direct
014	Insurance	Direct or Indirect
015	Salt Water Disposal	Direct or Indirect
016	Treating Expenses	Direct or Indirect
017	Environment and Safety	Direct
018	Overhead	Indirect
019	Shut-in and Minimum Royalties	Direct
020	Other Royalties	Direct
021	Pressure Maintenance	Direct
022	Other	Direct or Indirect

It may not be immediately clear how a particular cost is classified because subaccounts tend to be a mixture of classification by nature (salaries, supplies, insurance) and by function (well service, repairs, auto and truck). Each E&P company establishes its own practice. For example, if ABC Oil Company uses field labor in well services activities, the labor cost is charged to subaccount Salaries and Wages, rather than to subaccount Well Services and Workover. The classification system in use should be clearly understood and consistently followed by all personnel.

DIRECT PRODUCTION COSTS

Direct production costs are costs closely related to the production of oil or gas on specific mineral properties. Such expenses are largely controlled at the lease operating level. Several direct production costs are described in this section along with related accounting entries.

Salaries and Wages. Field employees consist of pumpers, gaugers, roustabouts, and other employees ranked below first-level supervisors. Employed directly on producing properties, they are concerned with the basic lease, facility operations, and routine maintenance. Time sheets are customarily used to record the hours spent on each job, well, or lease; these documents are the basis for charges to individual properties or wells, which normally occur during the monthly joint interest billing cycle.

Employee Benefits. Employee benefits are considered part of the total cost of labor and are allocated to individual leases. Many companies use estimates based on the ratio of employee benefits to direct labor costs. For example, ABC Oil Company assumes its employee benefits represent 20 percent of direct labor costs. Actual charges for health care premiums and other benefits are recorded in Account 903, Employee Benefits. At each pay period (or perhaps monthly), ABC debits the Lease Operating Expenses account and credits Employee Benefits for 20 percent of its actual labor costs.

Contract Pumping Services. It is common for individuals to render pumping and routine maintenance services to oil and gas companies on a contract basis. In this case, an individual enters into an agreement with a company to render certain services on selected properties for a defined amount. Compensation is tied to the number of wells, locations, type of services, time schedules, and other factors. The individual serves as an independent contractor and is not considered an employee of the company. Invoices cover all contract expenses, including time, vehicle usage, and travel. Unusual items are separately billed to the company for approval. Monthly invoices from contractors should provide the details necessary for accounting entries.

Well Services and Workovers. The accounting treatment accorded well services and workovers depends on the company. As noted in the glossary, workovers are remedial operations undertaken to maintain maximum oil-producing rates. Some companies include repairs to sucker rods, tubing, and wellhead connections in this category, while others treat them as repairs. Similarly, there is a question of which workover costs are charged to operating expense and which should be capitalized.

ABC Oil Company charges its Production Expense subaccount for costs of repairing sucker rods and tubing, costs of pulling rods and tubing, repairing well head connections, swabbing, **clean-out costs**, scraping paraffin, and replacing or servicing gas lift valves. In general, all repairs to wells or equipment in the wells are charged to this subaccount. Costs of outside services relating to reconditioning, repairing, or reworking a producing well are expensed to this subaccount. Similarly, it is charged for services to restore efficient operating conditions, such as reperforating casing, repairing casing leaks, or acidizing and shooting.

The costs of workovers that result in an increase in proved reserves are capitalized. Projects that call for deepening the well to another horizon or attempting to secure production from a shallower horizon (i.e., recompleting), or improving (not restoring) access to proved reserves from a producing horizon (e.g., fracing or lateral drilling), are treated as drilling costs. If the deeper drilling or attempted recompletion at a shallower horizon involves proved reserves at that horizon, then any costs are considered development costs and should be capitalized. Efforts to secure production in a horizon not already proved are treated as exploratory drilling costs; such costs are capitalized only if new proved reserves are found.

Repairs and Maintenance of Surface Equipment. Costs of repairing lease equipment (such as tank batteries, separators, flow lines, lease buildings, engines, motors, other above ground production equipment, and lease roads) are charged to this account. In general, costs related to repairs of the well or subsurface well equipment are charged to the Well Service and Workover account. When company employees are utilized, labor costs are usually charged to Salaries and Wages rather than to Repairs and Maintenance.

Ad Valorem, Production, and Severance Taxes. As discussed more fully in Chapter 13, ad valorem taxes are accrued as lease operating expenses based on a reasonable estimate of the amount to be assessed for the period. Production and severance taxes are recorded when the related production occurs or when the revenue on which they are based is recorded. These taxes are based on either the value of the product being sold or the volume of product sold (or a combination).

The following example illustrates how an entry for production taxes is recorded. Assume ABC Oil Company's share of production from the Magness lease for June 2006 was 10,000 barrels of oil, which sold for $60.00 per barrel. State production taxes imposed were six percent of gross value. The oil purchaser makes all necessary disbursements. The entry to record these items is:

120	Accounts Receivable—Oil and Gas Sales		564,000	
710.011	LOE—Production Taxes		36,000	
	601	Crude Oil Revenue		600,000
	To record production and sale of crude oil together with related taxes from the Magness lease for June 2006.			

INDIRECT PRODUCTION COSTS

Indirect production costs are: (1) costs not closely related to oil and gas production on specific leases, and (2) costs not controllable at the lease level. They are accounted for in much the same way as overhead costs: costs of a function or activity are accumulated and then allocated to individual properties on the basis of direct labor hours, direct labor costs, number of wells, time of equipment use, volume of service rendered, volume of production, or other reasonable basis. ABC chooses to accumulate such costs in its clearing and apportionment accounts (Accounts 350 through 369).

For some companies, there may be expenses incurred at the central administrative offices that might be production costs related to oil and gas producing activities. Companies should have a clear understanding of the nature of the expenses to ensure all production costs are appropriately accumulated and classified. General corporate overhead should not be included as a component of a company's production costs.

Depreciation of Support Facilities. Virtually all clearing and apportionment accounts involve the depreciation of tangible real and/or personal property. While Oi5.117 states that successful efforts accounting capitalizes the costs of all support equipment and facilities used in oil and gas producing activities, no mention is given to the method of depreciating these costs. The choice of depreciation method is left to the experience of the company. Support equipment and facilities are usually depreciated using either the straight-line or declining balance method.

Salt Water Disposal. Salt water is a frequent byproduct of oil and gas production. Because it is a waste item, it must be disposed of in an environmentally safe manner. Customarily, salt water from a well is gathered and reinjected into a subsurface formation.

If only one property is served by a particular salt water disposal system, expenses are considered direct costs and are charged to Lease Operating Expense, Account 710-015.

When more than one lease is served by a system, a means of apportioning the costs must be determined. If the ratio of water to oil does not differ significantly among properties served by a system, an apportionment based on the number of wells served is appropriate. However, if the oil-to-water ratio differs significantly among properties served, a charge based on the volume of salt water handled may be appropriate.

For example, assume that the oil-to-water ratio is about the same from each well in a reservoir served by salt water disposal system 24010. Costs of operating the system for the month of June 2006 were $40,000. This system serves the Magness B lease (24007), which has two producing wells, and Parker B (24008) and Parker C (24009) leases, each with four producing wells. The entry to apportion costs is:

710-015	Salt Water Disposal, Lease 24007	8,000	
710-015	Salt Water Disposal, Lease 24008	16,000	
710-015	Salt Water Disposal, Lease 24009	16,000	
352	Support Facilities Expenses		40,000
	To record apportionment of the expense of salt water disposal system.		

Other Apportionment Accounts. Other apportionment accounts (also called clearing accounts) may be used by E&P companies. Charges accumulated in these accounts are ultimately apportioned to individual lease operating expense accounts or asset accounts. The primary problems with apportionment accounts relate to choosing a reasonable basis for allocating and measuring the activity related to each lease. Typical methods for apportioning costs are:

- **District Expenses.** Allocated among acquisition, exploration, development, and production functions. The portion allocated to production is further allocated to individual properties based on the number of producing wells.

- **Region Expenses.** Relate to operation of the regional offices and other regional activities and are initially allocated to districts on the basis of individual district expenditures. They are then treated as other district expenses.

- **Drilling Equipment Expenses.** Apportioned to exploratory wells and development wells on a footage-rate or day rate basis.

- **Air Compressor Plant and Systems Expenses.** Normally apportioned on a volume basis.

- **Dwelling Expenses.** Allocated in the same manner as district expenses.

- **Electric Power System Expenses.** Apportioned based on power usage.

- **Fire Protection System Expenses.** Allocated according to the number of wells or facilities in the service area.

- **Gas Compressor Plant Expenses.** Apportioned based on volumes.

- **Gas Gathering System Expenses.** Apportioned based on volumes and/or wells served.

- **Oil Gathering System Expenses.** Apportioned based on volumes and/or number of wells served.

- **Salt Water Disposal System Expenses.** Apportioned based on volumes and/or wells served.

- **Water Flooding System Expenses.** Allocated by volumes of water used.

- **Other Services Facilities Expenses.** Allocated by number of hours or number of days used.

- **Transportation Equipment Expenses.** Allocated by number of miles driven or hours used.

- **Warehouse and Shop Expenses.** Allocated on the basis of number of items issued, cost of items issued, or direct labor hours for each lease.

The essential factor in the use of clearing or apportionment accounts is arriving at a reasonable basis for charging costs to the activities using the services.

PRODUCTION COSTS STATEMENTS

Production costs statements, or lease operating statements, are prepared monthly for each well, lease, or property. Since an individual property is often used as a cost center for successful efforts accounting, these statements serve as a kind of income statement. Some companies' statements include revenue from production, while others show expenses only. Details of all items are reported for the current month along with year-to-date totals. Any additional information provided depends on the entity. For ABC Oil Company, a portion of the Lease Operating Statement for Lease No. 24001 (having a one-eighth royalty) is shown in Figure 15-1.

Figure 15-1: Lease Operating Statement

ABC Oil Company			**Lease:**	Mag #24001
LEASE OPERATING STATEMENT			**WI:**	60.0%
2006			**NRI:**	52.5%

	January	February		Year To Date
8/8ths Volumes Sold:				
Oil bbls	315	312	*Ten more*	3,600
Gas Mcf	1,200	1,150	*monthly*	12,000
NGL bbls	0	0	*columns*	0
			exist on a	
ABC's Sales Prices:			*standard*	
Oil $/bbl	$60.50	$60.90	*lease*	$62.00
Gas $/Mcf	$5.42	$5.90	*operating*	$5.30
NGL $/bbl	$0.00	$0.00	*statement.*	$0.00
Per BOE at 6 Mcf: 1bbl	$49.63	$51.20		$51.21
Revenues @ 8/8ths:				
Oil	$19,057	$19,001		$223,200
Gas	6,504	6,785		63,600
NGL	0	0		0
Total revenues	25,561	25,786		286,800
Less Royalties & ORRIs	(3,195)	(3,223)		(35,850)
WI Revenues @ 100%	22,366	22,563		250,950
WI Expenses @ 100%:				
001 Salaries & wages	0	0		0
002 Employee benefits	0	0		0
003 Contract pumping	250	250		3,000
Other subaccounts	600	955		8,248
(Refer to App. 3 list of accts.)				
020 Other expenses	0	0		0
Total expenses	850	1,205		11,248
WI Net Cash Flow @ 100%	$21,516	$21,358		$239,702
ABC's Share:				
Revenue	$13,420	$13,538		$150,570
Expenses	(510)	(723)		(6,749)
Cash flow	$12,910	$12,815		$143,821
Revenue per BOE	$49.63	$51.20		$51.21
Expenses per BOE	(1.89)	(2.73)		(2.30)
Cash flow per BOE	$47.74	$48.47		$48.91

• • •

16

OIL AND GAS RESERVES

Key Concepts:

- **Definitions of reserves and categories of unproved, proved, probable, and possible reserves**

- **Classifications of proved reserves: proved developed and undeveloped reserves**

- **Methods for estimating and reporting proved reserves, including analogy, volumetrics, performance curves, and material balance analysis**

- **Elements of reserve production schedules**

INTRODUCTION

E&P financial reporting is highly dependent on proved reserves information as indicated in the following list:

- Under successful efforts accounting, exploratory well costs are capitalized only if they result in finding proved reserves (Chapter 6).

- Capitalized costs of proved properties are amortized on a units-of-production basis using the ratio of volumes currently produced to the sum of those volumes and remaining proved reserves (Chapter 17).

- Proved properties' net capitalized costs are limited to certain computations of value based on reserves (including proved reserves) (Chapters 18 and 19).

- Reserves (including proved reserves) are used in determining whether and to what extent a gain is recognized in certain conveyances of oil and gas property (Chapters 22 through 24).

- Reserves (including proved reserves) are used to determine the fair value of oil and gas properties in business combinations (Chapter 30).

- Public companies must disclose certain supplemental unaudited information on the proved reserves volumes (Chapter 29) and certain values attributable to the proved reserves (Chapter 31) with audited financial statements.

GENERAL DEFINITIONS AND CATEGORIES

Reserves are considered one of the categories of overall oil and gas resources. Reserves estimates are usually made by petroleum reservoir engineers, and occasionally by geologists.

Various definitions of reserves are used throughout the world, and many major countries such as Russia, China, and Norway have their own definitions. In the U.S., the SEC sets the definition of reserves, specifically proved reserves, for use in financial reporting and in other reports to shareholders of companies regulated by the SEC. Historically, reserves definitions also have been developed and maintained by certain professional societies, including the Society of Petroleum Engineers (SPE).

In March 2007, the SPE, in conjunction with the World Petroleum Council (WPC), the American Association of Petroleum Geologists (AAPG), and the Society of Petroleum Evaluation Engineers (SPEE), issued a common framework for reserves definitions known as the *Petroleum Resources Management System*. The system replaced joint industry guidelines issued in 1997, 2000, and 2001. Under the new framework, reserves of oil and gas are defined as:

> ...those quantities of petroleum anticipated to be commercially recoverable by application of development projects to known accumulations from a given date forward under defined conditions. Reserves must further satisfy four criteria: they must be discovered, recoverable, commercial, and remaining (as of the evaluation date) based on the development project(s) applied. Reserves are further categorized in accordance with the level of certainty associated with the estimates and may be sub-classified based on project maturity and/or characterized by development and production status.

Figure 16-1 provides an illustration of the industry's resources classification framework.

Figure 16-1
Resources Classification Framework

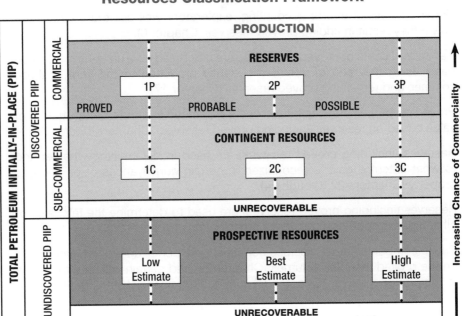

Source: Society of Petroleum Engineers,www.spe.org

Two significant attributes of the SPE/WPC/AAPG/SPEE (for brevity SPE/WPC) definitions are: (1) acceptance by four well-respected industry organizations, and (2) inclusion of deterministic and probabilistic methods for expressing reserves estimates. A method is considered deterministic if a single best estimate of reserves is made based on known geological, engineering, and economic data. Probabilistic describes the method when known geological, engineering, and economic data are used to generate a range of estimates and their associated probabilities.

Before addressing the categories of reserves, several important points must be noted:

- *Financial reporting uses a definition of proved reserves adopted by the SEC in 1978.* SEC definitions are not consistent with the new *Petroleum Reserves Management System*. In fact, many have expressed a view that the SEC reserves definitions need to be revised to consider the current environment, newer technology, market evolution and other issues. At the present time, however, no changes have been considered by the SEC staff.

- Reserves are expressed in volumes rather than in dollars or energy content. Some definitions refer to quantities rather than volumes and recognize that reserves may be expressed by weight (e.g., metric tons of oil) or energy content (e.g., MMBtu of gas).

- The amounts of reserves and recoverable resources change as economic factors change. In general, if the price of oil goes up faster than production costs, more oil can be commercially recovered, and reserves will increase.

If oil prices decline, reserves typically decrease. Reserves are estimated "as of" a given date (e.g., *as of* December 31, 2006, and not *for the year ended* December 31, 2006). The "as of" date should be included when reporting a reserves estimate.

- The terms estimated reserves, reserves quantities, and remaining reserves are redundant, since reserves are estimated remaining volumes. However, in the industry such terms are generally accepted in emphasizing key characteristics of reserves.

- The reliability of reserves estimates is subject to the reliability of available underlying geologic and engineering data and the experience, expertise, and judgment of the estimator.

- All reserves estimates reflect some degree of uncertainty.

Within the SPE/WPC definitions, proved reserves are:

...those quantities of petroleum, which by analysis of geological and engineering data, can be estimated with reasonable certainty to be commercially recoverable, from a given date forward, from known reservoirs and under current economic conditions, operating methods, and government regulations. . . . If deterministic methods are used, the term reasonable certainty is intended to express a high degree of confidence that the quantities will be recovered. If probabilistic methods are used, there should be at least a 90% probability that the quantities actually recovered will equal or exceed the estimate. [Author's note: SEC definitions are based on the deterministic approach.]

Subclassifications of proved reserves are addressed later in this chapter. These include proved developed producing reserves, proved developed non-producing reserves, and proved undeveloped reserves. *Petroleum accountants should be aware that SEC definitions are the ones always used for financial reporting purposes.*

Unproved reserves as defined by the SPE/WPC are:

...based on geologic and/or engineering data similar to that used in estimates of Proved Reserves, but technical or other uncertainties preclude such reserves being classified as Proved. Unproved Reserves may be further categorized as Probable and Possible Reserves.

Unproved reserves are not reported to the SEC or used for financial accounting purposes, such as in calculating DD&A. However, risk-adjusted unproved reserves, particularly probable reserves, may be used in developing expected cash flows and fair values in allocating purchase price in business combinations or accounting for impairment of long-lived assets (Chapter 18).

Probable reserves according to the SPE/WPC are:

...those additional Reserves that are less likely to be recovered than Proved Reserves but more certain to be recovered than Possible Reserves. It is equally likely that actual remaining quantities recovered will be greater than or less than the sum of the estimated Proved plus Probable Reserves. In this context, when probabilistic methods are used, there should be at least a 50% probability that the actual quantities recovered will equal or exceed the...[sum of estimated Proved plus Probable Reserves].

Probable reserves refer to additional reserves that will likely become proven with further drilling or successful testing (or implementation) of a new enhanced recovery project. They also refer to incremental reserves not recoverable under existing economic conditions, but recoverable based on expected favorable changes in economic conditions.

SPE/WPC defines possible reserves as:

> ...those additional reserves which analysis of geoscience and engineering data suggest are less likely to be recoverable than Probable Reserves. The total quantities ultimately recovered from the project have a low probability to exceed the sum of Proved plus Probable plus Possible..When probabilistic methods are used, there should be at least a 10% probability that the actual quantities recovered will equal or exceed the...[sum of estimated Proved plus Probable plus Possible Reserves].

SEC PROVED RESERVES DEFINITIONS

The SEC has adopted definitions of proved, proved developed, and proved undeveloped reserves. FAS 25, paragraph 7, provides that for FAS 19 and FAS 25 *petroleum accountants should use the SEC definitions in effect on the date(s) reserves disclosures are to be made*. Thus, as the SEC modifies its definitions, applicable FAS definitions automatically change to meet them. When this book was written in mid-2007, the SEC had not changed its definitions to accept the new SPE/WPC definitions.

PROVED RESERVES

Reg. S-X Rule 4-10(a)(2) defines proved oil and gas reserves as:

> ...the estimated quantities of crude oil, natural gas and natural gas liquids which geological and engineering data demonstrate with reasonable certainty to be recoverable in future years from known reservoirs under existing economic and operating conditions, i.e., prices and costs as of the date the estimate is made. Prices include consideration of changes in existing prices provided only by contractual arrangements, but not on escalations based upon future conditions... [Note: the SEC requirement uses the deterministic approach ("reasonable certainty") rather than the probabilistic approach ("90 percent certainty").]

Based on industry practices and the authors' observations, the following guidance is offered on how to apply the phrase "existing economic and operating conditions" to proved reserves as of the period-end (e.g., December 31 for calendar year-end companies):

- The phrase "the date the estimate is made" refers to the "as of" date of the financials, such as December 31– not the date when the December 31 reserves estimate is made which might be several weeks earlier or afterwards. If December 31 proved oil reserves are estimated in early December, based on a November 30 spot price of $60 per barrel, but the price at December 31 is $58 per barrel, then the estimate should be revised to reflect December 31 pricing. This is done even if by mid-January of the following year the price recovers to $60 per barrel.[1]

- Reserves should reflect oil, gas, and NGL spot prices at period-end, such as December 31, except to the extent of pricing determinable under sales contracts existing at December 31. The spot price should reflect the value of the proved reserves at the physical location, adjusted for quality differences. For example, assume for a given field, the December 31 spot price is $5.60/MMBtu. A contract in December calls for the sale of one Bcf of gas from the field in the subsequent calendar year at a price of $6.00 per MMBtu, while a second contract calls for the sale of two Bcf of gas at five cents over index prices. The $6.00 determinable price is used for one Bcf of reserves to be produced in the subsequent year. All other gas is priced at the $5.60 spot price (consistent with SAB Topic 12A, Item 2, Question 1). The contract price based on index pricing is not fixed and determinable at December 31.

- Absent fixed and determinable contract prices, the oil, gas, and NGL market (spot) prices on December 31 (for a calendar year-end company) should be used even though such prices may be materially higher or lower than the actual realized prices for December or January. Historically, many companies have used the December average actual prices received when such prices are close approximations of the month-end prices. However, as more fully explained in Chapter 29, the SEC staff issued an interpretation on its website that an average price for any period was not a suitable proxy for the year-end price required by FAS 69 for the standardized measure. SAB Topic 12A, Item 2, Questions 1 and 2, calls for determining year-end reserves by using "current market prices" at year-end. Hence, the SEC staff objects to average prices or any pricing that does not reflect the year-end spot price, unless it reflects firm contracts with determinable prices.

- Spot prices are volatile. Thus, average annual gas prices or projected average prices are often used for determining proved reserves for purposes other than GAAP financial. However, such prices are not suitable for determining proved reserves under the SECs definition. SEC rules unequivocally require the use of a period-end spot price for determining reserves under SEC definitions. The spot price used for proved reserves estimates is based typically on the cash market price as determined on the transaction date, adjusted for appropriate differentials. Methods of measuring the spot price must be consistently applied.

- Production and severance tax rates used to calculate the value of estimated proved reserves should reflect laws enacted as of period-end. For example, for a state law enacted in October 2006 raising the tax rate from five percent to six percent effective January 1, 2007, the rate for estimating the proved reserves recoverable under December 31, 2006, economic conditions would be six percent (for a company with a calendar year-end).

- Future operating costs should reflect rates incurred as of period-end applied to all expected future operations including major maintenance such as workovers.

The SEC definition of proved oil and gas reserves continues as follows:

Reservoirs are considered proved if economic productivity is supported by either actual production or conclusive formation test. The area of a reservoir considered proved includes (a) that portion delineated by drilling and defined by gas-oil or oil-water contacts, if any, and (b) the immediately adjoining portions not yet drilled, but which can be reasonably judged as economically productive on the basis of available geological and engineering data. In the absence of information on fluid contacts, the lowest known structural occurrence of hydrocarbons controls the lower proved limit of the reservoir.

Reservoirs that can be produced economically through application of improved recovery techniques (such as fluid injection) are included in the proved classification if successful testing by a pilot project, or the operation of an installed program in the reservoir, provides support for the engineering analysis on which the project or program was based.

Estimates of proved reserves do not include the following: (A) oil that may become available from known reservoirs but is classified separately as "indicated additional reserves"; (B) crude oil, natural gas, and natural gas liquids, the recovery of which is subject to reasonable doubt because of uncertainty as to geology, reservoir characteristics, or economic factors; (C) crude oil, natural gas, and natural gas liquids, that may occur in undrilled prospects; and (D) crude oil, natural gas, and natural gas liquids that may be recovered from oil shales, coal, gilsonite, and other such sources.

PROVED DEVELOPED AND UNDEVELOPED RESERVES

The same Reg. S-X Rule 4-10(a)(2) defines proved developed reserves as:

...reserves that can be expected to be recovered through existing equipment and operating methods. Additional oil and gas expected to be obtained through the application of fluid injection or other improved recovery techniques for supplementing the natural gas forces and mechanisms of primary recovery should be included as proved developed reserves only after testing by a pilot project or after the operation of an installed program has confirmed through production response that increased recovery will be achieved.

Reg. S-X Rule 4-10(a)(4) defines proved undeveloped reserves as:

...reserves that are expected to be recovered from new wells on undrilled acreage, or from existing wells for which a relatively major expenditure is required for recompletion. Reserves on undrilled acreage should be limited to those drilling units offsetting productive units that are reasonably certain of production when drilled. Proved reserves for other undrilled units can be claimed only if it can be demonstrated with certainty that there is continuity of production from the existing productive formation. Under no circumstances should estimates for proved undeveloped reserves be attributable to any acreage for which an application of fluid injection or other improved recovery technique is contemplated, unless such techniques have been proved effective by actual tests in the area and in the same reservoir.

The SEC reserve definitions for proved developed and proved undeveloped reserves specifically state that estimated quantities of oil expected to be obtained through application of fluid injection or other improved recovery techniques are proved only if testing or operations have been successful in the same (pressure-connected) reservoir. The SPE/WPC definition requires only that such tests or operations have been successful in a reservoir in the immediate area with similar rock and fluid properties. This is a most significant difference between the SEC and SPE/WPC definitions.

The SEC reserves definitions are augmented by SAB Topic 12, which is presented in CD Reference Exhibit A. Two points from the Topic 12 document should be noted in this discussion:

- Net NGL reserves are related to the leasehold in which ownership is held and not to NGL received for operating or owning the gas processing plant at which the NGL were recovered (SAB Topic 12A, Item 1).

- Coalbed methane is not gas derived from coal and should be included in proved gas reserves (SAB Topic 12G).

SUBCATEGORIES OF PROVED DEVELOPED RESERVES

Proved developed producing reserves are expected to be recovered from completion intervals producing at the time of the estimate.

Two types of *proved developed nonproducing reserves* exist—shut-in and **behind-pipe reserves**. Shut-in reserves are those reserves expected to be recovered from completion intervals that were open at the time of the reserves estimate, but were not producing for one of three reasons:

- The well was intentionally shut-in for market conditions such as a perceived temporary decline in oil or gas prices.

- The well had not yet begun production from the completed interval (perhaps because production equipment or pipelines were not yet installed).

- Mechanical difficulties have not been corrected as yet.

Behind-pipe reserves are those reserves expected to be recovered from completion interval(s) not yet open, but remain behind casing in existing wells. Such wells are usually producing, but from another completion interval. Additional completion work is needed before behind-pipe reserves can be produced. A requirement for behind-pipe reserves to be developed is that they can be produced with minimal capital expenditures relative to the cost of drilling another well. If the capital costs are large, these reserves must be called proved undeveloped reserves.

RESERVES ESTIMATION

Reserves estimation is a complex, imprecise process requiring a synthesis of diverse data about the geologic environment, reservoir rock structure and other characteristics, and engineering analyses of the interrelationships among reservoir fluids, pressure, temperature, operating practices, markets, prices, and operating costs. In estimating reserves, an engineer's judgment is influenced by existing knowledge and technology. Economic conditions, applicable statutory and regulatory provisions, and the purposes for the reserves information are also considered. As a field is developed and produced, more geological and engineering data become available for estimating the reserves.

GENERAL ESTIMATION METHODS

In addition to deterministic and probabilistic methods of expressing reserves estimates, four common approaches to estimating reserves are used:

- Analogy
- Performance curves
- Volumetrics
- Material balance analysis

Analogy. Analogy employs experience and judgment to estimate reserves based on observations of similar situations (e.g., nearby producing wells) and consideration of hypothetical performance. Analogy is used when data is unreliable and/or insufficient to warrant the use of other estimating methods. For example, possible reserves for a proposed well are estimated at 500,000 barrels by analogy to similar nearby producing wells known to have average estimated ultimate cumulative production of 500,000 barrels. Analogy alone is considered to have a low degree of accuracy relative to other methods. However, any reserves estimation method employs some degree of analogy in application.

Volumetrics. The volumetric method is a calculation of the hydrocarbons in place, and an estimate of those recoverable by using a combination of measured physical data and estimates for certain unmeasured data. Factors such as rock and fluid properties are combined with estimates of the reservoir volume derived from seismic and/or drilling information to determine quantities that can be economically recovered. The percentage of original oil in place that is typically expected to be recovered can vary from less than 10 percent to more than 50 percent, depending on the rock and fluid properties. This compares to recovery factors for natural gas, which often vary between 50 percent and 90 percent.

The volumetric method is most commonly used in newly developed and/or nonpressure-depleting reservoirs (water-drive). Overall, it has a low degree of accuracy, although good rock quality, well control, and uncomplicated reservoirs can improve precision. Figure 16-2 provides a simple example of the volumetric method of estimating reserves.

Figure 16-2
Illustrative Proved Areas of a Reservoir

Two exploratory wells E1 and E2, drilled on 40-acre spacing, have proved reserves. Earlier G&G studies showed the producing structure to be a narrow ellipse, so only three offset locations are proved (D1, D2, and D3). The total proved area is 200 acres consisting of five drill spacing units on a 560 acre lease.

Top View:

Side View:

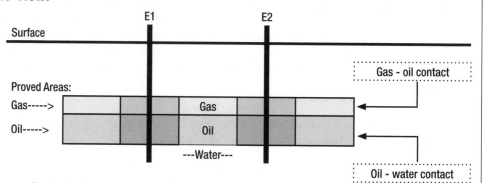

If the gas-oil and oil-water contacts are ten feet apart, then the 200-acre proved portion of the oil reservoir has ten feet of "pay" and a volume of 2,000 acre-feet. If such volume is 90% rock, 2% water, 5% unrecoverable oil and 3% recoverable oil (with 7,758 barrels in an **acre-foot**), then the proved oil reserves approximate 465,000 barrels [i.e., 2,000 x 3% x 7,758]. Fluid properties could be used to estimate the change in volume as the oil moves from reservoir temperature and pressure to the surface.

Performance Curves. For many properties, oil and gas production rates and reservoir pressures decline in patterns or curves that can be extrapolated to estimate future production. Figure 16-3 shows a graph with a production **decline curve** for a property producing for four years. Historical production for the period is plotted on the graph to reveal a trend in production rate over time. Engineers often use logarithmic graph scales to identify these trends, which are extrapolated five years into the future to provide an estimate of future production. The engineer ends the curve extrapolation and future production when the production rate declines to the property's economic limit. This limit occurs when production is too low to provide monthly cash inflow from production sales in excess of monthly cash outflow for operating costs.

Although the process can be done by hand, computer programs are often used to calculate recoverable reserves from inputs such as the current production rate, estimated decline, and various economic parameters (including operating expenses and product prices) that determine the economic limit.

Performance curves are generally considered to provide more precise estimates than volumetric or analogy approaches. Most commonly used after production is established, accuracy generally improves as historical production data accumulate. Analysis of decline curves (plotting the log of producing rates versus time) requires special attention when: (1) wells are not producing at capacity, (2) the number of producing wells is changing, (3) operating practices change, or (4) completion zones are not consistent over time. Reasons for wells not producing at capacity include seasonal curtailments, regulatory prorationing, and operational problems.

In some circumstances, engineers use combinations of several types of curves: investigating the decline trends of oil and/or gas compared against time, cumulative production volumes, declining pressures, increasing water production, or even the changing ratio of oil to gas over time to determine the appropriate reserves assignment. Due to changes in geologic settings and rock and fluid properties, the appropriate techniques for a particular oil and/or gas field may be inappropriate for fields in the same vicinity.

In general, production declines in one of two patterns:

- In an exponential decline curve, the percentage decline per year is relatively constant, such as a 10 percent decline per year, or

- A hyperbolical decline curve occurs when the percentage decline per year decreases over the well's productive life.

When production is plotted on a logarithmic scale, the exponential decline is a straight line, as in Figure 16-3, whereas the hyperbolic decline curve drops steeply with initial production and curves or flattens to an almost horizontal line. The historical production pattern and analogy with older wells in the same or similar reservoirs indicate which curve is applicable and the likely annual decline rate(s).

"A basic rule of thumb in the upstream (or producing) sector of the oil and gas industry is that the best place to find new crude oil or natural gas is near where it has already been found."

– *David F. Morehouse*, "The Intricate Puzzle of Oil and Gas 'Reserves Growth,'"
Energy Information Administration, Natural Gas Monthly, *July 1997.*

Figure 16-3
Production Decline Graph

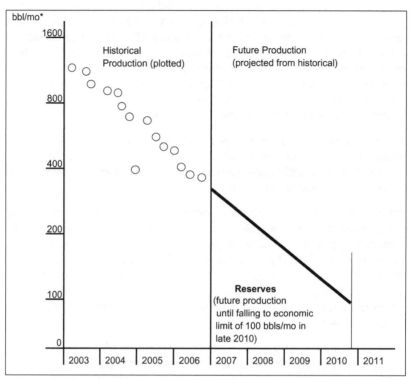

* Production is usually expressed on a logarithmic scale for graphing

Material Balance Analysis. This method involves complex calculations based on analysis of the relationship of production and pressure on well performance. It recognizes that reservoir pressure declines as more fluid (oil, gas, and water) is removed from the reservoir. Essentially, material balance means that the mass of all material (oil, gas, water) removed must equal initial material less the material remaining. From this simple equation, more complex relationships are developed based on reliable pressure and temperature data, production data, fluid analysis, and knowledge of the reservoir characteristics. Accuracy of this method is directly related to the quantity and quality of relevant data, and obtaining the data necessary to justify such a detailed study is relatively expensive.

A simple variation of this method generates a p/z curve where a gas reservoir's pressure (p), divided by a gas compressibility factor (z), provides a p/z amount that declines in a pattern as the reservoir produces. By extrapolating this pattern or curve, total cumulative gas production and gas reserves can be reasonably estimated. It requires shutting-in wells for several days at a time to periodically measure pressure at the bottom of the well (**bottom hole pressure, or BHP**). Analysis of curves showing declining reservoir pressure versus cumulative production requires special attention if: (1) wells are not properly tested, (2) several wells produce from the same reservoir, (3) the reservoir had greater than normal original pressure, or (4) the reservoir is suspected of having a water drive (as opposed to pressure depletion). Failure to provide the required special attention when such conditions are present will generally result in unreasonably high estimates.

A more complex example of material balance involves the use of reservoir simulators. These are computer programs that create a mathematical model of the reservoir. Using measurements of rock and fluid properties obtained from drilled wells and a volumetric model, the reservoir is subdivided into thousands or perhaps millions of "cells." While simple reservoir simulation models can be run on personal computers, simulations of larger fields require supercomputers. As the field is produced, production declines and field pressures are compared with the values predicted by the model. This "history matching" is used over time to refine the model, and results in greater accuracy in the model's predictions. Output from reservoir simulators is seldom sufficient for assigning proved reserves early in the life of a field, but as accuracy improves over time, it can become an important tool in the reserves assignment process.

SUPPORTING DATA

In addition to the geologic and engineering data referred to above, other important data for determining reserves quantities are:

- **Records of Production.** These are historical records of daily or monthly production (as opposed to sales) kept in production files and updated periodically by engineering assistants. These files are kept for both operated and nonoperated properties. Engineers use them to establish a production decline curve for determining the remaining recoverable reserves.

- **Records of Ownership.** For ownership interests (before and after payout), the entity's net share of reserves is the only one reported. These interests come from the lease records department and must agree with the interests being used for revenue and joint interest billing. Ownership interests can change over time based on agreements among the owners. Such changes typically occur when all well costs have been recovered and are referred to as **before payout** and **after payout** interests.

- **Records of Gas Imbalances.** Imbalances occur when owners of production do not sell quantities in proportion to their ownership interest. Companies can choose to account for imbalances by the sales method or the entitlement method, as explained in Chapter 14. Companies using the sales method adjust reserves for the amount of any imbalance. Those using the entitlements method reflect the imbalance on the balance sheet, but do not adjust reserves.

- **Records to Determine Current Pricing and Operating Costs.** For proved reserves that are by definition based on current economic and operating conditions, engineers use current prices and operating costs to determine the economic limit. Lease operating costs are usually available from lease operating statements but require analysis to identify recurring costs, repairs, and maintenance. A thorough analysis is necessary to identify fixed and variable portions. This analysis is useful in projecting costs in the later years of a field as the number of wells and the daily producing rates decline.

RESERVES SCHEDULES

Reserves estimation normally includes developing schedules of how the reserves will be produced over time. Timing is impacted by market conditions, producer decisions, and the availability of investments to develop proved undeveloped reserves. Both historical conditions and future plans are important in making reasonable projections.

Figure 16-4 provides a simplified version of a production schedule of proved reserves. Additionally, Figure 16-5 illustrates a simplified future cash flow estimate for a 10 percent net revenue interest in the gross reserves of Figure 16-4. Schedules may be prepared for each well, field, state, country, and reserves classification.

Figure 16-4
Reserves Production Schedule (simplified example)

(as of 12/31/06, assuming 10% annual decline in the well's production rate)	
Past:	**Oil (bbl)**
2002	10,000
2003	9,000
2004	8,100
2005	7,290
2006	6,561
Cumulative to 12/31/06	40,951
Future:	
2007	5,904
2008	5,314
2009	4,782
2010	4,304
2011	3,874
2012	3,486
Reserves at 12/31/06	27,664
Estimated Ultimate Recovery	68,615

Figure 16-5
Simplified Schedule of Estimated Future Cash Flow from Production

Year	Gross Oil (bbl)	Net Oil (bbl)	Revenue ($60/bbl)	Operating Costs	Net Cash Flow	Cash Flow Discounted at 10%
2007	5,904	590	$ 35,400	$ 10,000	$ 25,400	$ 23,091
2008	5,314	531	31,860	10,000	21,860	18,066
2009	4,782	478	28,680	10,000	18,680	14,034
2010	4,304	430	25,800	10,000	15,800	10,792
2011	3,874	387	23,220	10,000	13,220	8,209
2012	3,486	349	20,940	10,000	10,940	6,175
Total	27,664	2,765	$165,900	$ 60,000	$105,900	$ 80,367

In practice, reserves schedules provide much more extensive information than shown in Figures 16-4 and 16-5 including:

- Production and cash flow are shown in columnar form for each year (for 10 to 20 years) along with a grand total.

- Production columns will usually include gross production (oil, gas, and NGL) as well as the owner's share, or net production, of oil, gas, and NGL.

- Cash flow columns may include oil price, gas price, combined revenue, severance taxes, lease operating costs, net operating cash flow, investments, abandonment costs, salvage value, net cash flow, and net cash flow discounted to a present value.

The schedules may also contain estimates of federal income taxes and after-tax cash flow, both undiscounted and discounted.

RESERVES REPORTS

Reserves reports are prepared by either company employees or independent third-party engineering firms, or both. Communication with the engineer is advisable for better understanding of how the work was performed and for an assessment of any data utilized.

Reserves reports are designed to meet SEC disclosure requirements and have many other uses including:

- Historical financial and income tax reporting for amortization of certain costs

- Determination of FAS 144 impairment of proved property (Chapter 18) and calculation of the full cost ceiling test (Chapter 19)

- Development of long-range plans and budgets

- Management decisions regarding field development and reservoir management

- Bank loans and lines of credit collateralized by future production

- Valuation of developed oil and gas properties, or valuation of a company being considered for acquisition or divestment

- Regulatory hearings or litigation

Different purposes may require different definitions, assumptions, and methods, which may lead to very different results. Yet, each can be a perfectly correct and valid report for its stated purpose. In all cases, the report should include a letter identifying who requested the report, its purpose, effective date, description of properties evaluated, sources of data, significant assumptions, reserves definitions employed, summary results, a statement of the evaluator's independence, and the definition of proved reserves used (such as the SEC definition required for financial reporting). The letter typically contains statements of the estimator's limited responsibility for the accuracy of underlying data, and remarks about the imprecise nature of the estimates. If the estimator is a registered professional engineer, a seal will usually be affixed to the letter.

The report can include summary reserves schedules and schedules by property. One type of summary ranks all properties according to the total present value with the most valuable listed first. Graphs of production decline curves and p/z curves, as well as maps showing the locations of existing wells and proved undeveloped locations, may also be provided.

Financial auditors read reserves reports and cover letters to assist in compliance with applicable auditing standards including AU 336 on the use of specialists, and AU 558 and related Interpretation 9558 on supplementary information. The cover letter provides most of the information needed for compliance and may reveal areas to be investigated more thoroughly. For instance, a letter may discuss inconsistencies in the assumptions or methods used, such as the use of prices other than market prices at the reserves estimation date.

AU 336 provides "guidance to the auditor who uses the work of a specialist in performing an audit in accordance with generally accepted auditing standards."[2] According to standard, the types of matters that a financial auditor may conclude to require the work of a specialist could include such things as: valuations, the determination of physical characteristics relating to the quantity or condition of minerals or mineral reserves, or technical interpretations.

AU 558 "Required Supplementary Information" provides financial auditors with guidance on "the nature of procedures to be applied to supplementary information required by the FASB, GASB, or FASAB and describes the circumstances that would require the auditor to report such information." The auditor is required to consider whether or not supplementary information is required by the FASB or GASB. If it is required, then the auditor must follow specific procedures outlined in this standard.

In AU 9558.1, the PCAOB extends the supplemental information guidance specifically for oil and gas reserves. "Estimating oil and gas reserves is a complex process requiring the knowledge and experience of a reservoir engineer. In general, the quality of the estimate of proved reserves for an individual reservoir depends on the availability, completeness, and accuracy of data needed to develop the estimate and on the experience and judgment of the reservoir engineer. Estimates of proved reserves inevitably change over time as additional data become available and are taken into account. The magnitude of changes in these estimates is often substantial. Because oil and gas reserve estimates are more imprecise than most estimates that are made in preparing financial statements, entities are encouraged to explain the imprecise nature of such reserve estimates."[3]

SPE STANDARDS FOR ESTIMATING AND AUDITING RESERVES

In March 2007, the SPE adopted amended standards for estimating and auditing oil and gas reserves information (SPE Standards). The SPE Standards are not binding on petroleum engineers, but they do provide estimation and reporting guidance. Many petroleum engineering consulting firms do not issue reserves estimation reports that purport to comply with the SPE Standards. Compliance is not mandatory and purported compliance might expose the firms to unnecessary legal liabilities.

The SPE Standards provide guidance for engineers on reserves estimated by another party. However, the FASB and SEC do not require reserves data to be included in audited footnotes to the financial statements. Such data appears as unaudited supplemental information (as explained in Chapters 28 and 29). Nevertheless, the reserves audit is a popular service offered by independent petroleum engineering firms because it can be less expensive than an independent reserves determination. Reserves audited by an independent petroleum engineering firm, not by financial statement auditors, still appear in the unaudited information supplementing audited financial statements. In addition, many public companies have independent petroleum engineers conduct audits of proved reserves, and in SEC transactional filings the engineering firms will provide consents to the use of their reports.

Unlike an audit report under the AICPA or Public Company Accounting Oversight Board (PCAOB) standards, a petroleum engineer's reserves audit report can express positive assurance without the engineer testing or verifying the accuracy and completeness of underlying data. However, the engineer's reserves audit report should disclose the lack of such testing or verification.

A copy of the SPE Standards may be found on the SPE website: www.spe.org.

• • •

---

1 An exception to this rule is found in applying the full cost ceiling test as more fully described in Chapter 19. The ceiling for capitalized costs may reflect higher oil and gas prices occurring after the balance sheet date.

2 AU Section 336, "Using the Work of a Specialist," PCAOB, http://www.pcaobus.org/standards/interim_standards/auditing_standards/index_au.asp?series=300&section=336

3 AU Section 9558.03, "Required Supplementary Information: Auditing Interpretations of Section 558," http://www.pcaobus.org/standards/interim_standards/auditing_standards/index_au.asp?series=500&section=558

17 DEPRECIATION, DEPLETION, AND AMORTIZATION (DD&A) UNDER THE SUCCESSFUL EFFORTS METHOD

Key Concepts:

- Depreciation, depletion, and amortization (DDA) of capitalized proved property costs using successful efforts accounting

- Calculations of amortization expense based on unit-of-production and other methods

- Revision of reserves estimates

- Properties grouped for amortization purposes

- Exclusion for certain development costs when all wells in a group have not been drilled

- Amortization based on total equivalent units of oil and gas

SUMMARY OF REQUIREMENTS OF Oi5

Proved property acquisition costs and proved property well and development costs are amortized on a unit-of-production basis. This method matches amortization expense to related oil and gas production.

Both types of capitalized costs are amortized, but their calculations can differ. Proved property acquisition costs are depleted (amortized) over total proved reserves. Costs of wells and related equipment and facilities are depreciated (amortized) over the life of proved developed reserves that can be produced from assets represented by those capitalized costs. If a property is fully developed, proved reserves and proved developed reserves are the same. When a property is only partially developed, proved developed reserves are a subset of total proved reserves.

Depreciation, depletion, and amortization (DD&A) may be computed for each individual property. Alternately, properties can be aggregated on the basis of a common geological structural feature or stratigraphic condition, such as a reservoir or field. Royalty interests and other nonoperating interests may also give rise to aggregation of properties.

Oil and gas are often found together on a property or group of properties. In this case, the amortization per unit generally should be calculated on the basis of estimated total equivalent units—based on energy content—of oil and gas reserves. Unit-of-production rates are revised whenever the need is indicated, but must be reviewed at least once each year.

BASIC UNIT-OF-PRODUCTION COMPUTATIONS OF AMORTIZATION

The basic computation of unit-of-production amortization utilizes either of the following essentially identical formulas:

$$\frac{\text{Unamortized Costs at End of Period}}{\text{Reserves at Beginning of Period}} \quad \times \quad \text{Production for Period}$$

or

$$\frac{\text{Production for Period}}{\text{Reserves at Beginning of Period}} \quad \times \quad \text{Unamortized Costs at End of Period}$$

To illustrate the general computation, assume the following data at the end of an accounting period:

Capitalized costs at end of period	$1,000,000
Amortization taken in prior periods	$250,000
Estimated reserves at beginning of period	1,000,000 bbls
Production during period	40,000 bbls

Amortization expense for the period is $30,000:

$$\frac{\$1,000,000 - \$250,000}{1,000,000 \text{ bbls}} \quad \times \quad 40,000 \text{ bbls} = \$30,000$$

Note: the accounting period for public companies is considered a quarter.

REVISION OF ESTIMATES

Oi5.121 specifies amortization rates and reserves estimates be revised "whenever there is an indication of the need for revision but at least once a year..." Changes in reserves estimates should be done on a prospective basis as required by FASB Statement No. 154 (FAS 154), *Accounting Changes and Error Corrections*, Sec. A07. Thus, a change in the estimate affects current and future periods only. No adjustment is made in the accumulated amortization applicable to prior periods. This prospective treatment presents unique implications for public companies in computing amortization for interim reporting periods, and is examined later in this chapter.

The following formula is commonly used for computing periodic unit-of-production amortization:

$$\frac{CC - AA}{EREP + CPP} \times CPP$$

CC is total capitalized costs

AA is accumulated amortization

EREP is estimated reserves at end of current period

CPP is current period production

To illustrate this computation, assume the following facts, which are identical to the preceding example except the estimate of reserves was revised during the period:

Capitalized costs at end of period	$1,000,000
Amortization taken in prior periods	$250,000
Estimated reserves at beginning of period	1,000,000 bbls
Production during period	40,000 bbls
Estimated reserves at end of period	560,000 bbls

In calculating amortization for the period, the estimate of reserves originally made at the beginning of the period is ignored. Instead, amortization for the period is based on the revised reserves estimate at the end of the period added to current period production.

Based on the revised facts, amortization for the period is $50,000:

$$\frac{\$1,000,000 - \$250,000}{560,000 \text{ bbls} + 40,000 \text{ bbls}} \times 40,000 \text{ bbls} = \$50,000$$

Capitalized costs and related amortization for proved reserves are found in Account 221—Proved Property Acquisition Costs and Account 226—Accumulated Amortization of Proved Property Acquisition Costs in the Appendix 3 Illustrative Chart of Accounts.

GROUPINGS OF PROPERTIES FOR AMORTIZATION PURPOSES

It has been noted previously that proved properties in a common geological structure may be combined for computing DD&A. Oi5.121 states:

> Under the unit-of-production method, amortization (depletion) may be computed either on a property-by-property basis or on the basis of some reasonable aggregation of properties with a common geological structural feature or stratigraphic condition, such as a reservoir or field.

As a general rule, a cost center is either an individual property or an aggregation of properties by field. Combining properties by well can be difficult, since a property often encompasses acreage greater than the well's spacing unit. Of the nine successful efforts respondents to the *2001 PricewaterhouseCoopers Survey of U.S. Petroleum Accounting Practices*, two-thirds aggregated the capitalized costs of oil and gas producing properties into cost centers by field (note: the companies provided multiple responses to the survey question):

Percent	Aggregated by:
67	field
22	property
22	well
0	reservoir
0	other methods

To illustrate a grouping of proved properties, assume four leases overlying a reservoir are drilled and developed in the current period. Data relating to the four leases follows:

	Lease				
	A	B	C	D	Total
Net capitalized costs, end of period	$800,000	$1,400,000	$ 400,000	$2,000,000	$4,600,000
Estimated reserves, end of period (bbls)	180,000	680,000	1,500,000	380,000	2,740,000
Production during period (bbls)	20,000	20,000	100,000	20,000	160,000

If amortization is computed for each property individually, the total amortization for the period will be $245,000:

Property A: $\dfrac{\$800,000}{200,000 \text{ bbls}}$ X 20,000 bbls = $ 80,000

Property B: $\dfrac{\$1,400,000}{700,000 \text{ bbls}}$ X 20,000 bbls = 40,000

Property C: $\dfrac{\$400,000}{1,600,000 \text{ bbls}}$ X 100,000 bbls = 25,000

Property D: $\dfrac{\$2,000,000}{400,000 \text{ bbls}}$ X 20,000 bbls = 100,000

Total amortization $245,000

Alternatively, if the properties are combined into a single group, amortization for the period will be $253,793:

$\dfrac{\$4,600,000}{2,900,000 \text{ bbls}}$ X 160,000 bbls = $253,793

Under the successful efforts method, costs of unproved properties are not subject to depletion but are subject to an impairment test. Unproved properties whose costs are not individually significant may be combined into groups and their costs amortized on the basis of experience. In this instance, the petroleum accountant considers the company's track record with respect to write-offs of unproved property.

If impairment of unproved properties has been recorded on a group basis – and the properties have since been proved – then the proved properties account contains the gross cost of the formerly unproved properties. However, if impairment of an unproved property was recorded on an individual basis, then the proved properties account reflects the net impaired cost (original cost less the impairment allowance) once the property becomes proved. Chapter 18 contains a detailed discussion of impairment of long-lived assets.

ILLUSTRATION OF AMORTIZATION (DEPLETION) COMPUTATION

To illustrate Oi5.121 when a single proved property is treated as a cost center, assume the following data:

Cost initially transferred from unproved properties	$200,000
Depletion taken prior to beginning of this period	$20,000
Estimated proved reserves at beginning of this period	4,000,000 Mcf
Production during this period	80,000 Mcf
Revised estimate of proved reserves at end of period	4,920,000 Mcf

Amortization for the period is $2,880:

$$\frac{\$200,000 - \$20,000}{4,920,000 \text{ Mcf} + 80,000 \text{ Mcf}} \quad \times \quad 80,000 \text{ Mcf} = \$2,880$$

Amortization for the period would be recorded as follows:

726	Amortization (Depletion) of Proved Property Acquisition Costs	2,880	
	226 Accumulated Amortization of Proved Property Acquisition Costs		2,880

A detailed record of the amortization applicable to each property is maintained when calculating amortization by individual cost center. Amortization (depletion) of costs of a group of properties is computed in exactly the same manner as shown, except that data for all properties in the group are combined. A record is kept of accumulated depletion applicable to the entire group, rather than to individual properties.

DEPRECIATION OF PROVED PROPERTY WELL AND DEVELOPMENT COSTS

The capitalized costs of wells and related facilities include both tangible and intangible costs. In the general ledger accounts of ABC Oil Company, these costs are kept separately in Account 231 for intangibles and Account 233 for tangibles. Oi5.126 suggests the term "depreciation" may be given to amortization of tangible and intangible costs, although many companies still refer to the amortization of intangibles as depletion. This terminology likely stems from the fact that if intangible drilling costs (IDC) are capitalized for federal income tax purposes, they are subject to depletion for income tax reporting.

Oi5 provides that capitalized costs of wells and related facilities are amortized over proved developed reserves, whereas acquisition costs are amortized over total proved reserves:

> Capitalized costs of exploratory wells and exploratory-type stratigraphic test wells that have found proved reserves and capitalized development costs shall be amortized (depreciated) by the unit-of-production method . . . on the basis of total estimated units of proved developed reserves rather than on the basis of all proved reserves, which is the basis for amortizing acquisition costs of proved properties. (Oi5.126)

For example, assume a group of partially developed leases in a field has been combined into a single amortization pool as follows:

Proved property acquisition costs	$240,000
Proved property intangible costs	$3,800,000
Proved property tangible costs	$600,000
Accumulated amortization of acquisition costs	$20,000
Accumulated amortization of intangible costs	$760,000
Accumulated amortization of tangible costs	$120,000
Proved developed reserves at year-end	900,000 bbls
Proved reserves at year-end	1,400,000 bbls
Production during period	100,000 bbls

Depletion and depreciation for the period are recorded as follows:

726	Amortization of Proved Property Acquisition Costs	14,667*	
732	Amortization of Intangibles	304,000**	
734	Amortization of Tangibles	48,000***	
226	Accumulated Amortization of Proved Property Acquisition Costs		14,667
232	Accumulated Amortization of Intangibles		304,000
234	Accumulated Amortization of Tangibles		48,000
	To record amortization for period—computed as follows:		

$$* \quad \frac{\$240,000 - \$20,000}{1,400,000 \text{ bbls} + 100,000 \text{ bbls}} \quad \text{X} \quad 100,000 \text{ bbls} \quad = \quad \$\ 14,667$$

$$** \quad \frac{\$3,800,000 - \$760,000}{900,000 \text{ bbls} + 100,000 \text{ bbls}} \quad \text{X} \quad 100,000 \text{ bbls} \quad = \quad \$304,000$$

$$*** \quad \frac{\$600,000 - \$120,000}{900,000 \text{ bbls} + 100,000 \text{ bbls}} \quad \text{X} \quad 100,000 \text{ bbls} \quad = \quad \$\ 48,000$$

EXCLUSION OF PORTION OF SIGNIFICANT DEVELOPMENT PROJECTS

Development costs are amortized as the related proved developed reserves produce oil and gas. However, distortions in the amortization rate will occur unless the amortization formula is adjusted for substantial development costs relating to both proved developed and proved undeveloped reserves.

To illustrate, assume an offshore platform is constructed at a cost of $50,000,000 to be used to drill 15 development wells expected to extract an estimated 30,000,000 barrels of proved reserves. Prior to construction of the platform, two successful stratigraphic evaluation wells were drilled at a cost of $12,000,000. At the end of the current period, only two development wells have been drilled, at a cost of $3,000,000. During the current period 250,000 barrels were produced, and at the end of the period estimated remaining proved developed reserves from the two wells are 4,750,000 barrels.

Dividing total capitalized costs of $65,000,000 by the 5,000,000 barrels of beginning proved developed reserves results in an inflated current amortization rate of $13 per barrel. If all 15 wells had been drilled, total capitalized costs would increase to $84,500,000, all 30,000,000 barrels of proved reserves would be classified as developed, and the amortization rate would be $2.82 per barrel. Clearly, to better match DD&A expense to revenue and production, it is appropriate to exclude a portion of the $65,000,000 of capitalized costs from the amortization formula until all proved reserves are developed.

Oi5.126 provides for such an adjustment to the formula:

> If significant development costs (such as the cost of an offshore production platform) are incurred in connection with a planned group of development wells before all of the planned wells have been drilled, it will be necessary to exclude a portion of those development costs in determining the unit-of-production amortization rate until the additional development wells are drilled.

Oi5.126 does not specify the method to be used in determining what portion of the platform costs and stratigraphic well costs are to be excluded from the amortization calculation. Presumably, the exclusion would be based on either the:

- portion of total proved reserves estimated to be recoverable from wells already producing, or
- ratio of wells already productive to the total number of wells projected.

Under the first approach, the amortization rate would be [($62,000,000 x 5/30) + $3,000,000] divided by 5,000,000 barrels, or $2.67 per barrel. Under the second approach, the amortization rate would be [($62,000,000 x 2/15) + $3,000,000] divided by 5,000,000 barrels, or $2.25 per barrel of production.

Capitalized costs temporarily excluded from amortization would eventually become part of the amortization base as additional wells are drilled. Costs of development wells drilled are included in the amortization calculation as they are incurred, and the related reserves are transferred to proved developed reserves. Also, exclusion from the amortization base applies not only to the platform costs, but also to the capitalized costs of stratigraphic test wells that led up to the construction of the platform.

A third approach exists for amortizing capitalized costs, available only to companies using the full cost method of accounting. Under this method, capitalized costs plus expected future development costs are amortized over total proved reserves. For the previous example, the amortization rate would be calculated as $84,500,000 divided by 30,000,000 barrels, or $2.82 per barrel.

Oi5.126 also provides for situations in which companies using the successful efforts method have developed reserves that may require additional costs to be incurred before the reserves can be produced:

> Similarly, it will be necessary to exclude, in computing the amortization rate, those proved developed reserves that will be produced only after significant additional development costs are incurred, such as for improved recovery systems.

This problem should not be commonly encountered, however, because paragraph (a)(3) of Reg. S-X Rule 4-10 defines proved developed reserves as follows:

> Proved developed oil and gas reserves are [proved] reserves that can be expected to be recovered through existing wells with existing equipment and operating methods. Additional oil and gas expected to be obtained through the application of fluid injection or other improved recovery techniques for supplementing the natural forces and mechanisms of primary recovery should be included as "proved developed reserves" only after testing by a pilot project or after the operation of an installed program confirmed through production response that increased recovery will be achieved.

In addition, the definition of proved undeveloped reserves in Reg. S-X Rule 4-10(a)(4) includes the following:

> Proved undeveloped oil and gas reserves are reserves that are expected to be recovered from new wells on undrilled acreage, or from existing wells where a relatively major expenditure is required for recompletion.

In summary, reasonably matching revenue and production with applicable costs is the goal of these rules. Unit-of-production computations, while useful, can present problems in later years of production. These issues are discussed briefly at the end of this chapter.

DISMANTLEMENT, RESTORATION, AND ABANDONMENT COSTS

Oi5.128 requires:

> ...estimated dismantlement, restoration, and abandonment costs and estimated residual salvage values shall be taken into account in determining amortization and depreciation rates.

Chapter 20 addresses accounting for such costs under existing standards. In the 1980's and 1990's, the future cost of dismantlement, restoration, and abandonment (DR&A) was added to the current amortization base to increase DD&A. This allowed petroleum accountants to accrue for DR&A over the property's productive life without adding estimated future costs to asset accounts.

In June 2001, the Statement of Financial Accounting Standards No. 143 (FAS 143), *Accounting for Asset Retirement Obligations,* was issued which calls for DR&A liability to be recognized when the obligation is incurred (e.g., when the well is drilled or when the producing property is acquired). The amount of the recognized liability is added into the amortizable capitalized costs of acquiring or developing a property. Unlike prior rules that used undiscounted future DR&A, FAS 143 recognizes the liability at the discounted present value of future DR&A.

JOINT PRODUCTION OF OIL AND GAS

If oil and gas are found together on a property (or a group of properties forming an amortization group), the basis for amortization is the estimated total equivalent units of oil and gas. Equivalent units are expressed in terms of relative energy content such as Btu. (An equivalent unit based on revenues is specifically prohibited for companies using the successful efforts method, yet is allowed for full cost accounting.)

The energy content of both oil and gas varies from reservoir to reservoir, and even within a single reservoir. Many companies use the rule-of-thumb formula that one barrel of oil contains six times as much energy as 1,000 cubic feet (Mcf) of gas. Other companies seek to be more precise in their calculations by using the actual equivalent energy content for oil and gas in the property or group of properties that comprises the amortization unit.

To illustrate this concept, assume the following for a fully developed property:

Capitalized costs	$6,000,000
Amortization in prior periods	$240,000
Estimated oil reserves, end of period	620,000 bbls
Estimated gas reserves, end of period	3,300,000 Mcf
Oil production during period	70,000 bbls
Gas production during period	360,000 Mcf

The amount of amortization for the period is computed as follows, converting gas volumes to barrels of oil equivalent (BOE):

Reserves, end of the period:	
Oil (620,000 bbls x 1)	620,000 BOE
Gas (3,300,000 Mcf/6)	550,000 BOE
Total equivalent barrels, end of period	1,170,000 BOE
Production for the period:	
Oil (70,000 bbls x 1)	70,000 BOE
Gas (360,000 Mcf/6)	60,000 BOE
Total equivalent barrels produced	130,000 BOE
Total equivalent barrels, beginning of period	**1,300,000 BOE**

Amortization for the period would be $576,000, computed as shown:

$$\frac{130,000 \text{ BOE}}{1,300,000 \text{ BOE}} \times (\$6,000,000 - \$240,000) = \$576,000$$

Some companies, especially gas producing companies, may wish to convert oil to gas equivalents, an approach that will not change the results of the computation. This procedure is illustrated as follows:

Reserves, end of the period:	
Oil (620,000 bbls x 6 Mcf per bbl)	3,720,000 Mcfe
Gas (3,300,000 Mcf x 1)	3,300,000 Mcfe
Total equivalent Mcf, end of period	7,020,000 Mcfe
Production for the period:	
Oil (70,000 bbls x 6 Mcf per bbl)	420,000 Mcfe
Gas (360,000 Mcf x 1)	360,000 Mcfe
Total equivalent Mcf produced	780,000 Mcfe
Total equivalent Mcf, beginning of period	7,800,000 Mcfe

Amortization for the period would be $576,000:

$$\frac{780,000 \text{ Mcfe}}{7,800,000 \text{ Mcfe}} \quad \times \quad (\$6,000,000 - \$240,000) \quad = \quad \$576,000$$

Oi5.129 presumes amortization is based on the cost per equivalent unit, if both oil and gas are found in a property or group of properties forming an amortization group. Two exceptions are noted:

> However, if the relative proportion of gas and oil extracted in the current period is expected to continue throughout the remaining productive life of the property, unit-of-production amortization may be computed on the basis of one of the two minerals only; similarly, if either oil or gas clearly dominates both the reserves and the current production (with dominance determined on the basis of relative energy content), unit-of-production amortization may be computed on the basis of the dominant mineral only.

The first exception is illustrated using data from the preceding example. Since oil represents 53 percent of the energy content of minerals in the reservoir at the end of the period and 54 percent of the energy content of minerals produced during the current period, relative production of oil and gas in the current period is approximately the same as it will be in future periods. Thus, production and reserves of only one mineral (in this case, oil) may be used in the calculation. If only *oil* production and reserves are considered, amortization for the period would be $584,348:

$$\frac{70,000 \text{ bbls}}{690,000 \text{ bbls}} \quad \times \quad \$5,760,000 = \$584,348$$

In the previous example, since neither mineral is clearly dominant in both reserves and production, use of a single mineral could not be justified. Though Oi5.129 does not define the term "clearly dominates," it is reasonable to assume that if three-fourths or more of the energy content of both production and reserves is attributable to one mineral, then that mineral clearly dominates. However, if the energy content of either production or reserves attributable to one mineral is no more than three-fourths of the total energy content of that category, then one mineral cannot be considered clearly dominant.

REVISIONS OF INTERIM ESTIMATES

In the examples given, DD&A has been computed for a period without a length of time specified. When reserves estimates change during the year, however, defining the period becomes important.

Oi5.126 requires amortization rates to "be revised whenever there is an indication of the need for revision but at least once a year." During a fiscal year, revisions in the rate may be indicated by events such as: (1) major discoveries, (2) other reserves additions or declines, or (3) major price changes that impact the volume of proved reserves. Companies are cautioned against blindly using predetermined DD&A estimates, and thereby failing to revise the reserves estimates or amortization rate until year-end.

Changes in reserves estimates are considered a change in accounting estimate under FAS 154 and, accordingly, are treated on a prospective basis. This requirement has been interpreted in several different ways in practice. Two general approaches were reported in the *2001 PricewaterhouseCoopers Survey of U.S. Petroleum Accounting Practices*. The following example illustrates both methods.

Assume amortization (depreciation) is being recorded quarterly and reported in quarterly financial statements. On January 1, 2006, the first day of the fiscal year, undepreciated costs of wells and facilities on a property are $6,000,000 and estimated proved developed reserves are 1,000,000 barrels. During the first quarter ending March 31, 2006, 20,000 barrels are produced; during the second quarter ending June 30, 2006, 18,000 barrels are produced; and during the third quarter ending September 30, 2006, 22,000 barrels are produced. Thus, depreciation recorded in the first three quarters was $120,000 [i.e., 6,000,000/1,000,000 x 20,000 for first quarter], $108,000, and $132,000, respectively. In October, 6,000 barrels are produced and in November, 8,000 barrels are produced. In December, a revised estimate of proved developed reserves is calculated showing that on December 1 estimated reserves are 626,000 barrels. The revised estimate as of October 1 is 640,000 barrels, and the revised estimate as of January 1, 2006, is 700,000 barrels. Production during December is 6,000 barrels.

In the first approach, the "period" refers to the last quarter in which reserves are revised. Amortization for the year is the sum of the four quarterly amortization amounts. Under this approach, and using the previous assumptions, amortization for 2006 is computed as follows:

Amortization for first three quarters	$360,000
Amortization for fourth quarter:	
$\dfrac{20,000 \text{ bbls}}{640,000 \text{ bbls}}$ x ($6,000,000 - $360,000) =	176,250
Total depreciation for year	$536,250

In the second approach, the period refers to the fiscal year-to-date. Using this approach, DD&A is computed for the interim period as follows:

Amortization for the year:	
$\dfrac{80,000 \text{ bbls}}{700,000 \text{ bbls}}$ x $6,000,000 =	$685,714
Less: prior interim amortization	(360,000)
Amortization for 4th quarter	$325,714

The SEC has indicated changes in amortization rates are required to be made prospectively as changes in estimates. When proved reserves estimates are revised prior to the release of operating results for a quarter, the SEC staff will not object to the reserves revisions being implemented in the registrant's DD&A as of the beginning of that quarter, rather than delaying implementation until the following quarter. However, taking the reserves revisions back to earlier quarters is not appropriate.

A public company is required to give effect to the change in proved reserves on a prospective basis following the guidance for a change in accounting estimate under FAS 154. However, public companies may follow the first approach, and if there is a proved reserves change at year-end, then the company may give effect to such change in the quarter for which the financial statements have not been issued (in the example, the fourth quarter of 2006). The public company should be consistent in the approach followed.

AMORTIZATION OF NONOPERATING INTERESTS

The costs of nonoperating interests, like the costs of operating interests, should generally be depleted or amortized on the unit-of-production basis. Oi5.121 provides that in certain circumstances other methods of computing amortization may be appropriate:

> If an enterprise has a relatively large number of royalty interests whose acquisition costs are not individually significant, they may be aggregated, for purpose of computing amortization, without regard to commonality of geological structural features or stratigraphic conditions; if information is not available to estimate reserves quantities applicable to royalty interests owned (refer to paragraph .160), a method other than the unit-of-production method may be used to amortize their acquisition costs.

There are two major difficulties in implementing the unit-of-production method for nonoperating interests. First, many nonoperating interests may be quite small in both cost and value, so that they are individually immaterial. Second, operating interest owners are quite likely to refuse to provide information to nonoperating interest owners concerning proved reserves underlying a property or field, especially when the royalty interest is small and the royalty owner is not an operating oil and gas company. The royalty owner may be able to approximate the reserves by projecting the decline curve from the property based on past production history.

Oi5.121 implies that, if a single royalty interest is significant, its capitalized costs should be amortized over the related proved reserves from the property. Royalty interests in a field or reservoir may also be combined without regard to geologic commonality and amortized as the related proved reserves are produced. More commonly, however, because of the lack of information necessary to compute unit-of-production amortization, royalty costs are combined and amortized on a straight-line basis over a period of eight to ten years (overall U.S. proved reserves are about eight to ten times overall production).

Although Oi5.129 refers specifically to royalties, including overriding royalties, the same basic concepts apply to net profits interests. Conceptually, the unamortized costs of a net profits interest would be depleted on the basis of: (1) the production on which the net profit for the period is determined, and (2) the fractional share of reserves represented by the net profits interest. However, working interest owners may be reluctant to inform a net profits interest owner of the estimated proved reserves underlying the property or properties. As a result, amortization based on the straight-line method may be a logical approach to computing depletion.

The holder of a production payment payable in product would amortize costs on the basis of production received if there is reason to believe the payment will be satisfied. For example, an entity obtained for $1,000,000 a production payment of 1,000,000 Mcf of gas and during the current period received the first 250,000 Mcf. With reasonable assurance that the remaining 750,000 Mcf will be received, depletion of $250,000 [$1,000,000 x (250,000 Mcf ÷ 1,000,000 Mcf)] is recorded and matched against the value of the gas received during the period.

If it is doubtful the total number of units deliverable under a production payment expressed in physical quantities of minerals will be received, but an estimate of product that will be received can be made, then a portion of the costs should be amortized based on the ratio of units delivered to total expected to be delivered. For example, if: (1) $1,500,000 is paid for a production payment to be satisfied by delivery of 1,000,000 Mcf of gas, (2) during the current period the first 100,000 Mcf of gas is received, and (3) it is estimated that only an additional 500,000 Mcf will be received in the future, then depletion is $250,000 [$1,500,000 x (100,000 Mcf/ 600,000 Mcf)].

If it is doubtful the full production payment will be satisfied, but there is no information available on the quantity that will ultimately be delivered, a good case can be made for ignoring depletion and treating the entire value of the gas received as a recovery of the $1,500,000 cost of the production payment.

ALLOWABLE METHODS OTHER THAN UNIT-OF-PRODUCTION

Although Oi5.126 specifies the unit-of-production method should be used in depreciating the costs of wells and related facilities and equipment, there are limited situations in which other methods may be used. Oi5.126 mentions one exception:

> It may be more appropriate, in some cases, to depreciate natural gas cycling and processing plants by a method other than the unit-of-production method.

Presumably, if a cycling or processing plant serves only one lease or one group of leases combined for amortization purposes, the unit-of-production method should be used. However, when a cycling or processing plant serves a number of properties subject to individual amortization, or when the plant is used to process gas for other operators on a contract basis, some other depreciation method becomes appropriate. This reflects the fact that many companies consider processing plants to be more akin to refining facilities than to oil and gas producing assets.

Another instance in which a depreciation method other than the unit-of-production method appears to be appropriate is one in which assets with significant costs have a useful life substantially shorter than the productive life of the property on which they are situated. However, this approach is not specifically addressed in Reg. S-X Rule 4-10 or Oi5.

DEPRECIATION OF SUPPORT EQUIPMENT AND FACILITIES

Support facilities such as warehouses, camps, trucks, office buildings, and communications equipment frequently provide services to two or more functions – exploration, acquisition, development, and drilling/production. For example, a district warehouse serves all four functions. Even in cases where support equipment is used in only one activity, such as production, it may be impossible to identify the asset with only a single property or group of properties in a single amortization base. Consequently, the unit-of-production method based on oil and gas produced may not be an appropriate method for depreciating support equipment. Instead, the straight-line method, the unit-of-output method based on some factor such as miles driven (for trucks), or other acceptable basis should be used.

Depreciation and other costs of owning and using support equipment should be allocated to operating activities on the basis of usage and, consequently, expensed or capitalized as appropriate. For example, to the extent an asset is used in development, its depreciation and operating costs are capitalized, whereas depreciation and operating costs related to its use in production activities will be charged to expense. This cost allocation may be accomplished through clearing and apportionment accounts as discussed in Chapter 4.

A SUCCESSFUL EFFORTS AMORTIZATION EQUATION

Based on issues raised in this chapter, the unit-of-production equation or formula may be expressed as follows for a given cost center (a specific property or a reasonable aggregation of properties):

> **Amortization expense = B x S/(S+R), where:**
>
> B = amortization base, defined below
>
> S = volume sold during the period (equivalent barrels or Mcfs or volume of the dominant hydrocarbon)
>
> R = volume of proved reserves at end of period, using proved developed reserves for well and equipment DD&A, and total proved reserves for property acquisition DD&A

Units sold (S) could arguably be replaced with units produced because the two volumes are nearly equal over quarterly or annual periods. In some instances, units sold are significantly less than units produced, the difference being referred to as "shrinkage." Shrinkage can arise from natural gas used on the lease, gas volumes lost in processing for extraction of NGL, removal of impurities and BS&W, and even theft or pipeline leaks. Where shrinkage is significant, amortization calculations should use units produced or sold (S) and proved reserves (R) that are consistently determined (i.e, *both* before shrinkage or *both* after shrinkage) so that costs are reasonably allocated over the productive life of the reserves.

The *2001 PricewaterhouseCoopers Survey of U.S. Petroleum Accounting Practices* shows when volumes sold differ from volumes produced, volumes sold are generally used for calculating amortization both under successful efforts and full cost accounting. Of 30 respondents, 20 (or 67 percent) used volumes sold; 9 (or 30 percent) used volumes produced; one respondent reported using another method.

> **The amortization base (B) = C-A-E, where:**
>
> C = incurred capitalized costs of mineral property interests or of wells and development
>
> A = prior accumulated amortization
>
> E = capitalized development costs excluded from the amortization base as allowed by Oi5.126

The formula for full cost accounting (addressed in Chapter 19) is very similar to this example, but is calculated on a country-by-country basis. It uses total proved reserves, and adds a new factor to the amortization base for estimated future development costs ("F") of properties in the amortization base.

TAX TREATMENT FOR DEPLETION AND DEPRECIATION

For federal income tax purposes, the IRS has established specific rules regarding the computation of depletion and depreciation of oil and gas properties. Tangible well equipment is capitalized as personal property and depreciated in accordance with IRS depreciation guidelines. Leasehold costs are generally depleted over the greater of the unit-of-production method or at a statutory rate based on the property's revenue and net income as explained further in Chapter 26.

A PROBLEM WITH THE UNIT-OF-PRODUCTION METHOD

The unit-of-production method mandated by Oi5.126 is far from perfect. Over the economic life of an oil field as production declines, net cash flow per barrel declines to zero, while amortization per barrel may remain relatively constant. The unit-of-production method mandated in Oi5.126 results in income per barrel generally declining over the life of the field (and even incurring a loss in later years). The following example shows a property expected to produce for seven years:

Year	Net Bbls	Revenue ($60/bbl)	Oper. Costs	Cash flow/bbl	DD&A per bbl*	Income per bbl	Net Income	Net Unamortized Cost	Future Cash Flow
0								$40,000	40,000
1	1000	$60,000	$20,000	$40.00	$5.00	$35.00	$35,000	35,000	33,400
2	890	53,400	20,000	37.53	5.00	32.53	28,950	30,550	26,800
3	780	46,800	20,000	34.36	5.00	29.36	22,900	26,650	21,400
4	690	41,400	20,000	31.01	5.00	26.01	17,950	23,200	16,000
5	600	36,000	20,000	26.67	5.00	21.67	13,000	20,200	11,800
6	530	31,800	20,000	22.26	5.00	17.26	9,150	17,550	10,600
7	510	30,600	20,000	20.78	5.00	15.78	8,050	15,000	--
TOTAL	5,000	$300,000	$140,000	$32.00	$5.00	$27.00	$135,000		

* Ignores application of FAS 144

For simplicity, this example assumes expected future cash flow based on a constant oil price of $60.00 per barrel and constant fixed operating costs of $20,000 per year. The property generates $135,000 net income (an average of $27/bbl) over its seven-year life. Arguably, to better match revenue and expense, DD&A expense should reflect the $27/bbl of net income every year. However, the example illustrates that unit-of-production amortization tends to overstate net income per barrel early in the life of a producing property and understate it in later years.

For an ongoing oil and gas producing company, the understatement of amortization for new fields' capitalized costs compensates, to some degree, for the overstatement of amortization of old fields' costs. Without new fields, a liquidating company will find that its net income per barrel declines over time.

Mismatching of revenue and expense also causes capitalized costs for any one field to become impaired over time. This necessitates impairment write-offs under FAS 144 to avoid losses in the later years of the field's productive life.

Revenues are better matched with costs, and income per barrel more level over the property's productive life, if the capitalized costs are amortized over projected cash flow from production of proved reserves, instead of over units-of-production. This method, not provided for in Oi5 or Reg. S-X Rule 4-10, seeks to arrive at a combined cost of amortization expense and lifting cost, per equivalent barrel, that is relatively constant over the life of a property. For the preceding example, DD&A would be adjusted so that net income per barrel was always $27 if oil and gas prices and lifting costs remained constant.

FAS 144 accounting for long-lived asset impairment (addressed in Chapter 18) and the full cost ceiling test (Chapter 19) partially compensate from time to time for any significant mismatching of revenue and expense arising from the unit-of-production amortization method applied to oil and gas producing activity.

• • •

18

ACCOUNTING FOR THE IMPAIRMENT OR DISPOSAL OF LONG-LIVED ASSETS

Key Concepts:

- **Application of FAS 144 to successful efforts companies**

- **Inherent impairment under unit-of-production amortization**

- **Impairment indicators**

- **Adjustments to asset carrying amount**

- **Asset grouping**

- **Calculation of expected future cash flows and determining fair value**

- **Assets to be disposed of**

- **Applicability to full cost companies**

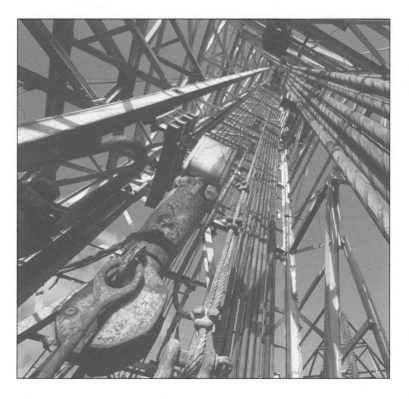

OVERVIEW

The FASB issued its Statement of Financial Accounting Standards No. 144, *Accounting for the Impairment or Disposal of Long-Lived Assets* (FAS 144), in August 2001 (see Current Text reference I08). The document addresses the accounting treatment of long-lived assets and related impairment issues; also, FAS 144 provides direction for petroleum accountants on the impairment and disposal of intangible assets being amortized.

For successful efforts companies, the impairment provisions of FAS 144 apply to proved properties and related equipment and facilities. Unproved properties are subject to the impairment provisions of FAS 19 and Reg. S-X Rule 4-10, as described in Chapter 7. Full cost ceiling provisions in Reg. S-X Rule 4-10 apply when assessing impairment of the full cost pool (reference Chapter 19).

FAS 144 requires a two-tiered approach for assessing impairment:

> **Step 1:** Whenever events or changes in circumstances indicate that the asset's carrying amount may not be recoverable, the entity estimates expected future cash flows from the asset's use and ultimate disposal. If the asset's carrying amount exceeds such cash flows (undiscounted and without interest charges), the entity must recognize an impairment loss as calculated in the following step. This comparison is usually based on pre-tax cash flows.
>
> **Step 2:** The impairment loss is measured as the amount by which the asset's pre-tax carrying amount exceeds its fair value.

Events and changing circumstances are indicators that an asset may be impaired. An asset's carrying value is required to be assessed only when there are indicators that its carrying value may not be recoverable. In summary, if an asset's expected undiscounted future cash flows, as calculated in Step 1 above, are more than its carrying value, the asset's carrying value is considered recoverable, and there is no impairment loss to measure.

FAS 144 is a broad-based standard that provides only general measurement guidelines. The following example demonstrates how a successful efforts company typically applies FAS 144 for its proved properties:

Assumptions

- Proved oil and gas properties and related equipment are grouped on a field basis for impairment purposes.

- The company has 20 proved fields.

- During the current reporting period, management made downward revisions in proved crude oil reserve estimates for three non-operated fields (Fields A, B, and C). These offshore Louisiana properties have experienced significantly reduced planned development activities as a result of new regulations for disposing of produced water.

- Fields A, B, and C have fair values of $3 million, $5 million, and $4 million, respectively (using expected future cash flows from reserves discounted at the market's current rate of return).

Example	(in millions)		
	Field A	Field B	Field C
Capitalized cost of proved properties	$5	$20	$10
Accumulated DD&A	(2)	(8)	(3)
Asset retirement obligations	(0)	(2)	(1)
Deferred revenue for volume production payment on Field C	0	0	(3)
Net book value	$3	$10	$3

Deferred income taxes are generally ignored for determining net book value. However, an exception to this rule is addressed later in this chapter.

Recognition test	(in millions)		
	Field A	Field B	Field C
Future undiscounted expected cash flows before taxes	$4	$8	$8
Net book value	$3	$10	$3
Impairment loss	No	Yes	No

Measurement of impairment

Net book value, ignoring deferred income taxes	$10
Fair value	(5)
Impairment loss	$5

Notice the measurement of impairment is considered a pre-tax amount. Net book value is not reduced by related deferred income taxes, and fair value is what the asset would sell for. The impairment loss is not based on any income taxes (or income tax benefits) resulting from selling the asset for fair value at a gain (or loss). Thus, the adjusting journal entry to record the impairment loss treats it like any pre-tax expense–its effect on the income tax provision must be computed and recorded.

For this example:

• The income statement's impairment loss account is debited for $5 million, and the impaired asset's accumulated DD&A is credited for $5 million.

• If the effective income tax rate is 40 percent, an additional entry debits the balance sheet deferred income taxes account for $2 million, and credits the deferred income tax provision for $2 million.

• The effect to net income is a reduction of $3 million (impairment of $5 million less related deferred tax benefit of $2 million).

In comparison, the ceiling write-down under the full cost ceiling test explained in Chapter 19 is an after-tax amount equivalent to the $3 million in the example.

Paragraph 25 of FAS 144 (I08.160) requires entities with multi-tier income statements to report impairment losses as a component of income from continuing operations before income taxes. Further, if a subtotal such as "income from operations" is presented, it should include the amount of that loss.

The company's policy for assessing and measuring impairment of its long-lived assets should be disclosed in notes to the financial statements. Paragraph 26 of FAS 144 (I08.161) requires the following disclosures in financial statements for each period in which an impairment loss is recognized:

- Description of the impaired assets (e.g., type of assets, location, fields) and facts and circumstances leading to the impairment.

- The way by which fair value was determined (whether based on a quoted market price, prices for similar assets, or another valuation technique.)

- The amount of impairment loss, disclosed either on the face of the income statement or in a note to the financial statements, indicating which caption on the income statement pertains to the impairment loss.

- The business segment impacted by the impairment loss, if applicable.

APPLICATION ISSUES

This section addresses several issues that may arise in applying FAS 144 to proved properties, including wells and facilities.

INHERENT IMPAIRMENT UNDER UNIT-OF-PRODUCTION AMORTIZATION

The last section of Chapter 17 addressed how property impairment is inherent if the required unit-of-production amortization method is used. The likelihood of impairment increases with time as an asset group's production declines to its economic limit. This is due to the calculation of unit-of-production amortization and the fact that operating costs tend to be fixed costs, rather than variable costs.

For example, if reserves are acquired at $5 per BOE, the expected DD&A rate is $5/BOE produced. However, as production declines with time, net cash flows per equivalent barrel also decline, eventually to zero. This occurs because operating costs, many of which are fixed, are spread over fewer units of production. Thus, in the asset group's later years, cash flow per BOE is less than the $5 per BOE needed to recover the asset group's unamortized carrying costs. Upward reserve revisions over the group's productive life may help restore value, but the problem remains attached to this amortization method.

Paragraph 28 of FAS 144 notes that the impairment assessment process may indicate a need to review depreciation policies. However, Oi5 permits only the unit-of-production amortization method for successful efforts companies (full cost companies can use a unit-of-revenue amortization method under certain circumstances). Thus, for older properties, the unit-of-production method continues to trigger impairment write-downs as properties approach their economic limits.

IMPAIRMENT INDICATORS

FAS 144 requires management to review the carrying value of proved, probable, and possible oil and gas properties–if events or changes in circumstances indicate that the carrying value may not be recoverable. Impairment indicators can include:

- The passage of time due to unit-of-production amortization, as explained in the last section.

- Lower expected future oil and gas prices (such as the prices used by management in evaluating whether to develop or acquire properties).

- Actual or expected future development costs are significantly more than previously anticipated for a group of properties (e.g., significant AFE overruns with no significant upward revisions in reserve estimates).

- Significant downward revisions to a field's reserve estimates.

- Significant adverse change in legislative or regulatory climate (e.g., an unanticipated increase in severance tax rates).

SEC registrants must address impairment in the operating results of the quarter in which the impairment-related events or circumstances occur that indicate an asset group may be impaired. Thus, impairment losses are reported in the quarter related to the event, as opposed to year-end operating results.

Some companies use quarterly benchmarks, such as their budgeted quarterly cash flow, to carefully monitor indications of impairment in a timely manner. For example, if the most recent analysis of expected future cash flow was $100,000 for the current quarter, and actual cash flow is significantly less than the benchmark, an updated analysis may be needed.

Companies that maintain a computer file of expected future cash flows by asset or asset grouping may find it prudent to update their records on a quarterly basis. Instead of looking for indicators, companies should update their expected future cash flow analysis for changes in future price expectations and for significant known changes in proved reserves. At a minimum, these companies should update their analyses at year-end when reserve estimates and the standardized measure are revised. Using E&P economic analysis software, the pre-tax standardized measure is routinely computed and saved on a per well basis. From that data, expected future cash flow from proved reserves is easily generated by changing pricing and cost-escalation assumptions. Arguably, the annual update process can be skipped for properties with capitalized costs well below expected future cash flows in the prior analysis. However, petroleum accountants may find it more efficient to update the analysis for all properties, rather than justify using a more selective update process to internal parties and outside auditors.

ASSET CARRYING AMOUNT

FAS 144 does not define what constitutes a long-lived asset's carrying amount. Generally, this is the asset's net book value, or cost less accumulated DD&A. Deferred income taxes are usually ignored, as discussed in this section.

For a fair comparison with expected undiscounted future cash flows and fair value, other balance sheet accounts may need to be consistently disregarded or considered, such as for accrued ARO costs and VPP (Volume Production Payment or Volumetric Production Payment) deferred revenue.

Ignoring Deferred Income Taxes—Usually. Unlike the full cost ceiling test, deferred income taxes typically do not impact an asset's carrying value for the purpose of comparing that value to related expected undiscounted future net cash flow (to determine whether there is potential impairment, as required by FAS 144). Thus, if an asset's carrying value is $1 million and the expected future cash flow is $1 million, then related future income taxes will equal or closely approximate related deferred income taxes. This is true because the entity's tax basis and the tax rate are typically the same in computing future income taxes as in computing deferred income taxes.

If expected pre-tax cash flow is significantly different from the asset's carrying value, future income taxes will similarly correspond to deferred income taxes, although not enough to change the decision whether impairment should be recognized. As a result, the consideration of future income taxes and recorded deferred income taxes in such a comparison is generally not needed.

Certain long-lived assets (such as E&P properties producing coalbed methane) generate substantial income tax credits that enhance asset value. In computing expected future cash flow, companies are free to consider any special income tax benefits.

Despite their use in the full cost ceiling test, deferred income taxes are not relevant in determining fair value or measuring impairment under FAS 144. Fair value is determined by using either pre-tax or after-tax cash flows, appropriately discounted, as discussed in Chapter 31. Fair value is what a third party will pay for the asset whereby the third party's purchase price becomes the property's new tax basis. Fair value of a producing property ignores how the seller's tax liability changes for any gain (or loss) relative to the asset's income tax basis. Thus, the asset's carrying amount is without regard to deferred income taxes in comparing it to fair value for measuring impairment loss.

Consideration of Accrued ARO Liabilities. As discussed in Chapter 20, the FASB issued FAS 143 (Current Text reference A50), *Accounting for Asset Retirement Obligations*. It requires asset retirement obligations (ARO) to be accrued as a liability when the obligations arise–as long as a reasonable estimate of fair value can be made.

At the time a field is explored and developed, a liability amount can be calculated. The initial liability accrual increases the carrying value of the asset. Paragraph 12 of FAS 143 (A50.112) states that the accrued liability and the corresponding future ARO liability are disregarded for FAS 144 impairment, i.e., ignored and not used to reduce expected future cash flow and asset fair value since the asset carrying amount has been increased by the initial ARO accrual.

Consideration of VPP Deferred Revenue. The sale of a VPP from a proved property is regarded as the sale of a mineral interest which reduces reserves according to FAS 19. It is common for cash proceeds to be credited to deferred revenue rather than to the oil and gas property asset account. This practice reduces reserves and expected cash flow without a corresponding reduction in the carrying amount of the asset. To properly apply FAS 144's impairment recognition test, an asset's carrying amount should be net of any related VPP deferred revenue.

Similarly, for measuring impairment loss, the asset's carrying amount should be net of any related VPP deferred revenue for comparison to the fair value of the net unsold property.

ASSET GROUPING

Producing Assets Are Commonly Grouped by Field. Paragraph 10 of FAS 144 states:

> ...assets shall be grouped with other assets and liabilities at the lowest level for which identifiable cash flows are largely independent of the cash flows of other assets and liabilities.

The *2001 PricewaterhouseCoopers Survey of U.S. Petroleum Accounting Practices* found that of the 10 respondents using successful efforts, six grouped assets by field (60 percent); none grouped by well; and one grouped by lease.

The grouping of proved properties on a field basis is generally appropriate due to sales arrangements or the existence of common field facilities. Most sales arrangements involve production from several wells within a given field, and production from a well can be dedicated to several purchasers. Sales proceeds from intermingled production of several wells are allocated based on each well's adjusted production volumes.

Purchasers do not typically seek production from a given well; instead, they contract to obtain a specific quantity of hydrocarbons. Thus, the terms and arrangements to sell a well's production depend on the quantity and quality of all wells within the sales contract coverage area.

Wells within a given field generally share common production facilities. Cost sharing is an indicator that cash flows from a given well or lease are not largely independent.

In addition, well operations typically succumb to, and are directly impacted by, operational and regulatory constraints of the field.

Grouping certain proved fields, or grouping proved fields with downstream activities, may be appropriate in assessing impairment if the cash flows of these operations are directly dependent upon each other. However, such groupings are the exception, not the norm.

DETERMINING EXPECTED FUTURE CASH FLOWS

FAS 144, paragraph 16 (I08.151), defines expected future cash flows as "the future cash flows (cash inflows less associated cash outflows) that are directly associated with and that are expected to arise as a direct result of the use and eventual disposition of the asset (asset group). Those estimates shall exclude interest charges that will be recognized as an expense when incurred." FAS 144, paragraph 17 (I08.152) states:

> Estimates of future cash flows used to test the recoverability of a long-lived asset (asset group) shall incorporate the entity's own assumptions about its use of the asset (asset group) and shall consider all available evidence. The assumptions used in developing those estimates shall be reasonable in relation to the assumptions used in developing other information used by the entity for comparable periods, such as internal budgets and projections, accruals related to incentive compensation plans, or information communicated to others. However, if alternative courses of action to recover the carrying amount of a long-lived asset (asset group) are under consideration or if a range is estimated for the amount of possible future cash flows associated with the likely course of action, the likelihood of those possible outcomes shall be considered. A probability-weighted approach may be useful in considering the likelihood of those possible outcomes.

A proper determination of expected future cash flows considers the following:

Reserves. Proved, probable, and possible reserves should be considered (and appropriately risk-reduced) in estimating expected future cash flows. Paragraph 17 of FAS 144 (I08.152) calls for considering the likelihood of possible outcomes, which allows companies to consider probable and possible reserves. However, the likelihood of possible reserves may be so remote the incremental effect on expected future cash flow is nominal.

As explained earlier, probable reserves are defined by the SPE and WPC as:

1. Unproved reserves more likely than not to be recoverable,

2. Where there is at least a 50 percent probability that the quantities actually recovered will equal or exceed the sum of estimated probable and proved reserves, and

3. Where expected future production is the sum of proved and probable reserves.

In seeming contradiction to the definition, the *2001 PricewaterhouseCoopers Survey of U.S. Petroleum Accounting Practices* found only 31 percent of successful efforts respondents considered probable reserves for determining FAS 144 impairment.

For expediency, a company is permitted to use only proved reserves in order to quickly eliminate many properties from the list of potentially impaired properties. For the remaining properties, a more refined determination of future cash flows can be made using: (1) proved reserves, (2) risk-adjusted probable reserves, and (3) possible reserves.

Prices. Future prices should be in nominal dollars (adjusted for expected inflation) and must reflect management's best estimates. Such prices must have a high correlation with the future pricing assumptions management uses in its long-range budgeting process, property acquisition, and property divestiture programs. Management's price estimates can be derived from actual contracts or independent public forecasts, such as the *Oil & Gas Journal*'s semi-annual price forecast compendiums or the SPEE annual *Survey[s] of Economic Parameters Used in Property Evaluations* noted in Chapter 31.

Future contracts (Chapter 33) available at the valuation date may be used to establish or reflect short-term expected prices adjusted for basis differential(s). Prices should reflect the value of hydrocarbons at the well-head or point of transfer from the asset group (e.g., at the gas plant tailgate if the plant is grouped with the producing wells for FAS 144 purposes). Thus, incremental profits or losses generated by subsequent downstream activities and some risk management activities are excluded from determining future hydrocarbon prices for the impaired asset group.

Costs. Future cost projections should be management's best estimates of the future capital expenditures, operating costs, and, perhaps, ARO costs directly associated with the impaired asset group. These costs should also have a high correlation with the future operating and capital expenditure assumptions management uses in its long-range budgeting process. In estimating future costs, current costs should be escalated by anticipated inflation factors consistent with using oil and gas sales prices in nominal dollars.

G&A Overhead. The *2001 PricewaterhouseCoopers Survey of U.S. Petroleum Accounting Practices* found that 100 percent of respondents using the successful efforts method ignored overhead in determining expected future cash flow for FAS 144 purposes. Overhead costs should be considered to the extent they directly relate to operations of the impaired asset group (e.g., operating personnel and project support staff located in district offices). Corporate or home office overhead not directly related to an impaired asset's activities should not be included.

Arguably, some home office overhead is necessary for utilizing the asset. Such overhead might be viewed as what FAS 144, paragraph 16, calls "future cash flows that are expected to arise" to obtain the future cash inflow generated by the asset. Indeed, some loans to E&P companies became substantially impaired when oil prices crashed in 1986. Lenders failed to consider the heavy G&A costs required to operate numerous small properties in order to generate cash flow loan repayment.

Income Taxes. Income taxes in foreign jurisdictions should be evaluated as to whether they are more appropriately classified as royalties or production taxes, both of which reduce future pre-tax cash flows.

DETERMINING FAIR VALUE

Paragraph 7 of FAS 144 (I08.142) states the impairment loss associated with an asset group is "the amount by which the carrying amount of a long-lived asset is not recoverable and exceeds its fair value." Paragraph 22 (I08.157) defines fair value as the "amount at which the asset could be bought or sold in a current transaction between willing parties." An asset's fair value is preferably indicated by a quoted market price in an active market. Otherwise, it is based on the best information available such as the price of a similar asset or the result of valuation techniques.

Two factors impact the assessment of fair value for proved oil and gas properties: (1) the lack of availability of quoted market prices, and (2) the variability of fair value according to future cash flows. As a result, companies prepare estimates–using a discounted cash flow analysis–of bid prices and the ultimate purchase and sales prices of oil and gas properties. Such a discounted cash flow analysis takes various forms and may include the following:

- Cash flows use nominal dollars (reflect inflation) or real dollars (ignore inflation)

- Tax expense as a separate cash outflow or adjust the discount rate to reflect tax expense (see Chapter 31 for further explanation)

- Risk-weight individual cash flow streams or discount the net cash flow streams considering underlying risks

Paragraph 22 of FAS 144 (I08.157) states the estimate of fair value should be based on the best information available. Therefore, valuation techniques that are merely rough rules of thumb, such as value per reserve barrel, should not be used when a better approach — discounted cash flow analysis — is available.

Expected future cash flows should be discounted using a rate commensurate with the risks involved, according to paragraph 23 of FAS 144 (I08.158). Further, Appendix B, paragraph 37, states that "the Board does not believe that discounting expected future cash flows using a debt rate is an appropriate measure for determining the value of those assets." Thus, the discount rate determined for each impaired asset group should be based on the rate of return the market expects for similar types of assets. Factors such as the company's internal hurdle rate for return on capital expenditures should be considered in determining discount rates.

It may be appropriate to separately risk-adjust certain cash inflows and outflows based on their probabilities, rather than indirectly adjusting for risk by modifying the discount rate. For example, if the probability associated with actually paying future ARO costs is significantly different from the probability that hydrocarbon production will occur, or that future sales prices will be realized, each cash flow stream is appropriately risk-weighted.

As previously noted, fair value and the amount of impairment are determined without regard to deferred income taxes. Likewise, the amount of income taxes due (or saved) by a seller for the taxable gain (or loss) on selling the property at a value different from the property's tax basis does not affect fair value or impairment amounts. FAS 144's measurement of impairment differs in this respect from the full cost ceiling test that is designed to consider such taxes.

ASSETS TO BE DISPOSED OF

FAS 144 also provides guidance for recognizing and measuring the impairment of long-lived assets to be disposed of. The statement superceded the accounting and reporting provisions of APB 30, *Reporting the Results of Operations—Reporting the Effects of Disposal of a Segment of a Business, and Extraordinary, Unusual and Infrequently Occurring Events and Transactions.* However, FAS 144 retained the requirement to report discontinued operations separately from continuing operations and extended that reporting to a component of an entity that either has been disposed of or is classified as held for sale. Proved oil and gas properties identified by management as held for sale are recorded at the lower of: (1) cost, or (2) fair value less costs to sell. Assets held for disposal should be distinguished from the company's other proved properties, either on the balance sheet or in notes to financial statements. A plan must exist for disposing of these assets, which should occur within one year of the plan date.

For assets to be disposed of, fair value is the amount of expected future net realizable value from sales, which has been discounted to the present value at the appraisal date. Fair value ignores estimated future oil and gas revenues and related operating expenses during the holding period prior to sale.

For example, a December 31, 2006, proposed sales contract is set to close March 1 for $1 million, with selling costs of $100,000. The asset has an expected future net realizable value of $900,000. Applying a discount factor to the $900,000 leads to a December 31, 2006, present value of $880,000. The resulting fair value for determining impairment at year-end is $880,000. Additional value from production in January and February is ignored, and the property's capitalized costs are not depreciated for the two month period.

FAS 144, paragraph 35, provides if the asset's fair value is measured by discounting expected future cash flows and if the sale is expected to occur beyond one year, the cost to sell should also be discounted (implying the cost to sell is not discounted otherwise).

Paragraph 34 states that assets identified as being held for sale should "not be depreciated (amortized) while they are being held for sale." Thus, oil and gas revenues and related operating expenses from assets held for sale are recognized, but no corresponding DD&A is allowed. This treatment is proper since the carrying values of assets held for disposal are recovered from their sale, not from use. If there is a subsequent revision of the fair value less costs to sell, an adjustment must be made in the carrying value of the assets held for sale. The value is adjusted to the new value provided it does not exceed the carrying value of such assets before the decision was made to dispose of them.

The following example illustrates the application of FAS 144 to long-lived assets to be disposed of. An E&P company signs a letter of intent on February 15, 2006, to sell its Texas properties for $100 million, less an estimated $5 million in operating cash flow through the expected closing date of September 28, 2006. Selling costs total $3 million. Expected sales proceeds are $95 million, and net sales proceeds are $92 million. The company has other properties so that the sale of the Texas properties is not considered a discontinuance of a business segment covered by APB 30. Instead, FAS 144 applies, and the Texas properties are treated as long-lived assets to be disposed of.

On February 29, 2006, the properties are carried at the lower of cost or fair value, less the cost to sell. Assume a four percent discount rate for six months. Thus, the expected $95 million in sales proceeds is discounted to $91.35 million in fair value at February 29, 2006. This fair value, less the undiscounted cost to sell, equals $88.35 million. If the properties' total carrying value at February 29 is $90 million, the company will write-down the assets' carrying value to $88.35 million and not depreciate that amount over the six-month holding period prior to sale. If the total carrying value is $85 million, no write-down will occur, and no depreciation is taken during the holding period.

Disclosure of impairment losses on assets held for sale is similar to the disclosures for assets held and used; however, the following additional disclosures should be made:

- Facts and circumstances leading to the expected disposal

- Expected manner and timing of the disposal and carrying amount

- Any gains or losses resulting from re-measurement of the assets

- Results of operations included in the income statement, if identifiable

Reporting of assets to be disposed of as a discontinued operation depends on whether they would be considered a component and whether certain other criteria are met. A component of an entity consists of operations and cash flows that can be clearly distinguished, operationally and for financial reporting purposes, from the rest of the entity. For a successful efforts company, a component may often be identified at the well, lease or field level.

The results of operations of a component of an entity that either has been disposed of or is classified as held for sale should be reported in discontinued operations in accordance with FAS 144 if both of the following conditions are met: (1) the operations and cash flows of the component entity have been (or will be) eliminated from the ongoing operations of the entity as a result of the disposal transaction, and (2) the entity will not have any significant continuing involvement in the operations of the component after the disposal.

EITF 03-13 clarifies questions that have arisen as to how paragraph 42 of FAS 144 should be interpreted and applied. There is a presumption that the continued sale of a commodity in an active market should be considered a migration of customers, and therefore the cash flows of a disposed entity have not been eliminated entirely. For purposes of this issue, a commodity is defined as products whose units are interchangeable and immediately marketable at quoted prices. This will reduce the number of reported discontinued operations in the oil and gas and other commodity type businesses.

APPLICABILITY TO FULL COST COMPANIES

Companies subject to SEC regulation and privately held full cost companies use the full cost ceiling test found in Reg. S-X Rule 4-10. They commonly ignore the FAS 144 impairment tests for the full cost pool.

SEC staff has issued comment letters calling for disclosure by full cost companies that the full cost ceiling test is used for proved oil and gas property in lieu of FAS 144. FASB staff has recommended that privately held companies using full cost follow the guidance for other full cost companies, presumably the full cost ceiling test used by publicly held full cost companies (based on minutes of the FASB meeting of September 14, 1994). Further, FAS 144 specifically comments in footnote 2 that accounting requirements for oil and gas properties accounted for using the full cost method are prescribed by the SEC.

Their recommendation is consistent with the concept that full cost companies, subject to Reg. S-X Rule 4-10(c) rules, effectively establish the practices for full cost (i.e., public companies' practices become the norm to be followed by privately held companies).

One Asset per Country-wide Cost Pool. In theory, publicly held full cost companies are subject to both the FAS 144 impairment rules and Reg. S-X Rule 4-10(c) ceiling test. However, the ceiling effectively limits aggregate costs to a level so far below undiscounted expected future cash flow that FAS 144 would rarely apply. One notable exception is when year-end pricing (used in the ceiling test) substantially exceeds expected pricing (used for FAS 144 impairment accounting).

The cost pool (i.e., a cost aggregation of successful and unsuccessful exploration activities) serves under full cost theory as a single asset—a probable future economic benefit indicated by proved reserves obtained by the company as a result of all prior exploration and development activity in a given country. It is subject to a single amortization per period and is not readily divisible into smaller assets.

In the SEC codification of financial reporting releases, Section 406.01.c.i, the SEC notes that once costs are included in the full cost pool amortization base, "they lose their identity for all future accounting purposes."

As a result, FAS 144 impairment is not recognized unless the capitalized aggregate costs exceed the aggregate expected future cash flows by country. Before that happens, the Reg. S-X ceiling test using discounted cash flows triggers a write-down to keep capitalized costs from exceeding undiscounted expected future cash flows. The only exception (rare) is when year-end pricing for the ceiling test substantially exceeds expected pricing.

Disregarding the Cost Pool as a Single Asset. Even if the full cost pool were to be treated as a grouping of assets with each field representing an appropriate grouping, the ceiling test using discounted cash flow would still minimize, if not eliminate, any write-downs for impairments under FAS 144.

Every quarter, full cost companies apply the ceiling test. The fair value of holdings in each field is estimated, and country-wide amortization is allocated among the fields based on relative fair value. This determines whether the net book value allocated to a field exceeds the corresponding undiscounted expected future cash flow. Fields with relatively little expected future cash flow have a relatively low fair value and are allocated relatively little net book value. Hence, to disregard the cost pool as a single asset for applying FAS 144 rarely changes the ultimate impairment, and any such change is likely to be insignificant.

FAS 144 HAS NO EFFECT ON THE DD&A METHOD OR ON COMPUTING THE FAS 69 STANDARDIZED MEASURE

Expected future cash flows under FAS 144 use expected prices, expected cost rates, and expected future production. As previously explained, expected future production might include risk-weighted probable and possible reserves. FAS 19 successful efforts and Reg. S-X full cost accounting pronouncements specifically require that DD&A be based on proved reserves. By definition, proved reserves are only those reserves recoverable with reasonable certainty using prices and cost rates as of the date the reserves estimate applies. FAS 69 requires that the standardized measure (addressed in Chapter 29) be based on proved reserves and year-end prices and cost rates–not on expected production, prices, and cost rates.

The method by which a company groups costs for DD&A amortization (such as by property) is independent of the way assets are to be grouped for FAS 144 impairment tests (such as by field). Cost aggregation for calculating an amortization base under full cost or under successful efforts is not a function of asset grouping for FAS 144.

• • •

19

THE FULL COST ACCOUNTING METHOD

Key Concepts:

- History of the full cost accounting method

- Definition of cost center

- Costs to be capitalized

- Calculation of the amortization base

- Amortization using unit-of-production and gross revenue methods

- The full cost ceiling

- Asset retirement obligations

- Discontinued operations

HISTORY OF FULL COST ACCOUNTING

Until the late 1950s, all oil and gas producing companies used some variation of the successful efforts method of accounting. At that time, a new approach to petroleum accounting was developed known as the full cost method. Under this concept, all costs incurred in acquiring, exploring, and developing properties within a large geopolitical or geographical cost center are capitalized and amortized as the reserves in that cost center are produced.

Full cost accounting regards all costs of acquisition, exploration, and development activities as necessary for the ultimate production of reserves, even though many costs do not directly relate to finding and developing reserves. Oil and gas companies expect the benefits obtained from prospects that prove successful, together with benefits from past discoveries, will be adequate to recover the costs of all activities, both successful and unsuccessful, and to yield a profit. Figure 19-1 (identical to Figure 4-2) summarizes the major full cost accounting rules explained in this chapter.

In the 1960s, many publicly held oil and gas companies, especially small, new companies, adopted the full cost method. By the mid-1970s and continuing today, nearly one-half of the publicly held companies were using full cost.[1]

Although the FASB rejected full cost as an acceptable accounting method in FAS 19, the SEC concluded in August 1978 (ASR 253) that the successful efforts method should not be the only acceptable approach. It announced that a full cost method to be developed by the SEC could be used by publicly held companies for their SEC filings. In ASR 258, which was issued in December 1978, the SEC adopted final rules for companies electing to use full cost. The initial rules were modified in 1983 and 1984 and are known as Reg. S-X Rule 4-10. Reproduced in Appendix 1, these rules clarify the nature of a cost center, costs to be capitalized and amortized, amortization methods, and computation of a ceiling on capitalized costs.

In response to the SEC's allowance of full cost accounting, the FASB issued FAS 25 in February 1979. It rescinded the FAS 19 rule requiring use of the successful efforts accounting method. However, FAS 25, paragraph 4, provides that because FAS 19 was issued, the specified successful efforts accounting method remains the preferable method. As a result, the SEC does not require an independent auditor's letter of preferability for an accounting change to the FAS 19 successful efforts accounting method, as noted in SEC Staff Accounting Bulletin Topic 12C, Item 1. The letter is required for a change to full cost accounting.

COST CENTER

Under the SEC's rules, cost centers are established on a country-by-country basis. A strict interpretation of this rule prohibits combining or grouping countries in a geographical area. For example, it is improper to combine a company's North Sea operations with its Norwegian and British territorial areas. Reg. S-X Rule 4-10(c)(6)(ii) provides a rare exception to the country-wide cost center:

> [S]ignificant purchases of production payments or properties with lives substantially shorter than the composite productive life of the cost center shall be accounted for separately.

The full cost accounting section in Chapter 22 discusses this exception further.

Figure 19-1
Full Cost Accounting for Costs

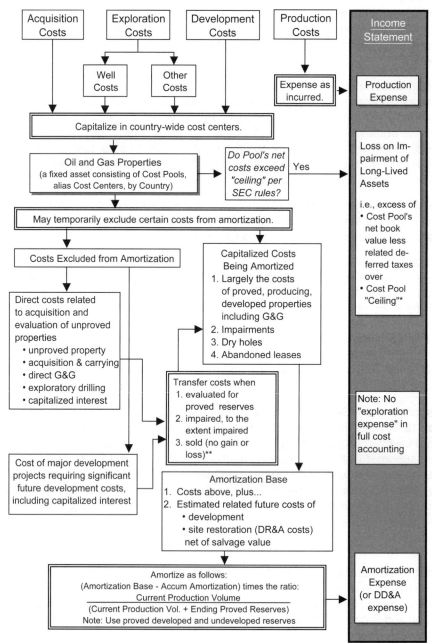

*Cost Pool Ceiling:

(a) a present value of projected future cash flow from proved reserves using hedge-adjusted prices.

(b) plus costs excluded from amortization,

(c) plus the lower of cost or fair value of unproved properties in amortization base,

(d) less estimated related income tax effects, i.e., (1) the present value of income taxes on taxable income relating to proved reserves' future cash flow, and (2) income taxes from hypothetically selling immediately the unproved properties and unevaluated projects at the values in (b) and (c) above.

**No gain or loss unless otherwise the ratio of cost to proved reserves would significantly change.

TREATMENT OF PROPERTIES HELD FOR PROMOTION OR SALE

Reg. S-X Rule 4-10 makes no reference to the possibility an oil and gas producing company might also be engaged in a lease brokerage business. However, SEC's Staff Accounting Bulletin No. 47 referred to the two lines of business concept. Many accountants argue that an E&P company can participate in two distinct businesses—oil and gas production and lease brokerage—by acquiring unproved properties for drilling purposes and other properties for the purpose of promoting them to limited partnerships.

SAB 47 originally indicated a "two lines of business" approach was acceptable and a property might be deemed to have been acquired for promotional activities and included in an inventory of properties held for such purposes if such distinction was made at the time of acquisition.

In May 1984, the SEC revoked this portion of SAB 47 and revised Reg. S-X Rule 4-10 to provide that sales of properties or transfers of unproved properties to partnerships, funds, or other entities, represent adjustments of the full cost pool. No gain or loss is recognized on these types of conveyances. Thus, costs of all mineral properties owned by a full cost company, including those acquired for resale or promotion, are treated alike and are included in a single, country-wide cost center.

COSTS TO BE CAPITALIZED

S-X Rule 4-10(c)(2) specifies the costs to be capitalized under the full cost method:

> *Costs to be capitalized.* All costs associated with property acquisition, exploration, and development activities (as defined in paragraph (a) of this section) shall be capitalized within the appropriate cost center. Any internal costs that are capitalized shall be limited to those costs that can be directly identified with acquisition, exploration, and development activities undertaken by the reporting entity for its own account, and shall not include any costs related to production, general corporate overhead, or similar activities.

Under these rules, all geological and geophysical costs, carrying costs such as delay rentals and maintenance of land and lease records, dry-hole and bottom-hole contributions, costs of exploratory wells (both dry and successful), costs of stratigraphic tests wells, costs of acquiring properties, and all development costs are capitalized. Only those overhead costs related directly to exploration, acquisition, and development activities should be capitalized. A special problem arises in determining the amount of interest to be capitalized by full cost companies, and is discussed later in this chapter. Even after leases are surrendered or abandoned, their costs remain a part of the capitalized costs of the cost center, as do costs of dry holes and other unsuccessful exploration.

Since all costs incurred in each country are capitalized into the cost center with the other mineral assets held within that country, individual properties and assets conceptually lose their identities. A single Oil and Gas Assets account (or similar title) for each country is used to accumulate the costs in that country. For example, a company with operations in the U.S. (onshore and offshore), Canada, and Norway would maintain accounts in three cost centers:

- Oil and Gas Assets—United States
- Oil and Gas Assets—Canada
- Oil and Gas Assets—Norway

Even though all oil and gas assets in a cost center are lumped into a single account, certain detailed records must be maintained for federal income tax and other regulatory purposes. In addition, companies can temporarily exclude certain unevaluated costs from the amortization base. Thus, companies using the full cost method must maintain subledgers for individual unproved properties and individual proved properties. Further, the method of accounting chosen does not alter the needs for management and internal control of operations. Basic accounting procedures, such as the use of an AFE, are not affected by the choice of successful efforts accounting or full cost accounting.

For these reasons, most companies use general ledger accounts similar to those used in successful efforts accounting, as shown in this book's Illustrative Chart of Accounts in Appendix 3.

AMORTIZATION OF CAPITALIZED COSTS

Amortization of capitalized costs under the full cost method differs significantly from the successful efforts approach. Reserve amounts and eligible costs for calculating unit-of-production amortization are unique to full cost accounting.

RESERVES TO BE USED IN THE AMORTIZATION CALCULATION

All capitalized costs within a cost center are amortized on the unit-of-production basis using total proved oil and gas reserves. (As mentioned previously, certain unevaluated costs may be temporarily excluded from amortization.) Oil and gas reserves are converted to a common unit-of-measure based on energy content or, in limited cases, current and future gross revenues.

COSTS TO BE AMORTIZED

Reg. S-X Rule 4-10(c)(3)(i) contains the basic description of costs to be amortized:

> Costs to be amortized shall include (A) all capitalized costs, less accumulated amortization, other than the.. [Author's note: costs of acquiring and evaluating unproved property, as explained on the next page]; (B) the estimated future expenditures (based on current costs) to be incurred in developing proved reserves; and (C) estimated dismantlement and abandonment costs, net of estimated salvage values.

A feature of the full cost method is all capitalized costs relating to oil and gas assets, other than specifically excluded costs, enter into the amortization computation at the time they are incurred. Another distinction is the general inclusion in amortizable costs of future expenditures for developing the proved reserves included in the amortization calculation. Inclusion of estimated future development costs, based on current cost levels, is necessary because all proved reserves are included in the calculation including those not yet developed. Omission of future development costs would result in a mismatching of costs applicable to the reserves used in the calculation.

Dismantlement and abandonment costs (asset retirement costs, or ARCs) impact the DD&A calculation for full cost companies as well. FAS 143, *Accounting for Asset Retirement Obligations* (discussed in Chapter 20), includes ARCs in the capitalized costs of the full cost pool for all asset retirement obligations (AROs) resulting from exploration and development activities completed to-date. Estimated dismantlement and abandonment costs described in item (C) for exploration and development costs incurred to-date are already included in item (A). Future development expenditures noted in item (B) create additional AROs when those activities are performed in the future and result in the capitalization of additional asset retirement costs when those future development costs are incurred and capitalized.

According to SAB 106, a company should estimate the amount of future ARCs to capitalize as a result of future expenditures to be incurred in developing proved reserves, and include those amounts in costs to be amortized. Item (C) requires the inclusion of estimated dismantlement and abandonment costs in the amounts to be amortized. No distinction was made in item (C) for estimated dismantlement and abandonment costs resulting from costs already incurred per item (A) or from costs to be incurred within item (B). The overall objective of full cost depreciation methodology is to estimate all the costs for proved reserves (both incurred and to be incurred) and amortize them over the production of proved reserves (both developed and undeveloped).

EXCLUSIONS FROM THE AMORTIZATION POOL

Two exceptions exist to the general rule that all capitalized costs in the cost center are included in the amortization computation when incurred. These exceptions are noted in Reg. S-X Rule 4-10(c)(3)(ii), as amended in 1983. Costs of unevaluated properties and major development projects expected to require significant future costs are exempted.

Costs Related to Unevaluated Properties

The first exclusion from amortization is the cost of acquisition and exploration directly related to unevaluated properties. Paragraph (c)(3)(ii)(A), of Reg. S-X Rule 4-10, as amended in 1983, provides:

(A) All costs directly associated with the acquisition and evaluation of unproved properties may be excluded from the amortization computation until it is determined whether or not proved reserves can be assigned to the properties, subject to the following conditions: (1) Until such a determination is made, the properties shall be assessed at least annually to ascertain whether impairment has occurred. Unevaluated properties whose costs are individually significant shall be assessed individually. Where it is not practicable to individually assess the amount of impairment of properties for which costs are not individually significant, such properties may be grouped for purposes of assessing impairment. Impairment may be estimated by applying factors based on historical experience and other data such as primary lease terms of the properties, average holding periods of unproved properties, and geographic and geologic data, to groupings of individually insignificant properties and projects. The amount of impairment assessed under either of these methods shall be added to the costs to be amortized. (2) The costs of drilling exploratory dry holes shall be included in the amortization base immediately upon determination that the well is dry. (3) If geological and geophysical costs cannot be directly associated with specific unevaluated properties, they shall be included in the amortization base as incurred. Upon complete evaluation of a property, the total remaining excluded cost (net of any impairment) shall be included in the full cost amortization base.

The exclusion refers to "all costs directly associated with the acquisition and evaluation of unproved properties." Although carrying costs are not specified, SEC Financial Reporting Release 14 (which provided for the exclusion) seems reasonably clear in allowing carrying costs to be included in the costs excluded from amortization and subject to annual impairment assessments.

Note that the rules for determining the impairment of unevaluated properties and related costs are similar to those given in Chapter 7 for determining impairment of unproved properties by successful efforts companies. In many instances, the SEC has adapted the rules for successful efforts accounting to specific problems in applying the full cost concept.

Exclusion from amortization is permitted in order to avoid distortion in the amortization per unit that could result if the cost of unevaluated properties with no proved reserves attributed to them was included in the amortization base. It is an effort to match proved reserves in the country-wide cost center with associated costs, including unsuccessful exploration costs.

The following calculation of a hypothetical cost center's amortization base illustrates the exclusion of unevaluated costs:

Capitalized costs as of period end		$140,000,000
Less amortization in prior periods		(30,000,000)
Net book value prior to current amortization		110,000,000
Add estimated future development costs		10,000,000
Total		120,000,000
Less costs related to unevaluated properties		
Cost	$25,000,000	
Less cumulative impairments	(5,000,000)	(20,000,000)
Amortization Base		**$100,000,000**

Unusually Significant Development Projects

The second permissible exclusion of capitalized costs from the amortization pool is provided in Reg. S-X Rule 4-10(c)(3)(ii)(B), as revised in 1983:

(B) Certain costs may be excluded from amortization when incurred in connection with major development projects expected to entail significant costs to ascertain the quantities of proved reserves attributable to the properties under development (e.g., the installation of an offshore drilling platform from which development wells are to be drilled, the installation of improved recovery programs, and similar major projects undertaken in the expectation of significant additions to proved reserves). The amounts which may be excluded are applicable portions of (1) the costs that relate to the major development project and have not previously been included in the amortization base, and (2) the estimated future expenditures associated with the development project. The excluded portion of any common costs associated with the development project should be based, as is most appropriate in the circumstances, on a comparison of either (i) existing proved reserves to total proved reserves expected to be established upon completion of the project, or (ii) the number of wells to which proved reserves have been assigned and the total number of wells expected to be drilled. Such costs may be excluded from costs to be amortized until the earlier determination of whether additional reserves are proved or impairment occurs.

(C) Excluded costs and the proved reserves related to such costs shall be transferred into the amortization base on an ongoing (well-by-well or property-by-property) basis as the project is evaluated and proved reserves established or impairment determined. Once proved reserves are established, there is no further justification for continued exclusion from the full cost amortization base even if other factors prevent immediate production or marketing.

To illustrate the exclusion of development costs from the amortization calculation, assume that capitalized costs of a discovery well, two evaluation wells, and a platform related to a major offshore project total $36 million. Two producing wells have been drilled from the platform at a cost of $2.5 million per well, and eight more wells expected to cost $2.5 million each will be drilled to formations containing an estimated 8.4 million barrels of probable reserves. It is projected that a total of 10 million barrels may finally be proved, although only 1.6 million have been proved by the two development wells.

In computing amortization for the year, reserves not yet proved are omitted from the proved reserve amount. That portion of the $36 million of common costs related to the excluded reserves is appropriately excluded from the amortization base. Calculations of the excluded portion using an allocation of common costs by well and an allocation by reserves follow:

Excluded costs using an allocation by well:	
Direct costs of the eight wells at $2.5 million each	$20,000,000
Plus common costs of $36 million x 8 wells / 10 wells	28,800,000
	$48,800,000
Excluded costs using an allocation by reserves:	
Direct costs of the eight wells at $2.5 million each	$20,000,000
Plus common costs of $36 million x 84%*	30,240,000
	$50,240,000

*8.4 million bbls / 10 million bbls.

Disclosure of Exclusions

Reg. S-X Rule 4-10(c)(7)(ii) provides several required disclosures for the costs excluded from the amortization base. An E&P company is required to state separately on the face of the balance sheet the aggregate capitalized costs of unproved properties and major development projects excluded from capitalized costs being amortized. In addition, notes to the financial statements must include a description of the current status of the significant properties or projects involved, including the anticipated timing of inclusion of the costs in the amortization computation. A table should be presented showing by category of cost— acquisition, exploration, development, and capitalized interest—(1) total costs excluded as of the most recent fiscal year, and (2) the amount of excluded costs incurred (a) in each of the three most recent fiscal years, and (b) in the aggregate for any earlier fiscal years in which the costs were incurred.

Excluded costs do not have to be disclosed by cost center, nor does the financial note need to provide the status of all properties and projects with excluded costs. For example, the balance sheet could show:

Oil and gas property and equipment:	
Proved properties	$40,000,000
Unproved properties and development costs	
not being amortized	10,000,000
	50,000,000
Less accumulated amortization	(8,000,000)
	$42,000,000

A financial statement note might read:

Costs withheld from amortization. The Company excludes from amortization the cost of unproved properties, exploratory wells in progress, and major development projects in progress. Oil and gas property and equipment costs not being amortized as of December 31, 2006, are as follows (in millions) by the year in which such costs were incurred:

	Total	2006	2005	2004	Prior
Acquisition costs	$ 5.0	$2.0	$2.0	$0.6	$0.4
Exploration costs	1.0	0.8	0.1	0.1	-
Development costs	3.7	3.7	-	-	-
Capitalized interest	0.3	0.3	-	-	-
	$10.0	$6.8	$2.1	$0.7	$0.4

The excluded costs include: (1) $5.1 million for the Some Day offshore field expected to be included in the amortization base in 2007, and (2) $2.3 million in the unproved, unevaluated Brittany Ranch lease expected to be evaluated in 2007.

UNIT-OF-PRODUCTION AMORTIZATION

Generally, amortization of capitalized costs of oil and gas assets is computed on the basis of physical units. Oil and gas volumes are converted to a common unit-of-measure on the basis of their relative energy content (with a single exception to be discussed later). Conversion to an equivalent barrel or Mcf is the same as illustrated in Chapter 17.

The full cost unit-of-production amortization formula is similar to the one given in Chapter 17 for successful efforts accounting, except as follows:

- The cost center is countrywide.

- The amortization calculation is based on total proved reserves.

- The amortization base includes estimated future development costs related to undeveloped proved reserves.

The full cost amortization formula is expressed as follows:

Amortization expense = $B \times S/(S+R)$, where:
   B = amortization base, as defined in the next paragraph
   S = volume sold during the period (BOE, Mcfe, or the volume of the dominant hydrocarbon)
   R = volume of total proved reserves at period's end
B, the amortization base, = C-A-V-E+F+D, where:
   C = incurred capitalized costs of acquisition, exploration, and development activities including ARCs for all AROs resulting from exploration and development activities completed to-date
   A = prior accumulated amortization
   V = estimated undiscounted future salvage value of the lease equipment (see Chapter 20)
   E = excluded capitalized unproved property costs and certain capitalized development costs [i.e., excluded from the amortization base as allowed in Reg. S-X Rule 4-10(c)(3)(ii)]
   F = undiscounted estimated future expenditures (based on current cost rates) to be incurred in developing proved reserves
   D = estimated undiscounted future ARCs to be incurred developing proved reserves
Amortization expense is calculated as: [C-A-V-E+F+D] x S/(S+R).

To illustrate a computation, assume that the following data applies to Public Company's oil and gas assets in a given country:

C:	Capitalized costs for the country	$260,000,000
Less A:	Accumulated amortization	(48,000,000)
Plus D:	Estimated ARCs on future development activities	10,000,000
Less V:	Estimated equipment salvage value	(8,000,000)
Less E:	Costs excluded from amortization	(12,000,000)
Plus F:	Estimated future development costs	14,000,000
Equals B:	Amortization base	$216,000,000
Times S:	Units sold in the year	x 4,000,000 BOE
Divided by (S+R) where R (proved reserves at year-end) equals 32 million BOE		÷ 36,000,000 BOE
Equals the current year's amortization		$ 24,000,000

Notice the formula adds the period's units sold (S) to reserves at the end of the amortization period (R) to calculate the best current estimate of proved reserves as of the beginning of the period (S+R) to correspond to the amortization base (B) prior to the current period amortization.

Shrinkage

As noted in Chapter 17, the figure for units sold (S) could arguably be replaced with units produced; however, the two volumes are nearly equal over a three- or twelve-month period. In some instances, units sold are significantly less than units produced due to shrinkage. Shrinkage arises from natural gas used on a lease, gas volumes lost in processing for extraction of NGL, removal of impurities and BS&W, and even theft or pipeline leaks. If shrinkage is significant, the amortization calculation should use units sold (S) and proved reserves (R) that are both before shrinkage or both after shrinkage so that costs are reasonably allocated over the productive life of the reserves.

GROSS REVENUE METHOD OF AMORTIZING COSTS

Although the conversion of oil and gas into a common measure is based on their relative energy content, paragraph (c)(3)(iii) of Reg. S-X Rule 4-10 provides an alternative. If oil or gas price regulations or economic circumstances indicate units of revenue is more appropriate for computing amortization, then that basis can be used. Recall from Chapters 1 and 12 that oil and gas price regulations ended in the U.S. by 1993. SAB Topic 12F clarified that the gross revenue method may still be used even when production is not subject to price regulation. Topic 12F states this method may be more appropriate:

> ...whenever oil and gas sales prices are disproportionate to their relative energy content to the extent that the use of the unit-of-production method would result in an improper matching of the costs of oil and gas production against the related revenue received. The method should be consistently applied and appropriately disclosed within the financial statements.

Historically, oil prices relative to gas prices are disproportionate to their relative energy content. The ratio of oil price to gas price will vary. In the past, the wellhead price of an oil barrel might approximate ten times the wellhead price of an Mcf of natural gas, despite an oil barrel having only six times the energy of an Mcf of gas. Particularly when the price ratio at year-end differs significantly from the average price ratio for the year, the gross revenue method could provide a significantly different amount of amortization expense.

Reg. S-X Rule 4-10 directs that unit-of-revenue amortization is computed on the basis of current gross revenues from production in relation to future gross revenues, based on current prices, from estimated production of proved oil and gas reserves. As used here, the term gross revenue means revenue net of royalty and net profit obligations, but not reduced by production costs. Changes in existing prices are considered only where they are provided by contractual arrangements.

To illustrate a gross revenue calculation of amortization, assume the same facts as the previous example. In addition, apply the following information:

Year's average price for the 4 million BOE produced	$48 per bbl
Year-end price per barrel of oil equivalent	$60 per bbl
B (the amortization base)	$ 216,000,000
Times S (the current year revenue, $48 x 4 MMBOE)	x $ 192,000,000
Divided by (S+R), where R = $60 x 32 MMBOE	÷ $2,112,000,000
Equals the current year's amortization	$ 19,636,364

Paragraph (c)(3)(iii) also states, "The effect of a significant price increase during the year on estimated future gross revenues shall be reflected in the amortization provision only for the period after the price increase occurs." This statement has been interpreted by some to suggest the effects on future revenues of insignificant price changes may be considered in computing amortization in the interim period in which the price change occurs, but the effects of a significant price change on future revenues are considered only in the next interim (quarterly) period. Such a literal interpretation seems inconsistent with the concept of using prices at the end of the period to determine proved reserves as of that date, future net revenues under Reg. S-X Rule 4-10(c)(4)(i), and the standardized measure disclosure under FAS 69. SAB Topic 12F on the gross revenue method does not address this interpretation.

Under a literal interpretation, the basic accounting period for amortization is the interim period. Although no guidelines are given for determining significance, unless the increase in the price of oil or gas is sufficient to increase overall future revenue from reserves by a material amount (perhaps more than five percent), the increase should not be considered significant.

As an example, assume quarterly financial statements are issued on a calendar quarter basis. On January 1, 2006, estimated reserves and unamortized costs were:

Oil reserves	10 million bbls
Gas reserves	200 MMcf
Unamortized costs	$360 million
Oil price	$60 per barrel
Gas price	$6 per Mcf

Production for the first quarter was 250,000 barrels of oil which sold for $15 million; 5 MMcf of gas were sold for $30 million. In April, gas prices increased from $6.00 per Mcf to $6.10 per Mcf. During the second quarter, 150,000 barrels of oil were sold for $9 million, and 4 MMcf of gas were sold for $24.4 million.

The company uses the gross revenue method of amortization. In computing amortization for the first quarter of the year, the increase in gas price from $6.00 to $6.10 in April is ignored because the increase did not occur in the first quarter. Thus, amortization for the first quarter is $9 million, which is computed as $360 million unamortized cost times the ratio of $45 million of first quarter revenues divided by $1.8 billion of future revenues at the beginning of the quarter. The first-quarter amortization reduces unamortized costs to $351 million.

For the second quarter, because the increase is not significant, it appears permissible (but not mandatory) to consider the 10 cent gas price increase in computing end-of-quarter future revenues. If the price increase is considered in computing amortization for the second quarter, the amount is $6,606,593, which is computed as $351 million unamortized cost times the ratio of $33.4 million in second-quarter revenues divided by $1,774,500,000, which is computed as follows:

Reserve revenues at the second quarter's end (R):		
Oil: $60/bbl x 9.6 million bbls	= $	576,000,000
Gas: $6.10/Mcf x 191 MMcf	=	1,165,100,000
Second-quarter revenues (S)	=	33,400,000
Total (R+S)		$1,774,500,000

Assume a further increase in gas prices occurred in August 2006 so that on September 30, 2006, the average price per Mcf was $7.20. This is a significant increase in prices and should not be considered until the following quarter. During the third and fourth quarters, there were no changes in estimates of quantities of proved reserves, and the revenues were as follows:

Third quarter:	
Oil 200,000 bbls	$12 million
Gas 5 MMcf	$36 million
Fourth quarter:	
Oil 150,000 bbls	$9 million
Gas 4 MMcf	$28.8 million

Amortization for the third quarter is $9,464,608 (computed as $344,393,407 of unamortized costs, times the ratio of $48 million in third quarter revenue, divided by $1,746,600,000, which is the future revenue in reserves as of the beginning of the third quarter). The $1,746,600,000 is computed as follows:

Reserve revenues at the third quarter's end (R):		
Oil: $60/bbl x 9.4 million bbls	= $	564,000,000
Gas: $6.10/Mcf x 186 MMcf	=	1,134,600,000
Third-quarter revenues (S)	=	48,000,000
Total (R+S)		$1,746,600,000

In the fourth quarter, the period following the significant price increase, the new higher price is considered in determining future revenues. Fourth-quarter amortization (assuming no change in reserve estimates) would be $6,652,117, i.e., the $334,928,799 of unamortized costs times the ratio of $37.8 million divided by $1,903,200,000, which is computed as follows:

Reserve revenues at the fourth quarter's end (R):	
Oil: $60/bbl x 9.25 million bbls	= $ 555,000,000
Gas: $7.20/Mcf x 182 MMcf	= 1,310,400,000
Fourth-quarter revenues (S)	= 37,800,000
Total (R+S)	**$1,903,200,000**

OTHER ASPECTS OF AMORTIZATION

Reg. S-X Rule 4-10(c)(3)(v) provides that amortization:

> ...shall be made on a consolidated basis, including investees accounted for on a proportionate consolidation basis. Investees accounted for on the equity method shall be treated separately.

Reg. S-X Rule 4-10(c)(3)(iv) permits depreciation of natural gas processing plants by a method other than unit-of-production. Presumably, this exception applies in instances such as when a processing plant treats not only the plant owner's gas, but also gas belonging to others on a contract basis.

Reg. S-X Rule 4-10(c)(6)(ii) states:

> ...purchases of proved reserves of oil and gas in place ordinarily are to be accounted for as additions to the capitalized costs in the cost center; however, significant purchases of production payments or proved properties with lives substantially shorter than the composite productive life of the cost center shall be accounted for separately.

Separate accounting of significant acquired production payments and short-lived properties usually increases the next year's total DD&A as illustrated in the following example:

Properties	Cost	Production	Opening Reserves	DD&A
Existing	$10 million	200,000 bbl	2,000,000 bbl	$1.0 million
Purchased	$5 million	100,000 bbl	500,000 bbl	$1.0 million
Aggregate	$15 million	300,000 bbl	2,500,000 bbl	$1.8 million

Separate accounting would result in a combined DD&A of $2 million. However, aggregation provides a combined DD&A of $1.8 million.

In the example, the purchased property's cost is 33 percent of the aggregate cost, and its life is half of the existing properties' average. Yet, the change in the first year's total DD&A is only an 11 percent increase. A question arises whether the purchased property is significant and if it possesses a substantially shorter life. There is no clear guidance on the issues. However, the SEC addresses significance in two closely related situations:

- The SEC has expressed that a full cost center's individually significant unproved properties under S-X Rule 4-10(c)(3)(ii)(A)(1) would generally have costs of more than 10 percent of the cost center's net book value (see Appendix 1).

- S-X Rule 4-10(c)(6)(i) calls for gain/loss recognition on the sale (not purchase) of property from the full cost pool when deferring the gain or loss would significantly alter the cost pool's amortization rate. Section (c)(6)(i) adds that a significant alteration is not expected to occur for sales involving less than 25 percent of reserves in the full cost center. Chapter 21's discussion of this statement suggests an alteration exceeding 10 percent is significant.

There is no specific guidance on what constitutes significance for this specific example. However, the situations described above would suggest this: to determine DD&A for such a purchase separately would need to change the combined DD&A expense by more than 10 percent immediately following the acquisition. A purchase involving the example above would need to be evaluated and judgment applied for the specific circumstances.

INTEREST CAPITALIZATION

Chapter 9 addresses the requirements of FAS 34 for capitalization of interest during a construction period. Interest should not be capitalized on assets "that are in use or ready for their intended use in the earning activities of the business."

FASB Interpretation No. 33 clarifies the interest capitalization rules for oil and gas producers using the full cost method. The FASB concludes that full cost companies should capitalize interest only on assets that have been excluded from the full cost amortization pool. Assets being amortized are deemed to relate to reserves being produced and, thus, are part of the earnings process. Interest related to those assets is not capitalized. Capitalized interest becomes a part of the cost of the related properties or projects and is subject to amortization when the asset costs are transferred to the amortization pool.

LIMITATION ON CAPITALIZED COSTS

One of the principal criticisms of full cost is the capitalization of costs such as dry holes, exploration costs, and surrendered leases creates a danger that unamortized capitalized costs in a cost center may exceed the underlying value of its oil and gas assets. This has led the SEC to establish a cost ceiling for each cost center.

Repeated informal SEC staff interpretations indicate the ceiling test is to be performed quarterly as of the end of the fiscal quarter. If the cost center's unamortized capitalized costs, less related deferred income taxes, exceed the ceiling, the net capitalized costs must be written down to the ceiling. A corresponding charge is made against income as of the balance sheet date. The write-down cannot be reversed in a subsequent reporting period.

The ceiling calculation is complicated and may be difficult to compute in some cases. The details are enumerated in Reg. S-X Rule 4-10(c)(4) and clarified in SAB 47 as found in SAB Topic 12D:

Reg. S-X Rule 4-10(c)(4): "Limitation on capitalized costs: (i) For each cost center, capitalized costs, less accumulated amortization and related deferred income taxes, shall not exceed an amount (the cost center ceiling) equal to the sum of: (A) the present value of estimated future **net revenues** [bold added] computed by applying current prices of oil and gas reserves (with consideration of price changes only to the extent provided by contractual arrangements) to estimated future production of proved oil and gas reserves as of the date of the latest balance sheet presented, less estimated future expenditures (based on current costs) to be incurred in developing and producing the proved reserves computed using a discount factor of ten percent and assuming continuation of existing economic conditions; plus (B) the cost of properties not being amortized pursuant to paragraph (c)(3)(ii) of this section; plus (C) the lower of cost or estimated fair value of unproven properties included in the costs being amortized; less (D) income tax effects related to differences between the book and tax basis of the properties referred to in paragraphs (c)(4)(i)(B) and (C) of this section. [Author's note: Part (D) is poorly worded, but the SEC has provided helpful interpretive guidance as explained later in this chapter.]

(ii) If unamortized costs capitalized within a cost center, less related deferred income taxes, exceed the cost center ceiling, the excess shall be charged to expense and separately disclosed during the period in which the excess occurs. Amounts thus required to be written off shall not be reinstated for any subsequent increase in the cost center ceiling."

THE FULL COST CEILING AND FAS 143

FAS 143 has provided some unique challenges for full cost companies due to its silence with respect to the ceiling test. Under FAS 143, ARCs:

- Represent the fair value that AROs had on the date liabilities were recognized, and

- Are additional historical costs of the related assets, which for oil and gas companies that follow Rule 4-10 of Reg. S-X represent the full cost pool.

Prior to FAS 143, such costs were generally accrued on an undiscounted basis in accumulated depreciation as an expense over the productive life of the oil and gas property. The accrual of such costs used to be a reduction of capitalized costs, whereas under FAS 143, the accrual of those costs results in an increase in capitalized costs.

Rule 4-10(c)(4) of Reg. S-X requires a company to calculate the limitation on capitalized costs (i.e., full cost ceiling) each quarter. Expected cash outflows necessary for settling these AROs have traditionally been incorporated into the determination of a company's present value of its estimated future net revenues used to calculate the full cost ceiling. As a result, the interaction of FAS 143 and Rule 4-10 results in the inclusion of ARCs as part of capitalized costs, while also reducing the ceiling limitation on those capitalized costs through the inclusion of the future cash outflows required for a settlement of the related AROs. This appears to double count the effect of asset retirement activities in the ceiling test. To address this, the SEC issued Staff Accounting Bulletin No. 106, which requires a company to increase the full cost ceiling by excluding the cash outflows (discounted at 10 percent in accordance with Rule 4-10) that are required to settle the AROs that have been accrued on the balance sheet. If an obligation for expected asset retirement costs has not been accrued under FAS 143 for certain asset retirement costs required to be included in the full cost ceiling calculation under Rule 4-10 (c)(4), such costs should continue to be included in the full cost ceiling calculation.

SAB 106 is consistent with FAS 143 paragraph 12's guidance regarding impairments for companies following the successful efforts method of accounting assessed under FAS 144. The total capitalized costs of the full cost pool recorded on the balance sheet are tested for impairment by referencing the future discounted net revenues to be realized from those oil and gas reserves, excluding cash outflows related to the settlement of AROs that have already been accrued on the balance sheet.

THE FULL COST CEILING AND FAS 144

For full cost companies, both the ceiling test and the FAS 144 impairment test apply in theory, but the FASB and SEC staff have informally indicated that the ceiling test is to be used for proved oil and gas properties in lieu of FAS 144 as explained in Chapter 18. The ceiling test is an SEC rule that is not eliminated by the issuance of a conflicting accounting standard by the FASB. However, the ceiling test is generally more stringent and conservative than the FAS 144 impairment calculation since the ceiling is based on discounted projected future cash flow; FAS 144 does not recognize impairment unless capitalized costs exceed undiscounted expected future cash flow. An exception to this general rule may occur when current oil and gas prices for the ceiling test significantly exceed expected future prices used for FAS 144 impairment.

PART (c)(4)(i)(A): PRESENT VALUE OF FUTURE NET REVENUES

The present value of future net revenues is essentially the discounted present value of future net cash flow from proved reserves. Future net cash flow is based on oil and gas prices and production cost rates as of the balance sheet date that are applied to the projected production of the company's proved reserves. Costs include estimated future development, production, and asset retirement costs. The calculation requires scheduling production, revenues, and costs by year to apply the 10 percent annual discount rate.

Discounted cash flow is computed under the following guidelines:

- Estimated future gross revenues (petroleum accountants would call these future revenues) are determined by multiplying expected future net production for each year by applicable sales prices in effect at the end of the current fiscal quarter, with consideration of price changes only to the extent provided by contractual arrangements, including hedging arrangements pursuant to SAB 103.[2] Average prices for the past year and expected prices may not be used. Favorable price changes subsequent to the balance sheet date and before release of the financials can be considered to avoid a write-down, but special disclosure is required as explained later in this chapter.

- Estimated future expenditures to be incurred to develop and produce the proved reserves each year are deducted from gross revenues. Estimates of future expenditures are based on current cost levels and cost rates.

- A fixed discount of 10 percent per annum is used to compute the present value of net revenues (gross revenues less development and lifting costs) to arrive at the net present value of proved reserves.

In this case, the present value is a sum of present values computed (using petroleum engineering software) on a well-by-well, property-by-property, or field-by-field basis. This is done because end of year prices and operating cost rates vary widely from one property or field to another as a result of the difference in quality of reserves, the existence of contractual sales prices, and numerous other factors.

As an example, assume KT Oil Company owns a single proved field in a cost center with estimated proved reserves of 2.4 million barrels on December 31, 2006. Production of proved reserves is expected as follows:

	Barrels
2007	1,000,000
2008	700,000
2009	400,000
2010	200,000
2011	100,000
Total	2,400,000

The year-end price per barrel is $60. Severance taxes are five percent of revenue. Other production costs are currently $3 million per year. Additional development costs of $9 million will likely be incurred in 2007 to develop the present proved reserves. Net cash flow and discounted net cash flow from production of proved reserves follow. In computing the cost ceiling, the value assigned to proved reserves will be $98,270,820.

Year	Gross Revenue	Lifting and Dev. Costs	Net Cash Flow	Discount Factor[3]	Discounted Cash Flow
2007	$60,000,000	$15,000,000	$ 45,000,000	.9535	$ 42,907,500
2008	42,000,000	5,100,000	36,900,000	.8668	31,984,920
2009	24,000,000	4,200,000	19,800,000	.7880	15,602,400
2010	12,000,000	3,600,000	8,400,000	.7164	6,017,760
2011	6,000,000	3,300,000	2,700,000	.6512	1,758,240
Total			$112,800,000		$98,270,820

PART (c)(4)(i)(B): COST OF PROPERTIES NOT BEING AMORTIZED

The costs of both unevaluated properties and unusually significant development projects being withheld from the amortization calculation are included in the ceiling at the current carrying cost (i.e., cost less any impaired costs used in the amortization base). Due to the nature of such costs and the impairment requirement, consideration of the fair value of such assets is apparently not necessary.

PART (c)(4)(i)(C): LOWER OF COST OR FAIR VALUE OF UNPROVED PROPERTIES BEING AMORTIZED

The lower of cost or estimated fair value of unproved properties included in the costs being amortized is zero—if the company's policy is to exclude from amortization all costs of unevaluated unproved property. When an exclusion option is adopted, the costs being amortized are the worthless impaired costs and worthless costs of "evaluated unproved property" (i.e., property evaluated as having no proved reserves and also considered worthless under normal circumstances). If unevaluated property costs are not being excluded from amortization, then this third component of the ceiling may have value.

The unproved properties included in the amortization base of the cost center are valued at the lower of cost or market. There is no indication in Reg. S-X Rule 4-10 whether the lower of cost or market for all unproved properties included in the amortization base is to be used or whether it should be done on a property-by-property basis. Given the nature of full cost, it is more practical to use the lower of total cost or total market.

PART (c)(4)(i)(D): INCOME TAX EFFECTS

In practice, this requirement is considered to be poorly worded; a literal interpretation is not used in industry or reflected in SAB Topic 12D on computing the income tax effects.

Reg. S-X Rule 4-10(c)(4)(i)(A), as amended by Financial Reporting Release 40A issued in September 1992, refers to future net revenues from proved reserves. Traditionally, the term future net revenues referred to net cash flow (not revenues) before reduction for income taxes, but traditionally the ceiling reflected cash flow after reduction for income taxes. The amended portion (c)(4)(i)(D) does not refer to income tax effects for the future net revenues in (c)(4)(i)(A) as it did before the 1992 amendments. An SEC representative informally clarified in late 1992 that the FRR 40A amendments were not intended to eliminate the income tax effects relating to future net revenues.

Subsection (c)(4)(i)(D) also refers to book basis when the term is intended to refer to the future net revenues (or alternatively, the present value of such future net revenues) referred to in section (c)(4)(i)(A) and to the ceiling values referred to in (c)(4)(i)(B) and (C), as indicated in SAB Topic 12D. The ceiling value for proved properties may be substantially different from book value, and hence the related income taxes may be substantially different from recorded deferred taxes that reflect the difference between book and tax basis.

However, the rule's language has yet to be corrected. Based on SAB Topic 12D and informal commentary from SEC staff, companies treat the amended (c)(4)(i)(D) as if it were corrected to read "income tax effects related to differences between (1) the future net revenues and values referred to in Reg. S-X Rule 4-10 (c)(4)(i)(A), (B), and (C), and (2) the tax bases of the related assets." Income tax effects are illustrated later in this chapter.

COST BASIS AS A NET NET BOOK VALUE

The ceiling is compared to capitalized costs less accumulated amortization (i.e., net book value) and less related deferred income taxes. This amount is referred to in this discussion as "net net" book value. Related deferred income taxes are the portion of recorded deferred taxes arising from the difference between the book value and tax basis of the oil and gas properties at the applicable balance sheet date.

Assume KT Oil Company has the following net net book value at December 31, 2006:

Proved property costs		$69,000,000
Unproved costs in amortization base ($0 fair value)		4,700,000
Amortization base		73,700,000
Costs excluded from amortization base		10,000,000
Less accumulated DD&A		(15,000,000)
Net book value		68,700,000
Related deferred income taxes:		
Net book value	$68,700,000	
Less tax basis of proved property	(5,000,000)	
Less tax basis of unproved property		
included in amortization base	0	
Less tax basis of excluded costs	(8,000,000)	
Equals book-tax difference	55,700,000	
Times 40% effective tax rate	x 40%	
Equals related deferred income taxes	$22,280,000	(22,280,000)
Net net book value		**$46,420,000**

ILLUSTRATION OF INCOME TAX EFFECTS CALCULATION

Theoretically, the income tax effect relating to future net revenue from proved property is calculated future year by future year using the future cash flow determined under Rule 4-10 (c)(4)(i)(A). These future taxes, calculated year-by-year, are discounted to a present value.

The income tax effects relating to the values in (c)(4)(i)(B) and (C) are the taxes on the difference (often minimal) between the values in (B) and (C) and the properties' tax bases as of the effective date of the ceiling test, as if the properties relating to (B) and (C) were sold on that date for the values used in (B) and (C).

The calculated income tax effects are then added together to determine the ceiling component for (c)(4)(i)(D). These calculations are collectively called a year-by-year approach because the largest component reflects income taxes on future net revenues calculated future year by future year and discounted to a present value.

A year-by-year approach to calculating the income tax effect has an acceptable alternative allowed under SAB Topic 12D known as the short-cut approach. It is similar in many ways to assuming that all the properties, including the proved properties, are sold as of the balance sheet date at the values in (c)(4)(i)(A), (B), and (C). The short-cut approach calculates related income taxes as the income taxes due on the gain from the "sale." However, statutory depletion (percentage depletion) can be used in the calculation. Thus, it is truly a short-cut to the year-by-year calculation, and not an approach that assumes immediate sales of proved properties.

In both approaches, income tax calculations consider the current tax bases of the oil and gas assets, as well as any related net operating loss carryforwards and tax credits.

Assume the previous facts for KT Oil Company and the following information:

- $7.5 million of 2007 development costs include $5.1 million immediately deductible as intangible development costs and $2.4 million of equipment costs depreciable for tax purposes on a unit-of-production basis.
- $5 million tax basis of proved property is deductible.
- KT Oil Company will have additional percentage depletion deductions.
- The combined federal and state income tax rate is 40 percent.
- On average, taxes are paid midway through the year whereby the same discount factors in the prior schedule are used.
- KT Oil Company has no income tax credits or net operating loss carryforwards.

The income tax effects relating to future net revenue are calculated as follows:

	2007	2008	2009	2010	2010	Total
Net cash flow	$ 26,000,000	$ 23,600,000	$ 12,200,000	$ 4,600,000	$ 800,000	$ 67,200,000
Add back '07 equipment costs	$ 2,400,000					$ 2,400,000
Depreciate '07 equipment	(1,000,000)	(700,000)	(400,000)	(200,000)	(100,000)	(2,400,000)
Deduct 12/31/06 tax bases	(1,825,000)	(2,138,000)	(550,000)	(425,000)	(62,000)	(5,000,000)
Deduct add'l % depletion	(200,000)	(300,000)	(200,000)	(200,000)	(1,000)	(901,000)
Taxable income	**25,375,000**	**20,462,000**	**11,050,000**	**3,775,000**	**637,000**	**61,299,000**
Income tax at 40%	10,150,000	8,184,800	4,420,000	1,510,000	254,800	$ 24,519,600
x Discount factor	0.9535	0.8668	0.788	0.7164	0.6512	n/a
Income tax present value	**9,678,025**	**7,094,584**	**3,482,960**	**1,081,764**	**165,926**	**$ 21,503,260**

Under the year-by-year approach, the income tax effect relating to the future net revenues is $21,503,260. The income tax effects relating to the values in (c)(4)(i)(B) and (C) are much smaller, and are computed as follows:

	(c)(4)(i)(B)	(c)(4)(i)(C)
Value	$10,000,000	$0
Less tax basis	(8,000,000)	(0)
Difference	$ 2,000,000	$0
Tax effect at 40%	$ 800,000	$0

For costs excluded from amortization, the corresponding tax basis is typically smaller because some of those costs may be tax deductions when incurred, such as intangible drilling and development costs and delay rentals. For the example, the combined income tax effect under the year-by-year approach is $21,503,260 plus $800,000, equaling $22,303,260.

Under the short-cut approach, the income tax effect is calculated as follows, assuming the present value of the additional percentage depletion is $800,000:

Present value of future net revenues		$ 58,677,480
(c)(4)(i)(B) value of excluded costs		10,000,000
(c)(4)(i)(C) value of unproved property being amortized		0
Ceiling value before income tax effects		68,677,480
Less tax bases and other deductions:		
Tax basis of proved property	$ 5,000,000	
Tax basis of excluded costs	8,000,000	
Tax basis of unproved property included in amortization base	0	
Present value of statutory depletion	800,000	
Net operating loss carryforwards	0	
	$13,800,000	(13,800,000)
Difference between value and tax basis		$ 54,877,480
Income tax effect at 40% combined tax rate using the short-cut approach		$ 21,950,992

In this example, the $21,950,992 income tax effect under the short-cut approach is two percent less than the $22,303,260 calculated under the year-by-year approach. Generally, the short-cut approach calculates tax effects to be slightly lower because it assumes the proved property tax basis is immediately deductible.

ILLUSTRATIVE CEILING TEST

For the example, the ceiling tests using both income tax calculation approaches are as follows:

	Year-by-year	Short-cut
Ceiling, pre-tax	$68,677,480	$68,677,480
Less income tax effect	(22,303,260)	(21,950,992)
Ceiling	46,374,220	46,726,488
Less net net book value	(46,420,000)	(46,420,000)
Excess book value [write-down]	$ (45,780)	
Excess ceiling [no write-down]		$ 306,488

Since SAB Topic 12D states that the short-cut approach is acceptable, companies using it may not need to record a write-down. However, if a write-down is recorded, it should adjust both the assets and related deferred income taxes. Assuming a write-down of $1 million and a 40 percent income tax rate, the journal entry is as follows:

761	Provision for Impairment of Oil and Gas Assets	1,000,000	
420	Deferred Income Taxes [liability a/c]	400,000	
	237 Accumulated Impairment of Oil and Gas Property Cost Centers		1,000,000
	945 Deferred Federal Income Tax Provision*		400,000
	To record impairment of carrying value of oil and gas properties in [country cost center] to cost ceiling.		

* For simplicity, Account 946 for state taxes is ignored here.

CEILING EXEMPTION FOR PURCHASED PROVED PROPERTY

Companies can purchase proved property at a cost that exceeds the related increase in the full cost ceiling. The property's cost might contain the value of expected price increases or probable reserves not reflected in the ceiling. It would be unfair to require a write-down due to purchase of a property at its fair value. SEC Accounting Series Release No. 258 addresses this issue. A registrant may request an exemption from the ceiling test when the write-down is attributable to purchased proved property, and the registrant believes the fair value of its properties exceeds the net book value.

SAB Topic 12D, Question 3, explains how the ASR 258 ceiling exemption can be obtained. The registrant requests from the SEC staff a temporary waiver from the ceiling test for the purchased property whereby the cost and ceiling value of the purchased property is excluded from the ceiling computation. Registrants should be prepared to demonstrate that the additional value exists beyond a reasonable doubt. The purchased property's fair value as of the ceiling test date should be, beyond a reasonable doubt, at least sufficient to eliminate the need for the write-down as illustrated by the following two examples:

[in thousands]	Ceiling	Net Net Book Value	Write-down
Example #1:			
Ceiling test with exemption	$19,000	$20,000	$1,000
+ Purchased property	8,000	10,000	2,000
= Ceiling test without exemption	$27,000	$30,000	$3,000
Example #2:			
Ceiling test with exemption	$20,500	$20,000	$ (500)
+ Purchased property	8,000	10,000	2,000
= Ceiling test without exemption	$28,500	$30,000	$1,500

In the first example, the registrant should demonstrate with reasonable certainty that the fair value of purchased property at the time of the ceiling test is at least equal to the $10 million purchase price, so that the ceiling write-down is limited to the $1 million write-down for other properties.

In the second example, the registrant should demonstrate with reasonable certainty that the fair value of the purchased property at the time of the ceiling test is at least $9.5 million. If that value were used in the ceiling, the total ceiling would equal the $30 million total net net book value, avoiding a write-down. In this case, the property's reasonably certain fair value can be less than its book value, and a write-down can still be avoided.

SUBSEQUENT EVENTS' EFFECTS ON CEILING TEST

SAB Topic 12D, Question 3, also allows a write-down to be avoided if the ceiling test considers one of two types of events occurring after the ceiling test date (the balance sheet date), but before the auditor's report on the affected financial statements:

- Additional reserves are proved up on properties owned at year end, or

- Price increases become known that were unknown as of the balance sheet date.

If the ceiling were recomputed giving effect to such event(s) (both cost and ceiling adjustments) and no write-down is calculated, then no write-down needs to be recorded. If a smaller write-down is calculated, it should be recorded.

By analogy, an interim ceiling write-down could be avoided if the subsequent events occurred prior to issuance of the unaudited quarterly financials.

Financial statements should disclose that "capitalized costs exceeded the limitation at [the balance sheet date]" and explain why the excess was not charged against earnings.

The registrant's supplemental disclosures of proved reserves (see Chapter 28) and of the related standardized measure (see Chapter 29) should not reflect the subsequent event(s). However, the effects could be disclosed separately with appropriate explanation.

Property acquisitions after the balance sheet date may not be considered.

Price declines after the balance sheet date do not need to be considered in the ceiling test, but substantial declines may require disclosure as a material subsequent event.

MINERAL CONVEYANCES AND PROMOTIONAL ACTIVITIES

Full cost companies are subject to many of the same rules applicable to successful efforts companies in accounting for mineral conveyances and promotional activities. In addition, a number of additional guidelines must be observed by those using full cost. These rules are discussed in Chapters 21 through 24. Figure 24-2 provides a decision chart on general accounting for property sales under full cost accounting.

ASSET RETIREMENT OBLIGATIONS

ARO settlements either through sale or satisfaction of the obligation represent another unique circumstance for full cost companies. An ultimate resolution of such AROs has not been determined; however, the predominant, yet varying, views are discussed below.

ACCOUNTING FOR SETTLEMENTS OF ARO'S THROUGH
SALE OF OIL AND GAS PROPERTIES UNDER THE FULL COST METHOD

Under Reg. S-X Rule 4-10(c)(6)(i), companies following the full cost method of accounting for oil and gas properties recognize sales or abandonments of oil and gas properties as an adjustment to capitalized costs, unless such adjustment would significantly alter the relationship between capitalized costs and proved reserves of oil and gas. Therefore, no gains or losses are recorded in sales of insignificant properties.

In situations where the buyer assumes the AROs related to an acquired property(ies), should any gain or loss on settlement of these AROs be recognized?

View A. Yes. Gains or losses on settlement of AROs should be recognized regardless of whether these liabilities were settled directly by the registrant or assumed by a third party as part of a sales transaction. Companies should estimate the fair value of the oil and gas property and the fair value of the ARO at the date the transaction is closed (the net of the two estimates agreeing to the sales proceeds received from the buyer). The difference between the fair value of the ARO at the transaction date and the amount accrued would be recognized in the statement of operations in accordance with FAS 143, whereas the difference between the fair value of the oil and gas property and its estimated cost basis would be recorded as an adjustment to the full cost pool under Rule 4-10(c)(6)(i).

View B. No. Rule 4-10(c)(6)(i) governs the accounting for the entire sales transaction including the assumption of the ARO by the buyer. Therefore, the proceeds from the sale and the reversal of the ARO assumed by the buyer should be recorded as adjustments to the full cost pool with no gain or loss recorded in the statement of operations.

In situations where a significant property(ies) is sold and as a result a gain or loss should be recognized under Rule 4-10, how should that gain or loss be calculated when the ARO liability is assumed by the purchaser?

View A. When an entity sells a significant amount of its reserves, for purposes of determining the resulting gain or loss from the sale, the recognized ARO related to the properties sold should be first be reversed against capitalized costs. Subsequent to such de-recognition, the total capitalized costs within the cost center should be allocated between the reserves sold and reserves retained pursuant to the guidance in Reg. S-X Rule 4-10(c)(6)(i) with the resulting cost basis for the properties sold used to determine the gain or loss on sale.

View B. When an entity sells a significant amount of its reserves, for purposes of determining the resulting gain or loss from the sale, the total capitalized costs within the cost center should be first allocated between the reserves sold and reserves retained pursuant to the guidance in Reg. S-X Rule 4-10(c)(6)(i). Subsequent to such allocation, the recognized ARO related to the properties sold should be reversed against the capitalized costs allocated to the properties sold. The resulting net cost basis for the properties sold would then be used to determine the gain or loss on sale.

ACCOUNTING FOR GAINS OR LOSSES RESULTING FROM THE SETTLEMENT OF ASSET RETIREMENT OBLIGATIONS UNDER THE FULL COST METHOD

FAS 143 provides for the recognition of an ARO at its fair value. Fair value is defined as the amount at which that liability could be settled in a current transaction between willing parties. Appendix A of FAS 143 goes on to explain that when estimating an ARO using a present value technique (the common method for many oil and gas entities) the estimates of future cash flows should include all costs and expenses, including overhead, profit margin, and other costs that would be incurred in settling the ARO. Therefore, to the extent internal resources are used to settle an ARO, the amounts representing profit margin will ultimately be de-recognized upon the complete settlement of the liability. Alternatively, some AROs could result in a loss upon settlement due to unplanned operational difficulties. For example, when decommissioning an offshore platform, several variables could affect the total cost of removing the platform that were unforeseen when establishing the liability (e.g., difficulties caused by weather and accidents) The issue is: should companies that follow the full cost method of accounting recognize gains or losses resulting from the settlement of asset retirement obligations?

View A. Yes. In paragraphs B39 and B41 of FAS 143, the FASB specifically contemplated that there could be differences between the fair value of the recorded ARO and the cost ultimately incurred by an entity to settle the ARO and that this would result in a gain or loss on that settlement. There is no specific exception to this guidance in FAS 143 for companies following the full cost method of accounting and Rule 4-10(c)(6)(iv) does not specifically address the settlement of asset retirement obligations. Therefore, any difference between the ARO liability accrued and the actual cost incurred by an entity to settle the ARO should be recognized in the statement of operations in the period when the ARO is settled.

View B. No. Companies that follow the full cost method of accounting should not recognize any gains or losses from the settlement of asset retirement obligations related to oil and gas properties. Any variances between the ARO liability accrued and the actual cost incurred by an entity to settle the ARO should be recorded as an adjustment to accumulated depreciation of the full cost pool. This is consistent with the overall theoretical basis of full cost accounting that transactions related to individual properties within the full cost pool should not result in the recognition of gains or losses except for certain circumstances prescribed by Rule 4-10. Proponents of this view also believe that the nature of settling an ARO is consistent with the nature of the services covered in Rule 4-10(c)(6)(iv) and therefore that guidance should be followed. GAAP, as generally defined, requires that variances between a recorded liability and the actual amount incurred to settle that liability be recorded in the statement of operations in the period the liability is settled (variances due to estimates). However, in the case of companies following the full cost method of accounting, there is specific GAAP in Rule 4-10 that prohibits the recognition of gains or losses in these transactions. The primary purpose of paragraphs B39 and B41 of FAS 143 was to explain why the FASB chose fair value as the appropriate measure of ARO's, even though this could result in the recognition of a gain on settlement by entities that settle these obligations internally in a more efficient manner. Proponents of View B believe that paragraphs B39 and B41 of FAS 143 were not mandating the recognition of gains or losses on the settlement of AROs under all circumstances.

DISCONTINUED OPERATIONS FOR FULL COST COMPANIES

When a full cost company exits an entire geographic area (representing substantially all of a cost center), the guidance in FAS 144 appears to be appropriate despite the indication that FAS 144 does not apply to full cost companies.

The intention of FAS 144 in relation to the disposal of long-lived assets is to broaden the presentation of discontinued operations to include more disposal transactions providing investors, creditors, and others with decision-useful information that is relevant in assessing the effects of disposal transactions on the ongoing operations of an entity.

Footnote 2 of FAS 144 indicates accounting requirements for oil and gas properties using the full cost method are prescribed by the SEC (Reg. S-X Rule 4-10). Despite this guidance, when a company disposes of substantially all of a cost center (e.g., including all liabilities and tax attributes) in addition to specific oil and gas properties, it appears appropriate that FAS 144 should govern the accounting treatment for the transaction.

FAS 144, paragraph 42, states the results of operations of a component of an entity that either has been disposed of or is classified as held for sale are reported in discontinued operations in accordance with paragraph 43 if both of the following conditions are met:

1. The operations and cash flows of the component have been (or will be) eliminated from the ongoing operations of the entity as a result of the disposal transaction, and

2. The entity will not have any significant continuing involvement in the operations of the component after the disposal transaction.

FAS 144, paragraph 41, states a "component of an entity" comprises operations and cash flows that can be clearly distinguished, operationally and for financial reporting purposes, from the rest of the entity. For full cost companies, a cost center meets the definition of a component and, therefore, justifies the use of discontinued operations treatment and presentation.

DISCLOSURE MATTERS

The SEC has recently indicated a concern with respect to the balance sheet classification of equipment and other depreciable assets. Certain companies have historically classified some equipment and other depreciable assets as unproved properties that are not subject to amortization. Certain full cost companies believe that such a grouping is consistent with the provision in Reg. S-X Rule 4-10 (c)(3)(ii)(A) that provides for "all costs directly associated with the acquisition and evaluation of unproved properties" to be put into one bucket, and excluded from amortization as the equipment and leasehold cost are viewed as components of the acquisition cost. However, this view does not appear to be consistent with the definition of acquisition of properties in Reg. S-X Rule 4-10 (a)(14) that does not indicate equipment is a component of acquisition cost. This equipment should be amortized using an appropriate method.

Another area of recent SEC attention is management fees. Companies using the full cost method should look to Reg. S-X Rule 4-10(c)(6)(iii) and (iv) regarding accounting for management fees and other income received for contractual services performed (e.g., drilling, well service, or equipment supply services) in connection with any property in which the registrant or an affiliate holds an ownership or other economic interest. Part (iv) does not distinguish between proved producing properties and unproved properties; the prohibition on income recognition applies to all properties. The rule's general prohibition of income recognition reflected the SEC view that current recognition of income for services rendered in connection with an owned property would be inconsistent with the full cost concept under which income is recognized only as reserves are produced. The SEC indicated income should be recognized only to the extent it exceeds a company's costs in connection with the contract and the properties, except for the limited circumstances described in Reg. S-X Rule 4-10(c)(6)(iii)(B) and Rule 4-10(c)(6)(iv)(A) and (B). Accordingly, registrants must treat management and service fees as a reimbursement of costs, offsetting the costs incurred to provide the services with any excess of fees over costs credited to the full cost pool and recognized through lower cost amortization only as production occurs.

The SEC has provided recent guidance that companies applying the successful efforts method of accounting for oil and gas producing activities should capitalize costs only as allowed by FAS 19. The costs of exploratory wells are initially capitalized, but may remain capitalized only if proved reserves are found within a year of capitalization. Cash expenditures for exploratory wells are appropriately classified within "investing activities" in the cash flows statement. FAS 19 specifies in paragraph 13 that certain costs of oil and gas producing activities, such as geological and geophysical costs, do not result in the acquisition of an asset and should be charged to expense. Cash expenditures for these costs should not be classified as investing activities in the statement of cash flows. There was no specific guidance in this area with respect to full cost companies. Given that a full cost company capitalizes geological and geophysical costs, which result in the acquisition of an asset through the full cost pool, it is unclear as to the appropriate treatment of these costs in the cash flows statement of a full cost company; however, prevalent industry practice is to classify these types of expenditures with the other additions to oil and gas properties in the investing activities section.

IFRS NO. 6 AND FULL COST ACCOUNTING

Although there is informal evidence that the International Accounting Standards Board (IASB) does not support the use of the full cost method of accounting, IASB has not specifically addressed this issue. International Financial Reporting Standard No. 6— *Exploration for and Evaluation of Mineral Resources* indicates an entity may continue to use the accounting policies applied immediately before adopting the IFRS. This includes continuing to use recognition and measurement practices that are part of those accounting policies.

• • •

---

1 In recent years, some companies that previously used the full cost method have changed to successful efforts. Nearly half (46%) of the top 100 exploration and production companies in the U.S. used full cost in 2006 according to SEC filings.

2 Issued in May 2003, SAB 103 indicates that hedge-adjusted prices must be used in the calculation as such prices represent the "best measure of estimated cash flows from future production."

3 The discount factor is the present value of one discounted at 10 percent per annum. This calculation assumes all cash receipts and expenditures occur at the mid-point of the year discounted to a present value as of December 31, 2006. Thus, the 2007 discount factor is calculated as $1/[(1+10\%)^{0.5} \text{ years}]$, and the 2008 discount factor is calculated as $1/[(1+10\%)^{1.5} \text{ years}]$.

20

ASSET RETIREMENT OBLIGATIONS

Key Concepts:

- Regulatory issues surrounding the retirement of production assets

- Current accounting for AROs

An asset retirement obligation (ARO) is an unavoidable cost associated with retiring a long-lived asset that arises as a result of either the acquisition or the normal operation of the asset. Asset retirement is a permanent (i.e., other than temporary) removal from service at the end of an asset's economic useful life. The term *retirement* includes sale, abandonment, recycling, or disposal in some other manner.

In the oil and gas industry, these obligations include the future dismantlement and removal of production equipment and facilities and the restoration and reclamation of the field's surface lands to an ecological condition similar to that existing before oil and gas extraction began. These costs are usually required by government regulations or lease contracts and are typically paid at the time oil and gas reserves are depleted and it is no longer economically feasible to continue production.

REGULATORY AND OPERATIONAL ENVIRONMENT

Regulations governing lease and well abandonment are dependent on the jurisdiction in which the related property resides. For purposes of this book, the most common practices are discussed. Because exploration and production companies often operate around the world, they frequently staff a compliance department to monitor the evolution of the regulatory environment in various locations.

A producer's first step is to obtain permits from local regulatory authorities. This should occur before dismantlement, restoration, and reclamation activities begin. Well logs or test flow data are usually required to confirm that the well is incapable of producing economic quantities of oil and gas. Regulators may also request detailed work plans and assurances that plugging and abandonment activities will not jeopardize nearby wells or pose an environmental hazard.

In mature-producing areas such as the Gulf of Mexico's outer continental shelf, abandonment procedures are firmly established. A permit can be obtained readily from the U.S. Minerals Management Service (MMS) as long as accepted procedures are followed. For example, toppling is an acceptable technique for offshore abandonment of production facilities. It involves removing the upper section of a platform (i.e., decks, jackets, and facilities) above a certain depth using either explosive or non-explosive cutting techniques. In most cases, clearance of at least 50-75 meters below the water's surface is required. The removed sections are then towed to shore where they are scrapped, placed on the adjacent seabed, or towed to designated reef sites and sunk. In many cases, regulations allow for subsurface structures to remain in place. Environmental impact studies have shown that sub-surface structures can benefit local ecology—a development that has benefited producers by significantly reducing the costs associated with removing the entire structure.

In other geographical areas, regulations can be much more stringent, such as requiring the ocean floor to be returned to its original state. This requires removal of the entire platform, including the casing, wellhead equipment, and pilings, to a specified depth below the ocean floor. Any associated flow lines can generally be flushed, cleaned of all hydrocarbon-bearing parts, plugged, and left in place. In most cases, salvage values of such lines do not justify the costs of bringing them to the surface.

Obtaining permits in less developed areas of the world can be onerous. Due to a lack of production history and ongoing regulatory and scientific debates as to what techniques qualify as environmentally friendly, producers in frontier areas may be required to perform detailed scientific and environmental impact studies. Alternative abandonment plans may have to be submitted before a permit is granted. In evaluating options, regulators give consideration to the following factors:

- Technical and engineering aspects of the plan

- Potential reductions in the consumption of natural resources as a result of re-use and recycling contemplated in the plan

- Potential environmental impact including exposure of biological habitation, atmospheric emissions, groundwater, soil, or surface fresh water

- Potential interference with other legitimate uses of the physical environment such as shipping lanes and commercial fishing

- Safety considerations

- Management measures to be implemented to prevent or mitigate adverse consequences of the plan

- The party responsible for future environmental monitoring activities associated with the plan

- The party liable for meeting claims for any damages caused by the planned abandonment activities

- Notification of authorities who maintain nautical charts and other physical environmental aids as to the modification or movement of structures

Much like the process for determining oil and gas reserves, estimating future abandonment and reclamation costs is not an exact science. Those responsible for estimating these costs must continually revise their assumptions to reflect changes in reserve life, current cost structures, technological advancements, and changes in the regulatory environment. In addition to evaluating the abandonment options permitted by local regulations, there are other factors and uncertainties that must also be considered including future contract labor rates, heavy equipment rental costs, expected levels of inflation, and future market values for scrapped parts. In addition, many contiguous production areas may reach the end of their operational life at the same time, thereby placing excess demand on local resources for abandonment services and further complicating the estimation of AROs.

CURRENT ACCOUNTING

Prior to the issuance in June 2001 of FAS 143, *Accounting for Asset Retirement Obligations*, accounting for AROs resulting from onshore development and production activities was a relatively simple matter. Most operators assumed that salvage values equaled the cost of dismantling facilities and performing clean-up and reclamation. Thus, net dismantlement costs were typically ignored. However, as a result of global expansion of the industry into more remote and environmentally sensitive areas, including offshore areas, and the continued evolution of federal, state, and local regulations, the costs to abandon and remediate oil and gas properties had become increasingly significant, to the point where these costs might exceed the costs incurred for original construction and installation.

The Financial Accounting Standards Board issued FAS 143 to address the various differences in previous accounting practices. FAS 143 requires that the fair value of a liability for an ARO should be recognized in the period incurred when: (1) the entity has an existing obligation associated with the retirement of a tangible long-lived asset, and (2) the amount of the liability can be reasonably estimated. The manner in which an ARO is incurred will affect the timing and pattern of liability recognition as follows:

- Obligations incurred upon the acquisition, construction, or development of an asset would be recognized when the cost of the long-lived asset is initially recognized;

- Obligations incurred (either ratably or non-ratably) during the operating life of the asset would be recognized over the life of the asset, concurrent with the events that give rise to the obligations; and

- Obligations incurred (a) upon a change in law, statute or contract provisions, or (b) because an entity otherwise assumed a duty or responsibility to another entity (or several other entities), would be recognized when the obligating event occurs. Obligations related to past operations would be recorded upon the enactment of the new law, whereas obligations created by future operations would be recorded as those obligations are created in the future.

A business must recognize an ARO, even if it intends to retire the asset using internal resources, when an obligating event takes place provided that it can reasonably estimate its fair value (or at the earliest date it can determine a reasonable estimate). In assessing the ARO fair value, the business can use either the amount at which the liability could be settled in a current transaction between willing parties in an active market or by using a substitute for market value such as the present value of estimated future cash flows associated with the obligation.

The present value of the estimated future cash flows discussed in FAS 143 is the most prevalent method for estimating the fair value of an ARO. A technique commonly used in determining the present value of the ARO in the oil and gas industry involves using current cost experience on retirement obligations multiplied by an inflation factor. The resulting expected future cash flows are then discounted back to present value using a company specific credit-adjusted risk-free interest rate. This expected cash flow approach can use multiple scenarios to reflect the range of possible outcomes to estimate fair value.

It is important to note that the appropriate rate of interest for the cash flows being measured should be determined based on the observable rates of interest on other liabilities with similar characteristics. Therefore, the risk-free interest rate is the interest rate on monetary assets that are essentially risk-free and that have maturity dates coinciding with the expected timing of the estimated cash flows required to satisfy the ARO. For example, a company should use a five-year credit-adjusted risk-free interest rate when the remaining number of years until payment of its retirement obligation is five years.

When the initial liability for an ARO is recorded, a corresponding increase (debit) is made to the related asset cost account, which is included as part of the cost of the related wells, equipment, and facilities. A systematic and rational method is then used to expense the asset cost over its useful life, generally on a unit-of-production basis for producing oil and gas properties. Revisions to the timing or amount of the original estimate of undiscounted cash flows are recognized as increases or decreases in:

- the carrying amount of the liability for an ARO

- the related asset retirement cost capitalized as part of the carrying amount of the related long-lived asset

Upward revisions in the amount of undiscounted estimated cash flows are discounted using the current credit-adjusted risk-free rate at the time the revision is made. Downward revisions in the amount of undiscounted estimated cash flows are discounted using the credit-adjusted risk-free rate that existed when the original liability was recognized. (See Figures 20-1 through 20-8 for a sample cash flow analysis and related journal entries.)

ARO liabilities must be accreted over time such that the balance initially recognized at present value is adjusted to reflect the passage of time. Oil and gas companies do this by applying an interest method of allocation to the beginning-of-period liability. The credit-adjusted risk-free interest rate—existing when the liability, or portion thereof, was initially measured—is used. The allocation is recognized as an increase in the ARO liability account and an increase to accretion expense, and is typically included in DD&A in the income statement.

For companies following the successful efforts method of accounting, capitalized asset retirement cost is included as part of the cost of the related wells, equipment, and facilities which is amortized over the remaining proved developed reserves (note: because capitalized asset retirement costs are directly linked to development activity, it would not be appropriate to treat such costs as acquisition costs to be depleted over total proved reserves). Undeveloped reserves, by definition, will require new wells or major expenditures before they can be classified as proved developed reserves. The construction of these new wells and the associated transfer of reserves from undeveloped to developed would result in additional obligations to retire these assets in the future.

For companies following the full cost method, capitalized asset retirement cost is included in the appropriate country-wide cost center and amortized over total proved reserves. Prior to FAS 143, the estimated dismantlement and abandonment costs net of salvage value were based on undiscounted net cash outflows and were included as part of future development cost in the full cost DD&A calculation. With the adoption of FAS 143, full cost companies now reflect the asset retirement costs that are associated with existing wells as part of their capitalized cost base.

In September 2004, the SEC issued *Staff Accounting Bulletin No. 106* (SAB 106) to clarify how AROs associated with undeveloped reserves (i.e., those that have yet to be incurred) should be treated in the full cost DD&A calculation. SAB 106 requires, to the extent estimated dismantlement and abandonment costs have not been included as capitalized costs under FAS 143, that a full cost company continue to include in its DD&A computation an estimate for dismantlement and abandonment costs net of salvage value that will be incurred as a result of future development activities. This estimate should be determined following the same approach applied pre-FAS 143 (i.e., on an undiscounted basis). It ensures that the estimated costs to abandon the undeveloped reserves that are included in the denominator of the full cost DD&A calculation are also reflected in the numerator of that calculation.

ILLUSTRATIONS OF ACCOUNTING TREATMENTS OF AROs

Figure 20-1 provides a sample cash flow analysis for an ARO at January 1, 2007, assuming an estimated cash outflow for settlement of the ARO of $100,000 on December 31, 2011, and a credit-adjusted risk-free rate (five-year term) of five percent:

Figure 20-1
ARO Cash Flow Analysis

	2007	2008	2009	2010	2011
Estimated cash outflow					$(100,000)
Discount factor using 5% discount rate	0.95238	0.90703	0.86384	0.82270	0.78353
ARO at January 1, 2007					$(78,353)

Based on the above cash flow analysis, the entry to record the ARO at January 1, 2007, is:

230	Capitalized Asset Retirement Cost (ARC)	78,353	
	410 Asset Retirement Obligation (ARO)		78,353

Assume at December 31, 2007, (1) the timing of the cash outflow is revised to occur in 2010, (2) the amount of the ARO is revised upward to $120,000, and (3) the credit-adjusted risk-free rate for the remaining three-year term is six percent.

An additional ARO would need to be recorded for the upward revision in the amount of cash outflows. Because this revision occurred at the end of the period, no accretion expense would be recorded for the incremental liability in 2007. The present value of the upward revision would be calculated as illustrated in Figure 20-2.

Figure 20-2
Calculation of Incremental ARO

	2008	2009	2010
Upward revision of cash outflow			$ (20,000)
Discount factor using 6% discount rate	0.94340	0.89000	0.83962
Incremental ARO at December 31, 2007			$(16,792)

According to FAS 143, the accretion for 2007 should be based on the liability at the beginning of the period prior to recognizing any adjustments to the ARO liability due to revisions in the timing or amount of estimated cash flows. The discount rate used in calculating accretion would be the rate used when the ARO was initially booked as illustrated in Figure 20-1. Thus, the accretion expense for 2007 would be calculated as follows in Figure 20-3:

Figure 20-3
Calculation of Accretion Expense

	2011
ARO at January 1, 2007 (Figure 20-1)	$78,353
Discount rate when ARO incurred	× 5%
2007 accretion expense	$3,918

The following entry would be required at December 31, 2007:

924	Accretion Cost on ARO	3,918	
	410 Asset Retirement Obligation (ARO)		3,918
	To record accretion expense for 2007.		

An additional ARO would need to be recorded for the accelerated timing of the cash outflows from December 31, 2011 to December 31, 2010, using the same credit-adjusted risk-free rate that was used upon establishment of the original ARO (i.e., five percent). This rate would not be updated as a result of a change in timing only. However, the discount factor used will reflect the accelerated timeframe expected until the ARO is settled (now three years from December 31, 2007). The additional ARO would be calculated as follows in Figure 20-4:

Figure 20-4
Calculation of ARO due to Timing Change in Cash Outflows

Undiscounted future cash outflows	$100,000
Discount factor using the same credit-adjusted risk-free rate used in the establishment of the original ARO (5%) reflecting the revised three-year expected accretion period	0.86384
Revised ARO balance to be recognized as of December 31, 2007	$ 86,384
Current ARO balance after recognizing 2007 accretion expense ($78,353 + $3,918)	(82,271)
Additional ARO to be recognized as of December 31, 2007	$ 4,113

The following entry would be required at December 31, 2007:

230	Capitalized Asset Retirement Cost (ARC)	20,905	
	410 Asset Retirement Obligation (ARO)		20,905
	To record additional asset retirement costs associated with the change in the estimated timing ($4,113) and amount ($16,792) of the ARO.		

If the revised amount of undiscounted cash flows had resulted in a reduction (rather than an increase) in the ARO, such changes would have been discounted using the credit-adjusted risk-free rate that existed when the original liability was recognized (five percent in this case).

As a result of the above entries, Figure 20-5 reflects the ARO liability at December 31, 2007:

Figure 20-5
Calculation of ARO at Year-End

ARO recognized at inception	$ 78,353
2006 accretion recognized	3,918
Additional ARO recognized in 2007	20,905
Book value of ARO at December 31, 2007	$103,176

As illustrated in Figure 20-6, subsequent to the initial recognition of the ARO, the carrying value no longer equals the fair value:

Figure 20-6
Calculation of Difference in Fair Value from Carrying Value

	2008	2009	2010
Revised estimated cash outflow			$(120,000)
Discount factor using 6% discount rate	0.94340	0.89000	0.83962
Fair value of ARO at December 31, 2007			$(100,754)

Note that the book value now differs from the fair value as follows:

Carrying value of ARO at December 31, 2007	$103,176
Fair value of ARO at December 31, 2007	(100,754)
Difference	$ 2,422

The difference between the ARO carrying value and fair value reflects the five percent rate differential applied to the original $100,000 undiscounted cash outflows estimate determined at inception (as adjusted for the change in timing), and illustrated in Figure 20-7.

Figure 20-7
Explanation of Difference in Discounted Future Cash Outflows

	Credit-Adjusted Risk-Free Rate		Difference
	5%	6%	
Undiscounted future cash outflows at inception	$100,000	$100,000	
Discount rate	0.86384	0.83962	
Discounted future cash outflows	$86,384	$83,962	$2,422

Accretion for each component of the ARO must be calculated separately based on the discount rate used when respective portions of the ARO balance were recognized. Figure 20-8 illustrates accretion expense for 2008 through 2010 as follows:

Figure 20-8
Calculation of Annual Accretion Expense

	Accreted at 5%	Accreted at 6%	Totals
ARO balance as of December 31, 2007	$ 86,384	$ 16,792	$103,176
Accretion expense recognized in:			
2008	4,319	1,008	5,327
2009	4,535	1,068	5,603
2010	4,762	1,132	5,894
Total ARO balance as of settlement	$100,000	$20,000	$120,000

Assume that on December 31, 2010, the company settles its ARO by using an outside contractor. The company incurs actual costs of $128,000 to settle this ARO liability resulting in the recognition of an $8,000 loss on the settlement of the obligation.

The following entry would be required at December 31, 2010:

410	*Asset Retirement Obligation (ARO)*		120,000	
801	*Loss on Settlement of ARO Liability*		8,000	
	301	*Vouchers Payable*		128,000
	To record the settlement of the ARO on December 31, 2010.			

APPLICATION ISSUES

ASSET IMPAIRMENT

FAS 144 requires that all cash inflows and outflows of the asset group be included in both the undiscounted cash flows used to test an asset group for recoverability and in the discounted cash flows used to determine the fair value of the asset group. However, while paragraph 12 of FAS 143 requires that capitalized asset retirement costs be included in the carrying value of the related asset when that asset is tested for impairment, it also states that the estimated cash outflows related to the liability for an ARO that has been recognized in the financial statements be excluded from the recoverability test and the determination of the asset's fair value. Although some may view such treatment to contradict the guidance in FAS 144, the cash outflows related to the recorded ARO should be excluded from the future cash flows used in both the recoverability test and the fair value test.

Full cost companies must also periodically calculate a limitation on capitalized costs (i.e., perform the full cost ceiling test). Capitalized costs that exceed this limit must be written off. The calculation of the full cost ceiling, as described in Rule 4-10, includes the future cash outflows that will be needed to settle the related AROs. If, after adopting FAS 143, a company were to continue calculating the full cost ceiling by reducing the expected future net revenues by the cash flows that are needed to settle the AROs, the effect would be to double-count such costs in the ceiling test since the associated asset retirement cost is already included in the full cost pool.

With respect to future cash outflows associated with settling an ARO, SAB 106 clarifies that cash outflows which have been accrued on the balance sheet should be *excluded* from the estimated future net revenues used in the full cost ceiling test. SEC staff pointed out that the exclusion of these future cash outflows is consistent with paragraph 12 of FAS 143 and avoids the double-counting issue noted above. If an obligation for expected asset retirement costs has not been accrued under FAS 143, such costs should continue to be included in the full cost ceiling calculation. For example, an ARO may not be recorded for wells associated with proved undeveloped reserves that are to be drilled in the future until the wells are actually drilled; thus, any cash outflow associated with abandoning such wells will continue to be included as a cash outflow in the full cost ceiling test.

CAPITALIZED INTEREST

With respect to the ARO liability, a company will measure the amount of accretion expense by multiplying the beginning carrying amount by the discount rate used to initially measure the liability. Accretion expense should be included in the operating section of the statement of income and should be shown separately, if material. The FASB concluded that accretion expense on the ARO does not qualify for interest capitalization because it does not represent an interest cost under FAS 34, *Capitalization of Interest Cost.*

FAS 69 DISCLOSURE CONSIDERATIONS

In February 2004, the SEC sent a letter to oil and gas producers clarifying its positions in regard to the impact of adopting FAS 143 on FAS 69 disclosures. A summary of the SEC staff's views are as follows:

- Asset retirement costs should be included in the Costs Incurred disclosures in the year that the liability is incurred, rather than on a cash basis.

- Accretion of the liability for an ARO should be included in the Results of Operations disclosure either as a separate line item, if material, or included in the same line item as it is presented on the statement of operations.

- Future cash flows related to the settlement of an ARO should be included in the Standardized Measure disclosure.

STATEMENT OF CASH FLOWS PRESENTATION

Under the consensus reached in the Emerging Issues Task Force (EITF) 02-6, *Classification in the Statement of Cash Flows of Payments Made to Settle an Asset Retirement Obligation within the Scope of FASB Statement No. 143*, cash payments made to settle an ARO should be classified in the statement of cash flows as an operating activity.

RECOGNITION OF AN ARO LIABILITY

Various contractual arrangements unique to the oil and gas industry raise a logical question as to whether the criteria for recognition of a liability under FAS 143 have been met. For example, a reversionary interest is a contractual arrangement in which an entity returns its economic interest in an oil and gas property to the former owner after a predetermined amount of production or income has been produced. If an oil and gas company has a 60 percent working interest in a field, but expects to lose one-fourth of such interest due to a reversion upon payout, the company would expect to bear only 45 percent of the future ARO costs. Depending on how specific contracts are written, other arrangements, such as net profits interests, rights to volume production payments, various production sharing contracts, or other foreign concessions, may give rise to assets without corresponding asset retirement obligations. Therefore, it is of utmost importance that contracts are read and the responsibility for asset retirement obligations is fully understood in determining whether an ARO liability has been incurred and should be recorded.

OFFSETTING AMOUNTS AGAINST AN ARO

FAS 143 prohibits the netting of an asset's salvage value against the ARO or the inclusion of the cash inflows resulting from the asset's salvage value in the cash flows used to estimate the fair value of the ARO.

Estimated salvage value should be considered in the determination of the unit-of-production depletion rate of the related asset. The capitalized costs included in the numerator of the DD&A calculation would be reduced by the expected salvage value. An amount equal to the salvage value would remain in the property account at the end of the asset's productive life to be offset when the proceeds from salvage are received.

Some entities provide assurances regarding their ability to satisfy their AROs. These assurances take many forms, including surety bonds, insurance policies, letters of credit, guarantees by other entities, and establishment of trust funds or identification of other assets dedicated to satisfy the asset retirement obligation. Providing such assurances will not satisfy or extinguish the ARO and therefore should not impact or offset the recognition of the ARO. However, these arrangements should be considered in determining the credit-adjusted risk-free rate of interest used to discount the cash flows associated with the liability.

CONDITIONAL ASSET RETIREMENT OBLIGATIONS

FASB Interpretation 47 (FIN 47) provides guidance on accounting for a legal obligation to perform an asset retirement activity within the scope of FAS 143 when the timing and (or) method of settlement are conditional upon a future event that may or may not be within the control of the entity.

Although the timing and (or) method of settlement may be conditional upon a future event, the obligation to perform the asset retirement activity is unconditional. Thus, an entity is required to recognize a liability for the fair value of a conditional asset retirement obligation if the fair value of the liability can be reasonably estimated. The fair value of a liability for the conditional asset retirement obligation should be recognized when incurred—generally upon acquisition, construction, or development and (or) through the normal operation of the asset. Uncertainty about the timing and (or) method of settlement of a conditional asset retirement obligation should be factored into the measurement of the liability when sufficient information exists.

An entity would have sufficient information to reasonably estimate the fair value of the liability if either of the following conditions exists:

- The settlement date and method of settlement for the obligation have been specified by others. In this situation, the settlement date and method of settlement are known, and therefore the only uncertainty is whether the obligation will be enforced (i.e., whether performance will be required).

- The information is available to make reasonable estimates of and to associate probabilities with:

  1) the potential settlement dates, and

  2) the potential methods of settlement.

Examples of information that are expected to provide a basis for estimating the potential settlement dates, potential methods of settlement, and the associated probabilities include, but are not limited to, information that is derived from the entity's past practice, industry practice, management's intent, and the asset's estimated economic life.

ENVIRONMENTAL REMEDIATION LIABILITIES

The provisions of FAS 143 do not apply to obligations that result from improper operation of an asset, including obligations subject to the requirements of SOP 96-1, *Environmental Remediation Liabilities*. FAS 143 provides guidance to help distinguish between obligations subject to FAS 143 and those that should be accounted for as part of an environmental remediation reserve.

The determination of whether an obligation should be accounted for in accordance with FAS 143 or other appropriate literature (such as SOP 96-1) is a matter of judgment based on individual facts and circumstances. However, consideration of timing is a factor that may help in making this determination. Environmental damage extensive enough to require immediate remediation generally arises from improper operation or other than normal operation of an asset (e.g., an oil spill, pipeline leak, or hurricane damage to production platforms). This type of environmental liability should be accounted for under FAS 5 and SOP 96-1. The ability to delay remediation until asset retirement suggests that the damage arose from normal operations and was inherent in operating the asset. Environmental damage arising from normal operations is subject to FAS 143, and the cost of such remediation should be included in the ARO measurement.

• • •

CHAPTER

21

ACCOUNTING FOR CONVEYANCES

Glossary Terms

assignee

assignment

assignor

Key Concepts:

- General principles of accounting for conveyances
- Sales of entire or share of working interest in unproved properties
- Sales of unproved nonoperating interests
- Sales of proved properties
- Sales and abandonment under the full cost method
- Accounting for overrides

A mineral conveyance is the transfer of an ownership interest in minerals from one entity to another. In an initial mineral lease agreement, a lessor conveys a 100 percent working interest in the property to a lessee, and the lessor retains a royalty interest. Later, a lessee may convey all or a part of the working interest to a third party and the lessor may convey all or part of the royalty interest to a third party.

For example, the lessee can sell all or a fractional share of its working interest. It may assign the working interest and retain a nonoperating interest (a sublease). Or the lessee could carve-out and transfer an overriding royalty, net profits interest, or production payment to a transferee. The holder of a royalty interest or other nonoperating interest may also convey all or a portion of that interest to another party.

There are many reasons why owners, especially working interest owners, convey interests in mineral properties. Shared risks of ownership and costs of exploration and development, financing issues, improved operating efficiencies, and tax benefits are a few of the advantages realized. Yet, conveyance contracts can be quite complex and may burden one of the parties with additional obligations and commitments.

GENERAL PRINCIPLES OF ACCOUNTING FOR CONVEYANCES

FAS 19 provided general guidelines for mineral conveyance accounting. Although FAS 25 suspended indefinitely most of FAS 19's rules, it did not suspend the rules relating to conveyances that are considered to be borrowings. In Reg. S-X Rule 4-10, the SEC adopted FAS 19's conveyance accounting rules (found in Oi5.133 through Oi5.138) for all publicly held oil and gas producing companies, including (with some modifications) those using the full cost method of accounting.

Oi5 and Reg. S-X Rule 4-10 offer the following guidelines:

1.　Some conveyances are, in substance, borrowings repayable in cash or its equivalent. These should be accounted for as borrowings, even by privately held companies.

2.　Gain or loss should generally not be recognized in pooling of assets in a joint undertaking intended to find, develop, or produce oil or gas from a particular property or group of properties.

3.　Gain should not be recognized (although loss may be[1]) at the time the following types of conveyance are transacted:

　A.　Part of an interest is sold, and substantial uncertainty exists about recovery of the cost applicable to the retained interest.

　B.　Part of an interest is sold, and the seller has a substantial obligation for future performance, such as an obligation to drill a well or to operate the property without proportional reimbursement for that portion of the drilling or operating costs applicable to the interest sold.

4.　Gain or loss should generally be recognized on other types of conveyances by successful efforts companies unless GAAP would prohibit such recognition.

5.　Exchanges of entire interests in oil and gas properties for entire interests in other oil and gas properties follow the guidance in N35.

6. With limited exceptions, no gain or loss should be recognized by a full cost company on a mineral conveyance. The major exception is a situation in which the conveyance is so large that to treat the proceeds as a recovery of cost would significantly distort the rate of amortization. This exception is discussed later in the current chapter.

Conveyance topics span three chapters in this book. Conveyances classified as sales and subleases in which the sole consideration is cash or cash equivalent are discussed here. Chapter 22 addresses conveyances in which payments out of oil or gas (production payments) are involved. Finally, conveyances in which the sole consideration is an agreement by the transferee to perform specified exploration or development work (sharing arrangements) are presented in Chapter 23.

Special rules for sales and abandonments under the full cost method adopted by the SEC are described at the end of this chapter. Knowledge of Oi5.133 through Oi5.138 and Reg. S-X Rule 4-10(c)(6) is important for companies following the full cost method.

Conveyance agreements may refer to transferred interests in different ways. Terms such as overrides, royalties, or term overrides may be used when, in fact, the conveyed nonoperating interest is a production payment or even a net profits interest. Accountants must be careful to record the substance of the conveyance regardless of the name given to the transaction by the property interest seller or buyer.

SALES AND SUBLEASES OF UNPROVED MINERAL INTERESTS

When mineral properties are sold or exchanged for cash or cash equivalent, several factors are crucial in determining the accounting treatment for a company using the successful efforts method of accounting.[2] These factors include whether the property is classified as proved or unproved, whether impairment of an unproved property is being recorded on an individual property basis or on a group basis, whether amortization of a proved property is being computed on an individual property basis or on the basis of a geological group, and whether an entire interest or only a partial interest is conveyed.

SALE OF AN ENTIRE WORKING INTEREST IN AN UNPROVED PROPERTY

If the entire interest in an unproved property is sold, recognition of gain or loss depends on the method used to record lease impairment. Oi5.138(g) provides that if impairment has been determined on an individual property basis, then gain or loss is recognized to the extent of the difference between the proceeds received and the net carrying value of the property.

For example, assume an unproved property had an original cost of $100,000. A $25,000 impairment allowance was recorded on an individual property basis. The property is now sold for $80,000. A gain of $5,000 is recognized on the sale as follows:

101	Cash		80,000	
219	Allowance for Impairment of Unproved Properties		25,000	
	211	Unproved Property Acquisition Costs		100,000
	620	Gains on Property Sales		5,000
	To record sale of lease.			

However, if the lease is part of a group of leases where an allowance for impairment was determined on a group or composite basis, the accounting outcome is different. No gain or loss is recognized because the sales proceeds of $80,000 do not exceed the $100,000 original cost of the lease. Oi5.138(g) states:

> For a property amortized by providing a valuation allowance on a group basis, neither gain nor loss shall be recognized when an unproved property is sold unless the sales price exceeds the original cost of the property, in which case gain shall be recognized in the amount of such excess.

As an example, assume a lease originally costing $100,000 had been subject to impairment on a group basis. It is sold in the current year for $125,000. The entry to record the transaction follows:

101	Cash		125,000	
	211	Unproved Property Acquisition Costs		100,000
	620	Gains on Property Sales		25,000
	To record sale of lease.			

Under full cost rules, cash proceeds from sales in each of the above instances are generally treated as a recovery of cost with no gain or loss recognized. The cost of the unproved property sold is transferred into the full cost pool, and the resulting cash proceeds are credited against the full cost pool.

SALE OF A SHARE OF A WORKING INTEREST IN AN UNPROVED PROPERTY

If only part of an interest in an unproved property—either a divided interest or an undivided interest—is sold under Oi5.138(h), no gain is recognized on the transaction unless proceeds from sale of the partial interest exceed the cost of the entire property. A loss on the sale is recognized either directly (according to FAS 19, paragraph 221) or indirectly through the impairment test (see endnote 1). According to Oi5.138(h):

> If a part of the interest in an unproved property is sold, even though for cash or cash equivalent, substantial uncertainty usually exists as to recovery of the cost applicable to the interest retained. Consequently, the amount received shall be treated as a recovery of the cost.[3] However, if the sales price exceeds the carrying amount of a property whose impairment has been assessed individually in accordance with paragraph .119, or exceeds the original cost of a property amortized by providing a valuation allowance on a group basis, gain shall be recognized in the amount of such excess.

Thus, proceeds from the unproved property sale are considered first as a return of capital. If proceeds from the sale of a portion of the property exceed the total carrying value of the entire property on which individual impairment has been recorded, or exceed the total cost of a property on which group impairment has been recorded, the excess of proceeds over the net book value is recognized as a gain.

Assume a successful efforts company owns Lease 15074 originally costing $1 million and having a $600,000 impairment allowance on an individual basis. An undivided three-fourths interest (having a $300,000 net book value) is sold for $380,000. No gain (or loss) is recorded because sales proceeds are less than the entire property's $400,000 net book value. The proceeds of $380,000 are treated as a recovery of capital.

101	Cash		380,000	
	211	Unproved Property Acquisition Costs		380,000
	To record sale of three-fourths interest in Lease 15074 for less than the lease's $400,000 net book value.			

On the other hand, if the three-fourths interest in the property is sold for $820,000, a gain of $420,000 is recognized. A nominal amount of $10 is left in the Unproved Property Acquisition Costs account for control purposes. Thus, the gain recognized is $420,010.

101	Cash		820,000	
219	Allowance for Impairment of Unproved Properties		600,000	
	211	Unproved Property Acquisition Costs		999,990
	620	Gains on Property Sales		420,010
	To record sale of three-fourths interest in Lease 15074.			

As mentioned earlier, losses on sales of unproved property are recognized either directly or indirectly by applying the impairment test. If the loss is recorded directly, the remaining cost may need to be reduced for some impairment.

For example, assume that unproved leasehold 15075 is held by a successful efforts company. The property cost $1 million and an individual impairment of $600,000 has been recorded. Three-fourths of the working interest (having a $300,000 net book value) is sold for $180,000. If the loss on sale is recorded, the remaining $100,000 of net capitalized costs would have an indicated value of only $60,000, which implies an impairment of $40,000. The loss on the sale and impairment on the remaining interest are recorded as follows:

101	Cash		180,000	
219	Allowance for Impairment of Unproved Properties		450,000	
930	Losses on Sales of Property		120,000	
	211	Unproved Property Acquisition Costs		750,000
	To record sale of three-fourths interest in Lease 15075.			

806	Impairment, Amortization and Abandonment of Unproved Properties		40,000	
	219	Allowance for Impairment of Unproved Properties		40,000
	To recognize lease impairment on Lease 15075.			

Alternatively, if impairment is recorded on a group basis, no further impairment may be necessary because the total value of properties in the group may exceed the net book value of the properties.

A full cost company generally would treat proceeds from the sale of unproved properties as a recovery of cost. This circumstance is illustrated in the latter part of this chapter.

SALES OF UNPROVED PROPERTY NONOPERATING INTERESTS

Journal entries illustrated in this chapter thus far have dealt with sales of unproved working interests. The same general rules apply to sales of nonoperating interests, basic royalties, overriding royalties, net profits interests, and production payments (if production payments are classified as mineral interests). The only complicating factor involving the sale of a nonoperating interest arises when the interest is carved out of the working interest and assigned.

Sale of an Unproved Nonoperating Interest. If the entire nonoperating interest in an unproved property is sold, the same rules apply as for working interests. For a successful efforts company, if the property is subject to an individual impairment test, the difference between the net book value of the interest and the selling price is treated as a gain or loss. However, if the nonoperating interest is part of a group impairment arrangement, any sales proceeds not in excess of the original cost of the interest are treated as a recovery of cost. If proceeds exceed cost, the difference is recognized as a gain.

For example, suppose that an unproved overriding royalty interest (ORRI) has a recorded cost of $16,000 and is included in a group on which impairment is being recorded. The unproved ORRI is a one-eighth interest in a 640-acre lease. Three-fourths of the ORRI (equating to a 3/32 net revenue interest in total production) is sold to a purchaser for $15,200. The following entry reflects the SEC's guidelines for recording the sale:

101	Cash	15,200	
	213 Unproved Royalties and Overriding Royalties		15,200
	To record sale of three-fourths of a one-eighth overriding royalty interest.		

However, if the sales price of the interest sold is $30,000, a gain of $14,000 is recognized.

A full cost company treats proceeds from the sale of nonoperating interests as a recovery of capitalized costs in the full cost pool.

Sale of a Carved-Out Nonoperating Interest in Unproved Property. Oi5 rules on conveyances make no distinction in the accounting treatment to be given to either the sale of a fractional share of a working interest or the sale of a carved-out nonoperating interest in an unproved property. In both cases, a successful efforts company treats proceeds as a recovery of cost until the book value of the property (or original cost, if group impairment is used) has been recovered; any excess is treated as gain. A loss on the sale of a fractional share of a nonoperating interest can be recognized (see endnote 1).

A full cost company treats proceeds from such sales as a recovery of cost in the full cost pool.

Conveyance of a Working Interest with Retention of a Nonoperating Interest

Conveyance for a Pooling of Assets. Oi5.138(b) provides that the retention of a nonoperating interest, such as an override, when assigning a working interest in return for drilling, development, and operation by the assignee is a pooling of assets in a joint undertaking. The assignor does not recognize a gain or loss. The assignor's lease cost becomes the cost of the retained nonoperating interest.

Subleases of Unproved Properties. A sublease occurs whenever the working interest owner transfers the operating rights to another party for cash or cash-equivalent consideration and retains an overriding royalty, net profits interest, or production payment that is considered to be equivalent to an overriding royalty. (See Chapter 22 for a discussion of production payments.) Under Oi5.138(h), a subleasing transaction is treated in the same way as the sale of part of an interest in an unproved property (i.e., the unrecovered book value of the working interest, or original cost if group impairment is used, is assigned to the nonoperating interest retained).

For example, assume ABC Oil Company uses the successful efforts method of accounting. For $300,000, it assigns an undeveloped lease that originally cost $1 million, and on which an individual impairment allowance of $600,000 has been established. ABC retains an overriding royalty of one-sixteenth of total production. The entry is recorded as follows:

101	Cash	300,000	
219	Allowance for Impairment of Unproved Properties	600,000	
213	Unproved Royalties and Overriding Royalties	100,000	
	211 Unproved Property Acquisition Costs		1,000,000
	To record sublease.		

The unproved ORRI retained is subject to the impairment test. A question arises if, as is likely to happen, the overriding royalty from a property on which individual impairment has been recorded is to be placed in a group of unproved properties for impairment purposes. Should further impairment be recorded on the overriding royalty before it is transferred to the group? If the value of the override clearly is substantially less than the residual book value assigned to it, then a write-down to its fair value should take place at the time of the sublease. This is reasonable because the decline in value actually applies to the working interest transferred. However, if individual impairment is to be continued on the overriding royalty interest, impairment is determined as in the previous manner, and no immediate impairment is necessary.

When an unproved working interest that is part of a group of properties on which impairment is being recorded is subleased, and an overriding royalty is retained, presumably the interest retained will be included in the account Unproved Overriding Royalties. If proceeds from the **assignment** are less than the original cost of the working interest, the amount received is treated as a recovery of cost. Conversely, if the consideration received is greater than the original cost of the working interest, a gain is recognized, and a nominal value such as $1 is assigned to the nonoperating interest for control purposes.

To explore these concepts, assume that ABC, a successful efforts company, assigns the working interest in an unproved lease to another operator for a cash consideration of $16,000; ABC retains a one-sixteenth overriding royalty. The lease, with an original cost of $14,000, is part of a group of unproved properties with a total cost of $2.1 million. A total impairment of $1.4 million has been recorded for the group. Assuming a control value of $1 is assigned to the overriding royalty, the entry to record the sublease follows:

101	Cash	16,000	
213	Unproved Royalties and Overriding Royalties	1	
	211 Unproved Property Acquisition Costs		14,000
	620 Gains on Property Sales		2,001
	To record sublease of unproved property at a gain.		

If the consideration received in the example had been $6,000, the appropriate entry is:

101	Cash	6,000	
213	Unproved Royalties and Overriding Royalties	8,000	
	211 Unproved Property Acquisition Costs		14,000
	To record sublease of property.		

A full cost company treats the proceeds as a recovery of cost in the full cost pool.

Retained ORRI with a Reversionary Working Interest. The holder of a retained ORRI may have the right to convert the ORRI to a future working interest in the property at an agreed-upon time or event, such as after the working interest owner(s) recover their drilling and completion costs from production. The right to convert the ORRI to a working interest contingent on some future event does not change the accounting for the initial conveyance of the working interest with retention of the ORRI. Reversionary working interests may also arise without converting an ORRI, such as in farmouts, carrying arrangements, and circumstances where some working interest owners elect to go nonconsent and not participate in a proposed development activity. This arrangement is described further in Chapter 23.

The following Figure 21-1 summarizes the creation of different types of nonoperating interests out of the working interest.

Figure 21-1
Creation of Nonoperating Interests out of Working Interest

1. Party A owns a mineral interest:

A
Mineral Interest (MI)

2. Party A leases the property to B retaining a 1/8 royalty interest (RI):

1/8	1/8	1/8	1/8	1/8	1/8	1/8	1/8

A	B
1/8	100% Working Interest (WI)
RI	with 7/8 Net Revenue Interest (NRI)

3. Party B transfers the working interest to C and reserves a 1/8 overriding royalty interest (ORRI):

A	B	C
1/8	1/8	100% Working Interest (WI)
RI	ORRI	with 6/8 NRI

4. Party C carves out to D a volume production payment interest (VPP) of X quantity, payable out of 2/3 of C's 75% NRI:

A	B	D	C
1/8	1/8	VPP out of 4/8 NRI.	100% WI &
RI	ORRI	After payout of X volume, the	2/8 NRI before
		4/8 NRI proceeds go to C.	payout (BPO)

5. Party C sells half the working interest to E, subject to ORRI & VPP:

A	B	D	C	E
1/8	1/8	VPP out of 4/8 NRI.	4/8 WI	4/8 WI
RI	ORRI	After payout of X volume, the	& 1/8	& 1/8
		4/8 NRI proceeds go to C&E.	NRI BPO	NRI BPO

SALES OF PROVED PROPERTIES

SALE OF AN ENTIRE PROVED PROPERTY

The sale of a proved property by a successful efforts company is handled in much the same way as the sale of any other item of plant and equipment. A determining factor is whether the lease is being amortized on an individual basis or as part of a group of properties.

As an example, assume ABC amortizes the cost of a proved 480-acre lease on an individual lease basis. Data relating to the property on January 1, 2006, are as follows:

Leasehold cost	$200,000	
Less accumulated amortization	(40,000)	
		$160,000
Wells and related facilities—IDC	800,000	
Less accumulated amortization	(160,000)	
		640,000
Wells and related facilities—Equipment	160,000	
Less accumulated amortization	(40,000)	
		120,000
Total		**$920,000**

If the entire interest in the property is sold, all balances relating to the lease are closed out, and the difference between the consideration received and the net book value of $920,000 is treated as a gain or loss. For instance, if the lease is sold outright for $3 million, a gain of $2,080,000 will be recognized.

SALE OF AN UNDIVIDED PORTION OF PROVED PROPERTY

If only a portion of a property is sold, the accounting treatment can be more complex. Oi5.138(j) gives general guidelines for handling this situation:

> The sale of a part of a proved property, or of an entire proved property constituting a part of an amortization base, shall be accounted for as the sale of an asset, and a gain or loss shall be recognized, since it is not one of the conveyances described in paragraph .135 or .136. The unamortized cost of the property or group of properties a part of which was sold shall be apportioned to the interest sold and the interest retained on the basis of the fair values of those interests. However, the sale may be accounted for as a normal retirement under the provisions of paragraph .132 with no gain or loss recognized if doing so does not significantly affect the unit-of-production amortization rate.

Assume ABC sells an undivided interest in a proved property that has been amortized individually. A proportionate share of each related account is removed, and the gain or loss recognized is the difference between the book value removed and the consideration received. The January 2, 2006, sale by ABC to Samsco for $3 million cash represents an undivided three-fourths share of the working interest in the 480-acre lease described in the preceding example. The appropriate entry by ABC is:

101	Cash	3,000,000	
226	Accum. Amortization of Proved Property Acquisition Costs	30,000	
232	Accum. Amortization of Intangible Costs ...	120,000	
234	Accum. Amortization of Tangible Costs ...	30,000	
	221 Proved Property Acquisition Costs		150,000
	231 Intangible Costs of Wells ...		600,000
	233 Tangible Costs of Wells ...		120,000
	620 Gains on Property Sales		2,310,000
	To record sale of three-fourths interest in a lease.		

SALE OF A DIVIDED PORTION OF PROVED PROPERTY

A difficulty is created when a successful efforts company sells a divided interest (e.g., 320 acres of a 480-acre tract in a proved property). If the portion sold is undeveloped and the portion retained is developed, no part of the cost of equipment or IDC should be removed from the accounts. Theoretically, the unamortized mineral property cost is allocated on the basis of relative fair values between the acreage conveyed and acreage retained.

Some practitioners interpret the terms "cost of the property" in Oi5 conveyance rules to include not only the mineral leasehold cost but also the cost of wells and related facilities and equipment. In measuring the cost to be "apportioned to the interest sold and the interest retained," the unamortized cost of all assets related to the property are included, even though the portion sold is undeveloped and the portion retained is developed. If this approach is followed, the value of the interest sold is presumably the sales price, and the value of the interest retained is the total value of the developed lease including equipment.

This interpretation may seem unusual when the interest sold is the entire working interest in a proved undeveloped property that is part of an amortization group. For example, assume that eight properties in a field, some developed and some undeveloped, have been grouped for amortization. No production (or amortization) has occurred yet. The unamortized balance of costs of the group is:

Proved leaseholds	$800,000
IDC	6,000,000
Equipment	1,000,000

An undeveloped lease in the group is sold for $2 million, and the remaining seven leases have a fair value of $18 million. The appropriate entry that allocates cost on the basis of relative fair value is:

101	Cash	2,000,000	
	221 Proved Property Acquisition Costs		80,000
	231 Intangible Costs of Wells ...		600,000
	233 Tangible Costs of Wells ...		100,000
	620 Gains on Property Sales		1,220,000
	To record sale of proved lease.		

This treatment is justified on the basis that once an amortization group has been formed individual leases lose their identities and one combined property replaces them.

SALE TREATED AS A NORMAL RETIREMENT

As noted in Oi5.138(j), if a portion of a property or group of properties is sold, the sale can be treated by a successful efforts company as a normal retirement, "with no gain or loss recognized if doing so does not significantly affect the unit-of-production amortization rate." Presumably, this treatment occurs only when the quantity of reserves sold is immaterial with respect to the total reserves retained or when the selling price per unit of reserves sold does not differ significantly from the cost amortization per unit (i.e., when the deferred gain or loss is quite small).

To illustrate this distinction, assume a proved property (or group of proved properties) has an unamortized balance of $10 million and the related proved reserves are two million barrels. Thus, the pre-sale amortization rate is $5 per barrel. If a portion of the property containing 600,000 barrels of proved reserves is sold for $3.6 million (i.e., $6 per barrel), and if no gain or loss is recognized, the remaining cost is $6.4 million (10,000,000 - 3,600,000), and the remaining reserves are 1.4 million barrels. The new amortization rate is $4.57 per barrel (6,400,000 ÷ 1,400,000). Further, assume that the portion retained has a fair value of $14.4 million ($10.29 per barrel[4]). If the sale had not been treated as a normal retirement, the $10 million total cost would have been allocated based on relative fair values. The portion sold would be allocated as follows: $10,000,000 x $3.6/($3.6 + $14.4), or $2 million. The portion retained would have an $8 million book value, which equates to $5.71 per barrel for the 1.4 million remaining reserves. Treating the sale as a normal retirement significantly affects the new unit-of-production amortization rate; it reduces the rate from $5.71 per barrel to $4.57 per barrel, a 20 percent change.[5]

Normally, the value per barrel of the portion sold equals the value per barrel of the portion retained. In this case, an allocation of cost based on relative fair value leaves the amortization rate the same as before the sale, which is $5 in the example provided. However, one should be careful to compare the new amortization rate to the alternative new amortization rate (not the pre-sale amortization rate) in evaluating the amortization effect of using cost recovery.

As illustrated later in this chapter, no gain or loss is recognized on such sales under full cost unless treating the proceeds as a recovery of costs would materially distort the amortization rate.

RETIREMENTS OF PROVED PROPERTIES

The surrender or release of rights in an unproved mineral property has been discussed earlier in this text. In summary, under the successful efforts method of accounting and if an unproved property on which impairment has been recorded on an individual basis is surrendered, the property's book value is written off as an abandonment loss. Alternatively, if an unproved property is part of a group on which amortization has been provided, when the property is relinquished its cost is charged to the Allowance for Impairment account. No loss is recognized on the transaction.

Under Oi5.132, the abandonment of proved mineral interests within a proved cost center is treated in the same way as the normal retirement of equipment or wells. Oi5.132 states:

> Normally, no gain or loss shall be recognized if only an individual well or individual item of equipment is abandoned or retired or if only a single lease or other part of a group of proved properties constituting the amortization base is abandoned or retired as long as the remainder of the property or group of properties continues to produce oil or gas. Instead, the asset being abandoned or retired shall be deemed to be fully amortized,

and its costs shall be charged to accumulated depreciation, depletion, or amortization. When the last well on an individual property (if that is the amortization base) or group of properties (if amortization is determined on the basis of an aggregation of properties with a common geological structure) ceases to produce and the entire property or property group is abandoned, gain or loss shall be recognized. Occasionally, the partial abandonment or retirement of a proved property or group of proved properties or the abandonment or retirement of wells or related equipment or facilities may result from a catastrophic event or other major abnormality. In those cases, a loss shall be recognized at the time of abandonment or retirement.

For example, assume the following costs and accumulated DD&A for a field:

Proved leaseholds	$ 1,000,000
Less accumulated amortization	(600,000)
	$ 400,000
Intangible costs of wells	$ 12,000,000
Less accumulated amortization	(7,200,000)
	$ 4,800,000
Tangible costs of wells	$ 600,000
Less accumulated amortization	(360,000)
	$ 240,000

An item of equipment costing $20,000 has been used on lease operations. Recently, it was retired from the lease and has been transferred to warehouse salvage inventory. Considering the equipment's current estimated value of $200, the appropriate entry is:

132	*Inventory of Materials and Supplies*	200	
234	*Accum. Amortization of Tangible Costs . . .*	19,800	
	233 *Tangible Costs of Wells*		20,000
	To record retirement of equipment on lease.		

Similarly, if an entire proved lease included in an amortization group of properties is abandoned, no gain or loss is recognized. Suppose a lease included in the previous group is abandoned. Original costs are: $32,000 for leasehold, $980,000 for IDC, and $63,000 for equipment. Equipment salvage proceeds total $1,000. The accounting treatment is:

101	*Cash*	1,000	
226	*Accum. Amortization of Proved Property Acquisition Costs*	32,000	
232	*Accum. Amortization of Intangible Costs . . .*	980,000	
234	*Accum. Amortization of Tangible Costs . . .*	62,000	
	221 *Proved Property Acquisition Costs*		32,000
	231 *Intangible Costs of Wells . . .*		980,000
	233 *Tangible Costs of Wells . . .*		63,000
	To record abandonment of lease in amortization group.		

Conceptually, if proved properties in a common geological structure are combined for purposes of computing amortization, the individual assets lose their identities. As a matter of practice, however, this does not occur because the IRS, federal regulatory agencies, and some state agencies can require separation of costs for each property. If it is not possible to determine costs applicable to individual properties, net salvage proceeds can be credited to the Tangible Costs of Wells and Development account or to the Accumulated Amortization of Tangible Costs account. This approach achieves the same net result as removing the costs from the asset accounts and charging them to the accumulated amortization accounts.

When the last well on the last lease of an amortization base is abandoned, or when the last well is abandoned on a producing lease that is being individually amortized, all asset accounts related to the properties (or property) are closed, and net book values less any salvage proceeds are recorded as a loss.

Oi5.132 addresses recognition of gains or losses from catastrophic events or other abnormalities. Fires, floods, earthquakes, hurricanes, or unusual governmental actions are considered abnormalities, whereas routine items such as well blowouts, abandonments of wells because of excess salt water intrusion, or other inherent industry risks are not considered abnormalities. For example, assume a flood occurs in the Smith field causing major destruction of equipment. Leases in this area have been combined for amortization purposes. Equipment with an original cost of $250,000 was damaged and removed. Net salvage proceeds of $28,000 have been received from its sale. Total capitalized equipment costs in the field are $750,000, and amortization of $375,000 has been accumulated. A loss of $97,000 is computed and the journal entry is recorded as follows:

Cost of equipment damaged	$ 250,000
Less accumulated amortization:	
$\dfrac{\$375,000}{\$750,000} \times \$250,000 =$	(125,000)
Imputed book value	$ 125,000
Less salvage proceeds	(28,000)
Net loss	**$ 97,000**

101	*Cash*	28,000	
234	*Accum. Amortization of Tangible Costs . . .*	125,000	
933	*Casualty Loss*	97,000	
	233 *Tangible Costs of Wells . . .*		250,000
	To record flood loss on equipment from Smith field.		

SALES AND ABANDONMENTS UNDER THE FULL COST METHOD

Under the full cost method accepted by the SEC, all oil and gas properties in each country are combined into a common pool. Conceptually, each property loses its separate identity. Thus, sales and abandonments of properties are generally treated as adjustments of capitalized costs. No gains or losses are recognized. Reg. S-X Rule 4-10 (c)(6)(i) includes these rules:

The provisions of paragraph (h) of this section, "Mineral property conveyances and related transactions if the successful efforts method of accounting is followed,"[6] shall apply also to those reporting entities following the full cost method except as follows:

(i) Sales and abandonments of oil and gas properties. Sales of oil and gas properties, whether or not being amortized currently, shall be accounted for as adjustments of capitalized costs, with no gain or loss recognized, unless such adjustments would significantly alter the relationship between capitalized costs and proved reserves of oil and gas attributable to a cost center. For instance, a significant alteration would not ordinarily be expected to occur for sales involving less than 25 percent of the reserve quantities of a given cost center. If gain or loss is recognized on such a sale, total capitalized costs within the cost center shall be allocated between the reserves sold and reserves retained on the same basis used to compute amortization, unless there are substantial economic differences between the properties sold and those retained, in which case capitalized costs shall be allocated on the basis of the relative fair values of the properties. Abandonments of oil and gas properties shall be accounted for as adjustments of capitalized costs, that is, the cost of abandoned properties shall be charged to the full cost center and amortized (subject to the limitation on capitalized costs in paragraph (b) of this section). [Author's note: The limitation on capitalized costs appears in Reg. S-X Rule 4-10(c)(4).]

When trying to determine if a significant alteration has occurred, petroleum accountants should reference the SEC Financial Reporting Policies (FRP) 406.01.c.iv which made it clear that the 25 percent rule is merely a general guide. The test for determining whether a gain or loss is recognized is whether a significant distortion of the amortization rate results if proceeds are treated merely as a recovery of cost similar to the successful efforts rules for treating a sale as a normal retirement.

Substantial economic differences between the properties sold and those retained occur when the fair value per reserves BOE of properties sold is substantially different from the fair value per reserves BOE of properties retained. Such differences can arise where: (1) production life is substantially different, (2) expected prices differ substantially because of quality or location, (3) degree of development of the reserves sold and of those retained is not comparable, or (4) production costs differ widely. In such cases, capitalized costs should be allocated on the basis of the relative fair values of the properties. Yet, this requirement may necessitate a complex and difficult calculation because of the difficulty in arriving at a fair value for the properties retained.

To illustrate the concepts of significant alteration and substantial economic differences, assume the following amounts for a full cost pool: $300 million in gross capitalized costs, $100 million in accumulated amortization, and 25 million barrels of reserves in the cost center. For simplicity, future development costs and future net DR&A costs are estimated at zero. The current amortization rate is $8 per barrel [($300 - 100)/25]. Certain properties, containing 7.5 million barrels of the estimated reserves are sold for $37.5 million ($5 per barrel). The fair value of the remaining properties is $150 million ($8.57 per barrel).

In this example, substantial economic differences exist as evidenced by the $5 per barrel value of properties being sold versus $8.57 per barrel for retained properties. Allocating the $200 million net book value on the basis of relative fair values assigns 20 percent or $40 million to the properties sold for a loss of $2.5 million and assigns 80 percent or $160 million to the properties retained for a new amortization rate of $9.14 per barrel. Deferring the loss by crediting the $37.5 million of sales proceeds against capitalized costs gives the retained properties a net book value of $162.5 million for a new amortization rate of $9.29 per barrel. Deferring the loss does not significantly alter the new amortization rate (the relationship between capitalized costs and reserves) and is allowable despite the fact that the sold properties contained 30 percent of the cost center's reserves.

Changing the assumptions slightly, assume the value of the retained properties is also $5 per barrel, which allows allocation to be based on reserves. In this case, 30 percent or $60 million of costs are allocated to the properties sold for a loss of $22.5 million. Treating the sale like a normal retirement (deferring the loss) still leaves a new amortization rate of $9.14 per barrel. However, if the loss had been recognized, the new amortization rate would be ($200 - 60)/17.5, or $8 per barrel, the same as the old amortization rate. Deferral of the loss would not be allowable because it would significantly alter the new amortization rate ($9.14 versus $8.00).

Sales proceeds should not be simply credited to the accumulated amortization account. To illustrate, assume that Fullco, a full cost company, operates only in the U.S. Therefore, it has only one cost center. Total capitalized costs in the center are $364 million, and accumulated amortization of these costs is $120 million on January 1, 2006. A summary of certain January 2006 transactions follows:

- Unproved leases were surrendered and had a cost of $4 million.

- Proved leases were abandoned and had an original cost of $600,000.

- The above leases had equipment costing $380,000.

- Salvage proceeds from above equipment were $20,000.

- IDC originally incurred on abandoned leases totaled $3.9 million.

Although capitalized costs were associated with specific leases in the previous example, it is not necessary to record adjustments to specific leases under the full cost method, nor is it even possible in some cases. The only entry required is to reduce the carrying value of the cost pool by the salvage proceeds. This can be done by either crediting a capitalized cost account or crediting the accumulated amortization account for $20,000.

Obviously, the latter approach applied over many years would result in a continuing increase in the capitalized cost accounts and the accumulated amortization account because acquisition costs are never reduced for salvaged equipment no longer owned by the company. In practice, most companies remove the asset costs from the asset account and charge these amounts, less any net salvage, against the accumulated amortization account. The summarized journal entry that follows reflects the abandonments and surrenders based on the facts provided:

101	Cash		20,000	
226	Accum. Amortization of Proved Property Acquisition Costs		8,860,000	
	221	Proved Property Acquisition Costs		600,000
	211	Unproved Property Acquisition Costs		4,000,000
	231	Intangible Costs of Wells ...		3,900,000
	233	Tangible Costs of Wells ...		380,000
	Summary of abandonments and surrenders for the year.			

GAINS OR LOSSES ON PROMOTIONAL ACTIVITIES

In May 1984, the SEC issued Release 33-6525, which revised Reg. S-X Rule 4-10. The ruling clarified that full cost companies cannot record gains or losses on the sales or promotion of unproved properties. Revised Reg. S-X Rule 4-10(c)(6)(iii)(A) now states:

> Except as provided in subparagraph (i)(6)(i) of this section, all consideration received from sales or transfers of properties in connection with partnerships, joint venture operations, or various other forms of drilling arrangements involving oil and gas exploration and development activities (e.g., carried interest, turnkey wells, management fees, etc.) shall be credited to the full cost account, except to the extent of amounts that represent reimbursement of organization, offering, general and administrative expenses, etc., that are identifiable with the transaction, if such amounts are currently incurred and charged to expense.

Subparagraph (c)(6)(iii)(A) contains extremely minor exceptions to the basic rule. Thus, even though a full cost oil or gas company acquires an unproved property for the specific purpose of reselling it or transferring it to a drilling fund (or partnership) operated by the company, any gain or loss resulting from a sale or transfer is treated as an adjustment of the full cost pool. This rule is discussed further in Chapter 24.

ACQUISITIONS OF E&P PROPERTY

ACQUISITION OF UNPROVED PROPERTY FOR CASH OR CASH EQUIVALENT

Accounting for the acquisition of unproved property for cash or cash equivalent is addressed in Chapter 7.

ACQUISITION OF PROVED PROPERTY FOR CASH OR CASH EQUIVALENT

Oi5 and Reg. S-X Rule 4-10 are silent on the appropriate accounting for acquisition of proved property other than by capitalizing the total purchase price. A question arises over allocation of the purchase price among the three elements of cost: mineral rights, IDC, and equipment. Conceptually, the purchase price would be allocated among the three elements on the basis of relative values. Although the equipment's value can be estimated, and the sales contract often specifies the value of that element, it can be difficult to place a value on the IDC represented by the well. Because of this and the federal income tax treatment required, it is common to assign to the equipment an amount equal to its fair market value. The balance of the purchase price is allocated to the mineral property (leasehold) acquisition account. This treatment is satisfactory if the property is fully developed so that all proved reserves on the property are being used as the basis for amortization of both the IDC and the mineral acquisition cost.

If the property is only partially developed—reserves can be segmented into proved developed and proved undeveloped—then the aggregate acquisition cost is allocated for financial reporting purposes to acquisition costs (amortized over total proved reserves) and development costs (amortized over proved developed reserves) by considering the relative value of proved developed reserves and proved undeveloped reserves. One reasonable approach determines IDC value by computing a lease acquisition value based on the value of a proved undeveloped barrel.

For example, assume a property is acquired for $1 million, which reflects an $800,000 value for 160,000 net barrels of proved developed reserves and a $200,000 value for 100,000 of proved undeveloped reserves. Equipment is valued at $100,000. First-year production is 16,000 barrels. For tax purposes, $100,000 is allocated to used equipment to be depreciated as such, and $900,000 is allocated to lease acquisition costs to be subject to income tax cost depletion based on total proved reserves. This allocation is often used by the company for financial reporting purposes, but it understates initial amortization by amortizing the entire $900,000 over proved reserves. Of the $900,000, there is an indicated $520,000 value for lease acquisition costs (leaving $380,000 for intangible development costs) based on the proved undeveloped reserves value of $2 per barrel times 260,000 proved barrels. If $380,000 is allocated to IDC, amortization of development costs is (16/160) x ($380,000 + $100,000), or $48,000, in the first year. Amortization of lease acquisition costs is (16/260) x $520,000, or $32,000. Total amortization costs are $80,000—the same as under the logical (but generally unacceptable) approach of amortizing the $800,000 value of proved developed reserves over such reserves and postponing amortization of the $200,000 until proved undeveloped reserves come on production.

OVERRIDING ROYALTY CONVEYANCES

This section summarizes the accepted accounting methods for overrides and other types of ORRI conveyances.

SALES OF OVERRIDES

Override Sale from Unproved Property. Accounting for the sales of nonoperating interests from unproved properties, such as overrides, has been covered earlier in this chapter. In general, a sale is treated as a recovery of cost until the book value of the original property (or original cost if group impairment is used) has been recovered; any excess is treated as a gain.

Override Sale from Proved Property with No Working Interest Retained. When an override, or a portion of an override, is sold in a proved property with no retention of a working interest, the accounting is the same as for the sale of a working interest. In general, a sale of the entire override is the sale of an entire proved property interest whereby gain or loss is recognized for successful efforts and generally treated as a recovery of cost against the full cost pool. When an undivided portion of an override is sold, the seller recognizes a gain or loss by allocating the override's book value between the portion sold and portion retained based on their relative fair values.

Override Sale Carved from a Working Interest in Proved Property. Oi5 conveyance rules are unclear on how to account for the sale of an ORRI (or other nonoperating interest) carved from a working (operating) interest. Consider the following rules:

- Oi5.136(b) does not allow gain recognition for sales of a part of interest owned if the seller has a substantial obligation for future performance (e.g., to operate the property without proportional reimbursement for operating costs applicable to the interest sold).

- Oi5.138(j) provides that the sale of part of a proved property is accounted for as a sale of an asset with gain or loss recognized. The amount of gain or loss is measured by apportioning book value to the asset sold and the asset retained in proportion to their fair values.

- Oi5.138(j) and its reference to Oi5.136(b) add that a sale of part of a proved property is not part of an interest owned for which the seller has substantial obligation for future performance, such as operating the property without proportional reimbursement for that portion of the drilling or operating costs applicable to the interest sold. However, the sale of an ORRI carved from the working interest of a proved property does leave the seller with substantial obligation of future performance (paying 100 percent of the related costs for a reduced share of revenues).

- Oi5.138(k) provides the accounting is the same as in Oi5.138(j) for the sale of a working interest and retention of an ORRI.

- Oi5.138(a) on conveying a VPP carved from a retained working interest does not allow gain recognition because the seller has a substantial obligation for future performance (i.e., operating the property without proportional reimbursement for operating costs).

Consider the following in applying these rules to transactions:

- An outright sale for cash of an ORRI carved from a working interest is the partial sale of a mineral interest.

- The buyer has purchased an interest in the reserves of the working interest owner. The reserves pertaining to the ORRI are no longer included in the seller's reserves base.

- The working interest owner has the obligation for substantial future performance to operate the property and bear all operating costs relating to the ORRI sold.

The rules of Oi5.136(b) appear to be most applicable, whereby a loss is recognized at the time of conveyance, but not a gain. Gain or loss is measured to determine whether: (1) a loss exists and must be recognized, or (2) the sale proceeds can simply be credited to the cost of the asset. Under the guidance of Oi5.138(j), gain or loss is measured by apportioning book value to the asset sold and the asset retained in proportion to their relative fair values.

The following example illustrates the apportioning method. Assume ABC owns a working interest (WI) with a book value of $100,000. It sells a 10 percent ORRI for cash in the amount of $40,000. The remaining WI is evaluated to have a fair market value of $120,000. The 10 percent ORRI has 25 percent of the total fair value of the property [40,000/(40,000+120,000) = 25%]. Under these circumstances, a gain is calculated in the amount of $15,000 [40,000 − (.25 x 100,000)], which cannot be recognized. If the sale had been for an amount of $20,000 and the fair market value of the remaining working interest was $60,000, the override's allocated cost would be $25,000 for a recognized loss of $5,000. The retained working interest would be subject to FAS 144 accounting for impairment as addressed in Chapter 18.

Override Sale Treated as a Normal Retirement. As explained earlier in this chapter, Oi5.138(j) allows for the "sale of part of a proved property, or of an entire proved property constituting an amortization base . . . [to] be accounted for as a normal retirement under the provisions of paragraph .132 with no gain or loss recognized if doing so does not significantly affect the unit-of-production amortization rate." The specific rule does not preclude such accounting for a sale of an override in proved property. However, the option of accounting for the override as a normal retirement has limited application:

- The optional accounting provides no positive income effect if the override is sold at a gain.

- The income effect is no different if the gain must be deferred anyway because a working interest was retained.

- Using the optional accounting to defer a loss (by charging the loss to the cost of the retained interest) is of little or no value if FAS 144 accounting for impairment requires a write-down of the cost of the retained interest to fair value.

- In many cases, deferral of the loss significantly affects the unit-of-production amortization rate whereby normal retirement accounting may not be used.

It should be noted that normal retirement accounting (deferral of gain or loss) is not available to a conveyance of a working interest with retention of an override.

CONVEYING AN OVERRIDE TO A LENDER

In some instances, a company conveys an ORRI in a proved property in order to obtain a loan commitment from a financial institution. This is done to obtain more favorable terms on a loan and is similar to obtaining a discounted loan. The value of the ORRI should be removed from the oil and gas properties classification and treated as a debt discount. In effect, this allows the ORRI to be amortized over the life of the loan.

For example, an oil company seeks financing from a bank in the amount of $20 million at seven percent APR repayable in 10 years. The bank will loan the money only at a 10 percent rate. The company offers the bank an ORRI having an estimated fair value of $600,000, which will be carved from the working interest. Although the income statement effect is as if the money were loaned at 10 percent, the cash flow effect to the company is a seven percent loan. The general entry to record the loan is:

101	*Cash*		20,000,000	
408	*Debt Discount*		600,000	
	401	*Notes Payable*		20,000,000
	201	*Oil and Gas Properties (assuming full cost accounting)*		600,000
	To record debt proceeds and reclass ORRI conveyance.			

Under full cost, the property asset accounts are typically credited with the fair value of the debt discount, and no gain or loss is recognized. Under successful efforts, a loss may be recognized, but not a gain, for the conveyance of an override carved out of a retained working interest.

CONVEYING AN OVERRIDE TO A KEY EMPLOYEE

In some instances, companies have agreements with key employees to hold a carried working interest or a net profits interest on their behalf. While conveyed in substance to key employees, title may not transfer until certain future economic events take place with regard to specific properties or investments. Often, such conveyances occur before the property becomes proved and the value of the conveyance is usually nominal and immaterial. In theory, the conveyance should be recorded in the same manner as conveying an ORRI to a lender, except that wage expense is debited rather than debt discount, and the rules for unproved property conveyances apply.

RETENTION OF AN OVERRIDE WHEN A WORKING INTEREST IS CONVEYED

Override Retention in an Unproved Property. Oi5.138(b) provides that retention of a nonoperating interest when assigning a working interest in return for drilling, development, and operation by the assignee is a pooling of assets in a joint undertaking. The assignor does not recognize gain or loss and its lease cost becomes the cost of the retained nonoperating interest.

If a working interest is sold for cash or cash equivalent and an ORRI is retained, the conveyance is a sublease of unproved property whereby recoverability of the cost assigned to the ORRI in unproved property is uncertain. Sales proceeds are credited against the cost with any excess over the cost being recognized as a gain.

Override Retention in a Proved Property. Oi5.138(k) provides that the sale of a working interest with retention of a nonoperating interest is accounted for as the sale of an asset and "any gain or loss shall be recognized" under successful efforts. Reg. S-X Rule 4-10(c)(6)(i) generally requires the proceeds to be treated as a recovery of cost against the full cost pool.

The seller measures the gain or loss by allocating the property book value between the portion sold and portion retained based on their relative fair values.

Oi5.138(k) mirrors Oi5.138(j) except that no mention is made of the option to account for the conveyance as a normal retirement. The language of Oi5.138(j) and Oi5.138(k) suggests that normal retirement accounting is not an available option for the sale of a working interest with retention of a nonoperating interest.

TERM OVERRIDES

Certain types of overrides do not extend to the end of the economic life of the property (i.e., they have a shorter duration than the underlying working interest). These are called term overrides and can be limited in either quantity or time. Generally, term overrides are construed to be production payments. If so, they are accounted for as such, either as volume production payments or loans. Chapter 22 addresses this area of accounting.

GENERAL TAX TREATMENT OF SALES AND LEASES

For federal tax purposes, there is an important distinction between sales and leases (including subleases). In a leasing transaction, the consideration received—other than any applicable to equipment sold if a developed property is subleased—is classified as ordinary income and may be subject to depletion.

For example, if ABC owns an unproved lease with a basis of $50,000 and assigns the working interest to Developco for $180,000, retaining a one-eighth overriding royalty, the entire $180,000 is ordinary income to ABC. ABC assigns the $50,000 cost less any cost depletion that might be allowable on the $180,000 bonus as the basis of the override retained.

For tax purposes, a transaction is considered a lease if the working interest is assigned for cash or cash equivalent and a continuing non-working interest is retained (e.g., a royalty or overriding royalty interest, or in certain cases a production payment, is retained). If a developed property is subleased, consideration received is first treated as a sale of equipment equal to the equipment's fair market value, and the remaining consideration is treated as leasehold bonus.

A sale transaction is deemed to have occurred when: (1) all of the interest in a property is sold, (2) the type of interest sold is the same as that retained (e.g., a fractional part of a working interest is sold), or (3) the working interest is retained, but a continuing non-working interest, such as a royalty interest, overriding royalty interest, or net profits interest is carved out and assigned. In a sale transaction, the seller allocates the basis between the interest retained (if any) and the interest sold, and recognizes gain (or loss) to the extent the sales proceeds exceed the basis allocated to the interest sold. If a nonoperating interest is carved out and sold, the allocation is based on the relative fair value of the interest sold and of the interest retained.

• • •

1 FAS 19 prohibits only gain from being recognized. Paragraph 221 states that "recognition of a loss should not be prohibited," implying that loss recognition at the time of sale is optional. However, if the loss were not recognized at the time of sale of an unproved property, a loss would effectively be recognized when the remaining capitalized cost is subject to impairment analysis (FAS 19, Note 4). For example, if one sells 50 percent of an unproved property costing $10,000 for $2,000, it seems unreasonable not to recognize an impairment loss (i.e., to carry the unsold 50 percent interest at $8,000 when the sale demonstrates a value of only $2,000 and an impairment of $6,000. The amount of loss recognized due to impairment will depend in part on whether the unproved property is assessed for impairment individually or in a group.

2 Companies using the full cost method treat the sale or abandonment of oil and gas properties as discussed later in this chapter. See Chapter 19 for a discussion of the gains or losses resulting from the settlement of AROs under the full cost method.

3 Oi5 Note 4 mentions that the unrecovered cost is subject to impairment assessment.

4 It may seem odd that the portion sold had a value of $6 per reserve barrel, while the portion retained had a value of $10.29 per reserve barrel, but such disproportionate values may occur when the sold portion is largely a reversionary interest in the field's later production.

5 FAS 19 does not define the word "significantly." However, Oi5.158 (FAS 69, paragraph 8) has defined a company as having significant oil and gas producing activities when such activities represent 10 percent or more of revenue, combined operating profit, or identifiable assets. The SEC believes that individual properties are significant if their costs exceed 10 percent of a cost center's net capitalized costs (FRP 406.01.c.i located in Appendix 1). Therefore, if cost recovery changes the amortization rate by more than 10 percent, it may be argued the change is "significant."

6 The reference to deleted paragraph (h) of Reg. S-X Rule 4-10 is presumed to mean Oi5.133 through Oi5.138 (on conveyances under successful efforts accounting) which replaced Reg. S-X Rule 4-10(h).

CHAPTER

22

PRODUCTION PAYMENTS AND NET PROFITS INTERESTS

Key Concepts:

- Criteria for identifying conveyance agreements

- Conveyed production payments

- Volume production payments

- Retained production payments

- Net profits interests

This chapter discusses the conveyances of production payments and net profits interests in the oil and gas industry. For reference, the general accounting rules for conveyances of properties are found in Chapter 21. The guidance in this chapter relates primarily to the successful efforts method of accounting. A company that follows the full cost method will generally follow the conveyance guidance of a successful efforts company with several exceptions, some of which are discussed later in this chapter.

ACCOUNTING BASED ON THE ATTRIBUTES OF OWNERSHIP

A conveyance is categorized according to the substance of the transaction, rather than any terminology used by the parties or in the agreement. Sellers and buyers assume certain attributes when property is transferred. Owners assume the ownership risks such as future price changes and production variances. With respect to ownership risks, the four principal types of petroleum property conveyances follow (see Figure 22-1).

- **Loan.** The seller retains substantially all pricing and production risks, while the buyer has few or no pricing and production risks. The contractual interest is expressed in dollar terms, and either: (1) the underlying expected cash flow for repayment is significantly greater than the contractual obligation, or (2) the amount of the obligation is guaranteed by the seller. In substance, the owner is not selling the property, but is borrowing funds instead.

- **Prepaid Commodity Sale (or "Prepaid").** The seller retains all, or substantially all, production risks; the buyer assumes all, or substantially all, pricing risks. In a prepaid conveyance, the buyer pays before the delivery of the oil or gas. A seller sells oil or gas in advance and buys oil and gas, if necessary, to meet its commitment to deliver a fixed quantity of oil or gas in the future. On the seller's books, a debit entry is made to Cash, while a credit is recorded to Deferred Revenue. Proved reserves are unaffected and the transaction is not considered a sale of a mineral interest.

- **Volume (or Volumetric) Production Payment (VPP).** The buyer assumes significant production risks and assumes all, or substantially all, pricing risks. VPPs differ from prepaids because the VPP buyer receives agreed-upon quantities from specified future production. Later on, if production is inadequate, the seller has no obligation to make up for the shortfall. Thus, a VPP is treated as a sale of a mineral interest. Special rules are specified in Oi5.138(a) for a VPP conveyance; the seller debits Cash and credits Deferred Revenue, and treats the conveyance as a sale of a mineral interest including any related proved reserves. For sellers using full cost accounting, the proceeds would be credited to the full cost pool unless such adjustment would significantly alter the amortization rate. See the full cost accounting section later in this chapter.

    VPPs entered into in connection with a business combination can have a different accounting impact. See the discussion in Chapter 30 regarding VPPs entered into for this purpose.

- **Sale of a Mineral Interest.** A buyer assumes all, or substantially all, of the seller's ownership risks. The seller debits Cash, credits Property accounts, and recognizes gain or loss to the extent allowed under successful efforts or full cost accounting, as applicable.

Figure 22-1
Conveyance Types Based on Risks of Ownership

	Assumption of	
Conveyance Types	**Production Risks**	**Pricing Risks**
Loan, in substance	Seller	Seller
Prepaid commodity sale	Seller	Buyer
Volume production payment	Buyer, primarily	Buyer
Outright sale	Buyer	Buyer

PRODUCTION PAYMENTS

Production payment transactions obligate the grantor to pay the holder for a specified portion of production proceeds, or else deliver a specific amount of oil or gas before production ceases. In either form, the holder has no obligation to pay operating costs. The holder looks to specified production for a limited period to receive either cash or marketable production. Accounting for this type of transfer depends in part on whether the E&P company conveyed the production payment, or conveyed a working interest and retained a production payment.

CONVEYED PRODUCTION PAYMENTS

Commonly, production payments are conveyed in return for an immediate receipt of cash. The transaction resembles a financing arrangement where the mineral property owner pledges production, or proceeds from production, to collateralize repayment of funds advanced.

Complexities in accounting treatment arise because financial markets have become more creative in designing instruments for investors. Funds advanced may be considered equivalent to loans; in other cases, they represent sales of oil and gas interests or advance payments for the purchase of future production. Subtle wording differences in agreements can alter the nature of these transactions, even though they appear similar and are referred to by the same name.

The Emerging Issues Task Force of the Financial Accounting Standards Board addressed the accounting implications in its EITF Issue No. 88-18 (EITF 88-18), *Sales of Future Revenues*:

> The Task Force reached a consensus...that classification as debt or deferred income depends on the specific facts and circumstances of the transaction. The Task Force also reached a consensus that the presence of any one of the following factors independently creates a rebuttable presumption that classification of the proceeds as debt is appropriate:
>
> 1. The transaction does not purport to be a sale (that is, the form of the transaction is debt).
>
> 2. The enterprise has significant continuing involvement in the generation of the cash flows due the investor (for example, active involvement in the generation of the operating revenues of a product line, subsidiary, or business segment).

3. The transaction is cancelable by either the enterprise or the investor through payment of a lump sum or other transfer of assets by the enterprise.

4. The investor's rate of return is implicitly or explicitly limited by the terms of the transaction.

5. Variations in the enterprise's revenue or income underlying the transaction have only a trifling impact on the investor's rate of return.

6. The investor has any recourse to the enterprise relating to the payments due the investor.

The premise of the task force's discussion in EITF 88-18 is that financing arrangements made as advances for future production should be classified as debt, unless conditions justify otherwise. As illustrated later in this chapter, many conveyed production payments are, indeed, borrowings. However, conveyance of a volume production payment (in which the grantor pledges to deliver certain quantities out of future production, free and clear to the lender) is regarded as a sale of future production; such sales proceeds are classified as Deferred Revenue for successful efforts companies.

Four general types of financing arrangements are discussed in this section:

- Production loans

- Guaranteed recoupable exploration advances

- Conveyed production payments for repayment of loans

- Conveyed production payments payable in product

Production Loans. A basic financing arrangement is the production loan. E&P companies obtain funds from banks or other financing institutions, which are repaid (including interest) out of production proceeds from specified properties. If production proceeds are insufficient to repay the advance, other funds must be used by the operator to repay the lending institution. A production loan transaction has no effect on an E&P company's revenue accounting. Payments made on the loan are treated in the same way as any other debt. The E&P company includes all of the working interest's share of reserves in computing amortization and making disclosures because the lender does not possess a mineral interest.

Guaranteed Recoupable Exploration Advances. Historically, a gas pipeline company that needed gas supplies advanced funds to an operator for exploration or developmental drilling in return for the right to purchase all or part of the gas produced from specific properties. The pipeline bought production from the properties at either: (1) a set price per unit, or (2) the prevailing market price at the time of production. Any advances were offset against the purchase price of the gas. Additionally, repayment could be satisfied from the general assets of the E&P company, as well as from production of other properties specifically pledged, if the advance was not recouped within a specified period.

Given the enormous supplies of gas available today, the type of advance described above is now extremely rare. It is mentioned to illustrate a financing arrangement described in Oi5.134, which stipulates that a recoupable advance is accounted for as a receivable by the advancer of funds and as a payable by the operator:

> Enterprises seeking supplies of oil or gas sometimes make cash advances to operators to finance exploration in return for the right to purchase oil or gas discovered. Funds advanced for exploration that are repayable by offset against purchases of oil or gas discovered, or in cash if insufficient oil or gas is produced by a specified date, shall be accounted for as a receivable by the lender and as a payable by the operator.

As it does for a production loan, the E&P company includes all of the working interest's share of reserves in computing amortization and making reserves disclosures because the lender is not deemed to own a mineral interest. Also, such transaction has no effect on revenue accounting.

Production Payments Conveyed as Security for Repayment of Loans. One variation of the recoupable advances arrangement is treated as a true production payment. The operator carves out an interest in the minerals from one property or more and transfers it to a financing institution as security for a loan. Production payments become the source for repayment of the loan. The amount of production applicable to the production payment is a specified fractional share of proceeds from production from the property until principal and interest have been recovered. Satisfaction of payment is reasonably assured, and a lender bears little risk of nonpayment due to production or price declines.

Several features of such a production payment distinguish it from a traditional production loan. Most importantly, repayment is made from the proceeds of production on the basis of when, if, and as it is produced. This means the arrangement is nonrecourse, and the advance is repaid only from the specified proceeds of production from named properties. Neither other assets nor the general credit of the E&P company provides collateral to the creditor. Clearly, a financing institution lends money under these circumstances only if: (1) the property has a good history of production, (2) the amount of the loan is a small part of the value of estimated total reserves to be produced from the property, and (3) interest rates are favorable. The intention of the E&P company in this transaction is to obtain financing, not to sell future production. As with a traditional production loan, the E&P company (not the lender) retains substantially all risks of ownership of the reserves. Thus, a production payment carved out of a producing property is treated as a receivable by the financing institution and as a payable by the E&P company. Oi5.134(b) contains the following provision:

> Funds advanced to an operator that are repayable in cash out of the proceeds from a specified share of future production of a producing property, until the amount advanced plus interest at a specified or determinable rate is paid in full, shall be accounted for as a borrowing. The advance is a payable for the recipient of the cash and a receivable for the party making the advance. Such transactions . . . are commonly referred to as production payments.

All production proceeds are reported as revenue by the E&P company. This includes the working interest's share of reserves in the required reserves disclosures. Payments of interest and principal are recorded in the same manner as payment of other loans. Obligations are categorized as long- or short-term on the same basis as other debt, although *Accounting Research Bulletin No. 43* suggests only the amount accrued at the balance sheet date should be classified as a current liability. Production payments, by their nature, are generally long-term obligations. Reclassification of a portion of the production payment to current liabilities should coincide with any accrual for production revenues pertaining to satisfaction of the production payment.

Conveyed Production Payments Payable in Product. Customarily, production payments payable in product are created from a proved developed producing property. They take two forms:

- They are payable in set quantities from specified production and are non-recourse.

- They are payable in product, but not limited to specified production. The holder has recourse to receive payment through other means available to the E&P company.

The first form is a VPP described in Oi5.138(a):

> The seller's obligation is not expressed in monetary terms but as an obligation to deliver, free and clear of all expenses associated with operation of the property, a specified quantity of oil or gas to the purchaser out of a specified share of future production. Such a transaction is a sale of a mineral interest for which gain shall not be recognized because the seller has a substantial obligation for future performance. The seller shall account for the funds received as unearned revenue to be recognized as the oil or gas is delivered.[1] The purchaser of such a production payment has acquired an interest in mineral property that shall be recorded at cost and amortized by the unit-of-production method as delivery takes place. The related reserves estimates and production data shall be reported as those of the purchaser of the production payment and not of the seller....

The second type of production payments payable in product is considered a prepaid commodity sale and has been described earlier in this chapter. It is not regarded as a mineral interest sale since the obligation to deliver product is not solely dependent on any specified production or reserves.

Since a VPP obligation is to be satisfied solely from future production, the seller has a substantial obligation for future performance (i.e., to produce the product and pay for related production costs).[2] Thus, no gain is recognized at the time the conveyance contract is entered into. Under successful efforts accounting, the seller is deemed to have received unearned revenue, which is recognized as the oil or gas is delivered. Yet, the oil or gas reserves that give rise to the revenue are to be excluded from the reserves reported by the VPP seller.

The treatment required by the purchaser of a VPP appears inconsistent with that of the VPP seller: the VPP purchaser also reports revenue as the oil and gas is produced. It would seem more logical for the VPP seller to defer a gain, not revenue, since the conveyance is a sale of a mineral interest—the operator no longer owns the reserves that, when produced, generate the revenue. For a production payment from proved property, gain or loss would be based on apportioning property costs between property sold (the production payment) and property retained on the basis of relative fair value consistent with Oi5.138(j). In accordance with Oi5.136, gain would be deferred because the VPP seller is obligated to pay all associated production costs and may be obligated to continue production and pay such costs even when they exceed the operator's net proceeds after the production payment. However, this more logical approach is not allowed due to the specific accounting for a VPP set forth in Oi5.138(a).

Though not delineated in the rules, a second alternative is to record deferred revenue and have the VPP seller (i.e., grantor) deemed the owner of the reserves. In this way, the VPP conveyance would not be regarded as a mineral interest sale, but as the holder's prepayment for purchase of production, similar to a prepaid. Such accounting is appropriate for a true prepaid for which the specified future volume is not tied to specified production.

As an example of the second alternative, assume ABC Oil Company (ABC) receives a $1,000,000 prepaid transaction in the form of a VPP to deliver 166,667 Mcf of gas over the next five years, regardless of its production. In such a prepaid, the buyer assumes the price risks of ownership, but no production risks. ABC must buy gas in the open market to meet the prepaid obligation of delivering gas, if necessary. However, a true VPP is tied to specified production, and the buyer assumes both pricing risks and some production risks. Thus, it is more appropriate to treat the true VPP as the sale of a mineral interest.

The following example illustrates the required treatment under successful efforts accounting for an agreement that commences on January 2, 2006. For $3,000,000, ABC carves out and assigns a production payment of 500,000 Mcf of gas from producing Lease 16018 to Mid-Central Pipeline Company. The obligation will be satisfied by delivery out of the first 80 percent of the working interest's share of production. The total cost of producing Lease 16018 is $7,100,000, which after allocation based on relative fair values would be $1,200,000 for the production payment and $5,900,000 for the remaining unrecovered capitalized costs of the property. During 2006, the working interest's share of production was 450,000 Mcf of gas, of which 360,000 Mcf were delivered to Mid-Central under the production payment agreement.

On December 31, 2006, the working interest's share of proved reserves in the ground was 2,500,000 Mcf, of which 140,000 Mcf belong to the production payment owner. Journal entries to summarize the pertinent facts for both parties follow:

ABC Oil Company

101	Cash		3,000,000	
	430	Deferred Revenues		3,000,000
	To record sale of VPP.			

430	Deferred Revenues		2,160,000	
	602	Gas Revenues		2,160,000
	To record earned revenue applicable to VPP [(360,000 ÷ 500,000) x $3,000,000].			

In its supplemental disclosures as of December 31, 2006, ABC includes 2,360,000 Mcf (2,500,000 - 140,000) of proved reserves and 90,000 Mcf of gas production for Lease 16018. Because the gain associated with the production payment was deferred and capitalized costs of the property have not been impacted, the reserves and production applicable to the production payment and the property are considered in computing depreciation, depletion, and amortization for 2006. Thus, total DD&A recorded on the lease for 2006 is $1,080,735, which considers both the production payment and remaining cost of the lease. Calculations for ABC follow:

Production Payment	**Lease**
$\dfrac{360,000}{140,000 + 360,000}$ x $1,200,000 = $864,000	$\dfrac{90,000}{2,360,000 + 90,000}$ x $5,900,000 = $216,735

Although the cost allocated to the VPP is based on reserve quantities and the allocation of those costs to expense through DDA by the working interest owner is based on the VPP owner's share of production and reserves, in accordance with Oi5.138(a) the reserve amounts of the VPP and the production belonging to the VPP holder are not included in the working interest owner's reserve report and production data, but are included in the VPP owner's reserve reports and production data.

Mid-Central Pipeline Company

225	Proved Production Payments	3,000,000	
	101 Cash		3,000,000
	To record VPP to ABC.		

726	Amortization of Proved Property Acquisition Costs	2,160,000	
	226 Accumulated Amortization of Proved Property Acquisition Costs		2,160,000
	To record amortization of production payment from ABC [(360,000 ÷ 500,000) x $3,000,000]		

In its disclosure of proved reserves on December 31, 2006, Mid-Central Pipeline Company includes 140,000 Mcf of gas remaining to be received under the production payment.

In substance, conveyance of a production payment can be a borrowing, a VPP, or even a prepaid, depending on the terms of the conveyance. Five examples of conveyed production payments follow. The first two illustrate conveyances that would be considered borrowings. The third and fourth are VPPs. The fifth one is a prepaid. In each case, at the time of conveyance, the grantor and holder reasonably expect the production payment to be paid off before the underlying property ceases production.[3]

1. **A borrowing:** For cash received, a production payment is conveyed that entitles its holder to $5,000 per month for four years from revenue proceeds (net of production taxes) of grantor's 20 percent working interest in the ABC lease.

2. **A borrowing:** For cash received, a production payment is conveyed that entitles its holder to the proceeds of 75 percent of oil production attributable to grantor's 20 percent working interest in the MNO lease until the holder receives $100,000 and related interest at 12 percent annually.

3. **A VPP:** For cash received, a production payment is conveyed that entitles its holder to 75 percent of oil production attributable to grantor's 20 percent working interest in the ABC lease until the holder receives 20,000 barrels of oil.

4. **A VPP:** For cash received, a production payment is conveyed that entitles its holder to 75 percent of oil production attributable to grantor's 20 percent working interest in the ABC and XYZ leases for ten years.

5. **A prepaid:** For cash received, a production payment is conveyed that entitles its holder to 300 barrels per month for five years from grantor's 20 percent working interest in the ABC lease. The agreement provides the following: if at any time production is insufficient to provide 300 barrels in any one month, the grantor will make up the difference by delivering other oil of similar grade and quality.

In the first example, the production payment proceeds are fixed in terms of amount and timing: the holder assumes virtually no price or production risks. The conveyance is, in substance, a borrowing. The second example calls for the holder to be repaid $100,000 at 12 percent interest. The holder's price or production risks are similar to those of a bank loan with the property serving as collateral. Examples 3 and 4 fit the VPP requirement of repayment of a specified quantity from specified reserves, and where the holder assumes pricing risk and some production risk. The grantor must record the proceeds as deferred revenue and reduce its reserves by the specified quantity due to the holder.

In the fifth example, the conveyance also calls for a specified quantity from specified reserves, but contains a safety net clause—if production is insufficient, the grantor makes up the difference even if it has to buy oil to deliver to the holder. The holder has no production risk, only price risk, so the conveyance is, in substance, a prepaid. For a prepaid, the grantor still records the initial proceeds as deferred (or unearned) revenue, but it is viewed as continuing to own the underlying reserves.

Three concepts are expressed in Oi5.134 and Oi5.136 that are applicable to the accounting for production payments:

- Some conveyances are, in substance, borrowings repayable in cash or its equivalent and should be accounted for as borrowings.

- If part of an interest is sold and substantial uncertainty exists about recovery of the costs applicable to the retained interest, no gain should be recognized at the time of the conveyance.

- If part of an interest is sold and the seller has a substantial obligation for future performance, no gain should be recognized at the time of conveyance.

Proper accounting for production payments depends on the facts surrounding the contract that created the parties' rights and obligations. Individual circumstances will cause the arrangement to fall under one of the three Oi5 accounting rules.

CONVEYANCES SUBJECT TO RETAINED PRODUCTION PAYMENTS

A retained production payment is created when the owner of a working interest in a mineral property transfers its interest to a purchaser, but retains an oil or gas payment that will be satisfied when, if, and as oil or gas is produced out of the working interest assigned. This type of production payment may be created out of a group of properties rather than from a single property. Also, it is a non-recourse transaction—the holder can look only to production for satisfaction of the obligation. Retained payments can arise when the lessee of a mineral property assigns its working interest to another operator; they may also be created by the original lease contract between the mineral rights owner and lessee.

For example, an E&P company desires to sell a producing property for $1,000,000. Another E&P company is willing to purchase the property for that price, but lacks the needed financing. The first company sells the property to the second company for $1,000,000, with the buyer paying $200,000 in cash and the seller reserving a production payment of $800,000 plus interest, payable out of 90 percent of the working interest's share of revenues that would otherwise go to the buyer.

Accounting for such a conveyance depends in part on whether the underlying property is proved or unproved, and whether the retained production payment is: (1) expressed in monetary terms and reasonably assured, or (2) equivalent to an override.

RETAINED PAYMENTS CARVED FROM PROVED PROPERTIES

Expressed in Monetary Terms. The appropriate accounting treatment for a conveyance transaction that creates a retained production payment expressed in monetary terms depends on whether satisfaction of the payment is reasonably assured. Reasonable assurance of satisfaction from a proved property exists only in those cases where the reserves estimated to be necessary to satisfy the payment are appreciably less than the total working interest share of proved reserves in the particular property.

Oi5 is explicit in describing the accounting rules for retained payments expressed in monetary terms arising from the conveyance of proved properties. Oi5.138(l) specifies the treatment by a successful efforts company of a retained payment where satisfaction is reasonably assured:

The sale of a proved property subject to a retained production payment that is expressed as a fixed sum of money payable only from a specified share of production from that property, with the purchaser of the property obligated to incur the future costs of operating the property, shall be accounted for as follows:

1) *If satisfaction of the retained production payment is reasonably assured.* The seller of the property, who retained the production payment, shall record the transaction as a sale, with recognition of any resulting gain or loss. The retained production payment shall be recorded as a receivable, with interest accounted for in accordance with the provisions of Section 169, "Interest: Imputation of an Interest Cost." The purchaser shall record as the cost of the assets acquired the cash consideration paid plus the present value (determined in accordance with the provisions of Section 169) of the retained production payment, which shall be recorded as a payable. The oil and gas reserve estimates and production data, including those applicable to liquidation of the retained production payment, shall be reported by the purchaser of the property (refer to paragraphs .160 through .167)....

As indicated in the rules, if satisfaction of the payment retained on transfer of a proved property is reasonably assured, the retained production payment is, in substance, a note receivable. It should be measured and recorded using the general rules specified in APB Opinion No. 21. In general, such a receivable is recorded at the discounted present value of the payments to be received. If the contract includes interest at a reasonable rate, the face amount of the payment is its appropriate measure. For example, assume ABC conveys to Red Company the working interest in a producing leasehold where capitalized costs and accumulated amortization are as follows:

	Leaseholds	Intangibles	Tangibles
Cost	$ 60,000	$480,000	$ 90,000
Less accumulated amortization	(20,000)	(160,000)	(30,000)
Net book value	$ 40,000	$320,000	$ 60,000

The consideration for the transfer is $1,000,000 cash and a production payment of $1,600,000 bearing interest at 12 percent (assumed to be a reasonable interest rate), payable out of the first 75 percent of the working interest's share of production. Satisfaction of the production payment is reasonably assured. On ABC's books, the required entry for this transaction is:

101	Cash		1,000,000	
226	Accum. Amortization of Proved Property Acquisition Costs		20,000	
232	Accum. Amortization of Intangible Costs of Wells and Development		160,000	
234	Accum. Amortization of Tangible Costs of Wells and Development		30,000	
271	Notes Receivable—Production Payments		1,600,000	
	221	Proved Property Acquisition Costs		60,000
	231	Intangible Costs of Wells and Development		480,000
	233	Tangible Costs of Wells and Development		90,000
	620	Gains on Property Sales		2,180,000
	To record sale of lease.			

Assuming the agreed-on value of the equipment is $70,000, the purchaser records the transaction in the following way:

233	Tangible Costs of Wells and Development		70,000	
221	Proved Property Acquisition Costs		2,530,000	
	101	Cash		1,000,000
	404	Production Payments Payable as Debt		1,600,000
	To record purchase of lease.			

Conceptually, the purchaser would allocate the basket purchase price among equipment, IDC, and mineral interest accounts on the basis of their relative fair values. However, because of the difficulty in making an allocation between IDC and leasehold, it is customary to apportion the purchase price to equipment first (equal to its fair value), and charge the remaining cost to the mineral interest. This treatment is generally required for federal income tax purposes.

The purchaser of the property subject to the retained production payment records all revenue and expenses applicable to the property. Payments made to the holder of the production payment are allocated first to interest expense in the manner specified in the contract. The balance is treated as a reduction of the principal amount of the payment. Similarly, the holder of the production payment treats the proceeds as interest income first, with any remaining proceeds treated as recovery of principal.

Expressed as a VPP. Oi5.138(l)(2) explains how to handle the sale of a proved property subject to a production payment expressed as a fixed sum of money, but without reasonable assurance of repayment:

> (2) *If satisfaction of the retained production payment is not reasonably assured.* The transaction is in substance a sale with retention of an overriding royalty that shall be accounted for in accordance with paragraph .138(k).

Oi5.138(m) addresses accounting for a retained VPP:

> The sale of a proved property subject to a retained production payment that is expressed as a right to a specified quantity of oil or gas out of a specified share of future production shall be accounted for in accordance with paragraph .138(k).

Transactions of this nature are treated in the same way as sales of operating interests in proved properties with retention of a nonoperating interest, such as the ORRIs discussed in Chapter 21. In essence, the sale of an operating interest in proved property subject to (1) a retained production payment not reasonably assured, (2) a VPP, or (3) a nonoperating interest (such as an ORRI) is accounted for as a sale with a gain or loss recognized. Book value is allocated to the interest sold and interest retained based on relative fair values, which is similar to the accounting for an undivided portion of an operating interest in proved property discussed in Chapter 21.[4]

Paragraph 232 of FAS 19 (from which the SEC drew the rules) elaborates on this situation and clearly states the accounting method to be followed:

> [Paragraphs .138(l) and .138(m)] have been added to clarify that accounting for the sale of a property with retention of a production payment shall be compatible with the accounting for the sale of production payments with retention of the operating interest. A retained production payment expressed in money may sometimes be so large that it is highly improbable that the production payment will be satisfied before the reserves are fully depleted. In those situations, therefore, paragraph [.138(l)] provides that the retained production payment shall be treated as an overriding royalty interest rather than a receivable or payable.

In Chapter 21, it was noted if an operating interest in a proved property is sold with retention of a nonoperating interest (e.g., an overriding royalty), the seller allocates the cost of the proved property to the operating interest sold and the nonoperating interest retained on the basis of the fair values of those interests. To illustrate this accounting treatment for a retained production payment, assume from the preceding example that satisfaction of the production payment of $1,600,000 is not reasonably assured. Based on known reserves, the production schedule, selling prices, costs, and appropriate discount rates, the production payment is estimated to have a fair value of $600,000. Sales proceeds are allocated first to the equipment in an amount equal to its fair value, resulting in a recognized gain of $10,000 ($70,000-$60,000) on the equipment sale. The remaining unrecovered cost of $360,000 (leasehold cost and IDC) is allocated next between the interest sold and that retained on the basis of relative fair values:

Value of interest sold (cash proceeds)	$ 930,000
Value of production payment retained	600,000
Total	**$1,530,000**
Cost allocable to interest sold:	$930,000 x $360,000 = $218,824
	$1,530,000
Cost allocable to production payment retained:	$600,000 x $360,000 = $141,176
	$1,530,000

The gain on the sale of the mineral interest and IDC is $711,176 ($1,000,000 - $70,000 - $218,824). Total gain on the sale is $721,176 ($711,176 on mineral interest and IDC and $10,000 on equipment) as reflected in the following entry:

101	*Cash*	1,000,000	
225	*Proved Production Payments*	141,176	
226	*Accum. Amortization of Proved Property Acquisition Costs*	20,000	
232	*Accum. Amortization of Intangible Costs of Wells and Development*	160,000	
234	*Accum. Amortization of Tangible Costs of Wells and Development*	30,000	
221	*Proved Property Acquisition Costs*		60,000
231	*Intangible Costs of Wells and Development*		480,000
233	*Tangible Costs of Wells and Development*		90,000
620	*Gains on Property Sales*		721,176
	To record sale of property.[5]		

Whether satisfaction of a retained production payment is reasonably assured has a profound impact on the accounting treatment given the transaction, especially if the payment is large when compared to the cash consideration received. Yet, reasonable assurance can be a most subjective measure. If satisfaction is reasonably assured, the payment is, in effect, a monetary asset (or debt); however, if satisfaction is not reasonably assured, the retained production payment is equivalent to an overriding royalty interest.

Retained Payments in Unproved Properties. A production payment retained on the assignment of an unproved property is likely to be expressed in terms of Mcf of gas or barrels of oil, and under Oi5.138(m), it is considered a nonoperating mineral interest. The transaction is treated as a sublease (see the preceding chapter) with cash proceeds from the transaction recorded as a return of book value, or of the property's original cost if group impairment is followed. The carrying value of the production payment is the unrecovered book value (or unrecovered cost). The unproved production payment is, of course, subject to the impairment test.

Under Oi5.138(l), a production payment expressed in a monetary amount is, conceptually, a cash equivalent asset. However, that concept was severely restricted by the conclusion in Oi5.138(l)(2) (and in paragraph 232 of FAS 19) that if satisfaction of a retained payment in a proved property is not reasonably assured, the payment takes on characteristics of a mineral interest rather than a monetary asset. Oi5.138(l) does not specifically discuss payments retained out of unproved properties. But, by their very nature, these payments have no assurance of satisfaction. It is logical to conclude that payments retained out of unproved properties are equivalent to overriding royalties and should be treated as such.

Prepaid Price Swaps. In one variation of the VPP, an oil and gas producer receives an advance from a financial institution in exchange for the revenue relating to a set volume of production for a specific time period. The producer sells its production in the normal course of business at market prices and remits the proceeds to the financial institution. This arrangement differs from a traditional VPP because the producer sells the product first and then delivers the proceeds to its financing company. This variation has been characterized as a prepaid price swap.

As defined in FAS 19 and given that both price and production risks are transferred to the financial institution, the economics of a typical prepaid price swap are the same to the producer as a VPP. Therefore, successful efforts accounting requires proceeds from the advance to be recorded as unearned revenue and amortized relative to periodic sales over the life of the agreement.[6]

NET PROFITS INTEREST

NET PROFITS INTEREST DEFINED

Accounting for the conveyance of net profits interest (NPI), retained NPI, carved-out NPI, and term NPI is addressed in this section.

A net profits interest (or Net Profit Interest) is an interest in production that is created from a property's working interest. Governed by contract, it is measured using a stated percentage of the net profits from the operation.[7] NPI holders are never obligated to pay a share of losses; however, net profits may be considered cumulative and incorporate losses from prior periods.

NPI is similar to an ORRI, but is measured on net profits, not revenue. The holder is not liable for net costs or losses. For example, on January 1, 2006, ABC Company conveys a net profits interest of 20 percent of the net profits from its 50 percent working interest in an ABC field. The conveyance agreement defines net profits as revenue less severance taxes and other direct exploration and development costs and direct operating costs (usually net profits contracts treat outlays for exploration and development as deductible expenses). Amortization, indirect administration costs, interest expense, and income taxes are ignored in computing net profits. Net profits are to be cumulative. If ABC had no revenue or operating expense from the field during January 2006, but had $50,000 in development costs, there were no net profits that month. The NPI holder receives nothing for its interest in the property. However, in February 2006, ABC's share of operations is the following: revenue of $100,000, severance taxes of $10,000, and other direct operating expenses of $30,000. February net profits are calculated at $60,000, while cumulative net profits are $10,000. ABC will pay the NPI holder 20 percent of $10,000.

ACCOUNTING FOR CONVEYANCE OF A NET PROFITS INTEREST

Oi5 conveyance rules are silent on the proper accounting for an NPI conveyance. A net profits interest is classified as a nonoperating interest, and could be compared to the override conveyances discussed in Chapter 21. However, the accounting differs when an NPI is conveyed with retention of a working interest.

Unlike the sale of an ORRI carved from a retained working interest, the accounting required for the sale of an NPI on proved property allows for immediate recognition of any gain under successful efforts accounting. When the NPI share is based on cumulative net profits, the retained working interest holder may have a very limited future obligation to bear a cumulative loss (i.e., a disproportionate share of future development and operating costs). Absent a cumulative loss, the NPI indirectly bears the costs since the costs determine cumulative net profit. The computation of gain itself (reflecting fair value in excess of allocated cost) is indicative that overall fair value exceeds overall book value whereby future cumulative loss to the WI holder is not expected. Under some circumstances, such as an NPI based on periodic, noncumulative net profit, the WI holder may have substantial future obligations that preclude an immediate recognition of gain.

GENERAL ACCOUNTING FOR NET PROFITS INTERESTS

Net profits interests are uncommon, and accounting for them varies as noted in the *2001 PricewaterhouseCoopers Survey of U.S. Petroleum Accounting Practices.* Of 30 survey respondents, only 11 of them addressed net profits interests. The responses are summarized as follows:

	NPI Owned	NPI Obligation
Treatment of Related Revenue and Expenses:		
• Record gross; report both revenues and costs as though a WI	20%	37%
• Record net as though an ORRI	70	36
• Record net as an operating expense	N/A	27
• Other	10	0
	100%	100%
Assignment of Reserves to Interest:		
• Assign gross reserves as though a WI	22%	36%
• Assign net reserves as though an ORRI	56	27
• Do not assign reserves	22	27
• Other	0	10
	100%	100%

An E&P company would be prudent to record net profits received or paid, and assign reserves to such net profits, on a consistent basis.

TERM NET PROFITS INTERESTS

Term NPIs are limited to a specified: (1) time period, (2) net profits amount, or (3) underlying production volume. They are similar to production payments in having a limited economic life. Term NPIs and VPPs are attractive partly because their sales may be treated as borrowings for tax purposes. Sometimes, they are treated for financial reporting purposes as sales, which reduce the full cost pool or give rise to a deferred gain or deferred revenue. The accounting treatment for specific NPIs may differ greatly depending on the characteristics found in the agreement.

For example, if a term NPI: (1) is limited to a stated quantity, (2) is not expected to extend for the full productive life of the underlying producing properties, (3) does not require the operator to deliver products to the term NPI holder, and (4) does not put the NPI holder at risk for cash payments to the operator should the expenses exceed revenues at any time during the life of the agreement, then one could conclude this instrument most closely resembles a VPP. Hence, it could be treated as a sale of mineral interests like a VPP (i.e., unearned deferred revenue is recognized under the successful efforts method).

Alternatively, if a term NPI does not require quantities to be delivered and its conveyance was not, in substance, a borrowing, the conveyance of a term NPI could be considered a sale of a portion of a property, whereby :

- for an unproved property (which would be rare), the proceeds simply reduce associated capitalized costs before any gain is recognized

- for a proved property, gain (or loss) is calculated, and gain must be deferred if the seller has a substantial obligation for future performance

Thus, proper accounting depends on the substance of the transaction.

ACCOUNTING RULES FOR OTHER PROPERTY CONVEYANCES

As pointed out previously, E&P companies and financial markets are interested in oil and gas reserves as a basis for the creation of securities or financial instruments available for purchase by investors. Cash-strapped oil and gas producers may seek ways to increase cash flow for a variety of reasons. Many transactions relate to an immediate inability to sell reserves on the open market at reasonable prices. As a result, an operator's desire to cash in its reserves in unconventional ways leads to unique financing methods and corresponding questions of how to account for them.

Accounting for unusual conveyances and financing methods requires consideration of the mineral conveyance accounting rules found in Oi5.133 through .138, which are substantially discussed in this chapter and Chapter 21. Another source of guidance is EITF 88-18, which is discussed in the production payment section of this chapter.

FULL COST ACCOUNTING

Accounting for production payments under full cost is similar to that for successful efforts with two notable exceptions described in the next section.

CONVEYANCE OF A VPP

Since a VPP conveyance is regarded as a sale of a mineral interest, Reg. S-X Rule 4-10(c)(6)(i) applies whereby "sales of oil and gas properties . . . shall be accounted for as adjustments of capitalized costs." Generally, no gain or loss is recognized "unless such adjustments would significantly alter the relationship between capitalized costs and proved reserves . . . attributable to the cost center." Reg. S-X Rule 4-10(c)(6) requires that (6)(i) supersede the conveyance rules of Oi5.138, including the VPP rules of Oi5.138(a). In situations where a significant alteration occurs, the proceeds from the conveyance of a VPP would be treated as deferred revenue following the guidance discussed above for a successful efforts company.

ACQUISITION OF SHORT-LIFE PROVED PROPERTY SUCH AS A VPP OR TERM NET PROFITS INTEREST

Reg. S-X Rule 4-10(c)(6)(ii) calls for "significant purchases of production payments or properties with lives substantially shorter than the composite productive life of the cost center [to] be accounted for separately." An acquired VPP, a term net profits interest, a term overriding royalty interest, or any working interest in rapidly depleting property may have to be amortized separately from other proved property located in the same country. Acquisition of a VPP does not require the VPP to be amortized separately; instead, the VPP must be significant and have a life substantially shorter than the composite productive life of the cost center.

The terms *significant* and *substantially shorter* are not clearly defined. Separate amortization of a large, short-life property may, or may not, have a significant effect on amortization. To illustrate, consider the following example:

	Old Properties	New VPP	Combined
Amortization base, net	$10,000,000	$4,000,000	$14,000,000
Next year's production (BOE)	1,000,000	1,000,000	2,000,000
Beginning reserves (BOE)	10,000,000	2,000,000	12,000,000
Next year's amortization	$1,000,000	$2,000,000	$2,333,333
Amortization rate	$1.00/bbl	$2.00/bbl	$1.17/bbl

If the cost of the VPP in this example is amortized separately, the total amortization is $3 million, whereas if the old properties and the VPP are combined, amortization totals $2,333,333 for a difference of $666,667. Yet, if the new, short-life VPP's beginning reserves were four million BOE (for an amortization rate of $1.00/bbl), then next year's total amortization would be $2 million (i.e., $1.00/bbl)—whether or not the new property is amortized separately.

TAX ACCOUNTING

GENERAL TAX TREATMENT OF PRODUCTION PAYMENTS

Since 1969, production payments have been typically treated as borrowings or loans for federal income tax purposes. Carved-out production payments have been treated as borrowings by both the operator/grantor and the lender, while retained production payments have been recorded as notes receivable in amounts equal to their fair values by the retainer/assignor and as purchase money mortgage payable by the assignee.

There are two exceptions to this general rule. One of the two exceptions arises when a production payment is retained in the initial lease by the mineral rights owner. In this case, the production payment retained is treated as an economic interest in the property. The transferor/lessor treats income received from the production payment as income subject to deductions for depletion. The lessee records the amounts paid to reduce the principal of the production payment as a capitalized installment bonus. This can result in the capitalized amount of depletable basis increasing during the period of the production payment even though reserves are decreasing. Knowledgeable lessees typically avoid this type of arrangement.

Though infrequent, a second exception arises when a production payment is carved-out and sold with the proceeds pledged for use in exploring or developing the properties from which the payment is carved. In this case, the production payment is considered to be an economic interest held by the lender of the proceeds. The lender treats income received from the production payment as income from its working interest in the well subject to deductions for depletion. The assignor of the production payment does not recognize income from the proceeds received on the assignment, but must reduce deductible exploration and development costs by the amount received.

GENERAL TAX TREATMENT OF NET PROFITS INTERESTS

For federal income tax purposes, an NPI is another form of nonoperating interest and is treated similarly to a royalty interest or an overriding royalty interest. Assume X owns the working interest and Y owns a 20 percent NPI. Total gross revenues to X and Y were $200,000. Net profits were $110,000. Y receives $22,000, which is equivalent to 11 percent of $200,000. Therefore, of 10,000 barrels produced in generating the $200,000, an 11 percent portion, or 1,100 barrels, is attributable to Y's NPI.

• • •

---

1 For full cost, the rule to treat VPP transaction proceeds as unearned revenue is superseded by Reg. S-X Rule 4-10(c)(6)(i) that requires a sale of a mineral interest to be acounted for as an adjustment of capitalized costs, with no gain or loss recognized, unless such adjustment would significantly alter the relationship between capitalized costs and proved reserves of the cost center.

2 This differs from an operator's sale of a working interest wherein the operator has a fiduciary obligation to manage future operations (i.e., to produce, but not an obligation to pay for the new owner's working interest share of production costs).

3 In that sense, the production payment is similar to a limited override that will cease or is expected to cease before the working interest ceases.

4 The sale of an operating interest in unproved property subject to: (1) a retained production payment not reasonably assured, (2) a VPP, or (3) a nonoperating interest such as an ORRI, is accounted for as a sublease of unproved property as discussed in Chapter 21.

5 For full cost accounting, no gain or loss would be recognized unless nonrecognition would significantly change the relationship of net capitalized cost to reserves. See the Full Cost Accounting section near the end of this chapter.

6 See endnote 1 above.

7 The contract should also address the NPI holder's right for accounting and right to audit the accounting as briefly discussed in *COPAS Accounting Guideline No. 13* (AG13).

CHAPTER

23

FARMOUTS, CARRIED INTERESTS, AND UNITIZATIONS

Key Concepts:

- **Definition of the term farmout**

- **Carried interests**

- **Accounting for unitization**

- **Tax accounting for farmouts, carried interests, and unitizations**

The pooling of capital concept has long been a part of accounting theory as well as an essential element in the federal taxation of extractive industries. It is common for an entity to acquire an interest in a mineral property through the contribution of money, property, or services, and assume all or part of the risk and burden of developing and operating it. One party may contribute a leasehold to the venture, another may provide equipment or services, such as drilling, and still another entity may contribute money. Members of the venture agree that they are contributing to a common pool of capital. Thus, each is viewed as making an investment in a venture or adding to the venture's reservoir of capital in return for ownership interest in the venture as a whole.

Many transactions of this type are also considered as exchanges of productive assets in return for similar productive assets, especially if mineral interests, intangible drilling costs, and equipment are viewed as similar. FASB Current Text Oi5.135 states no gain or loss is recognized at the time of conveyance in a pooling of capital or an exchange of similar productive assets.

Commonly encountered applications of these concepts are examined in this chapter. Generally, it is assumed that the successful efforts method is being followed. Although many of the same rules apply, special considerations for full cost companies are examined at the end of this chapter.

FARMOUTS

When the owner of a working interest transfers all or part of the operating rights to another party in exchange for the transferee assuming some portion of the cost of exploring or developing the property, the transaction is referred to as a farmout. One type of farmout is essentially a sublease without cash consideration. The original lessee assigns the working interest, but retains an overriding royalty or a net profits interest in return for the assignee's agreement to perform and pay for specified drilling and development activities.

For example, assume ABC Oil Company (ABC) assigns the working interest in Nellie Bell lease No. 26710 to Big Time Company, subject to a retained overriding royalty of one-eighth of total production from the property. As consideration, Big Time agrees to drill a well to a depth of 5,000 feet or to a specific sand formation, if shallower. Big Time is to complete the well and bear all equipment installation costs. It spends $340,000 for intangible drilling and development costs and $80,000 for lease and well equipment. ABC's original lease cost was $75,000 and it had a fair value of $400,000 at the time of the farmout agreement.

Oi5.138(b), specifies how this transaction should be accounted for by the two parties:

> An assignment of the operating interest in an unproved property with retention of a nonoperating interest in return for drilling, development, and operation by the assignee is a pooling of assets in a joint undertaking for which the assignor shall not recognize gain or loss. The assignor's cost of the original interest shall become the cost of the interest retained. The assignee shall account for all costs incurred as specified by paragraphs .106 through .132 and shall allocate none of those costs to the mineral interest acquired. If oil or gas is discovered, each party shall report its share of reserves and production (refer to paragraphs .160 through .167).

In this instance, both entities have contributed to the pool of capital. Each has benefited, yet no gain or loss is recognized by either party. ABC's leasehold cost of $75,000 becomes its cost for the overriding royalty retained and is recorded as follows:

223	*Proved Royalties and Overriding Royalties*	75,000	
	211 *Unproved Property Acquisition Costs*		75,000
	To record farmout of Nellie Bell lease and retention of one-eighth override.		

The entry assumes that no impairment of this property has been recorded on an individual lease basis. If such an impairment occurs, the net book value of the lease is assigned to the overriding royalty. For example, assume that individual impairment of $30,000 has been recorded on the lease in the preceding example. The entry to record the farmout is:

223	*Proved Royalties and Overriding Royalties*	45,000	
219	*Allowance for Impairment and Amortization of Unproved Properties*	30,000	
	211 *Unproved Property Acquisition Costs*		75,000
	To record farmout of Nellie Bell lease and retention of one-eighth override.		

Big Time classifies its investment in the property based on the type of expenditures made. No part of the costs incurred is allocated to the mineral rights obtained, and no gain or loss is recorded. The entry made by Big Time is summarized as follows:

231	*Intangible Costs of Wells and Development*	340,000	
233	*Tangible Costs of Wells and Development*	80,000	
	301 *Vouchers Payable*		420,000
	To record the costs of drilling and equipping well on Nellie Bell lease under a farmout agreement.		

If the well is dry, the costs incurred (less net salvage) are charged to Unsuccessful Exploratory Wells by Big Time. ABC would have recorded impairment of the overriding royalty.

FREE WELLS

When the owner of a working interest assigns a fractional share of the interest in return for another operator's drilling and equipping one or more wells without cost to the assignor, a free well has resulted. The term free well is used because the assignor retains a portion of the working interest and receives an interest in the well and equipment without bearing any part of the cost. The assignor also shares in the first production from the well.

A free well is considered a sharing arrangement under the pooling of capital concept, and no gain or loss is recognized by either party to the transaction. Oi5.138(c) addresses this issue:

> An assignment of a part of an operating interest in an unproved property in exchange for a "free well" with provision for joint ownership and operation is a pooling of assets in a joint undertaking by the parties. The assignor shall record no cost for the obligatory well; the assignee shall record no cost for the mineral interest acquired. All drilling, development, and operating costs incurred by either party shall be accounted for as provided in paragraphs .106 through .132. If the conveyance agreement requires the assignee to incur geological or geophysical expenditures instead of, or in addition to, a drilling obligation, those costs shall likewise be accounted for by the assignee as provided in paragraphs .106 through .132. If reserves are discovered, each party shall report its share of reserves and production (refer to paragraphs .160 through .167).

To illustrate a free well scenario, assume ABC owns several unproved leases in the Little River area. In January of the current year, it contracts with Freeco to drill and equip a well on the property—at Freeco's cost. In return, ABC assigns an undivided one-half working interest in the Downy lease to Freeco. ABC's original cost of the lease was $24,000. Freeco spends $125,000 on intangibles and $30,000 on equipment for the property, which is considered proved after the well is completed. Each party receives one-half of the production revenues, beginning with the first production, and each bears one-half of operating expenses and further developmental costs.

Since the transaction comes under the pooling of capital concept, the accounting treatment for both parties is essentially the same as accounting for farmouts. Assuming group impairment method is used, the entry required by ABC is:

221	*Proved Property Acquisition Costs*		24,000	
	211	*Unproved Property Acquisition Costs*		24,000
	To transfer cost of Downy lease to proved leaseholds.			

For Freeco, the transaction is expressed in the following summary journal entry:

231	*Intangible Costs of Wells and Development*		125,000	
233	*Tangible Costs of Wells and Development*		30,000	
	101	*Cash*		155,000
	To record costs of a free well drilled for a fractional interest in Downy lease.			

Under this procedure, ABC assigns no cost to IDC or equipment, and Freeco assigns no cost to the mineral interest. Each party reports only its share of production and proved reserves.

Another type of **free well agreement** calls for the lessor to retain all of the working interest and assign the driller a nonoperating interest in the property in return for drilling and equipping the well. Using data from the preceding example, assume ABC retains the entire working interest in a lease and assigns Freeco an overriding royalty of one-fourth of total production from the property in return for Freeco's drilling and equipping the well. This transaction represents a pooling of capital because each party contributes property, money, or services to a joint venture in return for some type of ownership interest. Thus, no gain or loss is recognized by either party.

As the holder of a nonoperating interest, Freeco has no ownership in either the IDC or equipment. It might appear that the entire $155,000 spent by Freeco should be treated as the cost of the overriding royalty. However, since Oi5.138c specifically prohibits classifying a portion of well costs to an earned mineral interest, it is more consistent with Oi5 conveyance rules for Freeco to treat the entire $155,000 as well costs.

CARRIED INTERESTS

For many years, carried interests have been widely used in the oil and gas industry. While various forms exist, all achieve the same economic result. A Manahan contract is a common type of **carried interests arrangement** and is illustrated in the following example.

ABC, the **carried party**, owns the working interest in an unproved lease named A1. It assigns its entire interest to Developco, the **carrying party**. Developco agrees to pay all costs of drilling, equipping, and operating the property until the entire amount is recovered out of working interest revenue. This period is referred to as the time of payout. Developco then reassigns one-half of the working interest to ABC (which has a 50% **reversionary interest**). At that time, ABC and Developco share equally in further revenues and production expenses and any additional expenditures for drilling or development.

ABC's cost of the lease is $20,000. Developco spends $100,000 for IDC and $32,000 for equipment placed on the lease. The well is completed and production begins on November 1, 2006. Working interest revenue is $30,000 per month (for 500 barrels) beginning with the first production and expenses are $8,000 per month. On December 31, 2006, proved reserves attributable to the working interest are 390,000 barrels. Based on these facts, Developco has $22,000 per month of net revenue ($30,000 revenue less $8,000 expenses) to apply toward recoupment of drilling and development costs. At the end of 2006, Developco has received $44,000 (two months at $22,000) and is entitled to recover an additional $88,000 ($132,000 - $44,000) out of revenue before ABC begins to share in production.

The accounting treatment specified by Oi5.138(d) for carried interests is summarized as follows:

1. No gain or loss is recognized by either party at the time of conveyance.

2. The expenditures or contributions of each party are accounted for in a proper manner by the party making the expenditure or contribution.

3. All revenue and cash expenses belong or apply to the carrying party until payout; except for the entry to transfer the property's cost to Proved Properties, no entries are necessary by the carried party until that time.

Since neither party records gain or loss on the conveyance transaction, ABC transfers the leasehold cost of $20,000 (or net book value, if impairment has been recorded on an individual lease basis) to Proved Leaseholds when the property becomes proved.

221	Proved Property Acquisition Costs	20,000	
	211 Unproved Property Acquisition Costs		20,000
	To record proving of the A1 lease carried by Developco.		

Since Developco is considered to own the full working interest until payout, its costs of drilling and equipping the well are recorded in the following journal entry:

231	Intangible Costs of Wells and Development	100,000	
233	Tangible Costs of Wells and Development	32,000	
	101 Cash		132,000
	To record drilling and equipment costs on the A1 lease.		

As mentioned, Developco is entitled to recover its expenses related to the property until it receives the entire amount due. If cash proceeds from the property are inadequate, ABC has no liability for unrecovered amounts. Developco has $22,000 per month of net revenue ($30,000 revenue less $8,000 expenses), which is $44 for each working interest barrel ($22,000/500 barrels) to apply toward recoupment of drilling and equipment costs. Thus, in November and December of 2006, Developco includes all the revenue and expenses in its income statement as summarized (for the two months) in general journal form:

101	Cash	60,000	
	601 Crude Oil Revenues		60,000
	To record production revenues from the A1 lease.		

701	Lease Operating Expenses	16,000	
	101 Cash		16,000
	To record production expenses on the A1 lease.		

Since all working interest production during payout belongs to the carrying party, its reserves disclosures should include all working interest production expected until payout, plus the carrying party's share of reserves at payout. The reserves quantity to be reported by the carried party prior to payout (and used in computing DD&A after payout) is the carried party's share of reserves at payout.

On December 31, 2006, the proved reserves attributed to each are computed as follows:

	Barrels
December 31, 2006, total working interest share of proved reserves	390,000
Less barrels expected to be produced from December 31 to date of payout attributed to the carrying party ($88,000 divided by $44 per barrel)	(2,000)
Expected reserves at date of payout	388,000
Reserves attributable to carrying party (Developco):	
Barrels to be produced until payout	2,000
One-half of reserves at payout	194,000
Total to carrying party	196,000
Reserves attributable to carried party (ABC):	
One-half of reserves at payout	194,000

ABC has no revenue from production during 2006 and records no DD&A for the year. Developco does not record leasehold costs. However, IDC and equipment amortization are recorded by Developco in 2006 and computed assuming net DR&A costs are zero:

		IDC	Equipment
$1,000/(1,000 + 196,000) \times \$100,000$	=	$508	
$1,000/(1,000 + 196,000) \times \$32,000$	=		$162

Once payout has been reached, each party reports its share of revenue, lifting costs, and additional drilling and development costs in the usual way. Continuing the preceding illustration, assume the following data in 2007 for the A1 lease:

- Production and sales (working interest share):

January through November 2007	**500 bbls per month**
December 2007	**750 bbls**

- Sales price per barrel for 2007   **$60 per bbl**

- Lifting costs:

January through November 2007	**$ 8,000 per month**
December 2007	**$12,000**

- Additional costs on well completed in November 2007:

IDC	**$120,000**
Tangible Equipment	**30,000**

- Proved developed reserves of 562,500 bbls for 100 percent working interest as of December 31, 2007

- No proved undeveloped reserves

Computations of revenue and expense items to be reported by each party in accordance with Oi5 conveyance rules are:

Revenues:

	Barrels	Price	Revenue
Developco:			
Jan 1 through payout on Apr 30	2,000	$60	$120,000
May 1 through Nov 30	1,750	60	105,000
December	375	60	22,500
Total	4,125		$247,500
ABC:			
Jan 1 through Apr 30	0	$ 0	$ 0
May 1 through Nov 30	1,750	60	105,000
December	375	60	22,500
Total	2,125		$127,500

Production Expenses:

Developco:			
Jan 1 through Apr 30	$8,000/mo x 4 mos	=	$32,000
May 1 through Nov 30	0.50 x $8,000/mo x 7 mos	=	28,000
December	0.50 x $12,000	=	6,000
Total			$66,000
ABC:			
Jan 1 through Apr 30			$ 0
May 1 through Nov 30	0.50 x $8,000/mo x 7 mos	=	28,000
December	0.50 x $12,000	=	6,000
Total			$34,000

Amortization of mineral interest cost:

Developco:			$0
ABC:	$\dfrac{2{,}125 \text{ bbls}}{2{,}125 \text{ bbls} + .50(562{,}500 \text{ bbls})}$	x $20,000 =	$150

IDC and equipment amortization (assuming net DR&A costs are zero):

Developco (assuming an annual computation):	IDC	Equipment
4,125/[4,125 + (.50 x 562,500)] x [$100,000 + (.50 x $120,000) - $508] =	$2,305	
4,125/[4,125 + (.50 x 562,500)] x [$32,000 + (.50 x $30,000) - $162] =		$ 677
ABC:	**IDC**	**Equipment**
2,125/[2,125 + (.50 x 562,500)] x (.50 x $120,000) =	$ 450	
2,125/[2,125 + (.50 x 562,500)] x (.50 x $30,000) =		$ 112

The information ultimately reflected in the accounts of the two companies for 2007 is shown in the following summary journal entries:

		Developco		ABC	
231	Intangible Costs of Wells and Development	60,000		60,000	
233	Tangible Costs of Wells and Development	15,000		15,000	
	101 Cash		75,000		75,000
	To record additional development costs on the A1 lease.				
101	Cash	247,500		127,500	
	601 Crude Oil Revenues		247,500		127,500
	To summarize 2007 production revenues from the A1 lease.				
710	Lease Operating Expenses	66,000		34,000	
	101 Cash		66,000		34,000
	To record 2007 production expenses on the A1 lease.				
732	Amortization of Intangible Costs of Wells	2,305		450	
	232 Accum. Amortization of Intangible Costs of Wells and Development		2,305		450
734	Amortization of Tangible Costs of Wells	677		112	
	234 Accum. Amortization of Tangible Costs of Wells and Development		677		112
	To record 2007 amortization on wells and facilities on the A1 lease.				
726	Amortization of Proved Property Acquisition Costs			150	
	226 Accumulated Amortization of Proved Property Acquisition Costs				150
	To record 2007 depletion on the A1 lease.				

As previously noted, contract terms that create carried interests can vary. For example, a nonconsent clause in a joint venture operating agreement may give rise to a carried working interest. ABC might propose that an additional well be drilled to fully exploit a reservoir. If Developco elects to not participate, it has gone nonconsent on the well. The operating agreement typically entitles ABC to drill and produce the well, receive all working interest revenues, and pay all operating costs until it recovers a specified multiple (e.g., 300 percent) of all costs of drilling and equipping the well. When the multiple is achieved, payout occurs. From this point forward, Developco participates in the well's revenues and costs based on its working interest—as though the nonconsent had not happened. See a nonconsent provision in CD Reference Exhibit E, Article VI, (B).

For additional guidance, refer to COPAS Accounting Guideline No. 13 (AG 13), *Accounting for Farmouts/Farmins, Net Profits, Carried Interests*.

PROMOTED VS. PROMOTING

In most joint ventures, the venturers share both costs and revenue in proportion to their ownership interests in the properties. For example, assume joint venture partners A and B each have a 50 percent working interest and a 45 percent net revenue interest in a venture (the lessor has a 10 percent net revenue interest in the form of a royalty interest). Since the parties share costs and revenues in the same proportions, this type of joint venture is sometimes referred to as a straight-up arrangement.

In some cases, costs and net revenue are not shared in the same ratios. A joint venture agreement may call for joint venturers X and Y to each receive 45 percent of the net revenue (the other 10 percent going to the royalty holder), but X bears 40 percent of costs and Y bears 60 percent of costs. In this situation, X is said to be the promoter or promoting party and Y the promoted party. Such an arrangement might occur if X originally owned 100 percent of the working interest in an attractive property and agreed to let Y have half of the working interest's 90 percent share of revenues in return for Y paying 60 percent of costs.

UNITIZATIONS

An important type of sharing arrangement is known as a unitization. In this case, all owners of operating and nonoperating interests pool their property interests in a producing area (normally a field) to form a single operating unit. In return, they receive **participation factors**, which are undivided interests in the total unit (and are either operating or non-operating based on the properties contributed).

Unitizations are designed to achieve the most efficient and economical exploitation of reserves in an area. The arrangement can be voluntary or it may be required by federal or state regulatory bodies. Unitizations are common in fields with primary production and are even more widely utilized for reservoir-wide enhanced recovery operations (explained in Chapter 32).

Unitizations are also popular on offshore properties where costs are high and reserves may be justified on an individual basis. Joint development of an area can make a unit more economically feasible. Units involve more than one lease and have diverse ownerships of various mineral interests and reservoirs that cross lease boundaries.

Shares in the unit that participating owners receive—participation factors—are based on acreage, reserves, or other criteria with respect to each lease to be placed in the unit.[1] Participation factors do not usually give weight to the stage of development of properties. Leases are often in different phases of development with some leases being fully drilled and equipped, others being partially developed, and some completely undeveloped.

Percentages are subject to revision within a specified subsequent period as additional information about the reserves becomes available. Accounting challenges resulting from subsequent adjustments are discussed later in this chapter.

EQUALIZATIONS

Unit participants with undeveloped leases in the unit are normally required to pay cash to participants with fully or partially developed leases in order to equalize the capital contributions of wells and equipment.

For example, assume the 600 acre Ajax lease is 100 percent owned by Company A. It will be unitized with an adjoining 400 acre tract known as the Brown lease, which is owned 100 percent by Company B. Unit participation factors are based on acreage. Thus, Company A receives a 60 percent participation factor, and Company B is allotted a 40 percent participation factor for both unit costs and unit revenue. Company A pays the Ajax lease royalty based on A's share of revenues. Company B pays the Brown lease royalty based on B's share of revenues. Prior to unitization, Company A spent $700,000 on two wells, and Company B spent $300,000 on one well. Terms of the unitization agreement require that $1,000,000 of prior well costs be reallocated so the sharing of prior well costs equals the sharing of post-unitization costs and revenue. As a result, Company B pays $100,000 to Company A at the time of unitization so that A's adjusted well cost is $600,000, or 60 percent of total well costs, and B's adjusted well cost is $400,000. Such adjustments are called **equalizations**.

Equalizing Pre-Unitization Costs. In new fields where development is not completed, it is common for an equalization agreement to be based on expenditures for exploration and drilling that occurred prior to the date of unitization. Four steps are involved in the unitization process:

1. Identifying pre-unit contributions to be allowed in computing equalization

2. Accumulating or collecting contributions from each pre-unit working interest owner

3. Calculating the obligation of each working interest owner for pre-unit costs

4. Determining settlement for underspent and overspent amounts

Generally, expenditures made for wells and facilities that directly benefit the unit are accepted for equalization; costs that relate to other wells and facilities that do not benefit the unit are not equalized. Costs to be equalized almost always include direct costs such as labor, employee benefits, taxes, construction charges, costs of special studies, and other expenditures that can be specifically identified with individual wells and equipment. In addition, geological and geophysical costs, permits, and environmental study costs may be considered direct charges.

Overhead not directly related to individual wells and facilities may be equalized. These costs include such items as offsite labor, administrative charges, and the cost of operating district or regional offices. Parties frequently limit overhead to a percentage of direct costs or a specified fixed annual fee. Actual time worked by personnel on the properties may also be equalized.

In addition to direct costs and overhead, unitization agreements may permit an equalization of risk charges or imputed risk charges. For example, insurance costs incurred in transporting equipment and facilities or the imputed costs of insurance to cover facilities prior to unitization may be considered. Finally, equalization agreements may provide for an inflation factor to reimburse parties for changes in purchasing power between the time of the original investment and ultimate recovery from other owners.

Cash Equalization. The unitization process is a pooling of capital to achieve a common benefit for all parties. Normally, no gain or loss is recognized by any party to the unitization.

A party making a cash equalization payment increases its recorded investment in wells and related equipment and facilities. On the other hand, a participant who receives a cash equalization payment reduces the recorded investment in the wells and related equipment. Oi5.138(f) contains the following accounting guidelines for unitizations:

> Because the properties may be in different stages of development at the time of unitization, some participants may pay cash and others may receive cash to equalize contributions of wells and related equipment and facilities with the ownership interests in reserves. In those circumstances, cash paid by a participant shall be recorded as an additional investment in wells and related equipment and facilities, and cash received by a participant shall be recorded as a recovery of costs. The cost of the assets contributed plus or minus cash paid or received is the cost of the participant's undivided interest in the assets of the unit. Each participant shall include its interest in reporting reserve estimates and production data.

The simplified example that follows demonstrates the financial accounting treatment required by Oi5.138(f) at the time of unit formation. Assume three E&P companies are involved in a unitization of their respective properties, all of which have been developed. Based on several factors, such as acre-feet of sand contributed, each party is allocated a one-third interest in the unit. The unitization agreement provides specifically:

> Inasmuch as the values of wells drilled and of wells and other operating equipment on the separately owned tracts is not in proportion to the participating interest of the owners of such tracts, and such values have not entered into the determination of the participation percentages, a separate exchange of interest in wells and well equipment, lease equipment, and other operating equipment will be made between the parties hereto.

In order to give each party credit for IDC and equipment, cash equalization calculations are made. In the following table, the undepreciated balance of well costs on each party's books is shown in Column (2). Column (3) represents the agreed-on value of the well costs contributed by each party based on current costs to drill the usable wells contributed by each party, and Column (4) reflects the share of the agreed-on value of well costs belonging to each party after the unitization. Cash is contributed or received by each party to equalize the value of well costs received and contributed as shown in Column (5). (In newly developed fields the agreed-on value is usually considered equal to allowable costs incurred by each party for exploration and development prior to the unitization.)

Equalization for IDC:

(1) Party	(2) Unamortized Balance	(3) Value Contributed	(4) Value Received	(5) Cash Equalization
A	$300,000	$ 550,000	$ 400,000	$ 150,000
B	260,000	375,000	400,000	(25,000)
C	320,000	275,000	400,000	(125,000)
Total		$1,200,000	$1,200,000	$ 0

Equalization for equipment:

(1) Party	(2) Unamortized Balance	(3) Value Contributed	(4) Value Received	(5) Cash Equalization
A	$20,000	$ 50,000	$ 60,000	$(10,000)
B	70,000	65,000	60,000	5,000
C	65,000	65,000	60,000	5,000
Total		$180,000	$180,000	$ 0

Mineral Rights Equalization. Monetary entries are not necessary to record the exchanges of mineral rights in property transferred to the unit for a share of minerals in return. Parties treat the book value of their contributed property as their investment in the mineral interest in the unit. Most unitization agreements, especially when some of the properties have not been fully developed, call for one or more subsequent evaluations and readjustment of participation factors. This topic is discussed later in the chapter.

IDC Equalization. Party A receives $150,000 cash as equalization for IDC. In accordance with Oi5.138(f), the cash received is treated as a reduction of investment:

101	Cash	150,000	
	231 Intangible Costs of Wells and Development		150,000
	To record receipt of cash on IDC equalization.		

Since the unamortized balance of A's IDC contribution is greater than the amount of cash received, the equalization payment merely reduces the investment.

Both B and C must make cash payments to equalize IDC. Under Oi5.138(f), payments are capitalized as additional investment in IDC.

Equipment Equalization. Both B and C receive cash in equalization of equipment contributions. In each case, the amount of cash received is less than the book value of equipment contributed; therefore, the full amount received is credited to Account 233, Tangible Costs of Wells and Development.

Equalization in Excess of Cost. Due to the valuation process, in which valuations are made and current pricing is taken into account, it may be possible to receive equalization credit in excess of cost. After equalization, the carrying value of a well may be negative for book purposes, but individual asset-carrying values within a proven property asset pool are generally not important under either successful efforts or full cost accounting methods.

Disproportionate Spending Equalization. Certain parties may strive to avoid cash equalization. In this case, equalization occurs by adjusting the amount of future expenditures to be paid by each party to compensate for disproportionate contributions. This technique is especially common in new fields where there has been little drilling activity up to the time of unitization.

To illustrate a cost-equalization program involving disproportionate spending, the following schedule shows the working interest ownership of each party, pre-unit costs, costs to be borne by each party, and over/underspent positions of each:

Table 1

Company	Working Interest Ownership	Pre-unitization Costs Incurred	Proportionate Share	Over (Under) Spent
Acorn	50%	$1,000,000	$ 750,000	$250,000
Barn	35	300,000	525,000	(225,000)
Check	15	200,000	225,000	(25,000)
		$1,500,000	$1,500,000	$ 0

Since actual expenditures incurred by Acorn Company prior to unitization exceed its proportionate share of total costs of $1,500,000, Acorn pays no part of costs after unitization until the other companies have overspent their shares by the same amount. The subsequent overspending by the two parties that were underspent is shared in the ratio of the proportionate interest of the shortfall. Thus, in the example above, Barn Company will absorb 90 percent (225/250), and Check Company will absorb 10 percent (25/250) of the first $250,000 of future expenditures to bring the parties back in balance to their proportionate working interests.

A reasonable interpretation of the provisions of Oi5.138(f) relating to sharing arrangements suggests that each party should account for actual expenditures in the regular manner.

Equalization Resulting from Redetermination of Interests. As pointed out previously, unitization agreements often contain provisions requiring the ownership to be redetermined and adjusted at dates subsequent to the date of unitization. These adjustments are based on changes in estimates of recoverable reserves that result from improved technical knowledge of the reservoir as the field is developed and oil and gas are produced. Between the dates of the unitization and subsequent readjustment, production revenues as well as operating expenses and development costs are allocated on the basis of the percentages of ownership interest in effect.

When a redetermination is made, it may be retroactively applied to the date the unit was formed. In other cases, the effective date occurs later such as when a discovery changes the size and extent of the proved portion(s) of reserves. As a result, an equalization computation is made at the date of redetermination to equalize production proceeds and costs incurred during the period. It is customary for equalization of production revenue to be handled through undertakes and overtakes of subsequent production, rather than through cash settlements. Equalization of post-unitization costs incurred is handled through disproportionate spending equalization as previously described.

For example, assume a unitization agreement becomes effective January 1, 2004, at which time equalization for prior expenditures is made through a cash settlement. The initial agreed-upon ownerships are 30 percent to Company X, 50 percent to Company Y, and 20 percent to Company Z. The agreement calls for a redetermination of ownership interests on January 1, 2007, based on revised estimates of oil and gas reserves contributed to the unit by the parties. During the three-year period prior to redetermination, production totaled 10 million barrels at an average price of $60 per barrel. Development expenditures of $30 million for drilling costs and $10 million for equipment and facilities were incurred. Operating expenses were $10 million. All revenue and costs were shared in the original agreed-upon ratio of 30 percent, 50 percent, and 20 percent.

On January 1, 2007, a redetermination is made and working interests are readjusted as follows: X receives 27 percent; Y receives 55 percent; and Z receives 18 percent.

Equalization for the over/undertake of production prior to the redetermination is accomplished by offsetting over/undertakes of production over the two-year period following redetermination. Equalization of over-expenditures and under-expenditures for development costs and operating expenses is accomplished through an adjustment of costs incurred after the redetermination of interests.

Thus, during each month of the two-year period following redetermination, Company Y receives 20,833 barrels in excess of its normal share of production, and shares of Company X and Company Z are reduced by 12,500 barrels and 8,333 barrels per month, respectively, in order to correct the misallocation of prior production.

Table 2
(in barrels)

Company	Initial Allocation of Production	Redetermined Allocation of Production	Over (Under) Produced	Monthly Equalization Over 24 Months
X	3,000,000	2,700,000	300,000	(12,500)
Y	5,000,000	5,500,000	(500,000)	20,833
Z	2,000,000	1,800,000	200,000	(8,333)

Assuming that production in the first month following redetermination is 300,000 barrels, it would be allocated as follows:

Table 3

Company	Percent of Working Interest	Normal Allocation of Production (bbls)	Equalization Adjustment (bbls)	Total Share of Production (bbls)
X	27	81,000	(12,500)	68,500
Y	55	165,000	20,833	185,833
Z	18	54,000	(8,333)	45,667
Total	100	300,000	0	300,000

The tables indicate equalization of production quantities, but not revenues. To equalize revenues, the actual monthly price of oil (or gas) after the redetermination is compared to the average price received prior to redetermination, which was $60 per barrel. Any variance in price is considered in the equalization redetermination. This calculation can be done monthly, but due to timing and information flow, the adjustment would normally be in arrears.

Table 4

Company	Monthly Equalization (bbl)	Pre-equalization Price	January 2007 Price	January Revenue Equalization
X	(12,500)	$60/bbl	$65/bbl	$62,500
Y	20,833	60/bbl	65/bbl	(104,165)
Z	(8,333)	60/bbl	65/bbl	41,665

Company X gave up 12,500 barrels in January worth $65 per barrel to compensate for taking 12,500 barrels in prior months at $60 per barrel, so the revenue equalization gives Company X $62,500 for the $5/bbl differential.

Equalization of development costs and operating expenses are accomplished through disproportionate spending equalization in the manner illustrated previously.

Under the general rules established for poolings of capital in Oi5.135 and Oi5.138, no accounting entries are necessary at the time of post-unitization redetermination of interests. It is appropriate for each owner to report revenues actually received, reflecting any increase or decrease due to an adjustment, and for each party to account in the usual way for all costs incurred. Reserve disclosures reflect readjusted amounts, and future depreciation, depletion, and amortization calculations are based on the revised estimates.

UNITIZATION ON FEDERAL LANDS

Unitizations on federal land have unusual features that complicate accounting for them. Federal unitization is a two-step process. First, lessees of federal mineral rights in a large prospective area of perhaps several thousand acres (the unit area) sign an exploratory unit agreement and a unit operating agreement to "adequately and timely explore and develop the committed leases within the unit area without regard to the interior boundaries of the leases."[2] Second, as proved areas within the unit become known, leaseholders within the areas (called a participating area or PA) are required to form a joint venture to develop and operate the participating area and share in costs and revenues. A PA expands as new wells extend the proved area, or it may contract as dry holes and uneconomic wells are drilled and define the productive area. Two or more PAs may combine into one large PA as new wells demonstrate the continuity of the underlying reservoir. A large unit area may have more than one PA when the unit area is ultimately developed.

Often, a PA interest is determined by relative acreage of the lease areas within the PA. A company's 100 percent working interest in a 320-acre lease with one well may become a 50 percent working interest in a two-well or three-well 640-acre PA. As the PA expands to 3,200 acres and 15 wells, the company's PA interest may fall to 10 percent. In this case, the company pays 10 percent of all 15 wells' costs and receives 10 percent of the PA revenues after royalties, assuming uniform royalty rates. Any PA formation, expansion, or contraction is approved by the U.S. Department of the Interior and is generally effective with (and retroactive to) the completion date of the well that justified the PA change. Hence, a company's working interest in a PA will vary as the PA expands or contracts. Accounting for a PA interest is complex and subject to retroactive adjustment.

A company can elect to go nonconsent and not participate in future wells within the PA or the unit, subject to a nonconsent penalty.[3] However, accounting for nonconsent interests is difficult and has been the subject of litigation due to internally inconsistent language in at least three versions of a standard unit operating agreement form used from 1954 through the early 1990s. Further discussion of this issue is beyond the scope of this book, but it is indicative of the complexity of accounting for PA interests.

Prudhoe Bay Example of Redetermination and Participating Areas. An example of post-unitization redetermination is described in the excerpt following from the forepart of the 1999 Form 10-K of BP Prudhoe Bay Royalty Trust. The trust has a net profits interest akin to a 16.4246 percent ORRI (royalty interest) in British Petroleum's first 90,000 barrels per day of production from the Prudhoe Bay Unit.[4]

THE PRUDHOE BAY UNIT

GENERAL

The Prudhoe Bay field (the Field) is located on the North Slope of Alaska, 250 miles north of the Arctic Circle and 650 miles north of Anchorage. The Field extends approximately 12 miles by 27 miles and contains nearly 150,000 productive acres. The Field, which was discovered in 1968 by BP [the Company] and others, has been in production since 1977. The Field is the largest producing oil field in North America. As of December 31, 1998, approximately 9.7 billion STB (Stock Tank Barrels[5]) of oil and condensate had been produced from the Field. Field development is well advanced with approximately $17.5 billion gross capital spent and a total of about 1,885 wells drilled. Other large fields located in the same area include the Kuparuk, Endicott, and Lisburne fields. Production from those fields is not included in the Royalty Interest.

Since several oil companies hold acreage within the Field, the Prudhoe Bay Unit was established to optimize Field development. The Prudhoe Bay Unit Operating Agreement specifies the allocation of production and costs to Prudhoe Bay Unit owners. The Company and a subsidiary of the Atlantic Richfield Company (ARCO) are the two Field operators. Other Field owners include affiliates of Exxon Corporation (Exxon), Mobil Corporation (Mobil), Phillips Petroleum Company (Phillips) and Chevron Corporation (Chevron).

PRUDHOE BAY UNIT OPERATION AND OWNERSHIP

...The Prudhoe Bay Unit Operating Agreement specifies the allocation of production and costs to the working interest owners. The Prudhoe Bay Unit Operating Agreement also defines operator responsibilities and voting requirements and is unusual in its establishment of separate participating areas for the gas cap and oil rim....

The ownership of the Prudhoe Bay Unit by participating area as of December 31, 1998, is summarized in the following table:

	Oil Rim	Gas Cap
BP	51.22%[a]	13.85%
Arco	21.87	42.56
Exxon	21.87	42.56
Mobil/Phillips/Chevron (MPC)	4.44	1.03
Others	0.60	0.00
Total	100.00%	100.00%

[a] The Trust's share in oil production is computed based on BP's ownership interest of 50.68% as of February 28, 1989.

CREATION OF JOINT VENTURES

Prior chapters have noted that E&P joint ventures are common in the U.S. Chapter 10 addresses joint venture operations, billing for joint venture costs, and day-to-day accounting for joint interests. Oi5.138(e) describes joint ventures and indicates how the formation of a joint venture is to be accounted for:

> A part of an operating interest owned may be exchanged for part of an operating interest owned by another party. The purpose of such an arrangement, commonly called a joint venture in the oil and gas industry, often is to avoid duplication of facilities, diversify risks, and achieve operating efficiencies. No gain or loss shall be recognized by either party at the time of transaction. In some joint ventures, which may or may not involve an exchange of interests, the parties may share different elements of costs in different proportions. In such an arrangement, a party may acquire an interest in a property or in wells and related equipment that is disproportionate to the share of costs borne by it. As in the case of a carried interest or a free well, each party shall account for its own cost under the provisions of this section. No gain shall be recognized for the acquisition of an interest in joint assets, the cost of which may have been paid in whole or in part by another party.

Two major points from Oi5.138(e) are illustrated in the following example. Assume two operators own contiguous unproved properties. For the sake of efficiency, they form a joint venture with ABC Company owning a two-thirds interest and South Company owning one-third. They cross-assign interests: ABC assigns to South Company a one-third undivided interest in a property (which had a book value of $120,000 and was being impaired individually), and South Company assigns a two-thirds interest in each of three leases (which had a cost of $260,000 and are part of a group subject to a group impairment test). Neither party recognizes a gain or loss on the exchange. ABC removes one-third of the cost of the lease in which it gives up an interest and one-third of the allowance for impairment of the lease. The net book value ($40,000) of the one-third interest is assigned to the two-thirds interest in the three leases acquired from South Company. A $40,000 allocation is made to individual leases (in which interests were acquired) based on relative market values of the interests. Similar entries are recorded by South Company.

The second point involves disproportionate sharing arrangements. In a different scenario, ABC, a successful efforts company, owns a lease which cost $30,000 and on which no impairment has been recorded. It retains one-fourth of the working interest and assigns three equal interests of one-third of three-fourths of the working interest to other parties, which will bear the entire cost of drilling the first well. If the first well is to be completed, all parties, including ABC, are to pay for a proportionate share of completing the well. This type of arrangement is a "third for a quarter" deal that was common years ago when oil prices escalated rapidly. The drilling cost on this well amounts to $600,000, which is paid in equal shares by the other three parties.

ABC retains $30,000 as its leasehold cost. ABC has no intangible cost and records its share of equipment costs when the costs are incurred. Each assignee accounts for the $200,000 contributed to the venture as IDC, and each properly accounts for its cost of equipment subsequently acquired. The assignees do not treat any part of their contributions as leasehold cost.

FULL COST ACCOUNTING

Reg. S-X Rule 4-10(c)(6) stipulates that, in general, the conveyance rules found in Oi5.133 apply not only to successful efforts companies, but also to companies using full cost.

However, Reg. S-X Rule 4-10(c)(6)(iii) adds that under the full cost method, no income is recognized from the sales of unproved properties or participation in various forms of drilling arrangements involving oil and gas producing activities, except to the extent of amounts that are identifiable with the transaction. Problems relating to the formation and operations of partnerships are discussed in Chapter 24.

TAX ACCOUNTING

Tax accounting for farmouts, carried interests, and unitizations can depend on individual circumstances and agreement terms. Certain accounting issues are unsettled due to conflicting court decisions.

For carrying arrangements, carrying parties typically pay 100 percent of IDC and equipment; however, a portion of these costs may be capitalized as depletable leasehold investment. If carrying parties own 100 percent of the working interest until payout, then they deduct (in the manner they would normally deduct their noncarried costs) 100 percent of the well costs as IDC and equipment depreciation. Upon payout, any undepreciated equipment costs are reclassified as depletable leasehold costs. Under other conditions (whereby the carrying parties are not entitled to 100 percent recoupment of the well costs), some or all of the carried costs are capitalized as depletable leasehold costs.

IRC Sec. 614(b)(3) provides that the taxpayer's properties in a compulsory unitization are treated as one property upon unitization. This rule applies to certain voluntary unitizations as well. Generally, a unitization is viewed as an exchange of the taxpayer's old properties for a new property. The transaction can give rise to taxable gain to the extent of cash received to adjust participants' share of unit costs. It may also give rise to an exchange of depreciable equipment costs for depletable leasehold costs—by delaying or eliminating deduction of such costs.

Joint ventures are not generally taxed as corporations, nor are they treated as partnerships. The joint venture owner's net share of joint venture revenue and expenses determines the owner's taxable income. To avoid corporate status, oil and gas joint venture agreements typically provide that each joint venture owner has an option to take its oil and gas in-kind. This option may never be exercised, but it has been viewed as sufficient to eliminate the joint profit objective regarded in tax rules as inherent to a corporation.

A joint venture can avoid being treated as a partnership by making an election in its first year (i.e., it elects out of Subchapter K). The election may be evidenced by a specific provision in the joint venture agreement. Opting out of partnership status has various advantages such as avoidance of: (1) filing partnership tax returns, (2) maintaining certain partnership accounting records, and (3) electing to deduct IDC as incurred.

● ● ●

---

1 A participant's fractional interest (or participation factor) may be based on any number of reasonable factors— acreage, estimated reservoir thickness under a given acreage, estimated reserves under a given acreage, number of producing wells on the acreage, and even prior production history for the acreage.

2 See the Unitization section of the U.S. Department of the Interior Bureau of Land Management's Handbook for a discussion of this topic.

3 The concept of nonconsent and nonconsent penalty is addressed briefly in Chapter 10.

4 The trust share in revenue is reduced for certain chargeable costs of several dollars per barrel.

5 Stock Tank Barrel refers to a marketable barrel of crude oil at 60° F and at an atmospheric pressure where: (1) solution gas has bubbled out of the crude oil, or (2) solution gas and water have been removed from the produced crude oil.

CHAPTER

24

ACCOUNTING FOR PARTNERSHIP INTERESTS

Glossary Terms

general partnership
limited partnership
managing partner

Key Concepts:

- **Accounting for general partnership investments using risk and rewards method, voting interest method, or proportionate consolidation method**

- **Reporting limited partnership investment**

- **Conveyance of mineral interests to the partnership under full cost and successful efforts accounting**

- **Treatment of management and service fees**

- **Master limited partnership issues**

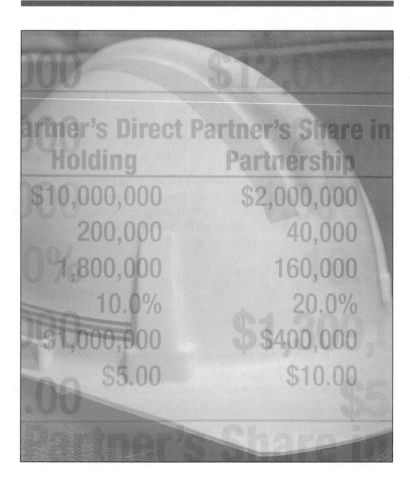

OVERVIEW

A partnership is a business entity with two or more parties that share in the profit or loss of an activity. Partnerships are legal organizations, which differ from joint operations that operate under contractual arrangements (see Chapter 10). Oil and gas companies often form partnerships involved in exploration and production activities for tax purposes. Whether they are sole proprietors or corporations, operators are eligible to buy into these entities set up as general or limited partnerships.

When an E&P company invests in a general partnership, it is entering a joint operation with one or more E&P companies. For tax law or other reasons, the partners do not follow the common approach to joint operations, which is to operate as undivided interest holders. Limited partnerships are also attractive forms of organization. Frequently, the E&P company serves as operating general partner. Limited partners that are individual or institutional investors are sources of financing for partnership business activities.

Whether an operator is a general partner or participating in a general or limited partnership, the accounting problems are much the same. Financial statements must be prepared, tax returns filed, and partners provided with tax information for their own returns. Layers of complexities are added when special allocations of revenue, expenses, costs to the partners, and reversionary interests are made. Additionally, filings with the SEC may be necessary because some limited partnerships are subject to regulations.

For both general and limited partnership investments, there are three major areas of concern: (1) reporting at the partnership level, (2) reporting at the partner level for the partnership investment, and (3) accounting for transactions between the partner and the partnership.

GENERAL PARTNERSHIPS

ACCOUNTING AND REPORTING AT THE PARTNERSHIP LEVEL

Partnerships are separate entities from their owners. A **general partnership** is one in which all of the partners are general partners and have the right to participate in management. The costs of organizing a general partnership are usually quite small and are expensed under the guidance of SOP 98-5, *Reporting on the Costs of Start-up Activities*. The **managing partner** is responsible for maintaining adequate business records, filing tax returns, and providing both financial accounting and tax information to the other partners. Selections of fiscal year and method of accounting (cash versus accrual) are made. Another choice is necessary if the partnership seeks to comply with GAAP: to elect either the full cost or successful efforts method of accounting. Sometimes, records are kept on a tax basis to simplify preparation of federal income tax returns by the partners. However, this complicates the partners' accounting for their investments in the partnership under GAAP.

REPORTING THE PARTNERSHIP INVESTMENT

In accounting for an investment in a partnership, one of three methods is appropriate depending on the facts and circumstances of the partnership arrangement:

1. Risk and rewards method under FASB Interpretation No. 46 (revised December 2003) (FIN 46R), *Consolidation of Variable Interest Entities*
2. Equity method (also called voting interest method)
3. Proportionate consolidation method (in limited circumstances)

In evaluating consolidation models, guidance under FIN 46R should be applied first. If it does not apply and the entity is not a variable interest entity (VIE), then the company needs to evaluate the voting interest/equity model. Each method is discussed in the chapter sections following.

Risk and Rewards Method. FIN 46R addresses consolidation of an entity where a company has the controlling financial interest. The rule makes two critical changes in the consolidation model: (1) it defines when a company should base controlling financial interest on factors other than voting rights, and (2) it requires a new risk and rewards model be applied in these situations. Consequently, GAAP now prescribes two accounting models for consolidation:

- The voting interest model where the investor owning more than 50 percent of an entity's voting interests consolidates.

- The risk and rewards model where the party who participates in the majority of the entity's economics consolidates. This party could be an equity investor, other capital provider, or a party with contractual arrangements.

To determine which accounting model applies under FIN 46R, and which party, if any, must consolidate a particular entity, the partnership must first determine whether the entity is a voting interest or a variable interest entity (VIE). The FASB coined the term VIE for entities subject to the risk and rewards model. An entity is considered a VIE if it possesses one of the following characteristics:

- The entity is thinly capitalized.

- Residual equity holders do not control it.

- Equity holders do not participate fully in an entity's residual economics.

- The entity was established with non-substantive voting rights.

Under FIN 46R, the party exposed to the majority of the risks and rewards associated with the VIE is deemed to be its primary beneficiary and must consolidate the entity.

The following are some FIN 46R considerations surrounding joint ventures:

- Reporting enterprises should first consider the business scope exception in paragraph 4(h) of FIN 46R. When evaluating this scope exception, joint ventures are excluded from the first criterion (the one that focuses the formation of the entity) as long as the entity meets the accounting definition of a joint venture. However, reporting enterprises must also meet the other three criteria in order to avail themselves of the scope exception.

- Many joint ventures are capitalized through stepped funding arrangements (equity or debt infusions) that occur over time, rather than at the formation of the entity. As such, a thinly capitalized joint venture would not have sufficient equity at risk, which would cause the entity to be considered a VIE under paragraph 5(a).

- Joint ventures are commonly structured to provide voting rights disproportionate to the investors' economic rights to the entity. In these situations, the reporting enterprise must apply the guidance in paragraph 5(c), and the first criterion would be met. If substantially all activities of the entity either involve or are conducted on behalf of the party with disproportionately low voting rights, the entity would be classified a VIE.

- The joint venture partners should consider whether or not they are related parties or de facto agents under FIN 46R. Often in these structures, transfer restrictions placed on one or both parties limit that party's ability to manage the economics of its investment in the partnership without prior approval. If such transfer restrictions do create a de facto agency relationship, the determination of the primary beneficiary will focus on which party is most closely associated with the entity. This would call for a qualitative analysis.

- In joint ventures, occasionally one of the joint venture partners manages the operations under a management contract. The question arises as to whether that contract constitutes a decision-making arrangement (covered by paragraphs B18-B21 of FIN 46R) or is merely a service contract (covered by paragraph B22 of FIN 46R). If all the significant decisions are made jointly by the joint venture partners, the management contract may be considered a service contract rather than a decision-making arrangement. As a service contract, such an arrangement could still be one of variable interest.

FIN 46R does not define a decision maker, but establishes the fee paid to a decision maker is not a variable interest if certain conditions are met. One of them is the ability to remove the decision maker. Paragraph B20 of FIN 46R discusses how to determine when the ability to remove the decision maker is substantive. It states:

The ability of an investor or another party to remove the decision maker (kick-out rights) does not affect the status of a decision maker's fees unless the rights are substantive. The determination of whether the kick-out rights are substantive should be based on consideration of all relevant facts and circumstances. Substantive kick-out rights must have both of the following characteristics:

a. The decision maker can be removed by the vote of a simple majority of the voting interests held by parties other than the decision maker and the decision maker's related parties.

b. The parties holding the kick-out rights have the ability to exercise those rights if they choose to do so: that is, there are no significant barriers to exercise of the rights. Barriers include, but are not limited to:

  (1) Kick-out rights subject to conditions that make it unlikely they will be exercisable, for example, conditions that narrowly limit the timing of the exercise

  (2) Financial penalties or operational barriers associated with replacing the decision maker that would act as a significant disincentive for removal

  (3) The absence of an adequate number of qualified replacement decision makers or inadequate compensation to attract a qualified replacement

  (4) The absence of an explicit, reasonable mechanism in the contractual arrangement, or in the applicable laws or regulations, by which the parties holding the rights can call for and conduct a vote to exercise those rights

  (5) The inability of parties holding the rights to obtain the information necessary to exercise them.

Comments on the Risk and Rewards Method. Appendix A of FIN 46R provides a simple example for calculating expected losses and expected residual returns on a pool of financial assets. Paragraph A1 includes the following assumptions for the example:

a. A single party holds all of the beneficial interests in the entity, and the entity has no liabilities.

b. There is no decision maker because the entity's activities are completely predetermined.

c. All cash flows are expected to occur in one year or not to occur at all.

d. The appropriate discount rate (the interest rate on risk-free investments) is five percent.

e. No other factors affect the fair value of the assets. Thus, the present value of the expected cash flows from the pool of financial assets is assumed to be equal to the fair value of the assets.

Appendix A of FIN 46R illustrates a set of six possible (or estimated) cash flow scenarios in Table 1. Each of these scenarios is probability weighted, the sum of which represents the entity's "expected cash flows." The entity's expected cash flows are $795,000, and the present value of those expected cash flows is $757,143.

FIN 46R, Appendix A, Table 1

Estimated Cash Flows	Probability	Expected Cash Flows	Fair Value
$650,000	5.0%	$ 32,500	$ 30,952
700,000	10.0%	70,000	66,667
750,000	25.0%	187,500	178,571
800,000	25.0%	200,000	190,477
850,000	20.0%	170,000	161,905
900,000	15.0%	135,000	128,571
	100.0%	$795,000	$757,143

In Table 2 of Appendix A, for each scenario where the estimated cash flow is less than the expected cash flow of the entity, there is an expected loss. For example, in the first scenario the estimated cash flows are $650,000 and the expected cash flows of the entity are $795,000, resulting in negative deviation in that scenario of $145,000. When probability-weighted and present-valued, the expected loss generated by the first scenario is $6,905. The sum of all of the scenarios in which the estimated cash flows are less than the expected cash flows equals the total expected losses of the entity ($26,667).

FIN 46R, Appendix A, Table 2

Estimated Cash Flows	Expected Cash Flows	Difference Estimated (Losses) Residual Returns	Probability	Expected Losses Based on Expected Cash Flows	Expected Losses Based on Fair Value
$650,000	$795,000	$(145,000)	5.0%	$ (7,250)	$ (6,905)
700,000	795,000	(95,000)	10.0%	(9,500)	(9,048)
750,000	795,000	(45,000)	25.0%	(11,250)	(10,714)
800,000	795,000	5,000	25.0%		
850,000	795,000	55,000	20.0%		
900,000	795,000	105,000	15.0%		
			100.0%	$(28,000)	$(26,667)

FIN 46R, Appendix A, Table 3

Estimated Cash Flows	Expected Cash Flows	Difference Estimated (Losses) Residual Returns	Probability	Expected Residual Return Based on Expected Cash Flows	Residual Expected Return Based on Fair Value
$650,000	$795,000	$(145,000)	5.0%		
700,000	795,000	(95,000)	10.0%		
750,000	795,000	(45,000)	25.0%		
800,000	795,000	5,000	25.0%	$ 1,250	$ 1,191
850,000	795,000	55,000	20.0%	11,000	10,476
900,000	795,000	105,000	15.0%	15,750	15,000
			100.0%	$ 28,000	$ 26,667

The same calculation is performed for the expected residual returns, only using the scenarios where the estimated cash flows are greater than the expected cash flows. In Table 3, the entity's expected residual returns are calculated as $26,667. It is no coincidence these two amounts are equivalent, since an entity's expected losses will always equal its expected residual returns as a result of this calculation.

While these examples demonstrate the mathematics behind the calculation of expected losses and expected residual returns, there is little guidance on how a reporting enterprise would derive the cash flow estimates necessary to perform these calculations. It is clear the first step for a reporting enterprise, according to the guidance in paragraph 8 of FIN 46R, is to identify the variable interests in the entity. Variable interests in an entity are those assets, liabilities, or equity that absorb an entity's variability. For purposes of the expected loss calculation, net assets of the entity are those assets and liabilities that create variability in the entity and, thus, are not variable interests. It is the estimated/ expected changes in the fair value of these net assets that drive the estimated cash flow scenarios in the calculation of an entity's expected losses and expected residual returns.

Voting Interest or Equity Method. Under the voting interest method (or equity method), a partner's initial investment is recorded in an account with a title such as Investment in OPQ Partnership. At the end of the fiscal period, the partner's share of income (or loss) is recorded as an increase (or decrease) in the investment account and appears as a single amount under a heading such as Income from OPQ Partnership in the income statement. The balance in the investment account is shown as a single amount on the partner's balance sheet under the heading of Investments.

Comments on the Voting Interest or Equity Method. Under the equity method, neither the share of the investee's reserves nor the share of the investee's oil and gas assets enter into the depreciation, depletion, and amortization calculation of the investor under either the full cost or successful efforts methods. Disclosures required by FAS 69 include separate disclosures of the enterprise's share of the investee's:

- Proved oil and gas reserves

- Standardized measure of discounted future net cash flows

- Capitalized costs relating to oil and gas producing activities

- Costs incurred in oil and gas property acquisition, exploration, and development

- Results of operations from producing activities

These requirements are discussed further in Chapters 28 and 29.

The equity method is used by many operators who invest in oil and gas partnerships. It is justified on the basis of APB No. 18, *The Equity Method of Accounting for Investments in Common Stock*. APB 18 was written to provide guidelines for investments in corporate stock, but AICPA *Accounting Interpretation No. 2* suggests many of the provisions of APB 18 are appropriate guides for investments in partnerships. The opinion suggests the equity method should be used when an investor has the ability to exercise significant influence over operating and financial plans of the investee. It presumes if the investor owns 20 percent or more of the investee's stock, the investor exercises significant influence.

APB 18 does not apply, however, when more than 50 percent of the investee's stock is owned. A full consolidation of the statements of the two entities is normally required in this case.

It would seem the same logic should apply to partnership investees. However, proportionate consolidation of the partnership, rather than full consolidation, is usually made when the investor's ownership interest is greater than 50 percent.

A major shortcoming of the equity method is full disclosure of all pertinent financial information is not given in the financial statements. Off-balance-sheet financing may result because the investor can be liable for significant partnership debts not reflected in the balance sheet. Paragraph 20 of APB 18 indicates disclosure of summarized financial information of such investees may be appropriate for material investments. (When the proportionate consolidation method is used, an investor discloses its proportionate share of each of the investee's applicable disclosure items, regardless of whether full cost or successful efforts is followed.)

Proportionate Consolidation Method. When using the proportionate consolidation method, a partner includes a proportionate share of each partnership asset and liability in the partner's balance sheet and each revenue and expense in the partner's income statement. Although it is possible for the partner to maintain actual accounts reflecting the ownership share in each partnership item, it may be easier in some cases for the partner to use the equity method of accounting for the transactions with the partnership during the fiscal period, and then at the end of the fiscal period eliminate the investment account and substitute the appropriate amounts of the partnership's assets and liabilities. Similarly, the Share of Income or Loss of the Partnership account would be eliminated, and the proper share of individual revenue and expenses would be substituted in the income statement.

As an example, assume X Corporation uses the successful efforts method of accounting, as does OPQ Partnership in which X Corporation owns a one-fourth interest. X Corporation invested $750,000 for that interest on January 2, 2006. For 2006, OPQ Partnership has a $1 million loss. OPQ's 25 percent share is $250,000 before $80,000 in related income tax reduction. Figure 24-1 illustrates the equity and proportionate consolidation methods for X Corporation's share of OPQ Partnership's loss.

Necessary data for the proportionate consolidation is obtained from financial reports provided by the partnership at the end of the fiscal period (as long as the partnership and the partner use the same accounting method and have the same fiscal year).

If there are special allocations of revenues or expenses, or if the accounting method used by the partnership is different from that of the partner, a reconstruction or reconciliation must be performed. This can be done based on the periodic reports of partnership expenditures and revenues prepared by the managing partner.

Figure 24-1
Example of Equity Method vs. Proportionate Consolidation

(thousands)

Equity Method	OPQ Partnership	X Corp. Pre-entry	X Corp. Entry	X Corp. Post-entry
Cash	$ 240	$ 500		$ 500
Receivables	200	2,000		2,000
Oil & Gas Properties	2,380	10,000		10,000
Investment in OPQ Partnership		750	$(250)	500
Other Assets	180	1,000		1,000
Total Assets	$ 3,000	$14,250	$(250)	$14,000
Liabilities & Deferred Taxes	$ 1,000	$ 5,000	$ (80)	$ 4,920
Partners' Capital	2,000			—
Stockholder's Equity		9,250	(170)	9,080
Total Liabilities & Equity	$ 3,000	$14,250	$(250)	$14,000
Revenue	$ 1,000	$20,000		$20,000
Production Expense	(200)	(6,000)		(6,000)
Exploration Expense	(1,500)	(5,000)		(5,000)
DD&A	(200)	(4,000)		(4,000)
G&A Expense	(100)	(1,400)		(1,400)
25% share of OPQ Loss			$(250)	(250)
Income Tax Provision		(1,200)	80	(1,120)
Net Income (Loss)	$(1,000)	$ 2,400	$(170)	$ 2,230

Proportionate Consolidation Method	OPQ Partnership	X Corp. Pre-entry	X Corp. Entry	X Corp. Post-entry
Cash	$ 240	$ 500	$ 60	$ 560
Receivables	200	2,000	50	2,050
Oil & Gas Properties	2,380	10,000	595	10,595
Investment in OPQ Partnership		750	(750)	—
Other Assets	180	1,000	45	1,045
Total Assets	$ 3,000	$14,250	$ 0	$14,250
Liabilities & Deferred Taxes	$ 1,000	$ 5,000	$ 170	$ 5,170
Partners' Capital	2,000		—	—
Stockholder's Equity		9,250	(170)	9,080
Total Liabilities & Equity	$ 3,000	$14,250	$ 0	$14,250
Revenue	$ 1,000	$20,000	$ 250	$20,250
Production Expense	(200)	(6,000)	(50)	(6,050)
Exploration Expense	(1,500)	(5,000)	(375)	(5,375)
DD&A	(200)	(4,000)	(50)	(4,050)
G&A Expense	(100)	(1,400)	(25)	(1,425)
25% share of OPQ Loss				—
Income Tax Provision		(1,200)	80	(1,120)
Net Income (Loss)	$(1,000)	$ 2,400	$(170)	$ 2,230

[This example assumes partnership's properties are in separate cost centers from X's.]

The SEC staff views pro-rata consolidation as inappropriate for interests in jointly controlled corporate entities, even if there is an agreement attributing benefits and risks to the owners as if they held undivided interests. Pro-rata consolidation would be appropriate for interests in partnerships and other noncorporate forms of joint ownership only if such interests are equivalent to holding undivided interests in assets (with severable liability for incurred related indebtedness) as described in SOP 78-9, *Accounting for Investments in Real Estate Ventures*.

EITF Issue No. 00-01, *Applicability of the Pro Rata Method of Consolidation to Investments in Certain Partnerships and Other Unincorporated Joint Ventures*, acknowledges pro-rata consolidation of an undivided oil and gas interest is appropriate. EITF 00-01 concludes a proportionate gross financial statement presentation is appropriate in an extractive industry, including oil and gas exploration and production.

Comments on the Proportionate Consolidation Method. The major advantage of proportional consolidation is the more complete economic picture it provides, such as an investor's share of investee liabilities.

Note that X Corporation's final net income in Figure 24-1 is the same as that under the equity method. This aspect is true for successful efforts accounting, but does not hold for full cost accounting. If the partner uses full cost, the proportionate share of the partnership's assets and proved reserves in each cost center must be included with those owned directly by the partner in computing depreciation, depletion, and amortization [per Reg. S-X Rule 4-10(c)(3)(v) as discussed in FRR 406.01.c.v.]. In such a case, the recomputed DD&A for consolidating the cost center likely will cause consolidated net income to differ from that under the equity method, even if the partnership uses the full cost method. This occurs because the ratio of production to reserves will likely change as shown in the following example:

Full Cost Example	Partner's Direct Holding	Partner's Share in Partnership	Consolidated
A. Cost basis	$10,000,000	$2,000,000	$12,000,000
B. Barrels produced	200,000	40,000	240,000
C. Barrels of reserves	1,800,000	160,000	1,960,000
D. Ratio of B/(B+C)	10.0%	20.0%	10.91%
E. Amortization (A x D)	$1,000,000	$400,000	$1,309,200
Amortization/bbl	$5.00	$10.00	$5.45

For this example, the combined amortization using the equity method is $1.4 million, whereas the consolidated amortization is $1,309,200 using the required partial consolidation of cost basis, production, and reserves.

If both the partnership and the partner use the successful efforts accounting method (as in Figure 24-1), it is a simple matter to combine the investor's separate statements with those of the investor's proportionate interest in the partnership's financial statements.[1]

Whenever both the partnership and the partner use full cost and the partnership has applied a ceiling test with a resulting write-down of capitalized costs, the partner's share of the write-down should be added back and the ceiling test applied to total cost and total value of the combined assets in the cost center.

If the partnership uses full cost and the partner uses successful efforts accounting, it may be difficult for the partner to convert all partnership statement items to the successful efforts method with a high degree of accuracy.

LIMITED PARTNERSHIPS

A limited partnership differs from a general partnership in that it consists of one or more general partners and at least one or more limited partners who have no right to participate in management or incur obligations on behalf of the partnership. In the last three decades, and especially in the 1970s and 1980s, thousands of limited partnerships were formed to finance oil and gas activities. Almost all of them utilized a single oil and gas operator serving as the sponsor and general partner. Individual investors accepted the role of limited partners.

These partnerships have been categorized as drilling funds, income funds, or hybrid versions. Drilling funds acquire mineral rights, explore, and drill on unproved properties, whereas income funds (also called production funds) are formed to acquire, fully develop, and operate proved producing properties.

ACCOUNTING AND REPORTING AT THE PARTNERSHIP LEVEL

In creating partnerships, certain organizational costs are incurred. Limited partnerships have significant fees related to legal services (e.g., attorneys' fees for drawing up and filing articles of partnership, filing fees and other state charges) and the work of promoters and organizers. If borne by the partnership, these costs should be expensed according to SOP 98-5, *Reporting on the Costs of Start-Up Activities,* just as they are for general partnerships.

Limited partnerships typically pay syndication fees, which are primarily broker commissions for selling limited partnership interests. Broker commissions are customarily paid from the proceeds of the limited partners' contributions; they range from five to 10 percent of the subscription price of the limited partnership interests. Syndication fees also include the cost of prospectuses or private placement memoranda, unless they are paid by the general partner. These up-front costs are treated as offsets against the partners' capital accounts in the same way corporations treat the costs of issuing capital stock. A few partnerships and general partners charge such costs to expense at the time they are incurred.

The general partner (or its affiliate) is reimbursed for costs incurred and also charges a fee for management services. Acquisition, exploration, and development are recorded based on the accounting method chosen. Fees and costs related to production are charged to current expense. Management fees may be paid in advance by a partnership. Such prepaid costs can be deferred and charged to asset accounts or expensed as the related services are performed by the general partner.

Limited partnership interests are sold in units of a specified amount. A limited partner either pays for an interest up-front, or may be obligated to make capital commitments for the life of the enterprise. In the latter case, the managing partner can make calls for capital contributions up to the total capital commitment amount, which usually involves large sums in the first year or two to fund acquisition, exploration, and development activities.

Limited partnerships, like general partnerships, may adopt either the full cost or successful efforts method of accounting; many use the income tax basis of reporting to partners because this is a concern of limited partners. In addition, partnerships may come under the jurisdiction of the SEC. Discussion of the legal requirements for exemption from SEC registration are outside the scope of this book.

REPORTING THE PARTNERSHIP INVESTMENT

As previously mentioned, general partners in limited partnerships use one of the three methods for reporting partnership investment: risk and rewards under FIN 46R, equity/voting interest, or proportionate consolidation. If the general partner controls the partnership (and limited partners do not have significant control), then full consolidation is required under the voting interest consolidation method. In evaluating the methods of accounting for the partnership, the guidance under FIN 46R should be applied first. If FIN 46R is not applicable and the entity is not a VIE, then the company needs to evaluate the voting interest method.

For several reasons, proportionate consolidations of interests in limited partnerships are more complicated than those for general partnerships. The sponsoring general partner may also own a limited partnership interest; this can make it more difficult to compute the general partner's total share of each item. Interests of the general partner and limited partners will be different for certain cost and revenue items, primarily because of federal income tax considerations.

Limited partners are often given special tax allocations to encourage them to invest. It is customary for limited partners to provide funds for intangible drilling and development costs, which are deductible for tax purposes when incurred. Conversely, general partners provide funds for capital outlays such as leasehold costs, seismic costs, and equipment costs. Revenues may be allocated in one proportion until payout, then on a different ratio thereafter. In many arrangements, relative interests may change depending on whether partners opt to participate in further assessments. Limited partners are required to pay in full for their limited partnership interests at the time the interests are acquired, but cash contributions of the general partner are often made only as such costs are incurred. Sometimes, the general partner is required to make minimum contributions by a specified date. As a result, it can be difficult to compute the portion of each asset and liability that should be assigned to each party in a proportionate consolidation.

Since a limited partnership may be viewed as a pooling of capital, the general partner and limited partners should follow the general guidelines of Oi5.138 (b) through Oi5.138 (f), which require each party to account for costs incurred according to their nature. Under full cost, all costs incurred for exploration and development are capitalized, whereas under successful efforts, only successful exploratory drilling and all development costs are capitalized.

The managing general partner prepares all financial reports for the partnership. If GAAP is followed, it is customary for partnership reports to be prepared on the same basis as the general partner. As noted, many limited partnership statements are prepared solely on a tax basis if the partnership interests are not publicly-traded. Books should be kept in sufficient detail to allow easy translation to both GAAP and tax bases.

The schedule that follows is typical of provisions for allocating revenues and costs between limited and general partners, although some schedules are much more complex.

	Percent Provided By:	
	Ltd. Partner	Gen. Partner
Organization costs	0	100%
Initial management fee (5% of subscriptions)	100%	0
Leasehold acquisitions	0	100%
Initial wells:		
Drilling and other noncapital costs, (tax*) including	99%	1%
Capital costs (tax)	0	100%
Subsequent wells abandoned within 60 days of		
Noncapital costs (tax)	99%	1%
Capital costs (tax)	0%	100%
Subsequent wells abandoned more than 60 days from		
Noncapital costs (tax)	50%	50%
Capital costs (tax)	50%	50%
Delay rentals	99%	1%
Operating expenses	50%	50%
Production proceeds	50%	50%

* Income tax allocation item

The consolidation guidance contained in SOP 78-9 should be applied to all partnerships regardless of their activities. Generally, if limited partners have important rights such as those specifically indicated in SOP 78-9 (including the right to review the general partner), the general partner is precluded from consolidating. If the only rights the limited partners have are liquidation or redemption rights, those rights in and of themselves would normally not preclude consolidation by a general partner. If the limited partners have the right to remove the general partner (i.e. that is they have kick-out rights), and no other important rights, those kick-out rights are important rights unless they are non-substantive. A kick-out right as contemplated by FIN 46R would be considered substantive.

In the past, companies may have concluded the right of the limited partners to remove the general partner with a voting level of other than a simple majority (e.g., 66.7 percent) is substantive and, thus, did not require the general partner to consolidate the limited partnership. With respect to modification of the existing partnership agreements, if the partnership agreement for those partnerships are substantively changed for reasons other than the level of vote required to replace the general partner, the level of vote also should be changed to conform with the criteria in paragraph B20 of FIN 46R.

EITF Issue No. 04-5, *Investor's Accounting for an Investment in a Limited Partnership When the Investor Is the Sole General Partner and the Limited Partners Have Certain Rights*, addresses whether rights held by limited partners preclude consolidation by the general partner in circumstances in which a sole general partner would otherwise consolidate a limited partnership absent existence of the rights held by the limited partners. This issue had previously been discussed by the Task Force in EITF 98-6, *Investor's Accounting for an Investment in a Limited Partnership When the Investor Is the Sole General Partner and the Limited Partners Have Certain Approval or Veto Rights*. A project to reconsider EITF 98-6 was dropped from the task force's agenda due primarily to the work AcSEC had undertaken at the time to revise the guidance in SOP 78-9. The task force agreed it was appropriate to re-address this issue and believed the model developed in EITF 98-6 was an appropriate starting point.

The model involves a two step analysis to determine if the presumption of consolidation by the general partner would be overcome. Step 1 would determine whether the limited partners have the substantive ability to dissolve (liquidate) the limited partnership or otherwise remove the sole general partner without cause. If yes, the presumption of control is overcome and the general partner would not consolidate the partnership. If the limited partners do not have that ability, under step 2, a decision is made as to whether the limited partners have substantive participating rights. If they do, then the presumption of control is overcome and the general partner would not consolidate the partnership. If they do not, control is presumed and the general partner consolidates.

As a result of EITF 04-5, many general partners in master limited partnerships (discussed later in this chapter) began consolidating the public limited partnership effective January 1, 2006. Each circumstance encountered by a petroleum accountant will need to be evaluated based on the specific facts and circumstances.

TRANSACTIONS BETWEEN THE PARTNER AND THE PARTNERSHIP

In both general and limited partnerships, transactions with the general partner can create difficult accounting issues. This is especially true in limited partnerships. Several transactions are examined in this section including the sale or transfer of properties to the partnership by the partner (or conveyances); management and service fees; and general and administrative reimbursements.

The appropriate accounting treatment of revenue received and costs incurred by the partner in such activities depends on whether the partner uses the full cost or successful efforts method of accounting.

CONVEYANCE OF MINERAL INTEREST TO THE PARTNERSHIP

The general partner may contribute unproved properties to the partnership in return for a partnership interest. Frequently, the general partner will sell to the partnership, for cash or other consideration, all or part of the interest in unproved properties for exploration and drilling. The accounting treatment for such conveyances when using the full cost method is quite specific.

General Rules for Conveyances under the Full Cost Method. Under the full cost method, an oil or gas operator is deemed to be in *one line of business* (oil and gas exploration and production) for all transactions involving properties in which the operator has an interest. Other activities related to such properties (e.g., lease brokerage, lease promotion, and management) are viewed as merely a part of the basic exploration and production function. Under the full cost theory, all costs incurred in exploration and development are treated as part of the full cost pool, and all proceeds related to mineral properties, other than from oil and gas production, are deemed to be recoveries of the full cost pool. As discussed in Chapter 21, Reg. S-X Rule 4-10(c)(6)(iii)(A), as amended in 1984, provides there is generally no recognition by a full cost company of any gains from the sale or conveyance of properties to entities or activities in which the transferor has an interest. All proceeds are to be treated as recovery of cost in years beginning after December 15, 1983:

> (iii)(A) Except as provided in subparagraph (c)(6)(i), all consideration received from sales or transfers of properties in connection with partnerships, joint venture operations, or various other forms of drilling arrangements involving oil and gas exploration and development activities (e.g., carried interest, turnkey wells, management fees, etc.) shall be credited to the full cost account.

The exception referred to above is for sale of properties that significantly alter the relation between capitalized costs and proved reserves. Prior to 1984, it was common for operators using the full cost method to segregate unproved mineral properties acquired for the purpose of resale or transfer to partnerships from the full cost pool. Segregated properties were treated as an inventory of assets held for resale and were excluded from the full cost pool in computing amortization and in applying the cost ceiling test. Since the properties were considered as inventory and reported as such in the balance sheet, gain or loss would be recognized on their resale or on their transfer to partnerships. Although the SEC previously recognized under certain circumstances this *two lines of business* concept, the change in rules eliminated the *inventory* concept for properties acquired in years beginning after December 15, 1983. Now all such properties are considered a part of the full cost pool and treated identically to properties acquired for exploration and drilling.

Reg. S-X Rule 4-10(c)(6)(iii)(A) generally prohibits recognition of income from a full cost company's sale or transfer of property related to partnerships, joint ventures, and other forms of drilling arrangements (e.g., carried interests, turnkey wells), except:

> ...to the extent of amounts that represent reimbursement of organization, offering, general and administrative expenses, etc., that are identifiable with the transaction, if such amounts are currently incurred and charged to expense.

As an example, if the partnership pays the general partner $500,000 for reimbursement of general and administrative expenses (G&A), when the general partner expensed only $200,000 in identifiable G&A costs, then only $200,000 of the reimbursement may be recognized as income. The rest must be credited against the full cost pool. These rules for property sales under full cost accounting are summarized in Figure 24-2.

Figure 24-2
Property Sales Under Full Cost Accounting

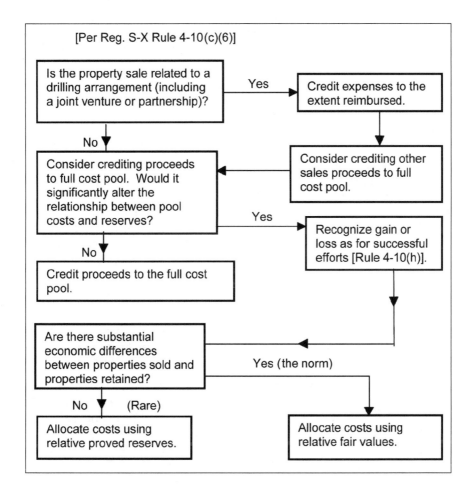

General Rules for Conveyances under the Successful Efforts Method. Section (c) of Reg. S-X Rule 4-10 applies only to companies using the full cost method. Operators using the successful efforts method are not affected by the rule. Thus, if a property originally purchased for exploration and drilling is transferred to a partnership by a successful efforts company, the transaction would be treated in the manner described in Chapters 21 through 23. Any cash or other consideration received is treated as a recovery of cost. Only if the consideration received exceeds the total cost of the property will gain be recognized (see Chapter 21).

In circumstances in which no cash is recovered but other partners provide contract drilling services or other services as assets, the transactions are to be viewed as a pooling of capital, and no gain or loss is recognized (see Chapter 23).

If the company maintains an inventory of unproved properties held for resale or promotion, Oi5.133 through Oi5.138 on mineral conveyances would appear to be applicable.

MANAGEMENT AND SERVICE FEES

Accounting Under Full Cost. In general, income is not recognized for management and service fees by a full cost company. An exception is made in certain circumstances for the promoters of income funds. Reg. S-X Rule 4-10(c)(6)(iii)(B) provides:

> Where a registrant organizes and manages a limited partnership involved only in the purchase of proved developed properties and subsequent distribution of income from such properties, management fee income may be recognized provided the properties involved do not require aggregate development expenditures in connection with production of existing proved reserves in excess of ten percent of the partnership's recorded cost of such properties. Any income not recognized as a result of this limitation would be credited to the full cost account and recognized through a lower amortization provision as reserves are produced.

The rules of paragraph (iii)(B) are illustrated by the following example. Assume ABC Oil Company organizes a production fund in which it is the general partner and manager. The total cost of the proved properties, most of which have been developed, is $28 million. Estimated costs to complete development of the properties are $5 million. During the year, management fees of $800,000 are received and related expenses are $320,000. Since the additional development costs required are more than 10 percent of the partnership's costs related to the properties, ABC treats the $480,000 excess of fees over actual costs as a reduction of the full cost pool. (If additional development costs had been only $2 million, less than 10 percent of the partnership's property cost, then net income of $480,000 [$800,000 less $320,000] would be recognized.)

Reg. S-X Rule 4-10(c)(6)(C)(iv)(c) provides if a full cost company is manager of the properties involved, then no income can generally be recognized from rendering contractual services such as drilling:

> Notwithstanding the provisions of (A) and (B) above, no income may be recognized for contractual services performed on behalf of investors in oil and gas producing activities managed by the registrant or an affiliate. Furthermore, no income may be recognized for contractual services to the extent the consideration received for such services represents an interest in the underlying property.

As an example, assume ABC Oil Company, a full cost company, is the general partner, sponsor, and manager of a limited partnership. During the year, ABC drills a well to the casing point for a fixed fee of $320,000. Its share of these costs is 25 percent, and the limited partners' share is 75 percent. Total costs incurred on the project are $280,000. ABC credits the full cost pool for the entire $40,000 drilling profit. Profit of $10,000 is credited to the pool by eliminating the intracompany drilling profit on ABC's 25 percent share of well costs. The additional $30,000 is credited to the pool to avoid recognizing drilling profit on the investors' well costs.

When a company maintains a separate contract drilling division, segmental income statements will normally be prepared. In preparing a consolidated income statement, the intracompany profit on the drilling contract is eliminated. Any profit resulting from that portion of the drilling contract applicable to partners is offset against the cost pool as demonstrated for ABC's transactions:

	Drilling Segment	Intracompany Elimination	Consolidated Amount
Contract Drilling Revenue	$320,000	$(80,000)	$240,000
Contract Drilling Expense	(280,000)	70,000	(210,000)
Net Income on Contract	$ 40,000	$(10,000)	30,000
Less Full Cost Pool Credit			(30,000)
Consolidated Net Income from Drilling			$ 0

Reg. S-X Rule 4-10(c)(6)(iv)(A) provides when an interest is acquired in connection with a service contract, income can be recognized to the extent cash consideration received exceeds all related contract costs, plus the partner's share of costs incurred and estimated to be incurred "in connection with the properties" (but only if the partner or an affiliate is not the manager of the oil and gas activity). "In connection with the properties" are vague terms. They appear to include acquisition, drilling, and development costs to be capitalized in the full cost pool, but not production costs to be expensed.[2]

To illustrate these concepts, assume ABC Oil Company performs drilling services and receives cash of $640,000 from the partnership. Total drilling costs are $560,000. ABC contributes cash of $64,000 for its 10 percent share of drilling costs, pays $10,000 for its 10 percent share of working interest in the lease, and pays $10,000 to an outside service company for its share of completion costs. $560,000 of contract costs plus $84,000 to be capitalized to the full cost pool exceed the $640,000 cash received by $4,000. No income is recognized, and the full cost pool is charged for a net $4,000. The following schedules show how these facts are reflected in ABC's income statement and balance sheet after eliminating intracompany profit on the 10 percent share of drilling costs.

Income Statement:	Drilling Segment	Intracompany Elimination	Consolidated Amount
Drilling Revenues	$640,000	$(64,000)	$576,000
Drilling Expenses	(560,000)	56,000	(504,000)
Net Drilling Income	$ 80,000	$ (8,000)	72,000
Less Full Cost Pool Credit			(72,000)
Recognized Profit			$ 0

Balance Sheet:	E&P Segment	Elimination Intraco. Profit*	Elimination Drilling Profit**	Consolidated Amount
Leasehold Cost	$10,000	$ 0	$ (6,000)	$4,000
Drilling Costs	64,000	(8,000)	(56,000)	0
Completion Costs	10,000	0	$(10,000)	0
	$84,000	$(8,000)	$(72,000)	$4,000

* Intracompany profit (see income statement schedule)
** Total drilling profit = $72,000 (eliminated first against drilling costs, $56,000; then against completion costs, $10,000; then against leasehold cost, $6,000.)

If total profit attributed to the other partners had been $9,000 greater (e.g., $81,000 instead of $72,000), a profit of $5,000 could have been recognized (as long as ABC or an affiliate did not manage the property); cash proceeds would have exceeded all related costs by that amount. Consideration received must exceed: (1) costs already incurred, and (2) those estimated to be incurred by the partner before profit can be recognized.

If an E&P company operates as an independent drilling contractor performing services for other entities in which it has no economic interest, and it is not the manager of the venture, then profit on drilling or other services may be recognized.

Reg. S-X Rule 4-10(c)(6)(iv)(B) allows profit to be recognized, even though the E&P company has an interest in the properties, provided the interest was obtained at least one year before the date of the service contract, and the interest is unaffected by the service contract. Income from such a contract may be recognized subject to the general provisions for eliminating intercompany profits under GAAP.

For example, assume for three years that ABC Oil Company has owned a 25 percent ownership interest in a partnership that holds a working interest in a prospect managed by another company. ABC's share of the leasehold interest cost has been $180,000. During the current year, it contracted to drill a well on the prospect for a contract price of $800,000. The well was successful, and total drilling costs were $680,000. ABC can recognize $90,000 of drilling profit ($120,000 total profit less the 25 percent intracompany profit).

ABC's consolidated income statement now reflects the following data:

Income Statement:	Drilling Segment	Intracompany Elimination	Consolidated Amount
Contract Drilling Revenue	$800,000	$(200,000)	$600,000
Contract Drilling Expense	(680,000)	170,000	(510,000)
Net Drilling Income	$120,000	$ (30,000)	90,000
Balance Sheet	E&P Segment	Intracompany Elimination	Consolidated Amount
Full Cost Pool:			
Leasehold Cost	$180,000		180,000
IDC	200,000	$ (30,000)	170,000

Accounting Under Successful Efforts. The special rules in Reg. S-X Rule 4-10 relating to partnerships, joint ventures, drilling arrangements, management fees, and service income are found in Section (c) relating to full cost companies. These limitations on income recognition do not appear to apply to managing partners using the successful efforts method. It is common for them to treat management fees as income when earned under the terms of the management contract.

Management fees paid up-front should not be reported in full as income in the year received, but should be deferred and recognized as the related services are rendered. If an up-front fee is designed, in part, to reimburse offering costs and other expenses associated with the partnership, the expenses may be charged appropriately to expense and the related reimbursement reported as income. A successful efforts company can expense non-reimbursed offering costs.

If the successful efforts method is followed by an operator, no special restrictions apply to the recognition of income, other than the standard rules for eliminating intracompany profit. For example, suppose a sponsor owns a 25 percent working interest and manages the limited partnership. The sponsor drills a successful well for the partnership for a contract fee of $500,000. Total costs incurred were $400,000. It is appropriate for the partner to recognize a profit of $75,000 ($100,000 less intracompany profit of $25,000) on the contract if the successful efforts method is used.

GENERAL & ADMINISTRATIVE REIMBURSEMENT

Most limited partnership agreements provide for reimbursement of general and administrative (G&A) expenses. Reimbursement may cover specific G&A expenses, which should be reported by the general partner as a reduction of expenses. The reimbursement may be a specified monthly amount, but normally it is computed as a percentage of partnership revenues or as a percentage of specified costs incurred. Frequently, the rate is higher during the drilling phase of the partnership than during production.

MASTER LIMITED PARTNERSHIPS

The mid-1980s brought the development of publicly-traded partnerships known as master limited partnerships (MLPs). Called depository units, MLP interests have been freely traded in the over-the-counter market and are sometimes listed on organized stock exchanges. In an MLP, the partnership's income (or loss) is passed through to the investors. MLP units that are publicly-traded also may be referred to as publicly-traded limited partnerships (PTLPs). Many MLPs have been acquired by corporations or were reorganized as taxable corporations. In recent years, MLPs are more likely to be utilized in the pipeline industry.

An MLP (often newly formed) that plans to operate as an E&P company may offer to issue its units of ownership in return for a direct or indirect interest in the properties. Frequently, units are offered to limited partners in return for their interests in existing partnerships. This allows two or more limited partnerships to combine forces. In other cases, units in the MLP are offered for working interests or royalties. The combining of existing limited partnerships and acquisition of properties through the issue of units of ownership in an MLP are referred to as roll-ups. The offer to exchange the units for mineral properties or partnership interests is referred to as an exchange offer.

PTLPs allow investors to minimize corporate taxes and provide a means for easily converting a limited partnership interest into cash. This contrasts dramatically with the ownership of regular partnership interests, which have little liquidity. An MLP roll-up permits a new company to own producing properties from the outset and offers advantages in financing activities as well as strong investor appeal. MLPs resulting from roll-ups may be substantially larger than their predecessor partnerships. A larger size can give a better competitive position to the new MLP.

In the past, some MLPs were formed when an existing corporation contributed interests in oil and gas properties to an MLP and then distributed limited partnership units to its existing shareholders in partial or complete liquidation of the corporation. Because of current tax laws, this is a far less desirable action than it was previously.

The major disadvantage of an MLP roll-up is the high cost of forming and administering the company. Complex administration and detailed investor information make MLPs costly and time intensive. Fees can be high for: (1) the securities firm retained as the dealer-manager, (2) the required attorneys, accountants, and engineers, (3) preparing, printing, and distributing offering documents, and (4) establishing an organization to manage the new company.

The sponsor of the exchange offer and other investors provide funds to administer the undertaking. Sponsors may be allocated some portion of the units in the acquiring MLP in return for funds to finance the venture and provide services to create and administer the roll-up. If the venture is successful, this interest may represent a substantial asset.

Accounting issues for MLPs are essentially the same as those for private limited partnerships. However, the accounting problems faced in forming an MLP, especially one that is publicly-traded, may be more complex. Major challenges arise in determining exchange values and in complying with FASB and SEC requirements for recording the formation of the enterprise.

DETERMINING EXCHANGE VALUES

One of the most important and difficult steps in an exchange offer is determining the number of units that will be offered to interest owners. Each offeree should be treated fairly; this can be accomplished by allocating shares based on the exchange value of the property interests included in the offering. Since proved reserves represent the most important asset involved in such offers, the estimated value of proved reserves attributable to each interest is a major factor in determining the shares offered for each interest.

The starting point in computing an exchange value is to project future production from proved reserves. The production schedule is converted into future net revenues based on assumptions about the future prices of oil and gas and future costs to develop and produce the reserves. Once future net revenue is estimated, it is reduced to a present value using a specified discount rate.

Exchange value calculations may also provide for probable reserves or even possible reserves. Since they are much more subjective, discounted cash flow from the production of these reserves is further reduced by an adjustment to allow for the uncertainties. For example, the value of an exchange offer could be based on the formula of 100 percent of proved, 50 percent of probable and 10 percent of possible reserves. If undeveloped acreage is included in the exchange offer, it should be evaluated by independent appraisers.

The specified present value discount rates and risk adjustments for probable and possible reserves are applied consistently among all partnerships forming the MLP. Ideally, exchange values should closely approximate fair values. However, the exchange values may be considered fair even without approximating fair values. The use of a uniform, consistent approach to determining the exchange values may be viewed as fair if the relationship to each other is generally the same as using fair values. For example, if all exchange values are 15 percent below their fair values, the proportionate ownership of the MLP would be the same. However, when properties are substantially different among the partnerships, caution is warranted in the use of a consistent discount.

At the time of the evaluation for exchange purposes, data is developed to comply with SEC disclosure requirements for proved reserves. This assumes the partnership is subject to SEC rules, which is likely the case. The basis for these disclosures may be different from the basis used in arriving at the exchange value. Disclosure requirements for the quantities and discounted present value of proved reserves are based on price and cost factors as of the date of the statements and on a uniform discount rate of 10 percent. Alternatively, the value for exchange offer purposes may be based on expected price and cost factors and on an assumed discount rate related to the cost of capital and other factors.

COSTS OF UNDERTAKING MLP EXCHANGE OFFERS

Paragraph 58 of Opinion No. 16 requires that the administrative costs of consummating business combinations be charged to current expense in the period incurred. Arguably, costs incurred in undertaking MLP exchange transactions are more akin to those necessary to create a new company than to consummate a business combination. In the past, many MLPs capitalized the exchange costs. Today, following the guidance of SOP 98-5, MLP start-up costs are expensed as incurred.

• • •

---

1 Oi5.121 and Oi5.126 regarding successful efforts DD&A do not specifically require that proportionate consolidation reflect recomputations of DD&A by consolidated cost centers. Such DD&A recomputation is consistent with Oi5.164(b) requirements to combine reserves, but recomputation rarely changes DD&A significantly by lease or field. Recomputing DD&A will not change total consolidated DD&A unless the ratio of production to reserves (P/R ratio) differs for the partner's direct and partnership interests, as occurred in the preceding full cost example. For a successful efforts cost center (typically a lease or a field), it is rare for a direct interest's P/R ratio to significantly differ from the indirect interest's P/R ratio, unless there is a reversion for one of the interests or the partner's reserves estimate differs from the partnership's reserves estimate.

2 The SEC's Codification of Financial Reporting Releases, 406.01.c.iv., includes an example computation that includes acquisition, exploration, and development costs, but not production costs.

25

ACCOUNTING FOR
INTERNATIONAL OPERATIONS

Key Concepts:

- General risks of operating in foreign lands

- Role of E&P subsidiaries in international markets

- Accounting issues and payments related to joint venture operations

- Concession and contract fiscal systems

- Elements of production sharing contracts (PSCs), including cost oil and profit oil

- Financial accounting for PSCs

- Nonrisked and risked service contracts

INTRODUCTION

International operations comprise a major segment of most large E&P companies. Operating outside the U.S. presents a diverse set of legal, accounting, and financial reporting issues. This chapter introduces readers to the challenges of international exploration and production of oil and gas.

Mineral interests outside the U.S. are commonly owned by the government of the host country, not by local citizens or private corporations. These governments act within their legal and economic environments to establish contracts with E&P companies to explore, develop, and produce those minerals. Contracts are subject to limited negotiations and bidding by an E&P company and its competitors.

Once terms are agreed upon, exploration and development activities commence in the targeted areas. Pre-approved work programs and budgets are established to guide the project. The E&P company may be obligated to fund all capital costs, and it bears the overall risk of failure. Minimum work requirements are established by contract between the government and E&P companies, which can result in significant commitments owed by the E&P companies.

Once production equipment is commissioned, landed-in-country, or placed-in-service, title normally passes to the host government. In other cases, title passes to the host government upon expiration of the contract. The company has the right to share in oil and gas produced or in proceeds from sales for a fixed number of years.

RISKS OF INTERNATIONAL E&P

Although countries outside the U.S. offer opportunities for petroleum exploration and production, international operations bring clear economic risks. In addition to the inherent risks of oil and gas operations, each country or region has its own set of challenges. Corporate management should understand these additional risks in order to assess the impact on company profitability.

POLITICAL INSTABILITY

The stability of a country's political regime is an important consideration. If a government changes hands, the new administration may not recognize existing agreements. Laws can change drastically and be applied on a retroactive basis. For example, in one country a new tax structure based on revenue, instead of income, was adopted resulting in an effective combined income tax rate exceeding 100 percent; this clearly eliminated any incentive for an E&P company to participate in the project.

Border disputes can also be problematic, especially on offshore sites. When an E&P company is awarded a license from a governmental agency, and it begins exploration activities, a neighboring country can step in and lay claim to the area. Boundary disputes of this nature, especially when reserves are involved, are not resolved quickly.

Geopolitical climate has become a major factor in E&P expansion. Internal conflicts, civil wars, polarization of religious and ethnic groups, and the rise of terrorism have led to greater risks of operating in foreign lands.

FOREIGN CURRENCY RISKS

Oil prices are generally quoted worldwide in U.S. dollars. Gas revenues and operating costs and expenses are often expressed in the local currency, which serves as the functional currency. Its stability in relation to U.S. dollars is important because unstable rates can lead to translation and hedging problems.

Other currency issues can involve settlements and repatriation. For example, the local currency may not be freely convertible into dollars or other currencies, or restrictions may exist on sending funds out of the country.

ACCOUNTING OPERATIONS RISKS

In some developing countries, accountants face conditions of limited logistical support, inadequately trained personnel, high staff turnover, limited or unreliable phone lines and computer equipment, and shortages of modern housing and other facilities. For these reasons, considerable time may be spent in the early stages of a project to establish local accounting departments and develop adequate information systems.

FORMS OF OPERATION IN A FOREIGN COUNTRY

AN E&P COMPANY'S LOCAL SUBSIDIARY

Often, E&P companies create foreign subsidiaries in countries where they plan to operate. Each subsidiary is registered with the host government before agreements are reached. The subsidiary negotiates contract terms and serves as the operator of record. It maintains separate books even though it may be little more than a shell company. Financial records for U.S. GAAP purposes are kept in the U.S. or other countries, which allows foreign subsidiaries to operate in some territories with little more than a field office.

Participation in the foreign subsidiary may be in the form of an undivided interest or an ownership interest determined through agreements which assign benefits and risks to owners in the subsidiary. Parties may include foreign governments as well as joint venture partners in the well. The structure may be different from a typical local subsidiary operation where: (1) each owner owns a discrete percentage of the local subsidiary equity, and (2) each owner uses the traditional consolidation approach depending on its ownership percentage and control.

The structure of the participation will determine how each party reflects its ownership interest. If participation takes the form of an undivided interest, each party typically would reflect its pro-rata share of the assets, liabilities, revenues, and expenses (i.e., pro-rata consolidation). If the ownership is effected through a corporation or entity similar to a corporation, even in cases where there is an agreement that assigns benefits and risks to the owners as if they held undivided interests, the participation would be evaluated following the guidance of the consolidation or equity method of accounting. EITF 00-01 provides guidance in applying the proportional consolidation method (also referred to as pro-rata) to ownership in unincorporated entities, such as partnerships and limited liability companies that are similar to partnerships. Each of these accounting models is discussed in more detail in Chapter 24.

OPERATING IN A JOINT VENTURE

Joint ventures are common business structures for international operations. Joint venture partners can include non-U.S. enterprises such as national oil companies from the host country. A venture operator should have an information system in place to manage the reporting requirements of the foreign government as well as those of the U.S.

INTRODUCTION TO FISCAL SYSTEMS

A significant issue for international petroleum accounting is how an E&P company and its host government will share in revenue. Sometimes called the fiscal system, the sharing arrangement determines how the parties allocate venture production and profits. Bonuses, royalties, profit sharing, and income taxes are key items addressed in the agreement.

While fiscal systems vary considerably, two types are most common:

- **Concession.** Concessions are much like leases in the U.S. The E&P company typically owns reserves discovered and has title to equipment and any oil and gas produced. Bonuses, royalties, production taxes, and income taxes flow into government coffers.

- **Contract.** Under a contractual arrangement, the government owns the reserves and possibly the field equipment. It contracts with an E&P company to perform or manage specified activities. The company's fee may be in cash (a service contract) or in a share of production (a production sharing contract, or PSC). The contract is designed to reimburse the company for its E&P costs before significant amounts are drawn by the government through production sharing and taxes.

In most instances, fiscal systems are complex, and they may also be vague or ambiguous. Multiple sharing formulas, artificial pricing, government inflexibility, changing regulations, cultural differences, and contractual inconsistencies can make the accounting for E&P profits a challenging experience.

Further complications can arise when several E&P companies enter into a joint venture arrangement and deal collectively with a host government. A joint operating agreement must be executed by the parties and the agreement itself introduces an additional tier of accounting-related issues. Further, oil taken by venture partners may routinely differ from entitled shares and give rise to oil and/or gas imbalances to be monitored and accounted for.

In general, E&P revenues are shared as follows:

- Up-front and periodic bonus payments to the host country
- Periodic royalty payments to the host country
- Recovery of investments and operating costs by the E&P company
- Profit sharing (or profit splitting)
- Taxation by the host country
- Infrastructure development for the host country

BONUS PAYMENTS

Upon execution of the agreement, payment of an up-front bonus to the host government may be required. Alternatively, a reduced up-front bonus could be specified with subsequent periodic bonuses. This allows an E&P company to retain more of its capital to fund exploration and development costs.

Production bonuses are paid to a host country when agreed-upon levels of production are met. As in the U.S., such bonuses are usually recorded as property acquisition costs.

ROYALTIES

Rates and formulas for determining royalties on international operations are far more diverse than in the U.S. When various grades of oil and gas are produced, different royalty rates can apply. Sometimes, sliding scale percentages are used to calculate royalties based on volumes produced.

Royalty arrangements based on units-of-production are common. This method is simple to use and audit because pricing information is not required. However, a royalty on a fixed percentage of revenues realized is arguably a more equitable arrangement. Thus, royalties based on actual sales prices (or published or posted prices) are also widespread. In some countries, royalties are credited against host country income taxes.

Revenue from operations in the U.S. is reported net of royalties. However, in international regions, accounting practices may call for revenue to be reported on a gross basis, and royalties to be recorded as expense items or elements of income taxes.

RECOVERY OF INVESTMENTS AND OPERATING COSTS

A host country typically requires the E&P company to bear all costs and risks of exploration and, perhaps, development. Production sharing contracts (PSCs) provide a substantial portion of initial revenue or production to the E&P company for cost recovery. Calculations for one type of PSC are illustrated later in the chapter.

Recoverable costs for a period depend on the terms of the individual PSC. Operating expenses incurred during a timeframe are generally recoverable, as well as an amortized amount of prior capital costs. Recovery of prior capital costs up to the maximum revenue available may be sought as reimbursement.

For example, assume an E&P company incurred $10 million in prior reimbursable costs. The PSC calls for 10 percent amortization each year that may be recovered (i.e., $1 million in the current period). Current period revenue available for reimbursement is limited to reimbursable costs not to exceed $4 million. If operating expenses are $500,000, then the total cost recovery/reimbursable expenses for the period are $1.5 million. Alternatively, the PSC may allow the operator to recover a total of $4 million during the year, consisting of $500,000 in operating costs from the current year and an additional $3.5 million of prior capital costs.

Under this concept, all cost recovery and/or deductions are restricted to production from a discrete license or field. Known as ringfencing, it limits cost recovery to expenditures attributable to that specific license. Costs incurred in one ringfenced license area cannot be recovered from an area outside those boundaries. Accounting for cost recoveries is a complex issue addressed later in the chapter.

PROFIT SHARING

After royalties are paid, revenue is shared by the E&P company and host country based on the sharing percentages set out in their agreement. An E&P company's revenue from a joint venture usually consists of two components: cost recovery revenue and profit sharing revenue. Profit-sharing revenue is usually net of the host country's share, much like the pro-rata consolidation of a joint venture's activities.

TAXATION

Another mechanism for host countries to collect their shares of E&P rewards is taxation — primarily income taxation. Some countries have formal income tax statutes; others include tax rules in their contractual arrangements with E&P companies. Petroleum accountants should be aware that the financial accounting guidelines for recording foreign income taxes are the same as for U.S. income taxes.

Determining gross taxable income can be difficult. If a company sells products to an affiliate at lower than free market prices, then free market prices are normally used to determine gross income for host country income tax purposes. In many countries, use of a free market price is replaced by the application of an artificial posted price for determining taxes (and sometimes royalties). This can be the case even if products are sold on the open market.

Tax systems around the world are dramatically different in the types of deductions allowed against taxable income. For example, an agreement may or may not allow the deduction of costs for negotiating an E&P arrangement with a host country, including costs incurred at the company's headquarters located elsewhere. Another example is the costs paid to affiliates. Host country tax laws or the E&P agreement may or may not allow deductions for all costs paid to related enterprises.

For tax purposes, recovered costs are generally deducted when the reimbursement is received. Alternatively, such costs can be deducted through a DD&A provision. Some countries allow bonus payments to be deducted, either in the form of a deduction similar to U.S. percentage depletion deductions based on gross income, or by allowing more than 100 percent recovery of certain expenditure categories in computing host country income taxes.

Debt financing may be necessary for the E&P company, at least during the development stage of a project. However, interest incurred on indebtedness required for operations in a host country may not be deductible for that country's income tax purposes. Certain host countries have disallowed all interest payments made outside their borders.

In most foreign jurisdictions, royalties are considered deductible expenses for host country income tax purposes, rather than as credits against income taxes. U.S. companies prefer royalties to be treated as foreign income taxes in order to reduce U.S. federal income tax liability. Contracts should clearly identify royalty and income tax amounts to verify their tax treatments, not only for host country income taxes, but also for home country income tax purposes.

In addition to income taxes, E&P companies operating outside the U.S. encounter other taxes. The U.K. and Australia are examples of countries that apply petroleum revenue taxes (PRT) or petroleum resource taxes to oil and gas operations. Other countries assess value-added taxes, or VATs. Customs duties and other importation fees are also forms of taxes assessed by host governments.

INFRASTRUCTURE COSTS

A host country may require certain infrastructure and other industrial investment as part of the arrangement. This can include training or employment of local personnel, as well as construction of public works projects. Some countries insist on these items when and if commercial petroleum reserves are found. Others mandate development activities in the earliest stages of exploration.

Thus, not only a company's capital is attractive to a host country, but also its knowledge base. Technology-sharing and other forms of expertise may be specified in contract packages. E&P company representatives are obligated to provide levels of training to host country personnel in order to foster local talent.

Contracts often call for a company to construct roads, utilities, housing, schools, hospitals, and other physical facilities in areas of exploration and production. These actions provide a secondary benefit of fostering goodwill and cooperation with residents. Occasionally, an E&P company finds it necessary to provide unplanned support to the local populace.

Accounting for costs of infrastructure and local support depends on the nature of the expenditures. Costs that are rightfully related to acquisition, exploration, development, or production are simply accounted for as such. Costs outside normal E&P activities are considered bonuses (e.g., helping to build a local hospital) or royalty compensation to the host country, and are accounted for as expenses.

CONCESSIONS

Concessions are fiscal systems in which a government grants the title of mineral rights to a concessionaire. The U.K. sector of the North Sea is an example of a concessionary system. Every few years, the government opens a bidding round of exploration and development proposals for petroleum licenses on blocks of offshore properties. It awards concessions to companies for the right to exploit any minerals found there. Awards are based primarily on development plans submitted by winning companies. Concessionaires own all risks and profits from reserves on government lands, as they do in the U.S. and Canada. Revenues are shared with the government through: (1) royalties and/or a tax on production, (2) VAT on specified costs, and (3) income taxes on company operations in the U.K.

EXAMPLE OF ALLOCATING NET PROCEEDS

Assume an E&P entity named Multico operates in a concessionary area in the North Sea. The contract between Multico and the U.K. requires the company to pay an eight percent royalty and a five percent VAT to the government; both calculations are based on gross revenue. Multico is responsible for all costs associated with exploration, development, and production, which include $10 million in exploration and development costs expended from 2004 to 2006. None of the exploration and development costs have been deducted in prior years. In 2006, the property began producing, and gross revenue of $5 million was earned. Local income tax laws allow Multico to deduct the total $1 million in operating costs incurred in 2006, as well as a pro-rata amortization of prior year exploration and development costs. Assuming an income tax rate of 40 percent, the share of net E&P proceeds accruing to Multico and the U.K. government in 2006 is shown in Figure 25-1.

Figure 25-1
Allocation of Net Proceeds for the Multico Example

	To Government	To Multico
Gross revenue		$ 5,000,000
Royalty 8%	$ 400,000	(400,000)
VAT 5%	250,000	(250,000)
Net revenue		$ 4,350,000
Operating expenses		(1,000,000)
1/5 of prior exploration and development costs*		(2,000,000)
Taxable income		1,350,000
Income taxes at 40%	540,000	(540,000)
Net to the parties	**$ 1,190,000**	**$ 810,000**

*Note: Multico actually paid the exploration and development expenditures in 2004-2006.

JOINT VENTURE CONCESSION

Many concessionary systems involve the host government participating as a working interest owner in oil and gas operations. These systems are known as joint venture arrangements. A government-owned oil company is set up to participate in the enterprise, and a joint operating agreement is executed. E&P companies typically agree to pay 100 percent of up-front costs, and the government-owned company is considered a carried working interest through the exploration phase. If commercial reserves are found, the government's company has an option to participate in development and production as a working interest owner at predetermined rates. In exercising this option, it agrees to share in all future drilling, development, and production costs.

Depending on contract terms, an E&P company may be allowed to recover all or a portion of its exploration expenditures. Two methods of recovery are commonly used. One involves direct payment by the government-owned company to the E&P entity. More frequently, E&P companies recover agreed-upon costs by retaining the government-owned company's share of production until expenses have been recouped. Many times, recoveries are subject to annual limitations and may take years to pay out. Afterwards, the government-owned company shares in costs and production just like any other working interest owner.

This type of arrangement does not alter the government's entitlement to royalty and income taxes; however, customs duties on imported materials and supplies and export duties on production are often exempted.

Accounting for a concession interest is similar to that of a working interest in a U.S. mineral lease. See Chapter 10 for a discussion of joint ventures.

CONTRACTUAL ARRANGEMENTS

In a contractual arrangement, the host government owns all minerals. The E&P company earns an interest in the minerals or receives proceeds from sales for its services (i.e., exploration, drilling, development, and production). Typically, the government (via a government-owned oil company) plays an active role in exploration, development, and production, and the E&P company acts as the operator.

These contracts require a joint management committee to oversee operations and vote on major decisions. It is comprised of staff from each company and government representatives. An annual work program and budget is submitted by the E&P entity for review and approval. The joint committee generally makes all major decisions concerning petroleum operations, including approving significant expenditures, evaluating exploration results, planning and drilling wells, and determining the economic feasibility of drilling results.

E&P companies are usually required to provide all technology and financing for a project. Equipment and facilities that are acquired locally or imported may become the property of the local government. This practice does not apply to leased equipment, equipment brought into the country temporarily, or assets owned by service companies. In some instances, title to equipment and facilities passes to the government at the time such goods are brought into the country or are installed. In other cases, title passes when the cost of equipment and facilities has been recovered by the E&P company.

As previously mentioned, two types of contracts are frequently encountered in international operations: production sharing contracts and service contracts.

PRODUCTION SHARING CONTRACTS

Production sharing contracts are probably the most common form of agreement between host countries and foreign E&P companies. Utilized worldwide, PSC terms and conditions vary widely although most involve a government-owned oil company.

E&P companies bear all costs and risks during exploration under most PSC arrangements. If commercial reserves are discovered, the government-owned oil company has the right to participate as a working interest owner at predetermined rates. E&P companies do not receive reimbursement for the government-owned company's share of costs; rather, they must recoup expenditures from future production. The government-owned company is responsible only for its working interest share of development and operating costs.

Cost Oil and Profit Oil. Cost recovery is a fundamental feature of PSCs. As stated in the last section, E&P companies typically pay 100 percent of costs incurred in exploration, and some or all of the costs during development and production phases. Oil (or gas) or other consideration accruing to the parties—with respect to cost recovery—is referred to as cost oil, while gross revenue accruing to the parties after cost recovery, or as a result of applying a profit factor, is referred to as profit oil.

The PSC agreement specifies which costs are recoverable, the order of recoverability, any limitations, and whether unrecovered costs in a period can be carried forward. Some contracts call for a type of amortization of capital costs recoverable in any year (e.g., only one-tenth of allowable capital costs are recoverable each year in the first ten years of production). Others simply employ an annual maximum to cap the amount of total recoverable capital costs in a given year.

Some contracts allow the recovery of interest incurred on capital expenditures. This may be a contentious point since governments assume that contractors are responsible for covering capital requirements. As an example, the typical Chinese PSC only allows cost recovery of deemed interest: that portion related to costs incurred during development work, but not during exploration.

The order of cost recovery is important given that it determines how quickly an E&P company is able to recover certain costs. For example, if the entity pays 100 percent of exploration costs and 49 percent of development costs, the company would prefer that exploration expenditures have priority. In general, costs are recovered as follows:

1. Current year operating costs

2. Unrecovered exploration expenditures

3. Unrecovered development expenditures

4. Deemed interest (if allowed)

5. Investment credit or capital uplift (if allowed)

6. Future abandonment cost fund (if required)

In many agreements, exploration and development expenditures are amortized or recoverable over a fixed number of years. If amortized capital costs are not recovered in any given year, the unrecovered portion may be carried forward to subsequent years. In other cases, however, carryforwards are not allowed and the potential recovery is lost.

After determining the amount of production or revenue for cost recovery, the profit oil is shared between the parties based on contract terms. Sometimes, a specified percentage of gross revenue is treated as profit oil and shared by the parties. In other cases, a percentage of the revenue remaining after cost recovery goes directly to the government; the E&P company and government-owned enterprise share the remainder.

Illustration of a Production Sharing Arrangement. Assume for this example that Jones Oil Company operates under a PSC agreement in the South China Sea. It has 49 percent of the working interest, and Sinhai Oil Company, which is owned by the Chinese government, has 51 percent. Their operating agreement calls for annual gross production to be split in the following order:

1. VAT equal to seven percent of annual gross production

2. Royalty of 13 percent of annual gross production

3. Cost oil limited to 62 percent of annual gross production with costs to be recovered in the following order:

   a) Operating costs

   b) Exploration expenditures (Jones Oil Company paid 100 percent)

   c) Development costs (Jones Oil Company 49 percent and Sinhai Oil Company 51 percent)

4. Annual gross production remaining after cost recovery becomes profit oil and is split as follows:

   a) Government receives 15 percent of profit oil.

   b) Remaining 85 percent is shared by Jones and Sinhai based on their working interests.

During 2006:

- Recoverable operating costs equal $4 million

- Unrecovered exploration costs equal $50 million

- Unrecovered development costs equal $100 million

- Gross production for the year is two million barrels of oil

- The "agreed upon" posted price is $60 per barrel

The allocation of production to the parties is shown in Figure 25-2. In addition, the government's proceeds are increased and Jones Oil Company's share is decreased by any income or other taxes levied by the Chinese government.

> **"PSAs** are essentially a vehicle to enable a country with proven hydrocarbon reserves but not the means to extract them to entice foreign capital investment into the country when the risks to ordinary investors are higher than normal."
>
> – *Tim Newman*, *"Misunderstanding Production Sharing Agreements Font Size," TSC Daily, March 7, 2007.*

Figure 25-2
Production Sharing Calculations

YEAR 2006	Barrels To Be Allocated	Chinese Government (in bbls)	Sinhai 51% (in bbls)	Jones Oil 49% (in bbls)
VAT (7% of 2,000,000 total barrels)	140,000	140,000		
Royalty (13% of 2,000,000)	260,000	260,000		
Cost oil (62% of 2,000,000)	1,240,000			
Cost oil allocation:				
For operating costs, $4,000,000/$60=66,667 bbls			34,000	32,667
For exploration costs, $50,000,000/$60=833,333 bbls limited to 1,240,000 - 66,667				833,333
For development costs, $100,000,000/$60=1,666,667 bbls limited to 1,240,000 − 66,667 − 833,333			173,400	166,600
Remainder			0	0
Profit oil: 2,000,000 x (100%−7%−13%−62%)	360,000			
Allocate 15% to government and split the rest 51% / 49%.		54,000	156,060	149,940
TOTAL	2,000,000	454,000	363,460	1,182,540

Capital Uplift. Often, host governments incorporate certain incentives into agreements in order to encourage capital investments in exploration, drilling, and development. These incentives may appear in PSCs or result from other negotiations.

Known as capital uplifts, the incentives are meant to encourage E&P companies to maximize their capital spending and to compensate for risks. A capital uplift, sometimes referred to as an investment credit, is an amount of cost recovery on capital expenditures over and above actual amounts spent. If a company spends $5 million in recoverable capital expenditures and a 10 percent capital uplift applies, then the company is allowed to recover 110 percent of actual spending, or $5.5 million.

Domestic Market Obligations. Some contracts specify that a certain percentage of an E&P company's share of profit oil must be sold to the local government. Occurring in situations where the country's demand for crude oil is greater than the government's share of production, these domestic market obligations help alleviate the government's need to rely on imported oil or oil from more expensive sources. Such sales are transacted at below market prices and are sometimes calculated in local currency. E&P companies will record net profit oil at market prices and reduce their profit by the amount of discount given to the local government.

Royalty Holidays and Tax Holidays. Royalty holidays and tax holidays are government incentives to encourage E&P companies to maximize investment early in the life of production. During a period of time (i.e., the first two years of production), royalty provisions may be waived. This leaves E&P companies with more money to invest in drilling and development. Similarly, a government may grant a tax holiday by specifying a period of time during which the E&P company is exempt from income taxes.

Un-ringfencing. Generally, only costs expended for work in a particular license area are recoverable from production in that area. Such costs are said to be ringfenced. Neither costs nor production can be transferred for recovery outside the contract area. Governments can choose to un-ringfence or allow cross-fence transfers of costs. This incentive is most effective when the government seeks to increase exploration in a particular area. It allows a company to immediately recover certain exploration expenditures in a frontier area against production from a currently producing area.

FINANCIAL ACCOUNTING FOR THE PSC

Regarded as Oil and Gas Producing Activity. Even though a host country may legally own the reserves in a PSC agreement, the E&P company has the right to explore, develop, and produce the oil and gas. These activities are substantially equivalent to owning mineral interests or shares of reserves; thus, Reg. S-X Rule 4-10 applies. PSC rights are viewed as the equivalent of concession rights and the basic financial accounting rules are the same:

- An E&P company records the PSC activity as oil and gas production, not as contractor services.

- Reserves are recognized by the E&P company to the extent of its share in future production under the PSC (although calculating that share can be much more difficult than for a concession).

The usual accounting for production sharing contracts is no different than that of concession activities. Proceeds are recorded as revenues from oil and gas production, and capitalized costs are amortized over the company's share of proved reserves.

In the *2001 PricewaterhouseCoopers Survey of U.S. Petroleum Accounting Practices*, eight of 11 respondents (73 percent) recorded the proceeds from the sale of cost recovery oil received under production sharing contracts as oil revenue. No respondents recorded the proceeds as a recovery of capitalized costs. Three respondents used methods not specified in published survey results.

When cost recovery proceeds were recorded as revenue, all respondents (100 percent) amortized capitalized exploration and development costs over the E&P company's entitled share of future production from proved reserves. No one reported that they amortized capital costs by the amount of the cost recovery proceeds.[1]

Disclosure of Proved Reserves. FAS 69 requires public companies to disclose the net quantities of the enterprise's interests in proved reserves. Paragraph 13 states such quantities are not to include:

> ...oil or gas subject to purchase under long-term supply, purchase, or similar agreements and contracts, including such agreements with governments and authorities. However, quantities of oil or gas subject to such agreements with governments or authorities as of the end of the year, and the net quantity of oil or gas received under the agreements during the year, shall be separately disclosed if the enterprise participates in the operation of the properties in which the oil or gas is located or otherwise serves as the *producer* of those reserves, as opposed, for example, to being an independent purchaser, broker, dealer, or importer.

The standardized measures of the two reserves disclosures may be combined (FAS 69, paragraph 30). End of year quantities separately disclosed are called proved reserves in Appendix A to FAS 69. However, FAS 69, paragraph 102, explains because such sharing in future production does not "represent direct ownership interests in reserves, those reserves quantities are to be reported separately from the enterprise's own proved reserves."

FAS 69 requires disclosure of the E&P company's net proved reserves under production sharing contracts. At issue is whether to disclose such reserves separately under FAS 69, paragraph 13, or within the table of directly-owned reserves. Arguably, for a true production sharing contract in which the E&P company does not directly own the reserves, paragraph 13 calls for those net reserves to be disclosed separately from net reserves directly owned. However, since (1) the standardized measure is combined, (2) direct reserves must be disclosed for each foreign geographic area in which significant reserves are located (FAS 69, paragraph 12), and (3) terms of production sharing contracts vary widely, there is little benefit in disclosing production sharing contract reserves in a separate table rather than including such reserves within the reserves amounts disclosed in the main table.

In a judgmental sampling of 2006 reports from large oil and gas companies, separate disclosure tables were not found, unless the production sharing contract reserves composed an individual geographical area. However, some of the companies reported (on a percentage basis) the amount of their reserves related to profit-sharing contracts.[2]

SERVICE CONTRACTS

Another type of agreement prevalent in a contractual system is a service contract. Service contracts are not as common as PSCs, but nonetheless present many accounting challenges. Service contracts are generally classified as being either nonrisked or risked.

In nonrisked service contracts, the E&P company agrees to provide services in the form of exploration, development, and production activities. The host government pays the E&P company a fee to cover incurred costs and provide a profit. Thus, the host country bears all risks of exploration and development. With respect to financial accounting, the service provider is not deemed to be engaged in oil and gas producing activities.

Nonrisked service contracts are used in areas such as the Middle East with substantial capital, but where industry expertise and technology are lacking. Fees earned differ widely over various ranges of success.

In practice, risked service contracts are more common than nonrisked service contracts. The E&P company incurs all costs and risks related to exploration, development, and production activities. In return, and if production is achieved, the company receives a fee representing recovery of its costs plus a profit. The fee is typically based on a sliding scale linked to the level of production achieved. During the past few years, risked service agreements have been used in many Latin American countries.

Accounting for risked service contract fees and costs are—for the most part—similar to that of PSCs. However, production revenue is not recorded, and no reserves are recognized by the service contractor (which does not have a share of oil and gas production). Fees are recognized based on the terms of the agreements. Exploration, development, and production costs are amortized according to the level of production achieved.

Risked Service Contract Example. Assume the Tyler Company enters into a risked service agreement with the government of Colombia. Tyler agrees to pay the government a U.S. $1 million signing bonus and initially bears all of the costs and risks associated with exploration, development, and production. The government agrees to pay Tyler an annual fee comprised of:

- All operating costs incurred in the current year

- One-tenth of all unrecovered capital expenditures

- A production fee of:

  $0.60 per barrel from 0 to 3,000 bbls per day (bopd)
  $0.80 per barrel from 3,001 to 10,000 bopd
  $1.00 per barrel above 10,000 bopd

The contract caps the E&P fee at $1.25 per barrel times the total number of barrels produced. If the maximum fee is reached and unrecovered operating or capital expenditures exist, then such costs can be carried forward indefinitely and recovered in future years.

After Tyler expends $5 million for exploration, drilling and development in 2006, production begins in the Verde Field. Operating expenditures for the year total $1.5 million. Production is 3,650,000 barrels or an average of 10,000 barrels per day. Tyler's total fee for 2006 is determined as follows:

Operating cost reimbursement	$1,500,000
Capital cost recovery ($5,000,000/10)	500,000
Production fee (3,000 bbls x 365 days x $.60)	657,000
Production fee (7,000 bbls x 365 days x $.80)	2,044,000
Total fee	**$4,701,000**

To assess if the maximum fee has been exceeded, the following computation is required:

$4,701,000/3,650,000 bbls = $1.288 per bbl

The computed fee of $1.288 per barrel is greater than the maximum allowed of $1.25; therefore, the actual fee paid to Tyler is:

$1.25 x 3,650,000 = $4,562,500

The difference between the computed fee and the maximum fee ($4,701,000 - $4,562,500 = $138,500) is to be treated as unrecovered capital costs and carried forward.

Tyler must pay income taxes on its local operations to the government of Colombia which decrease Tyler's profit and increase the government's share.

COMPARATIVE ILLUSTRATION OF SHARING ARRANGEMENTS

Figure 25-3 illustrates the four basic forms of sharing arrangements for exploration and development of a given area of interest. Projected costs and revenue (in millions of dollars) for each sharing arrangement are included.

Figure 25-3
Illustration of Sharing Arrangements
(in millions)

COSTS	Total for Venture	Company's Share Concession	50% Joint Venture Arrangement	Service Contract	Production Sharing Contract
Bonus to host country	$ 10	$ 10	$ 10	$ 10	$ 10
G&G studies	10	10	5	10	10
Exploration wells:					
Dry	40	40	20	40	40
Productive	20	20	10	20	20
Development costs	120	120	60	120	120
Indirect infrastructure costs	10	10	10	10	10
Total pre-production costs	**$ 210**	**$ 210**	**$ 115**	**$210**	**$210**
Cost subject to cost recovery				$200	$200

REVENUE Revenue sharing arrangements →		WI, net of royalty	WI, net of royalty	180% of cost	Cost recovery
Revenue share for 20 years		80%			
Revenue share			40%		
Share of cost production				90%	90%
Share of profit production for 20 years					25%
Share of first $222 million in revenue	$ 222	$ 178	$ 89	$200	$200
Share of subsequent revenue for 20 years	2,000	1,600	800	160	500
Share of revenues after 20 years	1,000	0	400	0	0
Total revenues	**$3,222**	**$1,778**	**$1,289**	**$360**	**$700**
Examples:					
Year 1 of production					
Revenue	$ 100	$ 80	$ 40	$ 90	$ 90
Operating costs	(10)	(10)	(5)	(10)	(10)
DD&A*		(7)	(3)	(40)	(21)
Income before taxes		**$ 63**	**$ 32**	**$ 40**	**$ 59**
Year 2 of production					
Revenue	$ 200	$ 160	$ 80	$180	$130
Operating costs	(20)	(20)	(10)	(20)	(20)
DD&A*		(14)	(6)	(80)	(30)
Income before taxes		**$ 126**	**$ 64**	**$ 80**	**$ 80**

*Assume for simplicity that successful efforts capitalized costs are amortized over assumed total current and future revenues.

OTHER ACCOUNTING MATTERS UNIQUE TO INTERNATIONAL OPERATIONS

GENERAL

There is no single, recognized set of international accounting standards for the oil and gas industry today. However, the International Accounting Standard Board (IASB) has begun to develop standards in its effort to issue a comprehensive set of rules aligned with current practices and to converge with U.S. GAAP. In December 2004, IASB issued its International Financial Reporting Standard 6 (IFRS 6), *Exploration for and Evaluation of Mineral Resources*. Effective on January 1, 2006, it was designed to improve the accounting practices for exploration and evaluation expenditures.

IFRS 6 defines elements of the cost of exploration and evaluation assets (although preparers of financial statements are allowed to continue applying accounting policies used prior to the adoption of the standard). It establishes how assets should be assessed for impairment; prescribes certain disclosures about exploration and evaluation assets; and sets levels at which such assets should be assessed for impairment, as well as how impairment losses are to be recognized.

Current international oil and gas accounting practices and procedures have largely evolved to handle exploration and development contracts. However, as previously noted, financial reporting policies should follow the substance of the transaction, not necessarily its legal form. Thus, there can be inherent conflicts in designing accounting practices and procedures which tend to follow the underlying contract's legal form versus its economic substance.

Accounting for foreign operations may require a company to keep two sets of accounting records. Financial systems must be designed to accommodate the accounting requirements of both the home country and the country in which operations are conducted. Problems in this area might not seem obvious until one looks more closely. For example, IDC is an important part of U.S. petroleum accounting, but is not recognizable to some foreign nationals. Certain countries allow interest to be capitalized, while others do not. The concepts of depreciation and amortization may not exist in locations where tax laws allow operators to expense everything as incurred. Finally, a few governments may require reports to be prepared in more than two currencies or demonstrate the effects of inflation. These differences can cause the accounting, reporting, and information systems to be very complex.

LIFTING IMBALANCES

Accounting for lifting imbalances may be especially difficult in international operations. Lifting imbalances occur when the volumes actually lifted from a site by an interest owner differ from the volumes to which the owner is entitled. The operator is responsible for notifying all participants of the following amounts used to calculate entitlements:

- Total production
- Actual royalty production
- Actual cost recovery production
- Actual investment credit production
- Actual profit production

The operator provides details of the overlift or underlift position of each party and the final overlift or underlift of each in relation to the others. When a party is overlifted at year-end, or other time period specified in the agreement, it should notify the operator and other parties of its intended method of settlement. Lifting imbalances can be settled in cash or in-kind.

In order to make an informed decision regarding the settlement of lifting imbalances, knowledge of available options is crucial. Pricing assumptions must be made for the relevant time period, and calculations are performed. After careful analysis, a decision can be reached. Notification is then given to the operator on a timely basis in order to execute a proper election.

RESERVES

A question sometimes arises about when proved reserves should be recognized in foreign operations. A host country's declaration that a field is commercial may be desired before the reserves estimator judges the reserves to be proved. FAS 69, paragraph 17 (Oi5.167), requires disclosure of host country requirements that restrict reserves disclosures or include unproved reserves. For instance, in certain countries, year-end reserves are priced at average year prices, as opposed to year-end prices. This practice is not acceptable under either FAS 69 or SEC rules. Various SEC technical releases state the use of average prices or prices other than year-end is not acceptable for the purpose of calculating the standardized measure of discounted future net cash flows.

Finally, for some countries, oil reserves quantities are estimated and reported in metric tons which must be converted to barrels for financial reporting in the U.S.

FULL COST

In the early stages of exploring for oil or gas in a foreign land, an E&P company may drill one or more dry holes and have no proved reserves for that country. Generally, the company defers dry hole costs when definitive plans exist for further exploration in that country. This is the practice for four of the five full cost companies that responded in the *2001 PricewaterhouseCoopers Survey of U.S. Petroleum Accounting Practices*. A fifth company expensed its dry hole costs.

SEC staff has indicated it is inappropriate to establish any minimum safe harbor period. Evaluation of the propriety of costs deferred for full cost companies should be based on specific facts and circumstances. Management has the responsibility for justifying costs deferred in a new cost center. SEC staff has also emphasized the importance of disclosure requirements, such as providing an aging of excluded costs and narrative of the properties or projects involved.

"What is the implication of global utilization of accounting information? In the simplest of terms, users must understand something about how accounting information is prepared to be able to effectively rely on it. What if each country had its own accounting rules? You can see that misinterpretation and lack of understanding could be a real problem. For example, what if a company reported their "turnover" as 10,000,000 euros? What would you conclude? For starters, you would need to know that "turnover" is synonymous with "revenue," and you would need to know how much a euro is worth....Terminology and methods are not consistent from country to country."

– Principles of Accounting.com, Chapter 15–Financial Reporting and Concepts, http://www.principlesofaccounting.com/chapter%2015.htm

MISCELLANEOUS ISSUES

INTERNATIONAL ACCOUNTING CONTROLS

The Foreign Corrupt Practices Act of 1977 (FCPA) requires certain companies to establish and maintain internal accounting control systems that satisfy particular objectives. The FCPA has two parts: one deals with specific acts and penalties associated with certain corrupt practices, and the second addresses standards relating to internal accounting controls.

Any domestic company—or its officers, directors, employees, agents, or stockholders—is prohibited from paying or offering to pay a foreign official to obtain, retain, or direct business to any person. The law prohibits payments to foreign officials, political parties, and candidates for the purpose of obtaining or retaining business by influencing any act or decision of foreign parties in their official capacity. It also applies to attempts to induce such foreign parties to use their influence with a foreign government to sway any act or decision of such government. This section of the FCPA applies to virtually all U.S. businesses, and noncompliance can result in significant fines for corporations and individuals who willfully participate in bribery of a foreign official. Violators may also be subject to imprisonment.

The internal accounting controls section of the FCPA imposes additional legal obligations on companies subject to the Securities Exchange Act of 1934. Failure by such companies to maintain appropriate books and records and internal accounting controls violates the Act. Criminal liability for failing to comply with the internal accounting control provisions is imposed if an individual knowingly circumvents, knowingly fails to implement a system of internal accounting controls, or knowingly falsifies any books, records, or accounts.

The primary intent of the FCPA is to prevent corrupt payments to foreign officials, and it requires accurate books and records and internal accounting controls to be maintained to help accomplish that objective. This necessitates management's direct involvement in designing and maintaining the internal control structure.

TRANSFER PRICING

If a U.S. company's foreign subsidiary sells crude oil to its U.S. parent at a transfer price of $60 per barrel when the market price is $58 per barrel, then $2 per barrel of profit is shifted from the U.S. parent to the foreign subsidiary. To prevent such shifts of income, the IRS imposes significant nondeductible penalties if transfer prices are not transacted at arm's length. To avoid such penalties, the company must:

- Determine a method to support transfer pricing at arm's length

- Maintain documentation supporting arm's length transfer pricing

- Provide this documentation in a timely manner to the IRS if requested

HOST GOVERNMENT AUDITORS

Auditors of the host government will periodically review the transactions and records associated with E&P venture operations. Depending on the nature of their audit and the location of supporting invoices and other documentation, they may request to work in the company's home office location as opposed to the field. These auditors are generally highly skeptical of the company's actions and are interested in determining the types of profits earned in the venture's activities.

A number of items are typically discussed and negotiated between a host country and an E&P company as a result of these audits:

- **Overhead.** What types of home office costs are the company being reimbursed for? Are they reasonable, supportable, and directly related to the venture's operations? What is the basis of the company's overhead allocation to the venture? Are such allocations consistent between years and consistently applied to the company's other ventures?

- **Technical Staff.** What is the nature of the work invoiced for home office technical staff? How are billing rates determined? What is the procedure for technical staff to account for time spent on each venture?

- **Costs in excess of AFEs.** What is the nature of costs incurred over the approved AFE amount? Are these excess costs subject to cost recovery?

Reports of audit findings and their subsequent resolutions are generally a lengthy and time consuming process that involves numerous levels of management.

DISMANTLEMENT, RESTORATION, AND ABANDONMENT OBLIGATIONS

Dismantlement, restoration, and abandonment of producing fields have become increasingly important to international E&P companies. Petroleum environmental issues are complex and depend heavily on local standards. The industry has sought to insulate itself from the impact of these obligations through the concepts of host country ownership of resources and reversionary production rights established in favor of the host country. Under most arrangements, economic production life remains with or reverts to the host country. With the transfer of a producing asset goes the obligation to abandon the field. Often, the contract provides that title to the fixed assets (wells, storage facilities, and pipelines) vests in the host country either at inception or at payout, and with the title goes the abandonment obligation.

If a host country requires environmental impact studies and the restoration of an area to its pre-existing conditions, the standard is clear. The extent of the obligation and costs associated with abandonment can be forecasted. Total costs and plans for abandonment are incorporated into the development plan.

Some PSCs require companies to put money into a sinking fund to pay for future abandonment and reclamation. If these sinking fund payments are considered recoverable costs (reducing profit oil), the government is actually sharing in dismantlement and reclamation costs to the extent it shares in the corresponding reduction in profit oil. When the company fully recovers all of its costs, money is deposited into a sinking fund, and it is allowed to recover those deposits from future production. The net cost is zero, and money is available to pay for dismantlement and reclamation expenses as they are incurred.

U.S. GAAP accounting for dismantlement, restoration, and abandonment obligations is the same whether for a U.S. property or a foreign property. Chapter 20 in this book provides additional information about these requirements.

By its very nature, petroleum exploration is risky and uncertain. Since most exploration ventures are unsuccessful, companies should carefully assess the impact of terminating their exploration efforts in a host country at certain well-defined times. A key factor to consider is whether the company will have the ability to withdraw without penalty after fulfilling certain benchmark work obligations.

• • •

---

1 Amortizing by the amount of cost recovery proceeds has the same effect on income as crediting the proceeds as a recovery of capitalized costs. The former increases revenue and expense by the proceeds amount; the latter does not.

2 2006 reports from ExxonMobil, Chevron, Marathon, ConocoPhillips, and Anadarko were reviewed for treatment of disclosures related to production sharing contracts.

26

BASIC E&P
INCOME TAX RULES

Key Concepts:

- **Definitions of property and economic interest in tax accounting**

- **Cost elements of a leasehold**

- **Tax elections for intangible drilling costs (IDC)**

- **Cost and percentage depletion calculations**

- **Sharing arrangements and forms of organizing E&P companies**

- **At-risk and passive loss rules**

- **Alternative minimum tax (AMT) calculations**

This chapter presents an overview of U.S. federal income tax laws and regulations unique to petroleum exploration and production. Countervailing tax policy considerations, as well as the unique nature of the oil and gas industry, combine to make taxation of oil and gas a complex and highly specialized area.

E&P companies should not rely solely on information found in this chapter. Outside professional advice and direct reference to current tax laws and regulations are advised.

OVERVIEW OF U.S. TAX ON OIL AND GAS

The U.S. does not levy a special federal tax on income from oil and gas production. This contrasts with countries such as the United Kingdom, which assesses a petroleum revenue tax, and Australia that applies a petroleum resource rent tax. Instead, income from oil and gas activity is taxed within the parameters of the regular income tax system.

Domestic tax laws provide many special rules for determining income and deductions from oil and gas exploration and production activities. To properly apply them, petroleum accountants must understand basic concepts in the industry including terms such as "property," "mineral interest," and "economic interest."

The federal tax system is complicated by the existence of a second, parallel system of income taxation that generates what is called the alternative minimum tax (AMT). As the name suggests, it was enacted to ensure that all profitable businesses pay some amount of tax. The federal income tax liability for a taxpayer is the higher of the regular income tax or AMT amount.

AMT has its own rules for determining taxable income. It is particularly relevant to the oil and gas industry because many deductions under the regular tax rules are added back, adjusted, or recalculated to arrive at AMT.

Numerous states and some cities levy their own income taxes. In most cases, state and local taxes are based on federal taxable income with certain adjustments allowed.

Local jurisdictions impose other taxes also, including real and personal property taxes and sales taxes. Virtually every state with oil and gas production imposes a tax (referred to as a production tax or severance tax) on the value or quantity of oil and gas produced within its jurisdiction.

THE OIL AND GAS PROPERTY

A clear understanding of the concept of property is important because it forms the cornerstone of U.S. oil and gas taxation. Almost all tax accounting for oil and gas activity is analyzed on a property-by-property basis, whether one is computing depletion deductions, calculating intangible drilling cost deductions, or figuring the gain or loss on property disposition.

Despite its emphasis, U.S. tax law is almost silent on how to define the term. IRC Sec. 614(a) states:

The term property means each separate interest owned by the taxpayer in each mineral deposit in each separate tract or parcel of land.

For purposes of this definition, the term interest means an economic interest. Thus, an oil and gas property constitutes:

1. Each separate economic interest owned by a taxpayer

2. In each separate mineral deposit

3. In each separate tract or parcel or land

In general, tax authorities have interpreted the brief definition literally: meaning that each mineral interest (e.g., royalty interest, working interest, overriding royalty interest, production payment, or net profits interest) is a separate property unless the same types of interests were acquired at the same time, from the same assignor, and in geographically **contiguous** tracts of land. If more than one operating interest in the same tract of land is held, a taxpayer must combine the interests and treat them as a single property unless an election is made to treat them as separate. Two or more separate nonoperating interests in the same tract of land may be combined, with the permission of the IRS, upon demonstration by a taxpayer that the principal purpose of the combination is not tax avoidance. Nonoperating interests cannot be combined with operating interests.

ECONOMIC INTEREST

Whether a property interest is considered an economic interest is an important distinction. Only the owner of an economic interest may deduct depletion from the oil and gas income generated by a producing property. U.S. tax regulations provide the following description of an economic interest:

> An economic interest is possessed in every case in which the taxpayer has acquired by investment any interest in minerals in place . . . and secures, by any form of legal relationship, income derived from the extraction of the mineral . . . to which he must look for a return of his capital. [Treas. Reg. Sec. 1.611-1(b)]

A large body of case law has developed around this description to clarify the concept. For tax purposes, an economic interest generally must meet all of the following four requirements:

1. The interest represents a capital interest in the minerals in place,

2. The interest provides the right to share in minerals produced or the right to proceeds from their sale,

3. The interest holder looks solely to the proceeds from extraction for a return on investment, and

4. The interest is held as a matter of legal right.

The following common property interests are considered economic interests and their holders are eligible to claim depletion on income derived from them: royalty interest, working interest, overriding royalty interest, and net profits interest.

A production payment may be treated as an economic interest for tax purposes if one of two conditions is met: (1) the production payment is carved out of a property and assigned to a party in exchange for an agreement to develop the property, or (2) the production payment is retained by the lessor in a leasing transaction. Production payments that do not meet these criteria are viewed as rights to repayment of a loan.

LEASEHOLD

Acquisition costs of an oil and gas property are commonly referred to as the leasehold basis, depletable basis, or leasehold. For tax purposes, the term leasehold reflects all the costs of acquisition that must be capitalized. Among these costs are:

- Geological and geophysical costs allocable to the property

- Purchase price allocable to the mineral interest in the case of an acquisition of a fee interest

- Lease bonus paid in the case of a leasing transaction

- Finders' fees, commissions, legal fees, and other professional fees incurred in the acquisition

- Delay rentals that have been capitalized

If an oil and gas property is productive, capitalized costs of the leasehold are recovered through depletion deductions over the productive life of the property. If the property is determined to be worthless (as a result of events such as abandonment, lease termination, cessation of production, or drilling of a dry hole), then capitalized leasehold costs must be deducted from income in the year the property is deemed worthless.

Timing of the deduction for worthlessness is often an issue; it is important for the property holder to identify with a specific event to fix the time of worthlessness. Actions of the property holder are important in determining whether the property should be deemed worthless for tax purposes. For example, even if a dry hole was drilled on a lease, the lease would not be deemed worthless if a delay rental is later paid or additional exploration and development work are undertaken.

GEOLOGICAL AND GEOPHYSICAL COSTS

In general, G&G costs that lead to the acquisition of a property must be capitalized as part of the cost of the property. Current tax law requires such costs after August 8, 2005, to be amortized over 24 months. Costs paid or incurred after May 17, 2006, by major integrated oil companies as defined in IRC Sec. 167(h)(5), are amortized over a period of five years. Costs not leading to an acquisition are deducted in the year paid or incurred.

Typically, G&G costs are incurred in two distinct phases:

1. Initial costs are incurred in a broad reconnaissance survey of a large area to determine which specific areas warrant closer study. All G&G costs incurred in this phase are allocated equally among the specifically identified areas—so-called areas of interest—without regard to their relative sizes. If only one area of interest is identified, all costs are allocated to that area. If no area of interest is identified, all of the G&G costs incurred in the initial survey are deducted in the year paid or incurred.

2. Once areas of interest have been identified, detailed surveys are conducted. Costs of these additional surveys are allocated to the specific area of interest.

If individual properties within an area of interest are leased, total geological and geophysical costs related to that area of interest, plus the costs of the detailed survey and an allocable portion of the reconnaissance survey, are allocated to the properties acquired on an acreage basis.

If no leases are acquired within areas of interest, then all costs incurred in or allocated to those areas are deducted in the year in which the areas are abandoned.

DEVELOPMENT COSTS

For tax purposes, costs incurred in developing an oil and gas property are divided into two categories: (1) tangible equipment costs, and (2) intangible drilling and development costs. Proper classification is important because their tax treatments differ significantly. In addition, petroleum accountants should understand tax rules that apply to the costs of dry holes.

TANGIBLE EQUIPMENT COSTS

Purchased equipment that has salvage value associated with it is recorded in the tangible equipment costs account. This category can include surface and production casing, wellhead equipment, tanks, pumps, separators, and other machinery.

Tangible equipment costs are capitalized and recovered over the life of the equipment by means of depreciation. IRS guidelines define the useful life of all types of tangible equipment for depreciation purposes. Under current law, most tangible production equipment has a tax depreciable life of seven years. Generally, a longer recovery life is required for AMT depreciation purposes.

Lease and well equipment may be depreciated under a units-of-production method also. This method is handled essentially the same way as cost depletion and requires no adjustment for AMT purposes.

Certain property located on current or former Indian reservation property may be depreciated using a depreciation life significantly shorter than regular depreciation allows. Most of this eligible property is located in the state of Oklahoma.

INTANGIBLE DRILLING COSTS

Intangible drilling costs (IDC) are costs that have no salvage value and are incidental to and necessary for drilling wells or preparing wells for oil and gas production. IDC is usually the single largest category of expense associated with drilling a well.

Examples of IDC include all amounts paid for labor, fuel, repairs, hauling, rents, and supplies used in the following activities:

- Drilling a well

- Clearing and draining ground, road-making, and surveying ground in preparation for drilling a well

- Assembling derricks, tanks, pipelines, and other physical structures necessary for drilling and preparing a well for production

A taxpayer holding an operating right to a U.S. oil and gas property must elect whether to capitalize IDC or deduct it currently. The election must be made in the first year the taxpayer pays or incurs IDC. In most cases, an election is made to deduct IDC.

Because of the binding nature of this election, taxpayers should carefully consider their options. An election to deduct IDC currently is made by simply deducting the costs on the tax return in the first year such costs are paid or incurred. Most taxpayers attach a statement to the income tax return for the year in which such costs are first incurred.

Those who fail to deduct IDC in the first year are deemed to have elected to capitalize them. These taxpayers must allocate IDC to the leasehold account and recover them through depletion. When expenditures are connected to the installation of tangible equipment, these amounts are allocated to the equipment account and are recovered through depreciation.

Taxpayers electing to deduct IDC in their first year of operations have subsequent annual elections available to them. They may elect to capitalize all or a portion of the IDC incurred in a tax year. The capitalized portion is amortized ratably over a 60-month period beginning in the month costs are paid or incurred. IDC capitalized under this option is not treated as a tax preference item for AMT purposes.

Integrated oil and gas companies may deduct only 70 percent of IDC at the time those costs are incurred. The remaining 30 percent must be capitalized and amortized ratably over a 60-month period beginning in the month the costs are paid or incurred.

IDC for wells located outside the U.S. may not be deducted currently. At the election of the taxpayer, such costs are included in the adjusted basis of the oil and gas property for purposes of computing depletion. Alternatively, the costs can be amortized over a 120-month period.

The election to deduct IDC for federal income tax purposes extends only to those intangible costs incurred in drilling a well and installing equipment in the well up through the point that valves are placed at the wellhead to control production. Thus, labor costs and other intangible costs to install flow lines, treating equipment, and storage tanks are not subject to the IDC election for tax purposes. Instead, they are treated as part of the cost of tangible equipment. Other intangible costs incurred after the wellhead is installed, but not related to installing equipment (e.g., removal of the rig from the drilling site and restoring the location), are treated as IDC for tax purposes.

In general, tax laws also govern the definition of tangible costs. Tangible asset costs are all costs of the physical assets (such as casing, pumps, production tubing, flow lines, and separators), along with installation costs of surface equipment. Accounting theory provides that the costs of installing equipment, including subsurface equipment such as casing, are included in the cost of tangible assets. Because most companies elect to expense IDC for income tax purposes, and because the tax laws include installation costs of equipment (up through the point that control valves are installed) in the election, these amounts are generally treated as intangible costs. For financial accounting purposes, the distinction is not important because intangible drilling costs are treated in the same way as tangible costs.

GUIDANCE ON WELL COST CLASSIFICATION

Proper classification of well costs as IDC or tangible costs is an important issue for an E&P company. It is critical for joint venture operators to properly classify the venture's well costs when billing joint venture partners for their share of costs. This allows all members of the venture to properly treat costs in accordance with their own elections.

Treas. Reg. Sec. 1.612-4 describes some items not included in IDC:

c) *Non-optional items distinguished.*

1. Capital items: The option with respect to intangible drilling and development costs does not apply to expenditures by which the taxpayer acquires tangible property ordinarily considered as having a salvage value. Examples of such items are the costs of the actual materials in those structures which are constructed in the wells and on the property, and the cost of drilling tools, pipe, casing, tubing, tanks, engines, boilers, machines, etc. The option does not apply to any expenditures for wages, fuel, repairs, hauling, supplies, etc., in connection with equipment, facilities, or structures not incident to or necessary for the drilling of wells, such as structures for storing or treating oil or gas. These are capital items and are returnable through depreciation.

2. Expense items: Expenditures which must be charged off as expense, regardless of the option provided by this section, are those for labor, fuel, repairs, hauling, supplies, etc., in connection with the operation of the wells and of other facilities on the property for the production of oil and gas.

Revenue Ruling 70-414 further explains items to be treated as IDC and those costs that should be excluded from IDC:

[IDC] excludes expenditures incurred in installing production facilities. The items thus excluded consist of expenditures relating to the installation of equipment such as pumping equipment, flow lines, separators, storage tanks, treating equipment, and salt water disposal equipment. Equipment of a character that is ordinarily considered as having a salvage value, whether it consists of production facilities or equipment necessary for the completion of a well, including cost of casing in a well (even though cemented in the well to such an extent that it has no net salvage value), is a depreciable item, the cost of which may be recovered only through the depreciation allowance. *Harper Oil Company v. U.S.*, 425 F. 2d 1335 (10th Cir. 1979), 70-1 USTC 9330. A producing well is completed when the casing, including the so-called *Christmas tree*, has been installed.

Costs of installing the following items are not subject to the IDC expense option provided for in Treas. Reg. Sec. 1.612-4(a):

- Oil well pumps (upon initial completion of the well) including the necessary housing structures

- Oil well pumps (after the well has flowed for a time) including the necessary housing structures

- Oil well separators including the necessary housing structures

- Pipelines from the wellhead to oil storage tanks on the producing lease

- Oil storage tanks on the producing lease

- Salt water disposal equipment including any necessary pipelines

- Pipelines from the mouth of a gas well to the first point of control such as a common carrier pipeline, natural gasoline plant, or carbon black plant

- Recycling equipment including any necessary pipelines

- Pipelines from oil storage tanks on the producing leasehold to a common carrier pipeline

Common IDC items appear in the following representative list:

1. Cost before drilling begins

   a) Work performed by the geologist to determine the exact location of the drill site (not G&G work to select leases)

   b) Bulldozer costs for clearing well site, digging slush pits, building roads, and survey costs involved in staking well location

   c) Cost of pads (such as gravel) for drilling rig

   d) Cost of bridges

   e) Laying flow lines for water to be used in drilling

   f) Installation of tanks for water and fuel for drilling purposes

   g) Moving and erecting drilling rig (if company owned)

   h) Construction of racks for drill pipe and other tubular goods to be used in the drilling process

2. Costs during drilling process

   a) If a contractor drills the well, the contractor's bill constitutes the majority of IDC costs in this category. Drilling mud and possibly other items may represent additional charges to the operator.

   b) If the well is drilled by the operator's rig, then the wages paid the crew, drilling rig maintenance and supplies, depreciation on the rig, mud, water, fuel, power, chemicals, bits, reamers, and company overhead related to the operation of the rig represent IDC charges.

3. Completion costs

   a) Drill stem tests, well logging, and other testing such as cores and side wall sampling

   b) Perforating, cementing, fracturing, acidizing

   c) Transportation and installation of subsurface equipment

4. Charges after well is completed

   a) Removing drilling equipment from the location (if operator owned)

   b) Restoring the land by filling slush pits and grading the area

   c) Repair of surface damages incurred during drilling

   d) Plugging and abandonment costs (if the well is a dry hole)

DRY HOLE COST

If a well is drilled and found to be a dry hole, the development costs associated with it should be deducted as dry hole costs. Leasehold costs may or may not be currently deductible depending on whether the lease is deemed worthless.

> *According to the Energy Information Administration (EIA), in 2006 there were 5,880 dry exploratory and developmental wells drilled in the U.S. Approximately 65% of these were development wells, and the remaining 35% were exploratory wells.*
>
> **Source:** *http://tonto.eia.doe.gov/dnav/pet/pet_crd_wellend_s1_m.htm, Energy Information Administration, as of April 19, 2007*

DEPLETION

By their nature, producing oil and gas properties are wasting assets. U.S. tax law recognizes this by providing a depletion deduction in limited cases to owners of the economic interest in the asset.

Two methods exist for computing a depletion allowance: (1) cost depletion, and (2) percentage (or statutory) depletion. Those taxpayers eligible to claim percentage depletion must compute depletion using both methods and claim the higher of the two.

COST DEPLETION

Under cost depletion, units of production from each property during the year are divided by total proved reserves attributable to the property at the beginning of the year to calculate a cost factor. This factor is multiplied by net leasehold costs of the property (capitalized minerals costs less depletion previously taken) to arrive at a cost depletion amount.

SAFE HARBOR ELECTION

During 2004, the IRS provided a safe harbor election that allows taxpayers to estimate probable or prospective reserves for purposes of computing cost depletion (reference Revenue Procedure 2004-19). By making the election, taxpayers can simplify the appropriate quantity of probable and prospective reserves for the tax cost depletion calculations. Once elected, the company's estimate of its total recoverable units for probable and prospective reserves is equal to 105 percent of its proved reserves. The oil and gas company must attach a statement electing the safe harbor to the federal tax return for the first taxable year of the election. The election is effective until revoked and is non-revocable in the first year elected.

PERCENTAGE DEPLETION

The percentage depletion method (also referred to as statutory depletion) provides for deduction of a specified percentage of gross revenue from each property. Currently, the depletion rate is 15 percent for nonmarginal well production. Such depletion is also limited to a percentage of the property's taxable income (before the deduction); in 2006, the ceiling was 100 percent of taxable income.

Percentage depletion is not generally available to integrated oil and gas companies' U.S. production. Foreign production is not eligible either. Independent producers and royalty owners also face limitations—their percentage depletion deduction is limited to U.S. production of 1,000 equivalent barrels of oil per day and cannot exceed 65 percent of total taxable income (before the deduction) for the year. Amounts disallowed due to the 65 percent cap may be carried forward subject to the 65 percent limit each year.

ALLOWABLE DEPLETION

Allowable depletion is the higher of cost or percentage depletion. It reduces a taxpayer's basis in each mineral property. Once the basis is reduced to zero, cost depletion can no longer be claimed. Percentage depletion can be claimed, however, for as long as the property continues to produce oil and gas.

A special concession exists for properties considered marginally profitable including:

1. Oil and gas produced from a domestic stripper well property (generally 15 barrel equivalent or less of production per day per well).

2. Oil from a domestic property which is substantially all heavy oil (gravity of 20 degrees API or less).

Independent producers or royalty owners holding marginal properties receive an increase of one percent for each whole dollar that the reference price for crude oil in the immediately preceding calendar year is less than $20 per barrel. Reference price is a defined amount based on the average wellhead price in the U.S.; it is published by the IRS each calendar year. For 2006, with a marginal depletion rate of 15 percent the maximum depletion rate under this concession was 15 percent (as the reference price was greater than $20 per barrel). In addition, the 100 percent of net income limitation is suspended for marginal properties for any taxable year beginning after December 31, 1997, and before January 1, 2008.

ILLUSTRATION OF DEPLETION CALCULATION

Operator O acquired a mineral lease and began drilling in January 2006. The well was successful and production began in April. Over the remainder of the year, 11,000 barrels (bbls) of oil were produced and sold for total gross revenue after royalties of $577,500. Drilling and production expenses on the property for the year amounted to $492,500, leaving $85,000 of taxable income from the property before deducting depletion. At December 31, 2006, the property had a leasehold basis of $500,000 before depletion for the current year. Mineral reserves at December 31, 2006, totaled 360,000 bbls. O's taxable income from all sources for the year, before depletion, was $120,000. The mineral interest is a U.S. property and Operator O is an independent producer.

Cost Depletion:

$$\frac{\text{2006 Production}}{\text{Beginning of year reserves}} \times \text{Leasehold basis at end of year}$$

$$\frac{11{,}000}{360{,}000 + 11{,}000} \times \$500{,}000 = \underline{\$14{,}825}$$

Percentage Depletion:

Gross revenue	$577,500
Statutory rate	x 15%
Percentage depletion before limitation	$ 86,625
Limited to pre-depletion taxable income from the property	$ 85,000
Taxable income (all sources) before depletion	$120,000
Limitation based on taxable income	x 65%
Taxable income limitation	$ 78,000
Percentage depletion after limitations	$ 78,000

Allowable depletion (greater of $14,825 cost depletion or $78,000 percentage depletion)	$ 78,000
Leasehold basis at beginning of next year ($500,000 - $78,000)	$422,000
Percentage depletion carryover to succeeding years ($85,000 - $78,000)	$ 7,000

SHARING ARRANGEMENTS

To reduce the costs and risks of developing oil and gas properties, it is common for two or more parties to join together in a sharing arrangement to explore jointly for oil and gas. A sharing arrangement occurs when one party contributes cash, property, services, or other consideration in exchange for an interest in the mineral property. Farmouts are a prevalent type of sharing arrangement where the owner of an operating interest assigns all or a portion of the operating interest to another party in return for the assignee's assumption of all or a portion of the costs of developing the property.

Sharing arrangements take many forms including:

- Drill a well in exchange for the entire operating interest (the assignor may or may not retain a nonoperating interest)

- Drill a well in exchange for a portion of the operating interest

- Drill a well in exchange for a nonoperating interest

- Pledge cash to the development of a property in exchange for an operating or nonoperating interest in that property

- Participate in a mixed sharing arrangement in which cash or other consideration, as well as development work, is contributed in exchange for an interest in a property

Simple, unmixed sharing arrangements are considered nontaxable transactions. If no consideration passes between the parties other than a contribution to or assumption of an obligation to develop a property then neither party realizes gain or loss from the transaction. This concept is frequently referred to as the pool-of-capital doctrine. Other U.S. tax principles generally applicable to sharing arrangements are:

- Only the party that incurs and pays a cost can deduct it for tax purposes.

- Only operating interest owners can deduct IDC and depreciation, and then only to the extent of their fractional share of the operating interest. The fractional share of IDC or equipment costs incurred in excess of the fractional share owned in the operating interest must be capitalized and added to depletable leasehold costs.

As an example, assume X agrees with Y to drill and equip a well on Y's undeveloped property, at no cost to Y, in exchange for a 75 percent operating interest. X incurs $100,000 of IDC and $40,000 in equipment costs.

- X can deduct $75,000 of IDC ($100,000 x 75%).

- X can depreciate $30,000 as equipment costs ($40,000 x 75%).

- The remaining $25,000 of IDC and $10,000 of equipment costs are added to depletable leasehold costs.

- Y has no right to deduct any costs since they were borne entirely by X.

The tax consequences of entering into a mixed sharing arrangement are more complex. In general, the transaction must be divided into two parts: (1) the pool-of-capital doctrine is applied to development work contributions, and (2) potential tax gain or loss flows from the contribution of cash or other consideration.

FORMS OF ORGANIZATION

Because of the economic uncertainties of exploring for and producing oil and gas, two or more parties often join together to locate and develop prospects. These joint efforts take a variety of legal forms: joint ventures, partnerships, corporations, and certain hybrid entities (such as S corporations and limited liability companies which combine the legal and tax characteristics of partnerships and corporations).

JOINT VENTURE

It is common in the U. S. for working interest owners to jointly develop a property. Their rights and obligations are spelled out in two documents: (1) a joint venture agreement, and (2) a joint operating agreement. Under a typical joint operating agreement, one working interest owner is designated as the operator of the joint venture, while others assume the role of nonoperators.

Joint venture participants have an important decision to make about their tax status— whether to be treated as a partnership or elect out of the partnership tax provisions. In practice, most choose to elect out. If participants meet the criteria and elect to be excluded from partnership provisions, then entity-level tax accounting is not required. Instead, participants independently report their shares of revenue and expenses for tax purposes. In addition, each participant can make an election to expense or capitalize IDC.

Joint venture participants may elect to be excluded from partnership provisions if the following three conditions are met:

1. Each participant owns an interest in the oil and gas property as a co-owner, either in fee or under a lease granting exclusive operating rights.

2. Participants reserve the right to take in-kind or dispose of their individual shares of production.

3. Participants do not jointly sell the oil and gas produced, although each may delegate the right to sell his or her share to one of the participants for a period not to exceed one year. This right can be renewed annually.

PARTNERSHIP

Partnerships are separate entities for tax and legal purposes. In contrast to a joint venture, accounting for revenues and expenses is performed at the entity level. Partnerships file tax returns, but pay no entity-level income tax. Instead, the partnership is treated as a conduit and individual partners account for their allocable shares of net income or loss and for their shares of credits.

Two types of partnerships are used: general and limited. In a general partnership, all partners have unlimited personal liability for the legal obligations of the partnership. A limited partnership has one or more general partners with unlimited personal liability and one or more classes of limited partners. In general, the personal liability of a limited partner does not exceed the partner's contributed capital. Because of relatively high risks in oil and gas exploration and production, limited partnerships are a common form of organization, particularly when operations are funded by outside investors. However, investors are often subject to passive loss rules if the form of entity limits an investor's legal liability.

Many important tax elections are made by the partnership rather than by individual partners. These actions are binding on all the partners. For example, the partnership elects whether to capitalize or expense IDC, and it determines whether oil and gas properties will be combined or remain separate for tax purposes. Frequently, a partnership is used to make special allocations of deductible items where one party contributes a disproportionate amount of the costs. Although most income and deduction items are accounted for at the entity level, depletion is calculated only at the partner level. The partnership is obligated to provide partners with enough information to calculate depletion deductions.

CORPORATION

A corporation is a separate legal entity organized under state law. It offers its shareholders legal liability limited to their investment in the corporation. Corporations file their own income tax returns and pay federal and state taxes on net income. Profits are distributed to shareholders in the form of dividends, which are subject to taxation at the shareholder level. Thus, the price paid for the limited liability provided by a corporation is two levels of tax on its distributed profit.

S CORPORATION

An S corporation is a hybrid entity that combines the legal characteristics of a corporation with many of the tax advantages of a partnership. Other than for federal income tax purposes, an S corporation acts like any other corporation. It is incorporated under state law and offers its shareholders limited legal liability. For income tax purposes, S corporations are conduit entities that pay no income tax at the corporate level. Line items of income, loss, and credit flow directly to shareholders' individual returns. Similar to oil and gas partnerships, crucial elections such as the treatment of IDC and whether to aggregate or separate oil and gas properties are made at the S corporation level.

Eligibility for S corporation status is strictly limited. A corporation must file an election statement subject to IRS approval, and five requirements must be met:

1. The corporation must be a domestic corporation that is not a member of an affiliated group.

2. The corporation may have no more than 100 shareholders for tax years beginning after December 31, 2004.

3. The shareholders may be only individuals, estates, or certain qualifying trusts.

4. No shareholder may be a non-resident alien.

5. The corporation may have only one class of stock.

The treatment of S corporations for state income taxes varies. Some states require a separate S corporation election for state tax purposes; others accept the federal election. Some states fail to recognize S corporations as pass-through entities and treat them like regular corporations for state tax purposes.

LIMITED LIABILITY COMPANY

A limited liability company is an entity formed under state statutes that allow it to combine the corporate characteristic of limited liability with the tax-conduit benefits of a partnership. Because of widespread use, most states now have limited liability company statutes in place. Oil and gas entities that seek the advantages of a hybrid form of organization, but do not meet S corporation rules, often consider limited liability company status.

LOSS LIMITATIONS

Investors in the oil and gas industry encounter the complex provisions of U.S. tax law that limit the use of losses to offset income from other unrelated activities. These loss limitation rules fall into two broad categories: (1) at-risk rules, and (2) passive loss rules.

AT-RISK RULES

Under current at-risk rules, individuals engaged in oil and gas exploration and production can deduct a loss for tax purposes only to the extent they are at-risk for such activity at year-end. An individual is considered at-risk to the extent of the cash and adjusted basis of any property he or she contributed to the activity, plus amounts borrowed to fund the activity for which the individual is personally liable or for which the individual has pledged property (other than property used in the oil and gas activity) as security for the loan. For purposes of deducting partnership losses, partners in an oil and gas partnership are at-risk to the extent of their contributions to the partnership (assuming the amounts contributed are at-risk at the individual level) and generally to the extent of loans to the partnership for which the partners could be held personally liable.

Loss deductions disallowed due to at-risk limitations are not necessarily lost. Disallowed losses can be carried forward indefinitely and deducted in succeeding tax years when at-risk amounts with respect to the activity are increased.

At-risk rules also contain anti-abuse provisions which address abrupt year-end increases in the at-risk amount. If a partner's at-risk amount decreases immediately after year-end, the partner/taxpayer must demonstrate the transactions were undertaken for valid business purposes and not merely to avoid the at-risk rules.

PASSIVE LOSS RULES

Passive loss rules provide that investors cannot use losses or tax credits generated by passive activities to offset wage and salary income, business profits from activities in which the investor materially participates, or investment income such as dividends, interest, or royalties. Instead, passive losses and credits can only be used to offset income from other passive activities.

Disallowed passive losses and credits are not irretrievably lost, but are suspended and carried forward to offset passive income in future years. Suspended losses and credits may be used in full in the year in which the passive investment is disposed of in a taxable transaction.

Passive loss rules apply to individuals, estates, trusts, and certain closely held subchapter C corporations. They do not apply directly to a partnership or a subchapter S corporation, but rather to a partner's or a subchapter S corporation shareholder's distributive share of passive losses and credits.

In general, a passive activity is any trade or business activity (including oil and gas activity) in which the taxpayer does not materially participate. To meet the material participation standard, a taxpayer must maintain regular, continuous, and substantial participation in the activity. Due to the nature of the oil and gas industry, passive loss rules do not apply to any investor who holds a working interest in an oil and gas property directly or through an entity that does not limit the investor's legal liability. The working interest exception applies regardless of the investor's level of participation in the activity.

For this purpose, a working interest is solely the interest burdened with the cost of developing the property. Interests created out of the working interest such as overriding royalties, net profits interests, or production payments do not qualify for the working interest exception.

ALTERNATIVE MINIMUM TAX

The alternative minimum tax (AMT) was enacted to ensure that profitable businesses, even those using lawful tax incentives to reduce income tax liabilities, pay some amount of federal income tax. A form of minimum tax has existed in the law since 1969; but it was after 1986 when the scope of AMT was broadened significantly. From that point forward, it became a major issue for taxpayers in general — and the oil and gas industry in particular.

AMT is effectively a separate tax system that runs parallel to the regular federal income tax system. Alternative minimum taxable income (AMTI) is calculated by increasing regular taxable income by certain tax preferences and adjustments.

For individuals, AMTI in excess of an exemption amount (which phases out over certain income levels) is subject to a 26 percent tax. Maximum AMTI at this tax level is $175,000. A 28 percent tax is levied on AMTI that exceeds $175,000. For corporations, AMTI in excess of an exemption amount ($40,000, and which also phases out over certain income levels) is taxed at a flat rate of 20 percent.

The AMT liability can be fully offset by foreign tax credits calculated under special rules. Amounts of AMT paid after 1986 may be carried forward indefinitely as a credit against any future regular tax liability in excess of the AMT for that year.

For tax years beginning before January 1, 1993, the AMT was of particular concern to the oil and gas industry because two of the most significant regular tax deductions—IDC and percentage depletion—were considered add-back preference items in the determination of AMTI.

The burden of AMT was greatly reduced with passage of the Energy Policy Act of 1992, which repealed the excess percentage depletion preference as well as the excess IDC preference (with some limitations). Repeal of these preference items is limited to non-integrated oil companies and is effective for taxable years beginning after 1992. Excess IDC is still considered an add-back preference item to the extent that repeal of the excess IDC preference results in a more than 40 percent reduction in a taxpayer's AMTI.

Under pre-1993 law, IDC was a tax preference to the extent that excess IDC exceeded 65 percent of a taxpayer's annual net income from oil and gas. Excess IDC is the amount of IDC deducted for tax purposes in excess of the amount which would have been deducted had the IDC been capitalized and deducted ratably over 120 months (beginning with the month in which production from the property began). This calculation must still be made under the current law to determine whether the repeal of the excess IDC preference has resulted in a greater than 40 percent reduction in what would have been AMTI prior to the repeal. The amount of excess IDC, which causes a greater than 40 percent reduction in AMTI, will remain a tax preference in the computation of AMT.

Taxpayers subject to AMT because of the IDC preference may be able to reduce their IDC preference by electing to capitalize all or a portion of IDC incurred in a particular year and amortize it over five years. Careful analysis is important so that neither too little nor too much IDC is capitalized and maximum tax benefits are obtained.

Most of the remaining adjustments required to determine AMTI are not unique to the oil and gas industry. Adjustments commonly encountered by E&P companies are:

- For purposes of regular tax computation, tangible assets are often depreciated using a special accelerated method of cost recovery over relatively short asset lives. For AMT purposes, depreciation must be recalculated by using a less accelerated method over generally longer asset lives (for tax years beginning after 1998, the depreciable life for AMT purposes is the same as the life used for regular tax purposes). This results in a smaller deduction for AMT purposes.

- Gain or loss on the disposition of depreciable tangible equipment must be recomputed using the adjusted basis computed using the AMT depreciation life and method.

- Net operating loss deductions must be recomputed using the AMT rules. These rules generally reduce the amount of allowable deductions.

- In the case of corporations with adjusted current earnings (ACE) in excess of taxable income, the calculation of AMT requires that 75 percent of the excess be included in the calculation of AMTI. ACE is a defined term generally modeled after the concept of U.S. tax earnings and profits.

It should be noted that small corporations are not subject to AMT. Average annual gross receipts not exceeding $7.5 million for the prior three-year period will generally qualify a company as a small corporation.

ILLUSTRATION OF CORPORATE AMT CALCULATION

Regular taxable income	$ 50,000
Plus (minus) adjustments:	
Depreciation adjustment	5,500
AMT adjustment to asset disposition	(2,000)
Plus tax preferences:	
Excess IDC	125,000
ACE adjustment	5,000
AMTI if excess IDC preference had not been repealed	183,500
IDC preference adjustment (repeal of excess IDC preference to it would result in not more than 40% reduction in AMTI)	(73,400)
AMTI	110,100
Exemption	(40,000)
AMT base	$ 70,100
AMT ($70,100 x 20%)	$ 14,020
Regular tax ($50,000 x 15% applicable corp. tax rate)	$ 7,500
Tax liability (greater of AMT or regular tax)	$ 14,020

INCOME TAX CREDITS

IRC SEC. 43 CREDIT FOR ENHANCED OIL RECOVERY

IRC Sec. 43 allows an income tax credit for qualifying costs paid or incurred as part of an enhanced oil recovery (EOR) project. The credit is equal to 15 percent of qualified costs attributable to a domestic EOR project. Domestic projects that involve application of a qualified tertiary recovery method are eligible. They must be located in the U.S. and meet other criteria specified in tax regulations. In addition, a petroleum engineer must certify that the EOR project meets the specified requirements in Section 43. Approved qualified tertiary recovery methods include:

- Cyclic steam injection

- Steam drive injection

- In situ combustion

- Gas flood recovery methods

- Carbon dioxide augmented waterflooding

- Immiscible carbon dioxide displacement

- Immiscible nonhydrocarbon gas displacement

- Chemical flood recovery methods

- Caustic flooding

- Mobility control recovery method

Qualifying EOR costs include qualified tertiary injectant expenses, intangible drilling and development costs, and tangible property costs paid or incurred with respect to an asset that is used for the primary purpose of implementing an EOR project. The credit is phased out ratably to the extent the average price of crude oil in the preceding calendar year is greater than $28 per barrel (inflation adjusted). A complete phase-out occurs when the excess is $6.00 or greater.

OTHER INCOME TAX DEDUCTIONS

As part of the American Jobs Creation Act of 2004 signed into law on October 22, 2004, a tax deduction is provided for Qualified Production Activities ("QPA") under IRC Sec. 199. The new code section provides for a three percent deduction in 2005 and 2006, six percent in 2007-2009, and nine percent in 2010 and thereafter. For corporate taxpayers, this generally will result in a reduced federal income tax rate of 33.95 percent, 32.90 percent, and 31.85 percent, respectively, for the phase-in years on qualified production activities income ("QPAI"). The deduction is calculated as three percent, six percent, or nine percent of the lesser of QPAI or taxable income.

E&P companies, as undertakers of various production activities, may be eligible for this deduction depending on the specifics of their operations. Eligibility for and calculation of this deduction should be determined on a company-by-company basis for each company's upstream, midstream, and downstream operations.

• • •

CHAPTER

27

ACCOUNTING FOR INCOME TAXES

Key Concepts:

- Balance sheet approach to accounting for income taxes

- Permanent tax differences

- Temporary tax differences

- Categorizing temporary differences: taxable and deductible differences

- Evaluating evidence and taxable income for valuation allowance

- Financial statement disclosures for income taxes

Basis at December 31, 2006	GAAP	Tax	
Lease & well equipment	$10,000	$9,300	
Leasehold costs	$10,000	$10,200	
Liabilities not related to taxes	$12,000	$12,000	
Equity contributed	$2,400	$2,400	
Pre-tax income	$5,600	$5,600	
Temporary Differences	**GAAP**	**Tax**	**Differe**
Depreciation expense	$1,000	$1,700	($7
Depletion expense	500	300	2
Totals	$1,500	$2,000	($5
State tax expense	$284	$258	$
Permanent Differences	**GAAP**	**Tax**	**Differ**
Meals & entertainment expense	$140	$70	$
Taxable Income Computation:			
Pre-tax income	$5,600		
Tax over book depreciation expense	(700)		
Book over tax depletion expense	200		
Non-deductible meals & entertainment	70		
State taxable income	$5,170		
Current state tax expense	(258)		
Federal taxable income	$4,912		
Tax Provision Computations:			
Federal taxable income	$4,912		
Federal rate	x 35%		
Current federal tax expense	$1,719		
State taxable income	$5,170		
State rate	x 5%		
Current state tax expense	$258		
Book over tax basis	$500		
Federal rate	x 35%		
Deferred federal tax expense	$175		
Book over tax basis	$500		
State rate	x 5%		
Deferred state tax expense	$25		
Federal tax benefit from state for deferred state	($25)		
Federal rate	x 35%		

FAS 109, *Accounting for Income Taxes*, prescribes a liability method or balance sheet approach to account for deferred income taxes. Under the balance sheet approach, deferred taxes represent the future tax consequences of transactions already reported in a company's financial statements. Deferred tax liability is calculated first, and the net change in the net liability becomes the provision for deferred income taxes.

BASIC FRAMEWORK

The balance sheet approach is consistent with FASB's conceptual framework, which is an asset-and-liability approach. FAS 109 focuses on the balance sheet and on the proper determination of deferred tax assets and liabilities. It encompasses the following principles:

- A current liability or current asset is recognized whenever current year taxes are payable or refundable.

- A deferred liability or asset is recognized whenever there will be future tax effects from existing temporary differences and carryforwards from operating losses and tax credits.

- The measurement of liabilities or assets is based on enacted tax law as of the balance sheet date. Effects of anticipated changes in tax laws or rates are not considered.

- Where applicable, deferred tax assets are reduced by a valuation allowance for amounts that are not expected to be realized.

An E&P company must develop a structured approach in order to comply with the principles of FAS 109. This chapter presents a step-by-step approach to:

- Identify the types and amounts of temporary differences

- Categorize the temporary differences

- Measure the tax effects of temporary differences

- Assess the need for a valuation allowance

- Determine financial statement presentation

- Make financial statement disclosures

IDENTIFYING TYPES AND AMOUNTS OF TEMPORARY DIFFERENCES

DIFFERENCES BETWEEN GAAP AND THE TAX CODE

The objective of financial reporting is to determine income by applying generally accepted accounting principles (GAAP). GAAP is designed to "present fairly the financial condition" of a company at a particular point in time. It requires subjective evaluation of the past, as well as certain future events expected to impact the company's financial condition. As a result, a company's financial reporting income is based primarily on:

1. matching costs with associated revenues

2. estimates of recovery periods and useful lives of assets

3. allowances for impairments in the carrying values of assets

In contrast, taxable income reflects events that occurred during each taxable period by applying specific rules of the taxing jurisdictions where the operations take place. U.S. federal tax rules are codified in the Internal Revenue Code (the Code), related regulations, and court decisions. Similarly, each state also has separate tax laws, regulations, and court cases. The rules define when income is recorded and costs are recovered.

The principal objective of the tax system is to measure the correct amount of tax due within the proper period. Tax rules are intended to restrict the ability to manipulate taxable income. In general, the Code:

- Specifically defines when a liability is accruable or fixed

- Does not allow, except in rare cases, the use of loss reserves, contingency reserves, or impairment allowances

- Identifies non-taxable transactions and non-deductible expenses

- Establishes specific rules of property classification for depreciation

- Does not allow anticipated future events to be considered

- Generally measures the timing of events based on closed transactions

Most companies experience significant differences between the years in which income and deductions are reported under GAAP, and the years in which they are recognized under income tax rules. FAS 109 requires taxpayers to determine the nature of these differences which take two forms: permanent and temporary.

PERMANENT DIFFERENCES

Permanent difference is an archaic term used in APB Opinion No. 11. While not referred to in FAS 109, it is still used in discussions of accounting for income taxes. Permanent differences represent income and/or expenses that are included in financial reporting income but are not taxable or deductible for tax purposes–and are never anticipated to be. Permanent differences impact a company's current tax provision and effective tax rate, but do not impact its deferred tax account.

Permanent differences also encompass deductions for tax purposes that have no associated financial statement costs. One common permanent difference for oil and gas exploration companies is percentage depletion. Statutory depletion deductions are measured as a percentage of gross oil and gas income. The provision was added to the Code in the 1920's as a tax incentive for oil and gas exploration. A company's allowable percentage depletion deduction is computed on a property-by-property basis and is subject to limitations explained in the preceding chapter. To the extent a company's allowable percentage depletion exceeds its adjusted tax basis, a permanent difference results.

Other examples of permanent differences:

- **Tax-exempt interest**   Included in income for financial reporting, but not in determining taxable income

- **Penalties**   Deductible for financial reporting but not for tax purposes

- **Non-deductible meals**   50 percent of such expense cannot be deducted for tax purposes

- **EOR**   Enhanced oil recovery (EOR) credits available to offset tax liability

- **Goodwill amortization**   Certain goodwill is deductible for tax purposes

- **Dividends received**   Nontaxable portion of dividends received by a corporation

- **IRC Sec. 199 deduction**   Deduction allowed for domestic manufacturers and producers

TEMPORARY DIFFERENCES

Temporary differences are those differences between the tax basis of assets or liabilities and their reported amounts in the corresponding GAAP balance sheet. FAS 109's balance sheet approach requires a company to maintain both a financial reporting balance sheet and a tax balance sheet. The difference in the balance sheets is principally the result of cumulative variances in the company's financial reporting income and previous tax returns. Additionally, variances can result from the different manner in which stock and asset acquisitions are accounted for under purchase accounting. These cumulative temporary differences comprise the bases for the company's deferred tax liability or asset.

The following example demonstrates the ways permanent and temporary differences impact a company's accounts including current taxes payable, deferred tax liability or asset, and tax rate reconciliation disclosure.

Example Assumptions:

U.S. statutory tax rate of 35 percent in the current year and thereafter.

Gross state income tax rate of five percent in the current year and thereafter.

Company started on January 1, 2006.

GAAP Meals & entertainment expense for the year is $140, of which only $70 is deductible for federal and state tax purposes.

GAAP Pre-tax income is $5,600.

Basis at December 31, 2006	GAAP	Tax	
Lease & well equipment	$10,000	$9,300	
Leasehold costs	$10,000	$10,200	
Liabilities not related to taxes	$12,000	$12,000	
Equity contributed	$2,400	$2,400	
Pre-tax income	$5,600	$5,600	
Temporary Differences	GAAP	Tax	Difference
Depreciation expense	$1,000	$1,700	($700)
Depletion expense	500	300	200
Totals	$1,500	$2,000	($500)
State tax expense	$284	$258	$25
Permanent Differences	GAAP	Tax	Difference
Meals & entertainment expense	$140	$70	$70

Taxable Income Computation:

Pre-tax income	$5,600
Tax over book depreciation expense	(700)
Book over tax depletion expense	200
Non-deductible meals & entertainment	70
State taxable income	$5,170
Current state tax expense	(258)
Federal taxable income	$4,912

Tax Provision Computations:	
Federal taxable income	$4,912
Federal rate	x 35%
Current federal tax expense	$1,719
State taxable income	$5,170
State rate	x 5%
Current state tax expense	$258
Book over tax basis	$500
Federal rate	x 35%
Deferred federal tax expense	$175
Book over tax basis	$500
State rate	x 5%
Deferred state tax expense	$25
Federal tax benefit from state for deferred state tax expense	($25)
Federal rate	x 35%
Deferred federal tax benefit	($9)

Total Tax Provision:	
Federal current	$1,719
State current	258
Federal deferred ($175-9)	166
State deferred	25
Total tax expense	$2,168

Rate Reconciliation:		
Tax Impact by Item	**Amount**	**Rate**
Pre-tax income	$1,960	0.3500
Non-deductible meals & entertainment	25	0.0044
State tax expense (Note 1)	184	0.0329
Total tax expense	$2,169	0.3872

Note 1: Amount represents total state tax expense net of the federal tax benefit ($184 = $283 x 65%)

Summarized Balance Sheet:	
Assets:	**GAAP**
Lease & well equipment	$10,000
Leasehold costs	10,000
Total assets	$20,000

Liabilities and Equity:	
Current tax payable	$1,977
Federal deferred tax liability	166
State deferred tax liability	25
Liabilities not related to taxes	12,000
Equity contributed	2,400
Retained earnings	3,432
Total liabilities and equity	$20,000

CATEGORIZING TEMPORARY DIFFERENCES

Once a company has identified all of its financial reporting and tax basis differences (cumulative temporary differences), FAS 109 requires the differences to be fragmented between taxable and deductible differences.

TAXABLE TEMPORARY DIFFERENCES

Temporary differences, which affect taxable income in future tax years, are referred to as taxable differences. These items produce a deferred tax liability for the company. In general, taxable differences relate to tax deductions claimed before the year in which the expense is reflected in financial reports. A prime example of a taxable difference is depreciable property that has a more rapid recovery period for tax purposes than for book purposes. For oil and gas exploration and production companies, depreciation and IDC are the most common taxable temporary difference.

Examples of taxable temporary differences are:

• **Depreciation**	Accelerated rates used for tax. Straight-line or unit-of-production used for financial reporting.
• **IDC**	Expensed for tax and capitalized for book under both successful efforts and full cost, except for exploratory dry holes charged to expense under successful efforts.
• **Delay rentals**	Expensed for tax purposes unless taxpayer elects to capitalize or is required to capitalize all or a portion under IRC Sec. 263A. For financial reporting, expensed under successful efforts and capitalized under full cost.
• **Dry hole costs:**	
• **Exploratory**	Expensed for tax purposes. For financial reporting, expensed under successful efforts and capitalized under full cost.
• **Development**	Expensed for tax purposes and capitalized for financial reporting under both successful efforts and full cost.
• **Installment sales**	Profit recorded in year of sale for financial reporting. Profit deferred and recorded as received for tax purposes and potentially subject to an interest charge.
• **Purchase accounting for acquisition of another company**	Stock acquisition treated as a purchase for financial reporting. For tax purposes, stock acquisition generally requires the purchaser to assume the (usually) smaller tax basis of the seller, which is similar to a pooling.

DEDUCTIBLE TEMPORARY DIFFERENCES

Deductible differences produce a tax benefit or deduction in a future tax year. Often, they are the result of a company's tax basis for an asset exceeding its financial reporting basis. Deductible temporary differences produce a deferred tax asset; such differences result from deductions that have been taken for financial reporting, but are not yet deducted for tax purposes. Net operating losses and tax credit carryovers are also treated as deductible temporary differences.

Examples of deductible temporary differences follow:

• **Reserves/allowances**	Generally not deductible for tax purposes until liability is fixed or actually paid.
• **Impairments**	Allowances for unproved property impairment are not deductible for tax purposes until the lease has expired and/or lease acreage is abandoned.
• **Geological and geophysical**	Expensed for financial reporting under successful efforts and capitalized/amortized for tax if leases are acquired as a result of G&G expenditures.
• **Sublease of unproved property**	Proceeds are ordinary income for tax purposes and generally treated as recovery of costs for financial reporting.
• **Sale of part of property**	Gain or loss recognized for tax purposes. Proceeds generally treated as recovery of cost for financial reporting.
• **Deficiency payment received under take-or-pay contract**	Taxable when received for tax purposes and treated as deferred revenue (if recoverable and recovery is likely) for financial reporting.
• **Bad debts**	Reserve method cannot be used by most taxpayers. For tax purposes, specific identification methods should be used. Estimated uncollectible accounts provided for in financial reporting.
• **Post-retirement benefits**	Reserve for post-retirement benefits per FAS 106 not deductible for tax until benefits are paid.
• **Equity method of accounting vs. cost**	Certain investments may be accounted for on the equity method for financial reporting and the cost method for tax purposes (generally because the subsidiary is less than 80 percent owned and not included in the consolidated tax return). In certain instances, due to the indefinite reversal criteria of APB Opinion No. 23, this difference may be treated as a permanent difference.
• **Organization expenses**	Expensed as incurred for financial reporting while capitalized and amortized over five years for tax purposes.
• **Inventory capitalization/self-constructed asset**	For tax purposes, additional costs are required to be capitalized on inventory and self-constructed assets pursuant to IRC Sec. 263A.
• **Carryovers—net operating losses, investment tax credits, AMT**	These tax assets result from losses, business tax credits, or alternative minimum taxes paid in prior years that are available to reduce future regular tax.

Categorizing temporary differences can be complicated when an asset's carrying value reflects both prior taxable and deductible temporary differences. For example, capitalized proved oil and gas property costs may reflect prior deductible temporary differences due to impairment (recorded for GAAP, but not for tax) and taxable temporary differences due to IDC tax deductions and accelerated tax depreciation. Accumulated DD&A for GAAP may exceed accumulated DD&A for tax because costs capitalized under GAAP include IDC deducted for tax purposes (not because GAAP DD&A occurs sooner than tax DD&A).

MEASURING TAX EFFECTS OF TEMPORARY DIFFERENCES

Once a company's temporary differences are identified and allocated between taxable and deductible, the impact on deferred taxes is measured by applying the appropriate tax rate. The tax rate includes not only federal taxes, but state and foreign taxes that may apply as temporary differences reverse in the future. Thus, the petroleum accountant considers the impact of state and foreign tax laws in each taxing jurisdiction where the company is active. State tax apportionment factors, state operating losses, and foreign tax credit utilization affect calculations of the tax rate also.

Oil and gas companies are often subject to the alternative minimum tax (AMT). As discussed in Chapter 26, AMT is a separate tax system intended to restrict companies from reducing their tax liabilities below a minimum amount. The AMT a company pays in excess of its regular tax liability in a given year produces an AMT credit. The credit can be carried forward indefinitely to reduce regular tax associated with both future taxable income and the reversal of temporary differences. As a result, the FASB ruled deferred income taxes should be measured using regular tax rates, not the AMT rate. This approach applies even if the company anticipates being subject to AMT for the foreseeable future.

The applicable tax rate is the enacted tax rate expected to apply in the future period in which the liability or asset is realized. Any change in the enacted tax rate is adjusted through the tax provision in the year of enactment.

ASSESSING THE NEED FOR A VALUATION ALLOWANCE

As described earlier, FAS 109 requires a company to compute tax on its separately identified taxable temporary differences. This computation arrives at the company's total deferred tax liability. The total deferred tax asset associated with separately identified deductible temporary differences must also be computed. This asset represents the tax benefits associated with expenses that have not been deducted for tax purposes, such as net operating losses and tax credit carryovers. Before reflecting the benefits of a deferred tax asset, the company should consider the need for a valuation allowance.

Under FAS 109, a company must determine if it will be able to utilize all or a portion of its deductible temporary differences. This requirement is met by applying a "more likely than not" standard, which is defined as a greater than 50 percent probability. To satisfy the standard, the company must evaluate: (1) both positive and negative evidence, and (2) all possible sources of taxable income. Positive evidence and evaluation of the company's sources of taxable income are key factors in analyzing a deferred tax asset.

POSITIVE EVIDENCE

A company's evaluation of positive evidence is critical to overcoming any negative evidence that a valuation allowance is not required. The following are examples of positive evidence mentioned in FAS 109:

- Existing contracts or firm sales backlog that will produce sufficient taxable income to realize the deferred tax asset.

- An excess of appreciated asset value over the tax basis of the entity's net assets in amounts sufficient to realize the deferred tax asset.

- A strong earnings history exclusive of the loss that created the future deductible amount and evidence the loss was an aberration.

NEGATIVE EVIDENCE

A company with an abundance of negative evidence has more difficulty in supporting a conclusion that a valuation allowance is not required. The following examples of negative evidence are mentioned in FAS 109:

- A history of operating loss or tax credit carryforwards expiring unused

- Losses expected in early future years by a currently profitable entity

- Unsettled circumstances, if unfavorably resolved, that would adversely affect future operations and profit levels

- A brief carryback or carryforward period limiting realization of the tax benefit

SOURCES OF TAXABLE INCOME

Once a company assesses both positive and negative evidence, it must evaluate possible sources of taxable income. The benefit of a deferred tax asset can be recognized if a company has sufficient sources of taxable income. FAS 109 defines four of them:

- Reversal of existing taxable temporary differences

- Taxable income in prior carryback years, if the carryback is permitted under tax law

- Future taxable income exclusive of temporary differences and carryovers

- Tax planning strategies

Not all sources of income are treated equally, however. The first two sources (reversal of taxable temporary differences and income in prior carryback years) are much easier to justify than the last two because: (1) they are based on historical transactions, and (2) they have an accompanying lower degree of risk.

The inherent risk (exploration success, fluctuation in oil and gas prices) of projecting future taxable income requires careful examination. Any income projection should correlate with the company's reserves report, FAS 144 expected future cash flows, and expected drilling and development expenditures (capital budget). Reliance on a tax planning strategy requires a company to consider actions that would not necessarily be taken in the ordinary course of business, but are taken to prevent a tax benefit from expiring. Tax planning strategy must be prudent, feasible, and not cost-prohibitive.

DETERMINING FINANCIAL STATEMENT PRESENTATION

Once a company has determined the appropriate deferred tax asset or liability, it selects the proper way to present the deferred account in its financial statements. FAS 109 requires each temporary difference to be classified as current or noncurrent based on classification of the related asset or liability for financial reporting. For example, a temporary difference relating to a noncurrent asset (such as depreciable property or IDC) is treated as a noncurrent deferred tax asset or liability. A temporary difference that relates to a current asset (such as inventory or accounts receivable) is classified as a current deferred tax asset or liability. A deferred tax liability or asset that is not related to an asset or liability for financial reporting is classified based on the expected reversal date.

All current deferred tax liabilities and assets are offset and presented as a single amount; likewise, all noncurrent deferred tax liabilities and assets are offset and presented as a single line item. Amounts are not offset for different taxpaying subsidiaries or for assets in different tax jurisdictions. Also, a company should allocate any valuation allowance between current and noncurrent deferred tax assets on a pro-rata basis.

For example, assume a taxpaying entity's unproved property assets generate a $100,000 noncurrent deferred tax asset, and proved property assets generate a $504,000 noncurrent deferred tax liability in the same tax jurisdiction. The balance sheet reflects a net $404,000 noncurrent deferred tax liability. As explained in the next section, the tax footnote to the financial statements discloses the components.

MAKING FINANCIAL STATEMENT DISCLOSURES

FAS 109 requires disclosure of information related to income tax accounts presented in the balance sheet and income statement of a company.

BALANCE SHEET

Components of a net deferred tax asset or liability presented in the balance sheet must be disclosed in a footnote, including the total of:

- All deferred tax liabilities

- All deferred tax assets

- Valuation allowance

A company must also disclose any net change in the total valuation allowance during the year. Public enterprises disclose the deferred tax effect of each type of significant temporary difference and carryforward; nonpublic enterprises should disclose the type of significant temporary differences, but may omit disclosure of the tax effect.

For example, assume a publicly held E&P company has net operating loss carryforwards and AMT credit carryforwards. These generate deferred tax assets subject to a valuation allowance. The footnote disclosure might read as follows:

For financial reporting, the components of the net deferred asset at December 31, 2006, were as follows (in thousands):

Deferred tax assets	
NOL carryforwards	$20,000
AMT credit carryforwards	1,000
Other	500
	21,500
Deferred tax liabilities	
Proved property	(15,000)
Other	(400)
	(15,400)
Deferred tax assets net of liabilities	6,100
Valuation allowance	(4,100)
Net deferred tax asset	**$ 2,000**

The December 31, 2006, valuation allowance was $1 million less than at December 31, 2005, due to the company's ability to utilize a larger deferred tax asset.

Companies must disclose information when a potential deferred tax liability is not required to be recognized. Two types of temporary differences are excepted from the required recognition of deferred tax, unless they are expected to reverse in the foreseeable future:

- An excess of the financial reporting amount over the tax basis of an investment in a foreign subsidiary or foreign corporate joint venture that is essentially permanent in duration

- Undistributed earnings of a domestic subsidiary or a domestic corporate joint venture that is essentially permanent in duration and that arose in fiscal years beginning on or before December 31, 1992

The following items should be disclosed: (1) a description of the types of temporary differences that have not been recognized, (2) events that could cause the differences to become taxable, and (3) the amount of unrecognized deferred tax liability.

INCOME STATEMENT

Companies are to provide details about the income tax expense attributable to continuing operations for each year presented. The amount of current tax expense or benefit and the amount of deferred tax expense or benefit should be disclosed. Also, a company must note the benefits of operating loss carryforwards, the impact of changes in enacted tax laws or rates, and any adjustments to the beginning of the year valuation allowance resulting from a change in circumstances about the realizability of the related asset.

Public companies disclose a reconciliation (using percentages or dollar amounts) of the reported income tax expense to the amount of income tax expense that would result from applying domestic federal statutory tax rates to pre-tax income. Information about the amount and nature of each significant reconciling item is required. A nonpublic company may disclose the nature of significant reconciling items, but can omit a numerical reconciliation. For example, a public company might disclose the following in the income tax note to the financial statements:

	2006	2005	2004
Federal statutory rate	35%	35%	35%
Tax-exempt income	-1%	-1%	-1%
Effect of tax on foreign income	3%	4%	2%
Utilization of net operating loss carryforwards	0%	-34%	-34%
Other	1%	0%	0%
Effective income tax rate	38%	4%	2%

Disclosures should include: (1) the amount and expiration of operating loss and tax credit carryforwards, and (2) any portion of the valuation allowance for which subsequent recognition will be required to be allocated to goodwill or other noncurrent intangible assets of an acquired entity. Members of a group that files a consolidated tax return will disclose the amount of current and deferred tax expense, the amount of any tax-related balances due to or from affiliates, and the principal provisions by which deferred taxes are allocated among members of the group.

RECENT DEVELOPMENTS IN FINANCIAL STATEMENT REPORTING

In order to promote increased relevance and comparability in the financial reporting of income taxes, the FASB issued FIN 48, *Accounting for Uncertainty in Income Taxes*—an interpretation of FASB Statement No. 109. FIN 48 is applicable to all uncertain positions for taxes accounted for under FAS 109. Its rules apply to the start of fiscal years commencing after December 15, 2006.

The following is a brief summary of FIN 48 guidelines:

- **Recognition:** A tax benefit from an uncertain position may be recognized only if it is "more likely than not" the position is sustainable based on its technical merits.

- **Measurement:** The tax benefit of a qualifying position is the largest amount of tax benefit that is greater than 50 percent likely of being realized upon ultimate settlement with a taxing authority having full knowledge of all relevant information.

- **Change in judgment:** The assessment of the recognition threshold and the measurement of the associated tax benefit might change as new information becomes available. Unrecognized tax benefits should be recognized in the period that the position reaches the recognition threshold, which might occur prior to absolute finality of the matter. Similarly, recognized tax benefits should be derecognized in the period in which the position falls below the threshold.

- **Interest/Penalties:** A taxpayer is required to accrue interest and penalties that, under relevant tax law, the taxpayer would be regarded as having incurred. Under FIN 48, interest starts to accrue in the period that it would begin accruing under the relevant tax law, and penalties are accrued in the first period for which a position is taken (or is expected to be taken) on a tax return that would give rise to the penalty. How a company classifies interest and penalties in the income statement is an accounting policy decision. The company should disclose the policy applied and the amounts recognized.

- **Balance sheet classification:** Liabilities resulting from this Interpretation are classified as long-term unless payment is expected within the next 12 months.

- **Disclosures:** The Interpretation requires qualitative and quantitative disclosures including discussion of reasonably possible changes that might occur in the recognized tax benefits over the next 12 months; a description of open tax years by major jurisdictions; and a roll-forward of all unrecognized tax benefits presented as a reconciliation of the beginning and ending balances of the unrecognized tax benefits on a worldwide aggregated basis.

- **Transition and Effective Date:** The Interpretation is effective as of the beginning of fiscal years starting after December 15, 2006. After considering other applicable guidance (such as the guidance the Emerging Issues Task Force specifies in Issue 93-7, *Uncertainties Related to Income Taxes in a Purchase Business Combination*), a company should record the change in net assets that results from the application of the Interpretation as an adjustment to retained earnings.

OTHER CONSIDERATIONS

INTERCORPORATE TAX ALLOCATION

FAS 109 provides rules for allocating taxes to subsidiaries that issue separate financial statements, but are included in a consolidated tax return. A single allocation method is not required; however, the method used must be consistent with the broad principles of the standard.

FAS 109 specifically prohibits a method that:

- Allocates only current taxes payable to a member of a group that has taxable temporary differences

- Allocates deferred taxes to a member of a group using a method fundamentally different (e.g., the APB Opinion No. 11 method) from the balance sheet method of FAS 109

- Allocates no current or deferred tax expense to a member of a group that has taxable income because the consolidated group has no current or deferred tax expense

BUSINESS COMBINATIONS

Deferred taxes must be recognized on differences between the assigned financial reporting and tax basis of acquired assets and assumed liabilities. However, four exceptions exist that allow a deferred tax liability to be unrecognized: (1) differences related to goodwill that are not tax-deductible, (2) unallocated negative goodwill, (3) acquired leveraged leases, and (4) APB Opinion No. 23 differences recognized in an acquisition (e.g., undistributed earnings of subsidiaries, investments in corporate joint ventures, and bad debt reserves of savings and loan associations).

A deferred tax asset resulting from an acquired entity's deductible temporary differences, operating loss, or tax credit carryforwards at the acquisition date may have a valuation allowance associated with it. The tax benefits for those items that are first recognized in financial statements (by elimination of the valuation allowance) after the acquisition date are applied in the following order:

1. Reduce to zero any goodwill related to the acquisition

2. Reduce to zero other noncurrent intangible assets related to the acquisition

3. Reduce income tax expense

If financial statements for prior years are restated, all purchase business combinations consummated in those years must be re-measured. Generally, for a business combination consummated prior to the beginning of the year for which FAS 109 is first applied, balances remaining, except for goodwill, are adjusted to their pre-tax amounts. When determination of the adjustment for any or all of the assets and liabilities is impracticable, none of the remaining balances of any assets and liabilities acquired in that combination are adjusted to pre-tax amounts (i.e., none of the remaining amounts that were originally assigned on a net-of-tax basis pursuant to FAS 141 should be adjusted).

INTERIM FINANCIAL REPORTING

At the end of each interim period, a company makes its best estimate of the annual income tax rate. It applies that rate to year-to-date pre-tax income in order to arrive at year-to-date income tax expense. The estimated annual effective tax rate reflects tax benefits expected to be realized during the year or recognizable at the end of the year as a deferred tax asset.

The effect of a change in beginning of the year balances of a valuation allowance as a result of a change in judgment about the realizability of a related deferred tax asset in future years should not be apportioned among interim periods; instead, it should be recognized in the interim period in which the change occurs.

• • •

28

NONVALUE DISCLOSURES ABOUT OIL AND GAS PRODUCING ACTIVITIES

Key Concepts:

- Historical background of disclosure requirements

- Description of FAS 69 and SEC disclosures

- Definition of significant oil and gas producing activities

- Publicly traded enterprises

- Method of accounting and disposition of capitalized costs

- Reserves quantity information

- Capitalized costs of oil and gas producing activities

- Property acquisition, exploration, and development costs

- Results of operations disclosures

- Standardized measure of discounted future net cash flows

- Capitalized exploratory well costs

- Full cost companies' special disclosures

- Current examples of disclosures from annual reports

This chapter focuses on the nonvalue disclosures required by the Statement of Financial Accounting Standards No. 69 (FAS 69), *Disclosures About Oil and Gas Producing Activities*, and reflected in the FASB Current Text, Oi5.156 through Oi5.408, Oi5.811, and Oi5.813. Related SEC disclosure rules and miscellaneous full cost disclosures are also addressed.

HISTORY OF DISCLOSURE REQUIREMENTS

Disclosure requirements for E&P companies have evolved over the past 30 years. (See discussion in Chapter 4.) Issued in December 1977, FAS 19 was the first authoritative literature to address disclosures for oil and gas producing companies. In it, the FASB not only adopted a form of successful efforts accounting, but specified certain supplemental data to be included in financial reports. Nonvalue disclosure requirements were scheduled to apply to: (1) mineral reserves quantities, (2) capitalized costs, and (3) costs incurred.

However, in August 1978—before FAS 19's effective date—another agency intervened. The SEC issued ASR No. 253, *Adoption of Requirements for Financial Accounting and Reporting Practices for Oil and Gas Producing Activities*. The release accomplished several purposes:

- Adopted the form of successful efforts accounting prescribed by FAS 19

- Indicated an intention to adopt the disclosures prescribed by FAS 19 (which was subsequently done)

- Indicated an intention to adopt a form of full cost accounting (which was subsequently done)

- Allowed the use of either successful efforts or full cost accounting for SEC reporting purposes

- Adopted rules that required disclosure of certain financial and operating information beyond FAS 19 requirements

- Adopted a definition of proved reserves different from those in effect at the time FAS 19 was issued

Four months later the SEC issued ASR No. 257, *Requirements for Financial Accounting and Reporting Practices for Oil and Gas Producing Activities*, and ASR No. 258, *Oil and Gas Producers — Full Cost Accounting Practices*, in which the SEC: (1) reaffirmed its conclusions reflected in ASR 253, (2) adopted definitions of proved reserves developed by the Department of Energy (DOE) for its Financial Reporting System, and (3) prescribed the form of full cost accounting acceptable as an alternative to successful efforts accounting for SEC reporting purposes.

The SEC undertook these actions from the position that neither the full cost nor the successful efforts method provided sufficient information on the financial position and operating results of oil and gas producing enterprises. A new system of accounting based on valuations of proved oil and gas reserves would be developed for primary financial statements—and it was envisioned to replace both the successful efforts and full cost accounting methods. Referred to as reserve recognition accounting (RRA), it would require supplemental disclosures on that basis until RRA could be developed as the basic accounting method.

The SEC also indicated (and subsequently carried out) its intention to require the disclosure of a supplemental earnings summary to reflect estimated additions to proved reserves and changes in the valuation of estimated proved reserves based on current prices and costs and a 10 percent annual discount rate. All costs associated with finding and developing such additions and all costs determined to be nonproductive during the period were to be deducted in determining that supplemental measure of earnings.

The issuance of ASR No. 253 presented a challenge to the industry. It meant FAS 19 would be imposed only on enterprises not subject to SEC reporting requirements, which would impede comparability of financial reports. As a result, the FASB issued FAS 25 in February 1979. It suspended the effective date of FAS 19 as to the accounting method to be used in financial statements, but not as to the disclosure requirements.

In September 1979, the SEC adopted rules in ASR No. 269, *Oil and Gas Producers— Supplemental Disclosures on the Basis of Reserve Recognition Accounting (RRA)*, for the supplemental disclosure of a summary of changes in the present value of estimated future net revenues from the production of proved reserves. Also adopted was a requirement for a summary of oil and gas producing activities prepared on the basis of RRA. The SEC anticipated that these supplemental disclosures—and previously adopted requirements for the reporting of reserves quantities, estimated future net revenues, and present value of future net revenues—would provide the basis for evaluating the feasibility of requiring RRA as a uniform accounting method in the primary financial statements.

By February 1981, the SEC changed directions and it issued ASR No. 289, *Financial Reporting by Oil and Gas Producers*, which stated the SEC no longer considered RRA to be a potential method of accounting in the primary financial statements of oil and gas producers. Because of the inherent uncertainty of recoverable quantities of proved oil and gas reserves, the SEC no longer supported RRA. ASR No. 289 also announced the SEC's "support of an undertaking by the FASB to develop a comprehensive package of disclosures for those engaged in oil and gas producing activities." The SEC indicated in the release that it expected to amend its rules to be consistent with the disclosure standards to be developed by the FASB for oil and gas producers.

In November 1982, the FASB issued FAS 69, which applies mostly to publicly-traded companies. Much of the discussion in this chapter derives from this pronouncement. A month later in December 1982, the SEC issued Reg. S-K §229.302. It adopted FAS 69 to replace the SEC's existing requirements for disclosure about oil and gas producing activities. (See Regulation S-K Excerpts in Appendix 1.)

OVERVIEW OF DISCLOSURES

The following is a list of disclosures that are required by FAS 69, SEC rules, and other accounting pronouncements for oil and gas activities:

- FAS 69 requires that every enterprise engaged in oil and gas producing activities, whether publicly-traded or not, must disclose in its financial statements: (1) its method of accounting for costs incurred in such activities, and (2) its manner of disposing of capitalized costs relating to those activities.

- Under FAS 69, every publicly-traded enterprise with significant oil and gas activities must disclose with complete sets of annual financial statements certain supplemental information (that need not be audited) as to the following:

  - Proved oil and gas reserves quantities

  - Capitalized costs relating to oil and gas producing activities

  - Costs incurred in property acquisition, exploration, and development activities

- – Results of operations for oil and gas producing activities

- – A standardized measure of discounted future net cash flows relating to proved oil and gas reserves quantities as of year-end and the year's change in the standardized measure.[1]

- For enterprises following the Reg. S-X Rule 4-10 full cost method, additional disclosures are required:

  - – Disclosure of total amortization expense for each cost center for each year an income statement is presented (per equivalent unit)

  - – A separate statement on the face of the balance sheet providing the total capitalized costs excluded from the amortization base and providing certain related disclosures in the notes to the financial statements

  - – Disclosures relating to any ceiling test write-down or subsequent events that eliminate or reduce the write-down

- FAS 69 requires interim financial statements to include information about any major discovery or other favorable or adverse event that causes a significant change from the most recent annual supplemental disclosures concerning oil and gas reserves.

- APB 22, *Disclosure of Accounting Policies*, requires significant accounting policies to be disclosed. Examples of significant policies related to E&P activities might include the following:

  - – Policy for capitalizing internal costs associated with E&P activities[2]

  - – Method of accounting for gas balancing (i.e., sales method or entitlement method)[3]

  - – Disclosures of policy for buy/sell transactions[4]

  - – Disclosures of policy related to accounting for suspended well costs[5]

- For oil and gas exchange offers, SEC SAB Topic 2D contains special disclosure requirements.

- The SEC industry guide requires additional disclosures of oil and gas operations outside of the financial statements, as further explained at the end of this chapter.

The remainder of this chapter further addresses these disclosure requirements (other than the standardized measure which is addressed in Chapter 29 and interim financial disclosure requirements discussed earlier). APB 22 accounting policy disclosure requirements are addressed in various other chapters.

WHAT ARE "SIGNIFICANT" OIL AND GAS PRODUCING ACTIVITIES?

FAS 69 disclosures are required for enterprises with *significant* oil and gas producing activities. Under FAS 69, an enterprise is regarded as having significant oil and gas producing activities if such activities are at least 10 percent of the company's total activities, as indicated by any one of the following three tests:

1. Revenues from oil and gas producing activities (including both sales to unaffiliated customers and sales or transfers to the enterprise's other operations) are 10 percent or more of the combined revenues (including

sales to unaffiliated customers and sales or transfers to the enterprise's other operations) of all the enterprise's industry segments.

2.   Results of operations of oil and gas producing activities (excluding the effects of income taxes) are 10 percent or more of the larger of the:

   a)   combined operating profit of all industry segments that did not incur an operating loss, or

   b)   combined operating loss of all industry segments that did incur an operating loss.

3.   The identifiable assets of oil and gas producing activities (tangible and intangible enterprise assets that are used by oil and gas producing activities, including an allocated portion of assets used jointly with other operations) are 10 percent or more of the assets of the enterprise, excluding assets used exclusively for general corporate purposes.

The SEC provides that an enterprise's oil and gas activities will be viewed by the SEC as significant for FAS 69 disclosure requirements if: "the discounted present value of a registrant's oil and gas reserves is significantly in excess of ten percent of consolidated total assets" even if the three tests noted above are not met.[6] SEC rules do not define what is significantly in excess of 10 percent.

WHAT IS MEANT BY "PUBLICLY-TRADED"?

FAS 69, footnote 2, provides for purposes of FAS 69, the term *publicly-traded enterprise* refers to:

> ...a business enterprise (a) whose securities are traded in a public market on a domestic stock exchange or in the domestic over-the-counter market (including securities quoted only locally or regionally) or (b) whose financial statements are filed with a regulatory agency in preparation for the sale of any class of securities in a domestic market.

Under the SEC's rules, some enterprises that are not technically publicly-traded may be required to provide FAS 69 disclosures in filings with the SEC. For example, certain limited partnerships, which file reports with the SEC, or certain private entities that offered securities under Regulation D of Securities Act of 1933[7], may also be required to have FAS 69 disclosures in their annual financial statements.[8] Certain limited partnerships may be able to secure a waiver from the SEC that will allow them to omit the present value disclosures. This waiver can be obtained if specific criteria are met. It extends only to value-based disclosures and not to reserves quantity disclosures or historical cost based information.[9] Other examples that require FAS 69 disclosures include significant investments accounted for under the equity method of accounting (i.e., Reg. S-X Rule 3-09) and significant acquisitions of a working interest in oil and gas producing properties (i.e., Reg. S-X Rule 3-05).[10]

DATES AND PERIODS OF THE DISCLOSURES

Under FAS 69, supplemental disclosures are required for producing complete sets of annual financial statements (whether audited or unaudited). A company should also disclose proved reserves and proved developed reserves information as of the beginning and end of each annual period.

SEC Reg. S-X Rules 3-01 and 3-02 require an annual report to be filed on Form 10-K. Audited balance sheets as of the end of each of the two latest years, and statements of income and cash flows for each of the latest three years are to be included. Accordingly, supplemental disclosures are required for the following dates and periods:

- Reserves quantities as of the end of the last four years and reserves quantity changes for each of the last three years

- Disclosures of capitalized costs and the related accumulated DD&A as of the end of the last two years

- Costs-incurred disclosures for each of the last three years

- Results of operations disclosures for each of the last three years

- Standardized measure as of the end of the year and standardized measure changes for each of the last three years.[11]

Figures in this chapter and Chapter 29 include examples of such disclosures from ExxonMobil's 2005 Annual Report as well as disclosures from the 2005 annual reports of other companies.

FAS 69 NONVALUE DISCLOSURES AND RELATED SEC RULES

DISCLOSING METHOD OF ACCOUNTING AND MANNER OF DISPOSING OF CAPITALIZED COSTS

Under FAS 69, all enterprises engaged in oil and gas producing activities must disclose in their financial statements the method of accounting for costs incurred (e.g., successful efforts) and the manner of disposing of capitalized costs relating to those activities (Accounting Method Disclosure). These are the only FAS 69 disclosure requirements that are not considered to be supplemental. Thus, the Accounting Method Disclosure is deemed to be an integral part of the financial statements. The accounting method can be disclosed on either the face of the financial statements, or in notes to the statements, or both, or in some other fashion indicating that the disclosure is an integral part of the statements.[12] The manner of disposing of capitalized costs is disclosed in the notes to the statements.

An example of the Accounting Method Disclosure is found in the *Notes to Consolidated Financial Statements* in ExxonMobil's 2005 Annual Report:

> **Property, plant and equipment.** . . . The Corporation uses the "successful efforts" method to account for its exploration and production activities. Under this method, costs are accumulated on a field-by-field basis with certain exploratory expenditures and exploratory dry holes being expensed as incurred. Costs of productive wells and development dry holes are capitalized and amortized on the unit-of-production method for each field.
>
> The Corporation carries exploratory well costs as an asset when the well has found a sufficient quantity of reserves to justify its completion as a producing well and where the Corporation is making sufficient progress assessing the reserves and the economic and operating viability of the project. Exploratory well costs not meeting these criteria are charged to expense.

Acquisition costs of proved properties are amortized using a unit-of-production method, computed on the basis of total proved oil and gas reserves. Significant unproved properties are assessed for impairment individually and valuation allowances against the capitalized costs are recorded based on the estimated economic chance of success and the length of time the Corporation expects to hold the properties. The cost of properties that are not individually significant are aggregated by groups and amortized over the average holding period of the properties of the groups. The valuation allowances are reviewed at least annually. Other exploratory expenditures, including geophysical costs, other dry hole costs and annual lease rentals, are expensed as incurred.

Unit-of-production depreciation is applied to property, plant and equipment, including capitalized exploratory drilling and development costs, associated with productive depletable extractive properties, all in the Upstream segment. Unit-of-production rates are based on the amount of proved developed reserves of oil, gas and other minerals that are estimated to be recoverable from existing facilities using current operating methods. Additional oil and gas to be obtained through the application of improved recovery techniques is included when, or to the extent that, the requisite commercial-scale facilities have been installed and the required wells have been drilled.

DISCLOSING RESERVES QUANTITY INFORMATION

FAS 69, paragraphs 10 through 17 (Oi5.160 through Oi5.167), requires publicly-traded enterprises to disclose annually certain data related to an enterprise's proved oil and gas reserves as supplemental information:

10. Net quantities of an enterprise's interest in proved reserves and proved developed reserves of (a) crude oil (including condensate and natural gas liquids)[13] and (b) natural gas shall be reported as of the beginning and the end of the year. *Net* quantities of reserves include those relating to the enterprise's operating and nonoperating interests in properties as defined in paragraph 11(a) of Statement 19. Quantities of reserves relating to royalty interests owned shall be included in *net* quantities if the necessary information is available to the enterprise; if reserves relating to royalty interests owned are not included because the information is unavailable, that fact and the enterprise's share of oil and gas produced for those royalty interests shall be disclosed for the year. *Net* quantities shall not include reserves relating to interests of others in properties owned by the enterprise.

11. Changes in the net quantities of an enterprise's proved reserves of oil and gas during the year shall be disclosed. Changes resulting from each of the following shall be shown separately with appropriate explanation of significant changes:

    a) *Revisions of previous estimates.* Revisions represent changes in previous estimates of proved reserves, either upward or downward, resulting from new information (except for an increase in proved acreage) normally obtained from development drilling and production history or resulting from a change in economic factors.

    b) *Improved recovery.* Changes in reserve estimates resulting from application of improved recovery techniques shall be shown separately if significant. If not significant, such changes shall be included in revisions of previous estimates.

c) *Purchases of minerals in place.*

d) *Extensions and discoveries.* Additions to proved reserves that result from (1) extension of the proved acreage of previously discovered (old) reservoirs through additional drilling in periods subsequent to discovery and (2) discovery of new fields with proved reserves or of new reservoirs of proved reserves in old fields.

e) *Production.*

f) *Sales of minerals in place.*

12. If an enterprise's proved reserves of oil and of gas are located entirely within its home country, that fact shall be disclosed. If some or all of its reserves are located in foreign countries, the disclosures of net quantities of reserves of oil and of gas and changes in them required by paragraphs 10 and 11 shall be separately disclosed for (a) the enterprise's home country (if significant reserves are located there) and (b) each foreign geographic area in which significant reserves are located. Foreign geographic areas are individual countries or groups of countries as appropriate for meaningful disclosure in the circumstances.

13. Net quantities disclosed in conformity with paragraphs 10-12 shall not include oil or gas subject to purchase under long-term supply, purchase, or similar agreements and contracts, including such agreements with governments or authorities. However, quantities of oil or gas subject to such agreements with governments or authorities as of the end of the year, and the net quantity of oil or gas received under the agreements during the year, shall be separately disclosed if the enterprise participates in the operation of the properties in which the oil or gas is located or otherwise serves as the *producer* of those reserves, as opposed, for example, to being an independent purchaser, broker, dealer, or importer.[14]

14. In determining the reserve quantities to be disclosed in conformity with paragraphs 10-13:

a) If the enterprise issues consolidated financial statements, 100 percent of the *net* reserve quantities attributable to the parent company and 100 percent of the *net* reserve quantities attributable to its consolidated subsidiaries (whether or not wholly owned) shall be included. If a significant portion of those reserve quantities at the end of the year is attributable to a consolidated subsidiary(ies) in which there is a significant minority interest, that fact and the approximate portion shall be disclosed.

b) If the enterprise's financial statements include investments that are proportionately consolidated, the enterprise's reserve quantities shall include its proportionate share of the investees' net oil and gas reserves.

c) If the enterprise's financial statements include investments that are accounted for by the equity method, the investees' net oil and gas reserves shall *not* be included in the disclosures of the enterprise's reserve quantities. However, the enterprise's (investor's) share of the investee's net oil and gas reserve quantities shall be separately reported as of the end of the year.

15. In reporting reserve quantities and changes in them, oil reserves and natural gas liquids reserves shall be stated in barrels, and gas reserves in cubic feet.

16. If important economic factors or significant uncertainties affect particular components of an enterprise's proved reserves, explanation shall be provided. Examples include unusually high expected development or lifting costs, the necessity to build a major pipeline or other major facilities before production of the reserves can begin, and contractual obligations to produce and sell a significant portion of reserves at prices that are substantially below those at which the oil or gas could otherwise be sold in the absence of the contractual obligation.

17. If a government restricts the disclosure of estimated reserves for properties under its authority, or of amounts under long-term supply, purchase, or similar agreements or contracts, or if the government requires the disclosure of reserves other than proved, the enterprise shall indicate that the disclosed reserve estimates or amounts do not include figures for the named country or that reserve estimates include reserves other than proved.

FAS 69 is the source for Figure 28-1, which illustrates the suggested format for disclosures of oil and gas reserve quantities. An example of such disclosures is provided in Figures 28-2A and 28-2B.

Figure 28-1
Illustrative FAS 69 Reserve Table Disclosure

Reserve Quantity Information*
for the Year Ended December 31, 20XX

	Total		United States		Foreign Geographic Area A		Foreign Geographic Area B		Other Foreign Geographic Areas	
	Oil	Gas	Oil	Gas	Oil	Gas	Oil	Gas	Oil	Gas
Proved developed and undeveloped reserves:										
Beginning of year	X	X	X	X	X	X	X	X	X	X
Revisions of previous estimates	X	X	X	X	X	X	X	X	X	X
Improved recovery	X	X	X	X	X	X	X	X	X	X
Purchases of minerals in place	X	X	X	X	X	X	X	X	X	X
Extensions and discoveries	X	X	X	X	X	X	X	X	X	X
Production	(X)	(X)	(X)	(X)	(X)	(X)	(X)	(X)	(X)	(X)
Sales of minerals in place	(X)	(X)	(X)	(X)	(X)	(X)	(X)	(X)	(X)	(X)
End of year	X	X	X	X	X	X	X	X	X	X
Proved developed reserves:										
Beginning of year	X	X	X	X	X	X	X	X	X	X
End of year	X†	X	X	X	X	X	X	X	X	X
Oil and gas applicable to long-term supply agreements with governments or authorities in which the enterprise acts as producer:										
Proved reserves — end of year	X	X			X	X				
Received during the year	X	X			X	X				
Enterprise's proportional interest in reserves of investees accounted for by the equity method — end of year	X	X	X	X	X	X	X	X	X	X

* Oil reserves stated in barrels; gas reserves stated in cubic feet.
† Includes reserves of X barrels attributable to a consolidated subsidiary in which there is an X percent minority interest.

Figure 28-2A
Oil and Natural Gas Liquids Reserves Table from ExxonMobil's 2005 Annual Report

Crude Oil and Natural Gas Liquids	United States	Canada	Europe	Africa	Asia Pacific/ Middle East	Russia/ Caspian	Other	Total
				(millions of barrels)				
Net proved developed and undeveloped reserves of consolidated subsidiaries								
January 1, 2003	2,909	1,285	1,333	2,626	592	353	527	9,625
Revisions	31	14	50	176	68	—	2	341
Purchases	1	—	—	—	—	—	—	1
Sales	(14)	—	(2)	—	—	—	—	(16)
Improved recovery	16	3	1	66	—	—	—	86
Extensions and discoveries	27	6	10	36	49	503	—	631
Production	(178)	(114)	(208)	(162)	(94)	(6)	(17)	(779)
December 31, 2003	2,792	1,194	1,184	2,742	615	850	512	9,889
Revisions	(46)	4	35	(39)	7	97	(14)	44
Purchases	—	—	—	10	—	—	—	10
Sales	(113)	(3)	—	—	(16)	—	—	(132)
Improved recovery	5	—	—	—	—	—	—	5
Extensions and discoveries	15	4	3	150	2	—	—	174
Production	(161)	(108)	(210)	(209)	(81)	(6)	(20)	(795)
Total before 2004 year-end price/cost revisions	2,492	1,091	1,012	2,654	527	941	478	9,195
Year-end price/cost revisions	101	(464)	2	(210)	(12)	(217)	—	(800)
December 31, 2004	2,593	627	1,014	2,444	515	724	478	8,395
Remove 2004 year-end price/cost revisions	(101)	464	(2)	210	12	217	—	800
Total before 2004 year-end price/cost revisions	2,492	1,091	1,012	2,654	527	941	478	9,195
Revisions	(235)	2	11	(53)	106	(96)	(2)	(267)
Purchases	—	—	—	—	—	113	—	113
Sales	(96)	(42)	(1)	—	(11)	(70)	(7)	(227)
Improved recovery	2	—	3	—	—	—	—	5
Extensions and discoveries	6	19	47	170	—	—	—	242
Production	(136)	(107)	(197)	(244)	(67)	(13)	(18)	(782)
Total before 2005 year-end price/cost revisions	2,033	963	875	2,527	555	875	451	8,279
Year-end price/cost revisions	80	(131)	8	(215)	(40)	(168)	—	(466)
December 31, 2005	2,113	832	883	2,312	515	707	451	7,813
Proportional interest in proved reserves of equity companies								
End of year 2003	426	—	20	—	767	973	—	2,186
End of year 2004	402	—	17	—	1,169	911	—	2,499
End of year 2005	413	—	11	—	1,381	873	—	2,678
Proved developed reserves, included above, as of December 31, 2003								
Consolidated subsidiaries	2,348	750	805	1,107	489	33	132	5,664
Equity companies	363	—	16	—	616	513	—	1,508
Proved developed reserves, included above, as of December 31, 2004								
Consolidated subsidiaries	2,204	561	763	1,117	403	34	129	5,211
Equity companies	347	—	15	—	642	600	—	1,604
Proved developed reserves, included above, as of December 31, 2005								
Consolidated subsidiaries	1,680	607	656	1,218	464	55	227	4,907
Equity companies	326	—	9	—	725	574	—	1,634

Figure 28-2B
Gas Reserves Table from
ExxonMobil's 2005 Annual Report

Natural Gas	United States	Canada	Europe	Africa	Asia Pacific/ Middle East	Russia/ Caspian	Other	Total
(billions of cubic feet)								
Net proved developed and undeveloped reserves of consolidated subsidiaries								
January 1, 2003	12,062	2,882	10,508	436	7,775	231	687	34,581
Revisions	124	(199)	411	157	19	—	(2)	510
Purchases	10	—	—	—	—	—	—	10
Sales	(90)	—	(3)	—	—	—	—	(93)
Improved recovery	9	1	—	—	—	—	—	10
Extensions and discoveries	156	45	333	1	872	238	—	1,645
Production	(999)	(388)	(1,103)	(11)	(727)	—	(40)	(3,268)
December 31, 2003	11,272	2,341	10,146	583	7,939	469	645	33,395
Revisions	31	19	(65)	165	(450)	47	164	(89)
Purchases	—	—	—	9	—	—	—	9
Sales	(142)	(18)	(16)	—	(301)	—	—	(477)
Improved recovery	2	—	31	—	—	—	—	33
Extensions and discoveries	121	36	39	39	44	—	—	279
Production	(846)	(399)	(1,092)	(25)	(633)	—	(40)	(3,035)
Total before 2004 year-end price/cost revisions	10,438	1,979	9,043	771	6,599	516	769	30,115
Year-end price/cost revisions	1,891	(96)	142	—	(208)	(1)	—	1,728
December 31, 2004	12,329	1,883	9,185	771	6,391	515	769	31,843
Remove 2004 year-end price/cost revisions	(1,891)	96	(142)	—	208	1	—	(1,728)
Total before 2004 year-end price/cost revisions	10,438	1,979	9,043	771	6,599	516	769	30,115
Revisions	1,369	128	221	35	1,879	(8)	(112)	3,512
Purchases	—	—	—	—	—	53	—	53
Sales	(105)	(23)	(73)	—	—	(26)	(2)	(229)
Improved recovery	—	—	—	—	—	—	—	—
Extensions and discoveries	288	27	116	57	33	315	—	836
Production	(764)	(376)	(1,072)	(22)	(546)	(3)	(36)	(2,819)
Total before 2005 year-end price/cost revisions	11,226	1,735	8,235	841	7,965	847	619	31,468
Year-end price/cost revisions	2,466	(30)	163	—	(686)	(26)	—	1,887
December 31, 2005	13,692	1,705	8,398	841	7,279	821	619	33,355
Proportional interest in proved reserves of equity companies								
End of year 2003	152	—	13,703	—	6,055	1,464	—	21,374
End of year 2004	140	—	13,557	—	13,455	1,367	—	28,519
End of year 2005	136	—	13,024	—	19,119	1,273	—	33,552
Proved developed reserves, included above, as of December 31, 2003								
Consolidated subsidiaries	9,513	1,962	7,196	155	5,785	3	328	24,942
Equity companies	124	—	7,770	—	2,689	709	—	11,292
Proved developed reserves, included above, as of December 31, 2004								
Consolidated subsidiaries	9,134	1,647	7,076	279	4,440	4	279	22,859
Equity companies	120	—	9,805	—	4,578	837	—	15,340
Proved developed reserves, included above, as of December 31, 2005								
Consolidated subsidiaries	10,386	1,527	6,332	376	6,067	227	313	25,228
Equity companies	113	—	10,226	—	7,276	835	—	18,450

INFORMATION ON CANADIAN TAR SANDS PROVEN RESERVES NOT INCLUDED

Tar Sands Reserves	Canada
	(millions of barrels)
At December 31, 2003	781
At December 31, 2004	757
At December 31, 2005	738

DISCLOSING CAPITALIZED COSTS OF OIL AND GAS PRODUCING ACTIVITIES

FAS 69, paragraph 18 (Oi5.168), requires disclosure as of the end of the year of the aggregate amount of capitalized costs relating to an enterprise's oil and gas producing activities and the aggregate related accumulated depreciation, depletion, amortization, and valuation allowances.

Paragraph 5 of APB Opinion No. 12, *Omnibus Opinion 1967*, requires disclosure of balances of major classes of depreciable assets, by nature or function. Thus, FAS 69, paragraph 18, notes that separate disclosures of capitalized costs for the following asset categories (listed in FAS 19, paragraph 11), or for a combination of those categories, often may be appropriate:

(1) mineral interests in properties, including (i) unproved and (ii) proved properties,

(2) wells and related equipment and facilities,

(3) support equipment and facilities used in oil and gas producing activities, and

(4) uncompleted wells, equipment, and facilities.

FAS 69, paragraph 19 (Oi5.169), requires significant capitalized costs of unproved properties to be reported separately. Capitalized costs of support equipment and facilities may be disclosed separately or included, as appropriate, with capitalized costs of proved and unproved properties.

FAS 69, paragraph 20 (Oi5.170), requires that if an enterprise's financial statements include investments that are accounted for by the equity method, the enterprise's share of the investee's net capitalized costs relating to oil and gas producing activities as of the end of the year must be disclosed separately.

Figure 28-3 shows the format suggested in FAS 69 for disclosing capitalized costs. Figure 28-4 shows an example from ExxonMobil's 2005 Annual Report. Note FAS 69 does not require disclosure of capitalized costs by major geographic area, but companies commonly do so.

Figure 28-3
Illustrative FAS 69 Disclosure of Capitalized Costs

**Capitalized Costs Relating to Oil and Gas
Producing Activities at December 31, 20XX**

	Total
Unproved oil and gas properties	$X
Proved oil and gas properties	X
	X
Accumulated depreciation, depletion and amortization, and valuation allowances	(X)
Net capitalized costs	$X
Enterprise's share of equity method investee's net capitalized costs	$X

Figure 28-4
Capitalized Costs Disclosure Table from
ExxonMobil's 2005 Annual Report

The amounts shown for net capitalized costs of consolidated subsidiaries are $5,541 million less at year-end 2005 and $4,769 million less at year-end 2004 than the amounts reported as investments in property, plant and equipment for the Upstream in note 8, page 60. This is due to the exclusion from capitalized costs of certain transportation and research assets and assets relating to the tar sands and LNG operations, all as required in Statement of Financial Accounting Standards No. 19.

Capitalized Costs	United States	Canada	Europe	Africa	Asia Pacific/ Middle East	Russia/ Caspian	Other	Total
				(millions of dollars)				
As of December 31, 2005								
Property (acreage) costs – Proved	$ 3,407	$ 3,336	$ 210	$ 184	$ 954	$ 460	$ 209	$ 8,760
– Unproved	587	266	29	544	858	99	227	2,610
Total property costs	$ 3,994	$ 3,602	$ 239	$ 728	$ 1,812	$ 559	$ 436	$ 11,370
Producing assets	34,306	11,261	39,355	11,818	15,024	857	1,006	113,627
Support facilities	620	199	478	410	1,158	217	51	3,133
Incomplete construction	1,862	789	1,073	4,903	751	3,109	154	12,641
Total capitalized costs	$40,782	$15,851	$41,145	$17,859	$18,745	$4,742	$1,647	$140,771
Accumulated depreciation and depletion	(26,071)	(9,573)	(28,899)	(5,115)	(13,070)	(330)	(437)	(83,495)
Net capitalized costs for consolidated subsidiaries	$14,711	$ 6,278	$12,246	$12,744	$ 5,675	$4,412	$1,210	$ 57,276
Proportional interest of net capitalized costs of equity companies	$ 1,386	$ —	$ 1,310	$ —	$ 1,043	$2,746	$ —	$ 6,485
As of December 31, 2004								
Property (acreage) costs – Proved	$ 3,739	$ 3,414	$ 235	$ 253	$ 998	$ 314	$ 209	$ 9,162
– Unproved	623	244	35	552	855	118	216	2,643
Total property costs	$ 4,362	$ 3,658	$ 270	$ 805	$ 1,853	$ 432	$ 425	$ 11,805
Producing assets	34,875	11,318	43,899	8,537	15,025	231	1,001	114,886
Support facilities	617	119	530	383	1,081	93	44	2,867
Incomplete construction	1,637	419	1,136	4,782	897	2,346	173	11,390
Total capitalized costs	$41,491	$15,514	$45,835	$14,507	$18,856	$3,102	$1,643	$140,948
Accumulated depreciation and depletion	(26,508)	(8,905)	(30,943)	(3,801)	(12,948)	(193)	(406)	(83,704)
Net capitalized costs for consolidated subsidiaries	$14,983	$ 6,609	$14,892	$10,706	$ 5,908	$2,909	$1,237	$ 57,244
Proportional interest of net capitalized costs of equity companies	$ 1,234	$ —	$ 1,277	$ —	$ 767	$2,427	$ —	$ 5,705

DISCLOSING COSTS INCURRED IN OIL AND GAS PROPERTY ACQUISITION, EXPLORATION, AND DEVELOPMENT ACTIVITIES

FAS 19 requires the disclosure of costs incurred in oil and gas property acquisition, exploration, and development activities regardless of whether the costs were capitalized or charged to expense. This requirement is also included in paragraphs 21 through 23 of FAS 69 (Oi5.171 through Oi5.173) and SEC Regulation S-X Rule 4-10(c)(7):

21. Each of the following types of costs for the year shall be disclosed (whether those costs are capitalized or charged to expense at the time they are incurred under the provisions of paragraphs 15-22 of Statement 19):[15]

    a) Property acquisition costs

    b) Exploration costs

    c) Development costs

22. If some or all of those costs are incurred in foreign countries, the amounts shall be disclosed separately for each of the geographic areas for which reserve quantities are disclosed (paragraph 12). If significant costs have been incurred to acquire mineral interests that have proved reserves, those costs shall be disclosed separately from the costs of acquiring unproved properties.

23. If the enterprise's financial statements include investments that are accounted for by the equity method, the enterprise's share of the investees' property acquisition, exploration, and development costs incurred in oil and gas producing activities shall be separately disclosed for the year, in the aggregate and for each geographic area for which reserve quantities are disclosed (paragraph 12).

The FAS 69 proposed format for disclosing costs incurred is shown in Figure 28-5. Such disclosures of costs incurred should not present separately the capitalized costs related to asset retirement obligations.[16]

Figure 28-6 from ExxonMobil's 2005 Annual Report provides an example of disclosing costs incurred by an E&P company.

Figure 28-5
Illustrative FAS 69 Costs Incurred Disclosure

Costs Incurred in Oil and Gas Property Acquisition, Exploration, and Development Activities for the Year Ended December 31, 20XX

	Total	United States	Foreign Geographic Area A	Foreign Geographic Area B	Other Foreign Geographic Areas
Acquisition of properties					
Proved	$X	$X	$X	$X	$X
Unproved	X	X	X	X	X
Exploration costs	X	X	X	X	X
Development costs	X	X	X	X	X
Enterprise's share of equity method investee's costs of property acquisition, exploration, and development	X	X	X	X	X

Figure 28-6
Costs Incurred Table from ExxonMobil's 2005 Annual Report

The amounts reported as costs incurred include both capitalized costs and costs charged to expense during the year. Costs incurred also include new asset retirement obligations established in the current year, as well as increases or decreases to the asset retirement obligation resulting from changes in cost estimates or abandonment date. Total consolidated costs incurred in 2005 were $10,784 million, up $1,767 million from 2004, due primarily to higher development and property acquisition costs. 2004 costs were $9,017 million, down $819 million from 2003, due primarily to lower development costs.

Costs incurred in property acquisitions, exploration and development activities	United States	Canada	Europe	Africa	Asia Pacific/ Middle East	Russia/ Caspian	Other	Total
				(millions of dollars)				
During 2005								
Property acquisition costs – Proved	$ —	$ —	$ —	$ —	$ —	$ 174	$ —	$ 174
– Unproved	11	6	—	53	41	156	12	279
Exploration costs	286	62	133	507	171	159	59	1,377
Development costs	1,426	624	1,302	3,189	541	1,774	98	8,954
Total costs incurred for consolidated subsidiaries	$1,723	$692	$1,435	$3,749	$753	$2,263	$169	$10,784
Proportional interest of costs incurred of equity companies	$ 269	$ —	$ 210	$ —	$319	$ 384	$ —	$ 1,182
During 2004								
Property acquisition costs – Proved	$ —	$ —	$ —	$ 68	$ —	$ 25	$ —	$ 93
– Unproved	14	1	—	24	2	—	—	41
Exploration costs	232	68	123	382	110	189	86	1,190
Development costs	1,427	694	1,232	2,788	494	985	73	7,693
Total costs incurred for consolidated subsidiaries	$1,673	$763	$1,355	$3,262	$606	$1,199	$159	$ 9,017
Proportional interest of costs incurred of equity companies	$ 155	$ —	$ 169	$ —	$205	$ 451	$ —	$ 980
During 2003								
Property acquisition costs – Proved	$ —	$ —	$ —	$ —	$ —	$ —	$ —	$ —
– Unproved	17	7	4	17	—	—	—	45
Exploration costs	252	102	153	264	144	170	67	1,152
Development costs	1,636	644	1,755	3,117	731	729	27	8,639
Total costs incurred for consolidated subsidiaries	$1,905	$753	$1,912	$3,398	$875	$ 899	$ 94	$ 9,836
Proportional interest of costs incurred of equity companies	$ 145	$ —	$ 231	$ —	$146	$ 289	$ —	$ 811

DISCLOSING RESULTS OF OPERATIONS FOR
OIL AND GAS PRODUCING ACTIVITIES

FAS 69 (and Oi5.174 through Oi5.179) requires disclosure of historical results of operations for oil and gas producing activities by major geographic area:

24. The results of operations for oil and gas producing activities shall be disclosed for the year. That information shall be disclosed in the aggregate and for each geographic area for which reserve quantities are disclosed (paragraph 12). The following information relating to those activities shall be presented:[17]

   a) Revenues

   b) Production (lifting costs)

   c) Exploration expenses[18]

   d) Depreciation, depletion, and amortization, and valuation provisions

   e) Income tax expense

   f) Results of operations for oil and gas producing activities (excluding corporate overhead and interest costs)

25. Revenues shall include sales to unaffiliated enterprises and sales or transfers to the enterprise's other operations (for example, refineries or chemical plants). Sales to unaffiliated enterprises and sales or transfers to the enterprise's other operations shall be disclosed separately. Revenues shall include sales to unaffiliated enterprises attributable to net working interests, royalty interests, oil payment interests, and net profits interests of the reporting enterprise. Sales or transfers to the enterprises' other operations shall be based on market prices determined at the point of delivery from the producing unit. Those market prices shall represent prices equivalent to those that could be obtained in an arm's-length transaction. Production or severance taxes shall not be deducted in determining gross revenues, but rather shall be included as part of production costs. Royalty payments and net profits disbursements shall be excluded from gross revenues.

26. Income taxes shall be computed using the statutory tax rate for the period, applied to revenues less production (lifting) costs, exploration expenses, depreciation, depletion, and amortization, and valuation provisions. Calculation of income tax expense shall reflect tax deductions, tax credits and allowances relating to the oil and gas producing activities that are reflected in the enterprise's consolidated income tax expense for the period.

27. Results of operations for oil and gas producing activities are defined as revenues less production (lifting) costs, exploration expenses, depreciation, depletion, and amortization, valuation provisions, and income tax expenses. General corporate overhead and interest costs[19] shall not be deducted in computing the results of operations for an enterprise's oil and gas producing activities. However, some expenses incurred at an enterprise's central administrative office may not be general corporate expenses, but rather may be operating expenses of oil and gas producing activities, and therefore should be reported as such. The nature of an expense rather than the location of its incurrence shall determine whether it is an operating expense. Only those expenses identified by their nature as operating expenses shall be allocated as operating expenses in computing the results of operations for oil and gas producing activities.

28. The amounts disclosed in conformity with paragraphs 24-27 shall include an enterprise's interests in proved oil and gas reserves (paragraph 10) and in oil and gas subject to purchase under long-term supply, purchase, or similar agreements and contracts in which the enterprise participates in the operation of the properties on which the oil or gas is located or otherwise serves as the producer of those reserves (paragraph 13).

29. If the enterprise's financial statements include investments that are accounted for by the equity method, the investee's results of operations for oil and gas producing activities shall not be included in the enterprise's results of operations for oil and gas producing activities. However, the enterprise's share of the investee's results of operations for oil and gas producing activities shall be separately disclosed for the year, in the aggregate and by each geographic area for which reserves quantities are disclosed (paragraph 12).

Figure 28-7 shows the illustrative FAS 69 Results of Operations Disclosure as presented in FAS 69. Figure 28-8 shows a corresponding excerpt from ExxonMobil's 2005 Annual Report disclosure.

In addition to the above disclosure requirements, FAS 69 also requires disclosure of a standardized measure of discounted future net cash flows from proved oil and gas reserves. The complex calculations required for this disclosure are discussed in Chapter 29.

Figure 28-7
Illustrative FAS 69 Results of Operations Disclosure

Results of Operations for Producing Activities
for the Year Ended December 31, 20XX

	Total	United States	Foreign Geographic Area A	Foreign Geographic Area B	Other Foreign Geographic Areas
Revenues					
Sales	$X	$X	$X	$X	$X
Transfers	X	X	X	X	X
Total	X	X	X	X	X
Production costs	(X)	(X)	(X)	(X)	(X)
Exploration expenses	(X)	(X)	(X)	(X)	(X)
Depreciation, depletion, and amortization, and valuation provisions	(X)	(X)	(X)	(X)	(X)
	X	X	X	X	X
Income tax expenses	(X)	(X)	(X)	(X)	(X)
Results of operations for producing activities (excluding corporate overhead and interest costs)	$X	$X	$X	$X	$X
Enterprise's share of equity method investees' results of operations for producing activities.	$X	$X	$X	$X	$X

Figure 28-8
Excerpt of Results of Operations Disclosure from
ExxonMobil's 2005 Annual Report
(Excludes amounts related to 2004 and 2003 for simplicity)

Results of Operations	United States	Canada	Europe	Africa	Asia Pacific/ Middle East	Russia/ Caspian	Other	Total
				(millions of dollars)				
2005 – Revenue								
Sales to third parties	$ 4,842	$3,216	$ 8,383	$ 40	$2,357	$357	$512	$19,707
Transfers	6,277	3,400	7,040	12,293	3,143	279	182	32,614
	$11,119	$6,616	$15,423	$12,333	$5,500	$636	$694	$52,321
Less costs:								
Production costs excluding taxes	1,367	1,265	2,174	840	567	123	105	6,441
Exploration expenses	158	36	64	310	122	164	101	955
Depreciation and depletion	1,181	983	2,133	1,319	666	137	58	6,477
Taxes other than income	738	53	690	1,158	839	2	3	3,483
Related income tax	3,138	1,482	6,572	5,143	1,313	111	159	17,918
Results of producing activities for consolidated subsidiaries	$ 4,537	$2,797	$ 3,790	$ 3,563	$1,993	$ 99	$268	$17,047
Proportional interest in results of producing activities of equity companies	$ 1,043	$ —	$ 1,003	$ —	$1,009	$701	$ —	$ 3,756

DISCLOSING MANAGEMENT'S EVALUATION OF CAPITALIZED EXPLORATORY WELL COSTS

In April 2005, the FASB issued a Staff Position entitled FSP FAS 19-1, *Accounting for Suspended Well Costs*. Prior to its issuance, paragraph 31(b) of FAS 19 required capitalized exploratory well costs to be expensed if the associated reserves could not be classified as proved after one year following completion of drilling. Pursuant to the FSP, there are circumstances that would permit the continued capitalization of exploratory well costs beyond one year if certain criteria are met. FSP FAS 19-1 also added disclosure requirements related to exploratory well costs. (See a sample disclosure at Figure 28-9.)

The disclosures required by FSP FAS 19-1 include:

- Amount of capitalized exploratory well costs that is pending the determination of proved reserves and changes in those capitalized exploratory well costs resulting from:

  - Additions to capitalized exploratory well costs that are pending the determination of proved reserves

  - Capitalized exploratory well costs that were reclassified to wells, equipment, and facilities based on the determination of proved reserves

  - Capitalized exploratory well costs that were charged to expense

  This disclosure should not include amounts that were capitalized and subsequently expensed in the same annual period.

- Amount of exploratory well costs that have been capitalized for a period of greater than one year and aging of those amounts by year, along with the number of projects to which those costs relate.

- For exploratory well costs that continue to be capitalized for more than one year after the completion of drilling, an enterprise should describe the projects and activities it has undertaken to evaluate the reserves and the projects, and the remaining activities required to classify the associated reserves as proved.

These disclosures are not required in interim financial statements; however, interim financial statements should include information about significant changes from the information presented in the most recent annual financial statements.[20]

Figure 28-9: Example of Disclosure of Suspended Well Costs – Excerpt from Exxon-Mobil's 2005 Annual Report[21]

Change in capitalized suspended exploratory well costs:	2005	2004	2003
		(millions of dollars)	
Balance beginning at January 1	$ 1,070	$ 1,093	$ 1,193
Additions pending the determination of proved reserves	233	139	217
Charged to expense	(62)	(98)	(238)
Reclassifications to wells, facilities and equipment based on the determination of proved reserves	(82)	(92)	(123)
Foreign exchange/other	(20)	28	44
Ending balance	$ 1,139	$ 1,070	$ 1,093
Ending balance attributed to equity companies included above	$ 2	$ 1	$ 30

Period-end capitalized suspended exploratory well costs:	2005	2004	2003
		(millions of dollars)	
Capitalized for a period of one year or less	$ 233	$ 139	$ 217
Capitalized for a period of between one and five years	485	510	453
Capitalized for a period of between five and ten years	167	172	162
Capitalized for a period of greater than ten years	254	249	261
Capitalized for a period greater than one year – subtotal	$ 906	$ 931	$ 876
Total	$ 1,139	$ 1,070	$ 1,093

[...]	2005	2004	2003
Number of projects with first capitalized well drilled in the preceding 12 months	16	8	13
Number of projects that have exploratory well costs capitalized for a period of greater than 12 months	56	61	76
Total	72	69	89

SPECIAL DISCLOSURES FOR COMPANIES USING FULL COST

Whether publicly-held or not, companies using the Reg. S-X Rule 4-10 full cost method are subject to various additional disclosure requirements.

DISCLOSING FULL COST AMORTIZATION PER UNIT-OF-PRODUCTION

Subparagraph (c)(7)(i) of Reg. S-X Rule 4-10 requires the following additional disclosures related to the amortization per unit-of-production for each cost center:

(i) For each cost center for each year that an income statement is required, disclose the total amount of amortization expense (per equivalent physical unit of production if amortization is computed on the basis of physical units or per dollar of gross revenue from production if amortization is computed on the basis of gross revenue).

An example of this disclosure is shown in Figure 28-10.

Figure 28-10
Example of Amortization per Unit-of-Production
Excerpt from Apache Corporation's 2005 Annual Report
(For simplicity, certain footnotes from the original report and data from
years 2004 and 2003 have not been reprinted in this example.)

	United States	Canada	Egypt	Australia	North Sea	Other International	Total
				(in thousands)			
2005							
Oil and gas production revenues	$ 2,824,522	$ 1,450,801	$ 1,358,183	$ 400,791	$ 1,274,470	$ 148,524	$ 7,457,291
Less operating costs:							
Depreciation, depletion, and amortization	556,922	261,195	221,230	100,798	186,675	57,892	1,384,712
Asset retirement obligation accretion	31,657	6,811	—	2,414	12,709	129	53,720
Lease operating expenses	477,780	229,592	116,160	55,666	146,015	15,262	1,040,475
Gathering and transportation costs	29,954	33,309	7,991	—	28,248	758	100,260
Production taxes	99,009	9,112	—	38,386	285,293	—	431,800
Income tax	578,366	332,435	486,145	69,199	246,212	24,697	1,737,054
	1,773,688	872,454	831,526	266,463	905,152	98,738	4,748,021
Results of operations	$ 1,050,834	$ 578,347	$ 526,657	$ 134,328	$ 369,318	$ 49,786	$ 2,709,270
Amortization rate per BOE	$ 8.78	$ 7.71	$ 6.34	$ 6.82	$ 7.76	$ 16.16	$ 7.99

DISCLOSING UNEVALUATED COSTS UNDER FULL COST ACCOUNTING

As discussed in Chapter 19, special disclosures related to unevaluated costs that have been excluded from amortization are required also. This requirement is found in paragraph (c)(7)(ii) of Regulation S-X Rule 4-10:

> (ii) State separately on the face of the balance sheet the aggregate of the capitalized costs of unproved properties and major development projects that are excluded, in accordance with paragraph (i)(3) of this section, from the capitalized costs being amortized. Provide a description in the notes to the financial statements of the current status of the significant properties or projects involved, including the anticipated timing of the inclusion of the costs in the amortization computation. Present a table that shows, by category of cost, (A) the total costs excluded as of the most recent fiscal year; and (B) the amounts of such excluded costs, incurred (1) in each of the three most recent fiscal years and (2) in the aggregate for any earlier fiscal years in which the costs were incurred. Categories of cost to be disclosed include acquisition costs, exploration costs, development costs in the case of significant development projects and capitalized interest.

DISCLOSING CEILING TEST RESULTS

Per Regulation S-X Rule 4-10 (c)(4)(ii), any expense resulting from the write-down of net capitalized costs in excess of the full cost ceiling should be separately disclosed. If such excess is not charged to expense because of certain subsequent events, as discussed in Chapter 19, the company should disclose that the excess existed and disclose why the excess was not charged to expense per SAB Topic 12D, Item 3(c). Note that the SAB does not specifically require the amount of the excess to be disclosed.

An example of a write-down disclosure is found in Anadarko Petroleum Corporation's 2005 Annual Report. The financial statement note disclosure reads as follows:

Ceiling Test. Under the full cost method of accounting, a ceiling test is performed each quarter. The full cost ceiling test is an impairment test prescribed by SEC Regulation S-X Rule 4-10. The ceiling test determines a limit, on a country-by-country basis, on the book value of oil and gas properties. The capitalized costs of proved oil and gas properties, net of accumulated DD&A and the related deferred income taxes, may not exceed the estimated future net cash flows from proved oil and gas reserves, excluding future cash outflows associated with settling asset retirement obligations that have been accrued on the balance sheet, generally using prices in effect at the end of the period held flat for the life of production and including the effect of derivative instruments that qualify as cash flow hedges, discounted at 10%, net of related tax effects, plus the cost of unevaluated properties and major development projects excluded from the costs being amortized. If capitalized costs exceed this limit, the excess is charged to expense and reflected as additional accumulated DD&A. For cash flow hedge effect information, see Supplemental Information on Oil and Gas Exploration and Production Activities — Discounted Future Net Cash Flows.[...]

[...] During 2005, 2004 and 2003, the Company made provisions for impairments of oil and gas properties of $78 million, $72 million and $103 million, respectively. The impairments in 2005 include $35 million related to unsuccessful exploration activities in Tunisia, $30 million related to exploration activities at various international locations and $13 million related to the disposition of properties in Oman. The impairments in 2004 and 2003 included ceiling test impairments of oil and gas properties in Qatar of $62 million and $68 million, respectively, as a result of lower future production estimates and other international exploration activities.

OTHER SEC DISCLOSURE REQUIREMENTS

In addition to the supplemental disclosures discussed previously, the SEC requires a number of other disclosures unrelated to the financial statements, but which are contained in the forepart of securities registration statements and of Form 10-K Annual Reports filed with the SEC. These requirements are found in the SEC's Regulation S-K and in *Guide 2, Disclosure of Oil and Gas Operations*, including the following:

For each of the last three fiscal years:

- Production-related information including:
    - Volumetric production data
    - Average sales price and production cost per unit (separately for oil and natural gas)
- Total net productive and dry wells drilled, broken down by exploratory wells and development wells drilled, by appropriate geographic area.

For the current date or end of the latest fiscal year:

- Total gross and net productive oil and gas wells
- Total gross and net developed acreage by FAS 69 major geographic area
- Total gross and net undeveloped acreage by appropriate geographic area and, if material, minimum remaining terms of leases and concessions

- Number of wells in progress, gross and net, waterfloods, pressure maintenance operations, by appropriate geographic area

- Information about obligations to provide fixed quantities of oil and gas in the future under existing contracts

- Difference between the reserves reported to other agencies and reserves included in the report, if such difference is in excess of five percent

- Instruction 3 to Item 102 of Regulation S-K requires material disclosure of information such as reserves, production, development, and the nature of the ownership interest regarding significant properties

• • •

1   See Chapter 29 for details of standardized measure disclosures.

2   In accordance with Reg. S-X Rule 4-10, any internal costs that are capitalized are limited to those costs that can be directly identified with acquisition, exploration, and development activities undertaken by the company for its own account, and do not include any costs related to production, general corporate overhead, or similar activities.

3   Under EITF 90-22, *Accounting for Gas-Balancing Arrangements*, an SEC registrant should disclose its method of accounting for gas balancing (i.e., sales method or entitlement method) as well as the amount of any imbalance in terms of both units and value, if significant. Additional disclosures may be necessary. In two known instances, the SEC staff asked registrants using the entitlement method also to disclose how revenues were recognized, how the company accounted for its share of production expenses, and how the receivable or liability was recorded.

4   Registrants who engage in buy/sell transactions should provide the disclosures required by EITF 04-13, *Accounting for Purchases and Sales of Inventory with the Same Counterparty*.

5   Under FSP FAS 19-1, *Accounting for Suspended Well Costs*, companies following the successful efforts method of accounting are required to disclose their policies related to management's evaluation of capitalized exploratory well costs.

6   SEC's Codification of Financial Reporting Releases, 406.02.d.i, reproduced at Appendix 1.

7   Regulation D of the Securities Act of 1933 established certain exemptions from the registration requirements of the act for private offerings of securities to qualified investors or at limited markets.

8   SEC's Codification of Financial Reporting Releases, 406.02.d.ii, reproduced at Appendix 1.

9   SEC's Codification of Financial Reporting Releases, 406.02.d.iii, reproduced at Appendix 1.

10 The SEC addresses financial statements for acquired oil and gas producing properties at http://www.sec.gov/divisions/corpfin/guidance/cfactfaq.htm.

11 FAS 69, paragraph 30, indicates that reserves information should be disclosed as of the end of the year. From a practical standpoint, in order to present the changes in the standardized measure for three years companies often disclose SMOG at the beginning and the end of each of the three years.

12 Reg. S-X Rule 4-10, Subsection (k), deleted in 1992 by Financial Reporting Release 40A, required that the method of accounting be disclosed on the face of the balance sheet. Today, the accounting method may simply be disclosed in the financial statement note on significant accounting policies.

13 Note 5 of FAS 69 states: "if significant, the reserve quantity information shall be disclosed separately for natural gas liquids." Author's note: Various methods of disclosing NGL reserves quantities are currently used. As noted above, most companies disclose natural gas liquids with oil reserves. Some companies disclose wet gas reserves (before removal of NGL), effectively including NGL reserves in natural gas reserves as opposed to oil reserves. Some of those companies also separately disclose NGL reserves, and financial statement users need to be careful to not double-count the NGL reserves.

14 See Chapter 25 for further discussion of this disclosure requirement.

15 FAS 69, footnote 6 states, "As defined in the paragraphs cited, exploration and development costs include depreciation of support equipment and facilities used in those activities and do not include the expenditures to acquire support equipment and facilities."

16 Refer to Basis of Conclusion of FAS 143, paragraph B42 and B44, and SEC sample letter sent to oil and gas producers dated February 24, 2004.

17 FAS 69, footnote 7, states: "If oil and gas producing activities represent substantially all of the business activities of the producing enterprise and those oil and gas activities are located substantially in a single geographic area, the information required by paragraphs 24-29 of the Statement need not be disclosed if that information is provided elsewhere in the financial statements."

18 FAS 69, footnote 8, provides: "Generally, only enterprises utilizing the successful efforts accounting method will have exploration expenses to disclose, since enterprises utilizing the full cost accounting method generally capitalize all exploration costs when incurred and subsequently reflect those costs in the determination of earnings through depreciation, depletion, and amortization, and in the valuation provisions."

19 FAS 69, footnote 9, states: "The disposition of interest costs that have been capitalized as part of the cost of acquiring qualifying assets used in oil and gas producing activities shall be the same as that of other components of those assets' costs."

20 In accordance with FSP FAS 19-1, any impairment of capitalized exploratory well costs that were capitalized for a period of greater than one year after the completion of drilling at the most recent annual balance sheet date will be considered significant for purposes of determining whether the change should be disclosed in interim financial statements.

21 The illustration does not include disclosures required by FSP FAS 19-1, paragraph 10(c), related to describing the projects and the activities the company has undertaken to date in order to evaluate the reserves and the projects, and the remaining activities required to classify the associated reserves as proved.

CHAPTER

29

VALUE-BASED DISCLOSURES

Key Concepts:

- Standardized measure disclosure rules

- Standardized measure computation example

- Income taxes: year-by-year vs. short-cut method

- Acquisition of reserves in place

- Disposition of reserves

- Changes in standardized measure

As explained in Chapter 28, Reserve Recognition Accounting (RRA) value disclosures required by the SEC in 1978 were replaced with certain disclosures prescribed by FAS 69, issued in late 1982. Among other items, FAS 69 required disclosure of "a standardized measure of discounted future net cash flows relating to proved oil and gas reserve quantities." The term is often called simply *the standardized measure*, or *SMOG*.[1] SMOG's calculation is almost identical to the earlier calculation required by the SEC, except that SMOG's calculation considers future income taxes.

DISCLOSURE RULES

The SMOG requirements are specified in Paragraphs 30 through 32 of FAS 69 (reproduced following) and in Oi5.180 through Oi5.182 of Appendix 2.

---

30. A standardized measure of discounted future net cash flows relating to an enterprise's interests in (a) proved oil and gas reserves (paragraph 10) and (b) oil and gas subject to purchase under long-term supply, purchase, or similar agreements and contracts in which the enterprise participates in the operation of the properties on which the oil or gas is located or otherwise serves as the producer of those reserves (paragraph 13) shall be disclosed as of the end of the year. The standardized measure of discounted future net cash flows relating to those two types of interests in reserves may be combined for reporting purposes. The following information shall be disclosed in the aggregate and for each geographic area for which reserve quantities are disclosed in accordance with paragraph 12:

   a. *Future cash inflows.* These shall be computed by applying year-end prices of oil and gas relating to the enterprise's proved reserves to the year-end quantities of those reserves. Future price changes shall be considered only to the extent provided by contractual arrangements in existence at year-end.

   b. *Future development and production costs.* These costs shall be computed by estimating the expenditures to be incurred in developing and producing the proved oil and gas reserves at the end of the year, based on year-end costs and assuming continuation of existing economic conditions. If estimated development expenditures are significant, they shall be presented separately from estimated production costs.

   c. *Future income tax expenses.* These expenses shall be computed by applying the appropriate year-end statutory tax rates, with consideration of future tax rates already legislated, to the future pre-tax net cash flows relating to the enterprise's proved oil and gas reserves, less the tax basis of the properties involved. The future income tax expenses shall give effect to [tax deductions] and tax credits and allowances relating to the enterprise's proved oil and gas reserves.[2]

   d. *Future net cash flows.* These amounts are the result of subtracting future development and production costs and future income tax expenses from future cash inflows.

   e. *Discount.* This amount shall be derived from using a discount rate of 10 percent a year to reflect the timing of future net cash flows relating to proved oil and gas reserves.

   f. *Standardized measure of discounted future net cash flows.* This amount is the future net cash flows less the computed discount.

---

31. If a significant portion of the economic interest in the consolidated standardized measure of discounted future net cash flows reported is attributable to a consolidated subsidiary(ies) in which there is a significant minority interest, that fact and the approximate portion shall be disclosed.

32. If the financial statements include investments that are accounted for by the equity method, the investees' standardized measure of discounted future net cash flows relating to proved oil and gas reserves shall not be included in the disclosure of the enterprise's standardized measure. However, the enterprise's share of the investees' standardized measure of discounted future net cash flows shall be separately disclosed for the year, in the aggregate and by each geologic area for which quantities are disclosed (paragraph 12).

The format suggested in FAS 69 for the standardized measure disclosure is shown in Figure 29-1.

In addition to an end of year disclosure of present value, FAS 69 also calls for disclosure of: (1) the aggregate SMOG change for the year, and (2) the significant reasons for the change in SMOG value from the beginning of the year to the end of the year. FAS 69, Paragraph 33 (Oi5.183), lists major reasons that may exist for SMOG changes and calls for their individual disclosures if the amounts are significant:

33. The aggregate change in the standardized measure of discounted future net cash flows shall be disclosed for the year. If individually significant, the following sources of change shall be presented separately:

     a.   Net change in sales and transfer prices and in production (lifting) costs related to future production

     b.   Changes in estimated future development costs

     c.   Sales and transfers of oil and gas produced during the period

     d.   Net change due to extensions, discoveries, and improved recovery

     e.   Net change due to purchases and sales of minerals in place

     f.   Net change due to revisions in quantity estimates

     g.   Previously estimated development costs incurred during the period

     h.   Accretion of discount

     i.   Other—unspecified

     j.   Net change in income taxes

In computing the amounts under each of the above categories, the effects of changes in prices and costs shall be computed before the effects of changes in quantities. As a result, changes in quantities shall be stated at year-end prices and costs. The change in computed income taxes shall reflect the effect of income taxes incurred during the period as well as the change in future income tax expenses. Therefore, all changes except income taxes shall be reported pre-tax.

Figure 29-1
First Half of Illustration 5 of FAS 69

	Total	United States	Foreign Geographic Area A	Foreign Geographic Area B	Other Foreign Geographic Areas
STANDARDIZED MEASURE OF DISCOUNTED FUTURE NET CASH FLOWS AND CHANGES THEREIN RELATING TO PROVED OIL RESERVES AT DECEMBER 31, 20XX					
Future cash inflows*	$X	$X	$X	$X	$X
Future production and development costs*	(X)	(X)	(X)	(X)	(X)
Future income tax expenses*	(X)	(X)	(X)	(X)	(X)
Future net cash flows	X	X	X	X	X
10% annual discount for estimated timing of cash flows	(X)	(X)	(X)	(X)	(X)
Standardized measure of discounted future net cash flows	$X**	$X	$X	$X	$X
Enterprise's share of equity method investees' standardized measure of discounted future net cash flows	$X	$X	$X	$X	$X

* Future net cash flows were computed using year-end prices and costs, and year-end statutory tax rates (adjusted for [tax deductions]) that relate to existing proved oil and gas reserves in which the enterprise has mineral interests, including those mineral interests related to long-term supply agreements with governments for which the enterprise serves as the producer of the reserves.

** Includes $X attributable to a consolidated subsidiary in which there is an X percent minority interest.

The format suggested in FAS 69 for disclosure of the reasons for changes is shown in Figure 29-2.

Figure 29-2
Second Half of Illustration 5 of FAS 69

The following are the principal sources of change in the standardized measure of discounted future net cash flows during 20XX:

Sales and transfers of oil and gas produced, net of production costs	$ (X)
Net changes in prices and production costs	X
Extensions, discoveries, and improved recovery, less related costs	X
Development costs incurred during the period	X
Revisions of previous quantity estimates	X
Accretion of discount	X
Net change in income taxes	X
Other	X

[*Authors' Note:* The above FAS 69 illustration does not list all of the sources of change noted in Paragraph 33, nor does it show the aggregate change as required in Paragraph 33. Figure 29-21 at the end of this chapter includes the items omitted above. The SMOG change for development costs incurred during the period is always a positive change as shown above; it is not a negative change as shown in Illustration 5 of FAS 69.]

SMOG COMPUTATION EXAMPLE

The next several pages illustrate how SMOG and SMOG changes can be computed. For this example, assume a company has proved reserves as of December 31, 2005, in only one field, Field No. 1. During 2006, the company discovers proved reserves in a second field, Field No. 2, and acquires a third field, Field No. 3, on May 31, 2006.

The following is a summary of worksheets that track various SMOG computations. SMOG for Field No. 1 is computed as of December 31, 2005, and again as of December 31, 2006. Next, individual components of Field No. 1's SMOG changes for 2006 are calculated. The example then demonstrates Field No. 2's SMOG as of December 31, 2006. Changes in SMOG for 2006 are calculated for Field Nos. 2 and 3, including changes related to discovery, acquisition, and subsequent changes from the date of acquisition for Field No. 3 to December 31, 2006. SMOG changes for Field No. 2 do not include changes other than those related to discovery and production during December 2006. (Other changes are not considered significant because this discovery was made late in 2006.) The SMOG and SMOG change computations by field are combined to determine the company's aggregate SMOG as of December 31, 2006, and its SMOG changes for 2006. The company's financial statements do not present the combined computation, but rather an aggregate computation of SMOG by geographical areas.

The combined disclosures included in this extended example are for illustration purposes only. They are intended to demonstrate how each field contributes to overall SMOG and changes in SMOG. Likewise, examples in this chapter may contain excerpts from actual SEC filings (Form 10-K) and are used for illustrative purposes only.

COMPUTING SMOG

Many companies calculate the standardized measure (and related changes) in the aggregate or by major geographical area, rather than by field. Field-by-field computations are often impractical. Calculations in the aggregate are generally less precise than by field, but can employ the same calculation concepts illustrated in the field-by-field example presented.

Assume the following information relating to the company's ownership in reserves in Field No. 1 on December 31, 2005, as shown in Figure 29-3.

Figure 29-3
Field No. 1 Assumptions as of December 31, 2005

Reserves as of December 31, 2005, to be produced in:

		Reserves		Future Development Costs	Future Income Taxes (a)
	bbls	**Mcf**	**BOE (b)**		
2006	30,000	165,000	57,500	$220,000	$ 497,000
2007	22,500	150,000	47,500		455,000
2008	15,000	90,000	30,000		294,000
2009	7,500	45,000	15,000		147,000
2010	3,750	20,000	7,083	10,000	67,667
Total	**78,750**	**470,000**	**157,083**	**$230,000**	**$1,460,667**

Price per barrel	$60.00		
Price per Mcf		$6.00	
Production costs per BOE			$20.00

(a) For simplicity it was assumed that income taxes are given numbers.
(b) Mcf was converted to BOE using the 6:1 factor.

Figure 29-3 presents the reserves amounts in barrels for oil and in Mcf for natural gas. The natural gas reserves are recalculated to the units of oil equivalent using a ratio of six Mcf per barrel of crude oil. Although the ratio is imprecise and the actual conversion ratio would depend on the physical qualities of natural gas, the ratio of 6:1 is commonly used to convert natural gas reserves and production amounts to equivalent units.

Computation of Future Income Taxes. For this example, future income taxes are provided as given numbers. However, actual SMOG disclosures employ two approaches to compute future income taxes applicable to the production of proved reserves.

The first method is a year-by-year calculation in which the projected revenues, projected operating expenses, depreciation, depletion, and other factors are considered in arriving at each year's tax outflow.

A second method of computing the tax liability is the *short-cut* approach, which is a lump-sum calculation rather than a year-by-year calculation.[3]

FAS 69's illustration of the standardized measure of discounted future net cash flows (shown in Figure 29-1) suggests that the effects of income taxes on future net cash flows from production of proved reserves are to be computed for each future year. This year-by-year approach seems to be required by Paragraph 30 of FAS 69 (Oi5.180), which states:

Future Income Tax Expenses. These expenses shall be computed by applying the appropriate year-end statutory rates, with consideration of future tax rates already legislated, to the enterprise's proved oil and gas reserves, less the tax basis of the properties involved. The future income tax expense shall give effect to tax deductions, tax credits and allowances relating to the enterprise's proved oil and gas reserves.

Further, FAS 69, paragraph 33 (Oi5.183), discusses changes in *future* income tax expense. The SEC has formally confirmed a staff position prohibiting use of the short-cut method for calculating income taxes for the purposes of SMOG calculations. On March 31, 2005, SEC staff issued its Frequently Requested Accounting and Financial Reporting Interpretations and Guidance [Section F.3.(j)], which includes the following:

(j) The calculation of the standardized measure of discounted future net cash flows relating to oil and gas properties must comply with paragraph 30 of SFAS 69. The effects of income taxes, like all other elements of the measure, must be discounted at the standard rate of 10% pursuant to paragraph 30(e). The "short-cut" method for determining the tax effect on the ceiling test for companies using the full-cost method of accounting, as described in SAB Topic 12:D:1, Question 2, may not be used for purposes of the paragraph 30 calculation of the standardized measure.

Computation of Future Net Cash Flows. Figure 29-1's illustration of the SMOG disclosure shows a line for *future net cash flows*. These are computed in Figure 29-4. The formula is: future cash inflows (i.e., future revenues), less future production costs and future development costs, equal future pre-tax net cash flows (often called by their old RRA term, *future net revenues*). Future net revenues less future income tax expense equal future net cash flows.

Figure 29-4
Schedule of Future Net Cash Flows for Field No. 1
As of December 31, 2005

		2006	2007	2008	2009	2010	Total
Future cash inflows	(b)	$2,790,000	$2,250,000	$1,440,000	$720,000	$345,000	$7,545,000
Future costs:							
Production costs	(b)	(1,150,000)	(950,000)	(600,000)	(300,000)	(141,667)	(3,141,667)
Development costs	(a)	(220,000)	–	–	–	(10,000)	(230,000)
Future net revenues		1,420,000	1,300,000	840,000	420,000	193,333	4,173,333
Future income taxes	(a)	(497,000)	(455,000)	(294,000)	(147,000)	(67,667)	(1,460,667)
Future net cash flows		$923,000	$845,000	$546,000	$273,000	$125,666	$2,712,666

(a) From Figure 29-3.
(b) Calculated from Figure 29-3.

Computation of the Present Value of Future Net Cash Flows. FAS 69 requires future net cash flows to be discounted at a standard rate of 10 percent per year. Reference to a table in Figure 29-5 shows the following *present value of 1* factors (PV factors) based on the assumption that the first year's cash inflow is received, on average, six months from the date of the standardized measure. This is commonly known as the mid-year convention.

Figure 29-5
Present Value of 1 Factors[4]

Year	PV Factor
1	.9535
2	.8668
3	.7880
4	.7164
5	.6512

Applying the PV factors from Figure 29-5 to the future net cash flows in Figure 29-4, the total present value of proved reserves (i.e., SMOG) as of December 31, 2005, for Field No. 1 is $2,320,185, as shown in Figure 29-6.

Figure 29-6
Computation of SMOG for Field No. 1 as of December 31, 2005

		2006	2007	2008	2009	2010	Total
Future cash inflows	(a)	$2,790,000	$2,250,000	$1,440,000	$720,000	$345,000	$7,545,000
Future costs:							
Production costs	(a)	(1,150,000)	(950,000)	(600,000)	(300,000)	(141,667)	(3,141,667)
Development costs	(a)	(220,000)	–	–	–	(10,000)	(230,000)
Future net revenues		1,420,000	1,300,000	840,000	420,000	193,333	4,173,333
Future income taxes	(a) [A]	(497,000)	(455,000)	(294,000)	(147,000)	(67,667)	(1,460,667)
Future net cash flows	(a) [B]	$923,000	$845,000	$546,000	$273,000	$125,666	$2,712,666
10% discount*	[B]x(1-[C])	(42,920)	(112,554)	(115,752)	(77,423)	(43,832)	(392,481)
Standardized Measure (SMOG)		$880,080	$732,446	$430,248	$195,577	$81,834	$2,320,185
*Present value factors used [C]		0.9535	0.8668	0.7880	0.7164	0.6512	
Supplementary calculations:							
Add back income tax							
present value*	[A] x [C]	473,890	394,394	231,672	105,311	44,065	1,249,332
Pre-tax standardized measure		$1,353,970	$1,126,840	$661,920	$300,888	$125,899	$3,569,517

(a) From Figure 29-4.

Pre-tax standardized measure is used in the calculation of changes in standardized measure, but is not included in the required disclosures prescribed by FAS 69. As discussed earlier, FAS 69, paragraph 33, requires all changes in the standardized measure to be presented on a before-tax basis.

Statement of Standardized Measure. Using the FAS 69 format, the standardized measure data relating to Field No. 1 as of December 31, 2005, is presented as follows:

Figure 29-7
Standardized Measure of Discounted Future Net Cash Flows
As of December 31, 2005

Future cash inflows	$7,545,000
Future production costs	(3,141,667)
Future development costs	(230,000)
Future income tax expenses	(1,460,667)
Future net cash flows	2,712,666
10% annual discount for estimated timing of cash flows	(392,481)
Standardized measure of discounted future net cash flows relating to proved oil and gas reserves	$2,320,185

COMPUTING SMOG CHANGES

To calculate individual factors leading to changes in the standardized measure of discounted present value of reserves in Field No. 1 during the year 2006, the standardized measure is computed as of December 31, 2006 (see Figure 29-8).

Figure 29-8
Field No. 1 Assumptions for the Year 2006 and
Data as of December 31, 2006

Data for the year ended December 31, 2006		bbls	Mcf	BOE (c)		
Production		27,000	180,000	57,000		
Revenues	$2,925,000					
Production expenses	1,224,000					
Revenues less production expenses	$1,701,000					
Previously estimated development costs incurred	$240,000					

					Future Development Costs	Future Income Taxes (a)
Data as of December 31, 2006			Reserves			
		bbls	Mcf	BOE (c)		
2007		24,000	180,000	54,000	$ 5,000	$ 598,850
2008		18,000	120,000	38,000		431,200
2009		9,000	60,000	19,000		215,600
2010		3,000	15,000	5,500	20,000	58,450
Total		54,000	375,000	116,500	$25,000	$1,304,100

		New Reserves Attributable to Extensions, Discoveries, and Improved Recoveries (b)			Future Dev. Costs - New Discoveries
Included in the above:		bbls	Mcf	BOE (c)	
2007		5,000	18,000	8,000	$ 5,000
2008		5,000	12,000	7,000	
2009					
2010					8,000
Total		10,000	30,000	15,000	$13,000

Price per barrel	$67.00
Price per Mcf	$7.50
Production costs per BOE	$23.00

(a) For simplicity it is assumed income taxes are given numbers.
(b) Reserve amounts attributable to extensions, discoveries, and improved recoveries are available from the reserves engineers' reports.
(c) Mcf was converted to BOE using the 6:1 ratio.

Figure 29-9
Computation of SMOG—Field No. 1
As of December 31, 2006

		2007	2008	2009	2010	Total
Future cash inflows	(b)	$2,958,000	$2,106,000	$1,053,000	$313,500	$6,430,500
Future costs:						
Production costs	(b)	(1,242,000)	(874,000)	(437,000)	(126,500)	(2,679,500)
Development costs	(a)	(5,000)	–	–	(20,000)	(25,000)
Future net revenues		1,711,000	1,232,000	616,000	167,000	3,726,000
Future income taxes	(a)	(598,850)	(431,200)	(215,600)	(58,450)	(1,304,100)
Future net cash flows		1,112,150	800,800	400,400	108,550	2,421,900
10% discount factor*		(51,715)	(106,667)	(84,885)	(30,785)	(274,052)
Standardized measure		$1,060,435	$ 694,133	$ 315,515	$ 77,765	$2,147,848
*Present value factors used		0.9535	0.8668	0.7880	0.7164	
Supplementary calculations:						
Add back income tax						
present value*		$ 571,003	$ 373,764	$ 169,893	$ 41,874	$1,156,534
Pre-tax standardized measure		$1,631,438	$1,067,897	$ 485,408	$119,639	$3,304,382

Effect of Extensions and Discoveries		2007	2008	2009	2010	Total
Future cash inflows from extensions	(b)	$ 470,000	$ 425,000	–	–	$ 895,000
Future costs:						
Production costs	(b)	(184,000)	(161,000)	–	–	(345,000)
Development costs	(a)	(5,000)	–	–	(8,000)	(13,000)
Future net revenues from extensions (pre-tax) undiscounted		$ 281,000	$ 264,000	–	$ (8,000)	$ 537,000
Future net revenues from extensions (pre-tax) discounted		$ 267,934	$ 228,835	–	$ (5,731)	$ 491,038

(a) From Figure 29-8.
(b) Calculated from Figure 29-8.

Based on the data provided, the standardized measure for Field No. 1 on December 31, 2006, is $2,147,848, as computed in Figure 29-9.

The aggregate change for the year 2006 in Field No. 1's standardized measure is a $172,337 decrease (the December 31, 2006, standardized measure of $2,147,848 less the December 31, 2005, standardized measure of $2,320,185).

Analysis of Reasons for Changes in Value. The major reasons for changes in SMOG are listed next. Each factor is analyzed in the following pages.

- Accretion of discount

- Sale of oil and gas produced, net of production costs

- Net changes in prices and production costs

- Revisions of previous quantity estimates

- Changes in estimated future income taxes

- Development cost changes

- Timing and other

Accretion of Discount. A basic feature of the FASB's standardized measure is the discounting of future cash flows at a standard rate of 10 percent per year. Thus, with all other factors remaining constant, the value of reserves in the ground increases with the passage of time by 10 percent per year. Because FAS 69, paragraph 33, requires all changes except income taxes to be reported pre-tax, the accretion is based on the pre-tax SMOG value as of the beginning of the year.

Figure 29-10 reflects both the actual year-by-year calculation of accretion as well as an approach using a simple computation of 10 percent of the beginning pre-tax SMOG to calculate the SMOG change attributable to accretion. The actual change illustrated in Figure 29-10 is slightly less than 10 percent of the year's beginning pre-tax present value (or *pre-tax* SMOG). First year cash flow accretion can only be as great as its discount as of the beginning of the year, or approximately five percent, not 10 percent. The assumption is that cash flow is received, on average, in the middle of the year.

Figure 29-10
Calculation of SMOG Changes due to Accretion–Field No. 1

Year-by-year calculation		2006	2007	2008	2009	2010	Total
Future net revenues at 12/31/05	(a)	$1,420,000	$1,300,000	$840,000	$420,000	$193,333	$4,173,333
x 12/31/05 PV factors	(b)	0.9535	0.8668	0.7880	0.7164	0.6512	–
= 12/31/05 pre-tax SMOG	[A]	1,353,970	1,126,840	661,920	300,888	125,899	3,569,517
Future net revenues (above)		1,420,000	1,300,000	840,000	420,000	193,333	4,173,333
x 12/31/06 PV factors		1.0000	0.9535	0.8668	0.7880	0.7164	–
= Accreted pre-tax SMOG	[B]	1,420,000	1,239,550	728,112	330,960	138,504	3,857,126
Accretion	[B]-[A]	$ 66,030	$ 112,710	$ 66,192	$ 30,072	$ 12,606	$ 287,609
Accretion as a % of [A]		4.9%	10.0%	10.0%	10.0%	10.0%	8.1%
Alternative Calculation							
Pre-tax SMOG at 12/31/05 (above)							$3,569,517
x 10% discount rate							10%
Accretion (increase) for 2006							$ 356,952
Difference between year-by-year calculation and alternative calculation of accretion ($356,952 - $287,609)							$ (69,343)

(a) From Figure 29-4.
(b) From Figure 29-6.

Sale of Oil and Gas Produced, Net of Production Costs. The production and sale of reserves obviously decrease the value of reserves in the ground and decrease SMOG. The resulting 2006 change in SMOG can be measured in two ways:

1. $1,701,000, which is calculated from Figure 29-8's actual 2006 revenues of $2,925,000 less actual production expenses of $1,224,000; or

2. $1,640,000, which is computed from projected 2006 revenues of $2,790,000 less projected production expenses of $1,150,000, as reflected in the December 31, 2005, SMOG per Figure 29-4.

The first measure (employing actual sales and production expenses) appears to be used universally. It is less confusing since actual sales and expenses are already disclosed in financial statements.

Actual production quantities are also considered in computing the SMOG effect of prices and cost changes (Figure 29-11), as well as reserves revisions (Figure 29-12).

Net Changes in Prices and Production Costs. FAS 69, paragraph 33, requires that the "effects of changes in prices and cost rates shall be computed before the effects of changes in quantities" whereby quantity changes are stated at current year-end prices.

The net change in the pre-tax SMOG due to changes in prices and production costs could be calculated similar to price variance in traditional cost accounting variance analysis. A December 31, 2005, value (V_{old}) equals the product of the December 31, 2005, reserves quantity (Q_{old}) times a net price (P_{old}) where net price is the discounted operating cash flow per BOE as of December 31, 2005. Similar, the December 31, 2006, value (V_{new}) $= Q_{new} \times P_{new}$.

The Q_{old} equates to a December 31, 2005, reserves estimate excluding 2006 production because the SMOG change due to 2006 production is disclosed separately. When applicable, Q_{old} also excludes any reserves additions attributable to proved property purchases, extensions, discoveries, or improved recoveries, as well as reserves sold during the year, because SMOG changes due to these factors are disclosed separately.

As required by FAS 69, paragraph 33, the price variance is ($P_{new} - P_{old}$) $\times Q_{old}$ and the quantity variance is ($Q_{new} - Q_{old}$) $\times P_{new}$. Thus, the basic formula providing the SMOG change attributable to price and cost rate changes is a *price variance* equal to the change in net price per BOE times the *old quantity* (i.e., estimated reserves at the beginning of the year, excluding the current year's production).

In general, SMOG changes due to prices and production cost changes can be calculated using the following steps:

1. Compute the net change in price and costs per unit.

2. Compute the units included in the estimate of beginning reserves that were not sold during the year.

3. Multiply (1) by (2) to determine the undiscounted net change from price and cost factors.

4. Multiply the undiscounted net change computed in step (3) by the year-end ratio of: (a) present value of future operating cash flow to (b) undiscounted future operating cash flow.

Figure 29-11
Net Changes in Prices and Production Costs in Field No. 1
Year Ending December 31, 2006

				BOE		
As of December 31, 2006						
Future cash inflows from production	(d)	$ 6,430,500				
Future production costs	(d)	(2,679,500)				
		3,751,000	(c)	116,500		
Less: portion attributable to						
Extensions and discoveries	(g)	(550,000)	(c)	(15,000)		
Purchases of reserves in place	(f)	–		–		
		3,201,000		101,500		$31.54
Add:						
Sales and transfers net of production cost	(c)	1,701,000	(c)	57,000		
Amounts attributable to prior years' discoveries and current year sales		4,902,000		158,500		$30.93 **[A]**
As of December 31, 2005						
Future cash inflows from production	(b)	$ 7,545,000				
Future production costs	(b)	(3,141,667)				
December 31, 2005, revenues net of prod.costs		4,403,333	(a)	157,083		
Less: Amounts related to sales of reserves in place	(f)	–		–		
Beginning of year amounts before revisions		$ 4,403,333		157,083 **[D]**		$28.03 **[B]**
Price change per equivalent unit (BOE) [A]-[B]						$2.90 **[C]**

Undiscounted **[E]=[D]*[C]**	$	454,853
Average pretax discount **[E]*[F]**		(65,810)
Effect of price change per BOE - Discounted	$	389,043　*

December 31, 2005			
Pre-tax net inflows before 10% discount	(e)	$ 4,173,333	**[H]**
Pre-tax net inflows after 10% discount	(e)	(3,569,517)	
Effect of 10% discount		$ 603,816	**[G]**
Discount %　　　　　　　　　　　**[G]/[H]**		14%	**[F]**

(a) From Figure 29-3.
(b) From Figure 29-4.
(c) From Figure 29-8.
(d) From Figure 29-9.
(e) From Figure 29-6.
(f) In this example there were no purchases or sales of reserves in place in 2006.
(g) Calculated from Figure 29-9. Future cash flows of $895,000 less Future production costs of $345,000 = $550,000).

*NOTE: The effect of price change per BOE is before tax. It is used in Figure 29-18 showing changes in SMOG.

Calculating the net change in pre-tax SMOG due to changes in prices and production costs using a short-cut method similar to price variance in traditional cost accounting variance analysis would be difficult because production costs cannot be clearly allocated between oil and gas produced. In addition, a short-cut method would not take into consideration any changes in the composition of reserves between oil and gas. However, such calculations may be done on the BOE basis.

The calculation above excludes 2006 production and reserves additions related to extensions and discoveries because the SMOG changes due to these factors are separately disclosed. It would also exclude any reserves attributable to mineral interests acquired or sold during the year, since SMOG changes due to mineral interest purchases or sales are also separately disclosed. Some of these factors are not relevant to the Field No. 1 example above, but are typical when a company computes its SMOG changes in the aggregate rather than by field.

Revisions of Previous Quantity Estimates. FAS 69, paragraph 33, requires that the SMOG change due to quantity revisions be based on current year-end prices and costs. SMOG changes due to quantity revisions can be described as follows:

1. Compute the quantity revision.

2. Compute its effect on *undiscounted* value based on end of year prices and costs.

3. Compute the present value effect by multiplying the undiscounted change by the ratio of the: (a) present value of future operating cash flow (i.e., future gross revenues minus future production costs) to (b) undiscounted future operating cash flow.

These steps are applied in Figure 29-12 to the data for Field No. 1 for 2006.

Figure 29-12
Net Change for Quantity Revisions – Field No. 1

Reserves Roll-Forward

		bbls	Mcf	BOE
Reserves as of December 31, 2005	(a)	78,750	470,000	157,083
Less:				
Production	(b)	(27,000)	(180,000)	(57,000)
Sales of reserves in place		–	–	–
Add:				
Purchase of reserves in place		–	–	–
Extensions and discoveries	(b)	10,000	30,000	15,000
		61,750	320,000	115,083
Reserves as of December 31, 2006	(b)	54,000	375,000	116,500
Revisions of previous estimates		(7,750)	55,000	1,417

SMOG changes due to revisions of previous estimates

Revisions of previous quantity estimates		1,417
Average price at the end of the year	(c)	$31.54
Changes in SMOG due to revisions of estimates - undiscounted		$44,677
Less: Discount*		(6,464)
Changes in SMOG due to revisions of estimates (discounted)		$38,213 *
*Average discount	(c)	14%

(a) From Figure 29-3.
(b) From Figure 29-8.
(c) From Figure 29-11.

*NOTE: The effect of revisions of quantity estimates is before-tax. It is used in Figure 29-18 showing changes in SMOG.

Changes in Estimated Future Income Taxes. FAS 69, paragraph 33, states: "all changes except income taxes shall be reported pre-tax." Consequently, the SMOG change attributable to changes in estimated future income taxes is simply the reverse of the net change in the present value of estimated future taxes as of the beginning and end of the year. If the present value of taxes decreases by $100,000, the related SMOG change is a $100,000 increase.

As presented in Figure 29-13, the SMOG change due to a change in income taxes is an increase of $92,798.

Figure 29-13
Computation of SMOG Change Attributable to
Net Change in Income Taxes, Field No. 1

		Discounted	Undiscounted
Future income taxes estimated at December 31, 2005	(a)	$1,249,332	$1,460,667
Future income taxes estimated at December 31, 2006	(b)	$1,156,534	$1,304,100
Net change in future income taxes to SMOG		$ 92,798	$ 156,567

(a) From Figure 29-6.
(b) From Figure 29-9.

Changes in Future Development Costs. FAS 69, paragraph 33, calls for disclosure of any SMOG changes attributable to: (1) "previously estimated development costs incurred during the period," and (2) "changes in estimated future development costs."

The amount of development costs actually incurred during the year that reduced previously estimated development costs should be presented separately from the development costs related to new extensions and discoveries. It is determined from analysis of the total development costs which were actually incurred during the year for each individual property. Many companies may find it impracticable to perform a detailed analysis by property to determine which part of the development cost incurred would relate to the prior year discoveries. In this case, the practical solution would be to perform such analysis for development costs related to major properties and presume that development costs associated with other properties relate to prior years' discoveries. Alternatively, since the company most likely would not engage in the significant development activities in the same year a major discovery is made, the development costs incurred in the subsequent year may be presumed to be related to prior years' discoveries.

The December 31, 2005, SMOG for Field No. 1 reflected $230,000 of future development and abandonment costs estimated to be incurred in 2006 (Figure 29-3). Actual costs were $240,000 (Figure 29-8). The related SMOG increase in 2006 attributable to development cost changes can be presented in one of two ways: (1) as actual costs incurred as one line and the estimated change in future development costs as another line, or (2) as previously estimated development costs incurred in 2006. Both approaches have merit. However, users of the second approach must be careful to exclude development costs incurred that were not related to proved undeveloped locations at the beginning of the year. Otherwise, the SMOG changes for both incurred costs and changes in estimated future development costs might be significantly overstated. To avoid this situation, future development costs attributable to reserves extensions and discoveries should be deducted from the changes in SMOG due to extensions, discoveries, and improved recovery of the reserves, as shown in Figure 29-14.

Changes in the estimated future development costs in Figure 29-14 were related to a $20,000 increase in development costs incurred in 2006 over what had been expected, plus a $2,000 increase related to revisions of the company's estimates of future development costs. The discounted amount of $10,498 attributable to changes in future development costs due to reserves extensions and discoveries was netted against the changes in SMOG due to extensions, discoveries and improved recoveries.

In February 2004, SEC staff issued a letter to oil and gas companies which, among other issues, discussed the impact of FAS 143 on the standardized measure. The SEC staff expressed the view that future cash outflows related to asset retirement obligations (AROs) should be included in SMOG calculations[5]:

We believe that an entity should include the future cash flows related to the settlement of an asset retirement obligation in its Standardized Measure disclosure.

Paragraph 30 states: "A standardized measure of discounted future net cash flows relating to an enterprise's interests in (a) proved oil and gas reserves ... and (b) oil and gas subject to purchase under long-term supply, purchase or similar agreements and contracts ... shall be disclosed as of the end of the year." We believe that the requirement to disclose "net cash flows" relating to an entity's interest in oil and gas reserves requires an entity to include the cash outflows associated with the settlement of an asset retirement obligation. Exclusion of the cash flows associated with a retirement obligation would be a departure from the required disclosure. However, an entity is not prohibited from disclosing the fact that cash flows associated with asset retirement obligations are included in its Standardized Measure disclosure as a point of emphasis.

Future cash outflows related to AROs are usually included in the future development cost data of the reserves report and SMOG calculations. The related changes in estimates for AROs are reflected in the change in the future development costs line of the SMOG changes disclosures.

Figure 29-14
SMOG Changes due to Changes in
Future Development Cost for Field No. 1 in 2006

	Estimated as of 12/31/2005	Attributable to new extensions and discoveries	Attributable to acquisition of properties	Actually expended during 2006	Other increases or (decreases) in future costs	Estimated as of 12/31/2006
2006	$220,000			$(240,000)	$20,000	
2007	–	5,000	–		–	5,000
2008	–	–	–		–	–
2009	–	–	–		–	–
2010	10,000	8,000	–		2,000	20,000
Total	$230,000	$13,000	–	$(240,000)	$22,000	$ 25,000

Changes in SMOG due to:		
Previously estimated development costs incurred during 2006	Fig. 29-3	$220,000
or		
Actual development costs incurred during 2006	Fig. 29-8	$240,000
Less: changes in estimated future development costs	(a)	(21,433)
		$218,567
Amount attributable to new extensions and discoveries		
Undiscounted		$ 13,000
Discounted	(b)	$ 10,498

(a) Calculated as change in estimate of future development costs of $22,000 above less discount of $567 calculated using a discount factor of 0.7164 as relates to 2010 amount.
(b) Calculated as change in estimate of future development costs of $13,000 above less discount of $1,502 calculated using a discount factors of 0.7164 as relates to 2010 amount and 0.9535 as relates to 2007 amount.

NOTE: Amount attributable to new extensions and discoveries will be netted against the overall effect of new extensions and discoveries in SMOG changes.

Changes due to Timing and Other. Aside from the standardized measure changes required to be delineated in FAS 69 disclosures, the SEC allows a catch-all category of *Other*, which many companies call *Timing and Other Differences*. Presumably, these amounts refer to changes in production profile differences and various other imprecise assumptions.

The total amount of Other changes reflects the net change in present value that is not specifically identified in one of the individual computations. The other amount reported depends in part on the approach taken to calculate accretion. As presented in Figure 29-10, if the company uses the short-cut approach to calculate accretion, the other category would potentially include a $69,343 difference between the two methods.

In the Figure 29-15 example, the Other category includes the effect of changes in timing of expected production between the 2005 and 2006 reserves estimates. The Undiscounted column is presented for illustration purposes to demonstrate all the other differences were accounted for in the overall analysis of SMOG changes.

Figure 29-15
Computation of Other Changes in Field No. 1

		Discounted (SMOG)	Undiscounted
Future Net Cash Flows as of December 31, 2005	(a)	$2,320,185	$2,712,666
Revenue less production and other costs	(b)	(1,701,000)	(1,701,000)
Changes in price, net of production costs	(c)	389,043	454,853
Development costs incurred	(d)	240,000	240,000
Net changes in future development costs	(d)	(21,433)	(22,000)
Extensions and discoveries, less related costs	(e)	491,038	537,000
Revisions of previous quantity estimates	(f)	38,213	44,677
Accretion of the discount	(g)	287,609	–
Net change in income taxes	(h)	92,798	156,567
Purchases of reserves in place		–	–
Timing differences and other		11,395	(863)
Future Net Cash Flows as of December 31, 2006	(e)	**$2,147,848**	**$2,421,900**

(a) From Figure 29-6.
(b) From Figure 29-8.
(c) From Figure 29-11.
(d) From Figure 29-14.
(e) From Figure 29-9.
(f) From Figure 29-12.
(g) From Figure 29-10.
(h) From Figure 29-13.

While the Other category is a valid line item in the disclosure and is utilized by many publicly held E&P companies, the amount included is arguably open to interpretation. Some companies prepare their standardized measure calculations in an organized manner with the idea that the Timing and Other category will be an insignificant number. They believe it is explained by production profile changes and leave it at that.

Other companies, specifically those with computer models and templates, can calculate the various prescribed changes in such a manner as to exclude production timing changes in Other. The argument here is that timing changes are often indistinguishable from quantity revisions, and sometimes from price revisions. Why not structure the calculation in such a way as to include the effects of timing changes with quantity variances or, perhaps, pricing changes? This point is valid for producing properties more so than for development properties. Independent of price changes or reserves revisions, uncertainties about government regulation and financing may change the time when proved undeveloped reserves begin producing.

As stated earlier, the Timing and Other category should be a relatively immaterial amount; if not, the reason for it should be understood, and an additional line item disclosure may be warranted. One approach to calculating the SMOG change due to timing changes compares: (1) the present value *ratio* of future cash flows projected at the beginning of the year, accreted to year-end (and excluding the year's actual oil and gas sales and proved property sales), and (2) the present value *ratio* of equivalent future cash flows projected at the end of the year. Hypothetically, if December 31, 2005, SMOG reflected a present value ratio of 0.74 for discounted cash flows (accreted to December 31, 2006) to undiscounted cash flows after 2006, but December 31, 2006, SMOG reflects a present value ratio of 0.68 for the equivalent cash flows, the decrease in present value ratio from 0.74 to 0.68 indicates timing of production has been delayed, causing a decrease in SMOG.[6] The decrease of 0.06 is multiplied by the undiscounted future operating cash flow to measure the SMOG changes due to timing differences.

DISCOUNTED PRESENT VALUE OF DISCOVERIES AND ADDITIONS

An important element of the disclosed SMOG changes is the increase caused by field extensions, new discoveries, and improved recoveries. To illustrate this computation, the information for Field No. 2 for 2006 is used as a basis.

Information about Field No. 2. Assume a discovery well and confirmation well were drilled in 2006 that proved up reserves. Relevant information for 2006 and data as of December 31, 2006, are presented in Figure 29-16.

Figure 29-16
Information About Discovery in Field No. 2 in 2006

Cost of exploratory drilling	$600,000
Cost of lease and well equipment	$280,000
Revenue	$807,000
Production expenses	$288,000

	bbls	Mcf	BOE (b)
Production in 2006	12,000	7,500	13,250

	Reserves			Future Development Costs	Future Income Taxes (a)
	bbls	Mcf	BOE (b)		
2007	187,500	90,000	202,500	$500,000	$ (2,828,000)
2008	150,000	75,000	162,500	100,000	(2,371,250)
2009	127,500	60,000	137,500		(2,040,500)
2010	90,000	45,000	97,500		(1,443,750)
2011	60,000	30,000	65,000		(962,500)
2012	30,000	15,000	32,500		(481,250)
2013	15,000	6,000	16,000	100,000	(203,700)
Total	660,000	321,000	713,500	$700,000	$(10,330,950)

Price per barrel	$67.00	
Price per Mcf		$7.50
Production costs per BOE		$23.00

(a) For simplicity, amounts for income taxes are given numbers.
(b) Mcf was converted to BOE using the 6:1 factor.

Calculation of Present Value, December 31, 2006. The SMOG value of proved reserves in Field No. 2 at December 31, 2006, is computed as $15,628,646, as shown in Figure 29-17. Since SMOG changes due to a new discovery must be computed based on pre-tax SMOG (i.e., discounted future net revenues), Figure 29-17 computes the present value of related income taxes and adds it to the SMOG value to calculate pre-tax SMOG.

Figure 29-17
Calculation of SMOG and Pre-tax SMOG for Field No. 2
As of December 31, 2006

		2007	2008	2009	2010	2011	2012	2013	Total
Production (BOE)		202,500	162,500	137,500	97,500	65,000	32,500	16,000	713,500
Future cash inflows		$13,237,500	$10,612,500	$8,992,500	$6,367,500	$4,245,000	$2,122,500	$1,050,000	$46,627,500
Future costs:									
Production costs	(a)	(4,657,500)	(3,737,500)	(3,162,500)	(2,242,500)	(1,495,000)	(747,500)	(368,000)	(16,410,500)
Development costs	(b)	(500,000)	(100,000)	–	–	–	–	(100,000)	(700,000)
Future net revenues		8,080,000	6,775,000	5,830,000	4,125,000	2,750,000	1,375,000	582,000	29,517,000
Future income taxes	(b)	(2,828,000)	(2,371,250)	(2,040,500)	(1,443,750)	(962,500)	(481,250)	(203,700)	(10,330,950)
Future net cash flows		5,252,000	4,403,750	3,789,500	2,681,250	1,787,500	893,750	378,300	19,186,050
10% Discount*		(244,218)	(586,580)	(803,374)	(760,403)	(623,480)	(364,650)	(174,699)	(3,557,404)
Standardized measure		$ 5,007,782	$ 3,817,170	$2,986,126	$1,920,847	$1,164,020	$ 529,100	$ 203,601	$15,628,646
Add back income tax present value*		2,696,498	2,055,400	1,607,914	1,034,303	626,780	284,900	109,631	8,415,426
Pre-tax standardized measure		$ 7,704,280	$ 5,872,570	$4,594,040	$2,955,150	$1,790,800	$ 814,000	$ 313,232	$24,044,072
*Present value factors used		0.9535	0.8668	0.7880	0.7164	0.6512	0.5920	0.5382	

(a) Assumes $23 per BOE.
(b) From Figure 29-16.

For purposes of disclosure of change in the standardized measure of discounted present value of reserves in Field No. 2 (see Figure 29-22), the components would include sales and transfers of oil and gas produced, net of production costs ($807,000 - $288,000 = $519,000), extensions and discoveries of $24,563,072 ($24,044,072 + $519,000) and income taxes of $8,415,426.

DISCOUNTED PRESENT VALUE OF ACQUIRED RESERVES

In May 2006, the company acquired a new producing property—Field No. 3—which primarily has oil reserves. The quantity of the reserves, future production expenses, and future development costs presented in Figure 29-18 were estimated by the company and its reserves engineers at the date of acquisition (May 31, 2006) and at December 31, 2006. The revenues, production expenses, and development costs presented in Figure 29-18 for the seven-month period ended December 31, 2006, represent actual amounts.

Figure 29-18
Information about Properties Acquired in 2006 – Field No. 3

	5 months ended May 31, 2006 (a)	7 months ended Dec. 31, 2006	Total
Production (bbls)	50,200	75,400	125,600
Revenue		$4,913,000	
Production expenses		$1,687,000	
Development costs incurred		$220,000	

Reserves as of 12/31/05 and 12/31/06 to be produced in:

		December 31, 2005 (a) bbls	May 31, 2006 bbls	December 31, 2006 bbls
	2006	120,000	70,000	–
	2007	140,000	150,000	145,000
	2008	120,000	125,000	130,000
	2009	90,000	87,000	90,000
	2010	60,000	60,000	60,000
	2011	40,000	40,000	40,000
	2012	20,000	20,000	20,000
	2013	8,000	8,000	10,000
	Total	598,000	560,000	495,000

Future development costs to be incurred:				
	2006	$450,000	$200,000	–
	2007	$750,000	$770,000	$800,000
	2008	$100,000	$100,000	$120,000
	2013	$50,000	$55,000	$55,000
Price per barrel		$60.00	$62.00	$67.00
Production costs per barrel		$21.00	$21.60	$23.00

(a) Information as of December 31, 2005, and for the five months ended May 31, 2006, is presented for illustrative purposes only and is not used for further calculations.

Reserves estimates prepared by the acquiring company may be substantially different from the reserves previously prepared by the seller due to changes in volume estimates, price changes from the previous period, and other reasons. Therefore, changes in SMOG related to acquisitions of reserves in place should be calculated at the date of acquisition and be based on the company's estimates and assumptions at that date, including prices per unit-of-production and future production and development costs. Subsequent changes between the date of acquisition and the end of the year in which the property is acquired would be reflected within categories required by FAS 69, paragraph 33.

Figures 29-19A and 29-19B illustrate for Field 3 the calculation of SMOG at the date of acquisition (May 31, 2006) and as of December 31, 2006, respectively.

Figure 29-19A
Calculation of SMOG and Pre-tax SMOG for Field No. 3
As of May 31, 2006

	2006	2007	2008	2009	2010	2011	2012	2013	Total
Future cash inflows	(a) $4,340,000	$9,300,000	$7,750,000	$5,394,000	$3,720,000	$2,480,000	$1,240,000	$496,000	$34,720,000
Future costs:									
Production costs	(a) (1,512,000)	(3,240,000)	(2,700,000)	(1,879,200)	(1,296,000)	(864,000)	(432,000)	(172,800)	(12,096,000)
Development costs	(a) (200,000)	(770,000)	(100,000)	–	–	–	–	(55,000)	(1,125,000)
Future net revenues	2,628,000	5,290,000	4,950,000	3,514,800	2,424,000	1,616,000	808,000	268,200	21,499,000
Future income taxes	(893,520)	(1,798,600)	(1,683,000)	(1,195,032)	(824,160)	(549,440)	(274,720)	(91,188)	(7,309,660)
Future net cash flows	1,734,480	3,491,400	3,267,000	2,319,768	1,599,840	1,066,560	533,280	177,012	14,189,340
10% discount*	(80,653)	(465,054)	(692,604)	(657,886)	(558,024)	(435,156)	(246,269)	(90,400)	(3,226,046)
Standardized measure	$1,653,827	$3,026,346	$2,574,396	$1,661,882	$1,041,816	$ 631,404	$ 287,011	$ 86,612	$10,963,294
Add back income tax present value*	851,971	1,559,026	1,326,204	856,121	536,693	325,268	147,854	44,618	5,647,755
Pre-tax standardized measure	$2,505,798	$4,585,372	$3,900,600	$2,518,003	$1,578,509	$ 956,672	$ 434,865	$131,230	$16,611,049
*Present value factors used	0.9535	0.8668	0.7880	0.7164	0.6512	0.5920	0.5382	0.4893	

(a) From Figure 29-18: May 31st bbls x price

Figure 29-19B
Calculation of SMOG and Pre-tax SMOG for Field No. 3
As of December 31, 2006

	2007	2008	2009	2010	2011	2012	2013	Total
Future cash inflows	$9,715,000	$8,710,000	$6,030,000	$4,020,000	$2,680,000	$1,340,000	$670,000	$33,165,000
Future costs:								
Production costs	(3,335,000)	(2,990,000)	(2,070,000)	(1,380,000)	(920,000)	(460,000)	(230,000)	(11,385,000)
Development costs	(800,000)	(120,000)	–	–	–	–	(55,000)	(975,000)
Future net revenues	$5,580,000	$5,600,000	$3,960,000	$2,640,000	$1,760,000	$ 880,000	$385,000	$20,805,000
Future income taxes	(1,897,200)	(1,904,000)	(1,346,400)	(897,600)	(598,400)	(299,200)	(130,900)	(7,073,700)
Future net cash flows	$3,682,800	$3,696,000	$2,613,600	$1,742,400	$1,161,600	$ 580,800	$254,100	$13,731,300
10% discount*	(171,250)	(492,307)	(554,083)	(494,145)	(405,166)	(236,966)	(117,343)	(2,471,260)
Standardized measure	$3,511,550	$3,203,693	$2,059,517	$1,248,255	$ 756,434	$ 343,834	$136,757	$11,260,040
Add back income tax								
Present value*	1,808,980	1,650,387	1,060,963	643,041	389,678	177,126	70,450	5,800,625
Pre-tax standardized measure	$5,320,530	$4,854,080	$3,120,480	$1,891,296	$1,146,112	$ 520,960	$207,207	$17,060,665
*Present value factors used	0.9535	0.8668	0.7880	0.7164	0.6512	0.5920	0.5382	

The discount rate used for 2006 in Figure 29-19A reflects the mid-year concept applied for the seven-month period from acquisition to December 31, 2006. Although the properties were acquired on May 31, 2006, for simplicity we still have used the standard mid-year discount rate of 0.9535. The remaining discount rates are the same as those included in Figure 29-5.

The changes in SMOG from the date of acquisition to December 31, 2006, for Field No. 3 are presented in Figure 29-20.

Figure 29-20
Calculation of Changes in SMOG for Field No. 3
For the Seven-Month Period ended December 31, 2006

1. Production (a)

Actual 2006 sales	$4,913,000	
Less actual 2006 production expenses	(1,687,000)	
2006 net (a decrease in SMOG)	$3,226,000	

2. Future Development Costs (a)

Previously estimated development costs incurred during the period	$150,000
Actual development costs incurred	$220,000
Changes in estimated future development costs	($70,000)

3. Net changes in prices and production costs

		Dollar Amounts		Quantity Amounts BOE	Average Realized Price
As of December 31, 2006					
Future cash inflows from production	(c)	$33,165,000			
Future production costs	(c)	(11,385,000)			
		21,780,000	(a)	495,000	
Extensions and discoveries		–		–	
Purchases of reserves in place		–		–	
		21,780,000		495,000	$44.00
Sales and transfers net of production cost	(a)	3,226,000	(a)	75,400	
		$25,006,000		570,400	$43.84 **[A]**
As of May 31, 2006					
Future cash inflows from production	(b)	34,720,000			
Future production costs		(12,096,000)			
Beginning of year amounts before revisions		$22,624,000	(a)	560,000 **[D]**	$40.40 **[B]**
Price Increase per BOE [A]-[B]					$3.44 **[C]**

Undiscounted [E] = [D] x [C]	$ 1,926,070
Average pretax discount **[E] x [F]**	(437,906)
Discounted	$ 1,488,164

May 31, 2006		
Pre-tax net inflows before 10% discount	(b)	21,499,000
Pre-tax net inflows after 10% discount	(b)	(16,611,049)
Effect of 10% discount		$ 4,887,951
Discount rate		23% **[F]**

(continued on next page)

Figure 29-20 (continued)
Calculation of Changes in SMOG for Field No. 3
For the Seven-Month Period ended December 31, 2006

4. Revisions of previous quantity estimates

(1) Compute the quantity revision:

		bbls
12/31/06 estimated reserves [G]	(a)	495,000
Proved reserves estimated as of the date of acquisition	(a)	560,000
Less 2006 quantities actually sold	(a)	(75,400)
Acquired estimated reserves not sold in 2006 [H]		484,600
Reserve revision increase [G-H]		10,400

(2) Compute the effect on undiscounted value:

Reserve revision - increase (decrease) (bbls)	10,400
Price less production expense per barrel as of 12/31/06	$44.00
Total increase (decrease) due to change in volumes	$457,600

(3) Compute the present value effect as of 12/31/06:

Ratio of discounted to undiscounted future operating cash flow (1-[F])	0.77
Change in SMOG due to quantity revisions:	$353,561

5. Change in Income Taxes

Income tax	December 31, 2006	May 31, 2006	
	(c)	(b)	Change
Undiscounted	$7,073,700	$7,309,660	$235,960
Discounted	$5,800,625	$5,647,755	($152,870)

6. Changes in SMOG

		Discounted (SMOG)	Undiscounted
Future net cash flows as of May 31, 2006	(b)	10,963,294	14,189,340
Revenues less production and other costs	(d)	(3,226,000)	(3,226,000)
Changes in price, net of production costs	(d)	1,488,164	1,926,070
Development costs incurred	(d)	220,000	220,000
Net changes in future development costs	(d)	(70,000)	(70,000)
Extensions and discoveries, less related costs		–	–
Revisions of previous quantity estimates	(d)	353,561	457,600
Accretion of the discount	(e)	1,532,862	
Net change in income taxes	(d)	(152,870)	235,960
Purchases of reserves in place		–	–
Timing differences and other		151,029	(1,670)
Future net cash flows as of December 31, 2006		11,260,040	13,731,300

(a) From Figure 29-18.
(b) From Figure 29-19A.
(c) From Figure 29-19B.
(d) From above.
(e) Calculated year-by-year accretion using information from Figure 29-19A. See example in Figure 29-10.

Figure 29-20 presents changes in SMOG from the date of acquisition to December 31, 2006, and does not include changes in the company's SMOG due to acquisition of the reserves as of May 31, 2006. From Figure 29-19A, the pre-tax SMOG at the date of acquisition was estimated to be $16,611,049. The related tax effect at the date of acquisition was $5,647,755. The future income taxes at the date of acquisition are estimated based on the company's effective tax rate expected to be realized in the respective years (in this example, taxes related to future net revenues are given). Because FAS 69, paragraph 33, requires all changes to be presented pre-tax, the amount of future income taxes associated with the future revenues is also presented separately from pre-tax SMOG changes related to acquisition of the reserves. As presented in Figure 29-20, the company's future tax amount as of December 31, 2006, is a total of $5,800,625 consisting of taxes related to acquired reserves ($5,647,755), plus $152,870 related to changes in income taxes after the date of acquisition.

RESERVES SOLD DURING THE YEAR

If a certain portion of reserves is sold during the year, the pre-tax effect of the cash flows eliminated from SMOG is reflected in the line item Purchases and Sales of Minerals in Place. The related tax effect is included in the Changes in Future Income Taxes line item.

In recent comment letters to oil and gas companies, the SEC has expressed a view that reserves associated with discontinued operations should be reflected as sales in the period in which the sale occurred. Prior periods should not be retroactively restated to remove the reserves associated with the discontinued operations in the FAS 69 disclosures despite the fact that the related revenues and costs associated with those reserves have been eliminated from prior period income statement totals in the primary financial statements.

COMBINED SMOG DISCLOSURE AS OF DECEMBER 31, 2006

The data from Field Nos. 1, 2, and 3 can now be combined as shown in Figures 29-21 and 29-22.

Figure 29-21
Combined SMOG as of December 31, 2006

	Field No. 1 (a)	Field No. 2 (b)	Field No. 3 (c)	Total
Future cash inflows	$6,430,500	$46,627,500	$33,165,000	$86,223,000
Future production costs	(2,679,500)	(16,410,500)	(11,385,000)	(30,475,000)
Future development costs	(25,000)	(700,000)	(975,000)	(1,700,000)
Future income tax expense	(1,304,100)	(10,330,950)	(7,073,700)	(18,708,750)
Future net cash flows	2,421,900	19,186,050	13,731,300	35,339,250
10% annual discount for estimated timing of cash flows	(274,052)	(3,557,404)	(2,471,260)	(6,302,716)
Standardized measure	$2,147,848	$15,628,646	$11,260,040	$29,036,534

(a) From Figure 29-9.
(b) From Figure 29-17.
(c) From Figure 29-19B.

Figure 29-22
Sources of Change in SMOG in 2006 - Combined

	Field No. 1 (a)	Field No. 2 (b)	Field No. 3 (c)	Total Worldwide
Sales and transfers of oil and gas produced, net of production costs	($1,701,000)	($519,000)	($3,226,000)	($5,446,000)
Net changes in prices and production costs	389,043	–	1,488,164	1,877,207
Development costs incurred during the year	240,000	–	220,000	460,000
Changes in estimated development costs	(21,433)	–	(70,000)	(91,433)
Extensions, discoveries, and improved recoveries	491,038	24,563,072	–	25,054,110
Revisions of previous quantity estimates	38,213	–	353,561	391,774
Accretion of discount	287,609	–	1,532,862	1,820,471
Net change in income taxes	92,798	(8,415,426)	(5,800,625)	(14,123,253)
Purchases and sales of mineral interests	–	–	16,611,049	16,611,049
Timing and other	11,395	–	151,029	162,424
Aggregate change in standardized measure	($172,337)	$15,628,646	$11,260,040	$26,716,349
Standardized measure as of 12/31/05 (d)	2,320,185	–	–	2,320,185
Standardized measure as of 12/31/06	$2,147,848	$15,628,646	$11,260,040	$29,036,534

(a) From Figure 29-15.
(b) From Figure 29-16 and 29-17.
(c) From Figure 29-19B and 29-20.
(d) From Figure 29-6.

Effects of the discovery of minerals in Field No. 2 are presented in the Extensions, Discoveries, and Improved Recoveries and in Net Changes in the Future Income Taxes lines. Because the discovery was made near the end of the year, it was considered impractical to calculate all other changes, except for actual sales. The Sales Net of Production Costs line represents sales after the date of discovery and before year-end; however, in most cases production will not be expected to start until subsequent years. At the same time, for Field No. 3 the SMOG changes are allocated between the Purchases and Sales of Mineral Interests line and lines related to Development Costs, Revisions of Estimates, Accretion, and others due to the fact that reserves were acquired on May 31, 2006. Addition of reserves at that date would be reflected in the line Purchases and Sales of Mineral Interests with the related tax effect going through the Net Changes in Income Taxes line. Other changes would represent the effect of changes in estimates and other changes for the period from May 31, 2006, to year-end. The Net Change in Income Taxes line includes both the effect of reserves acquisition on May 31, 2006, and the effects of other changes in SMOG, such as changes in prices, production costs, and other.

A different approach for the presentation of of reserves in the year of acquisition might be used. Some argue that because the reserves estimates may not be available at the date of acquisition, or that these reserves estimates may not be sufficiently supported by the reserves report, all the SMOG changes in a year of acquisition should be presented as Purchases and Sales of Mineral Interests with the related tax effect going through the Net Changes in Income Taxes line. Although this approach has merit, the allocation of SMOG changes between other lines is generally more informative.

When reserves are sold during the year, the SMOG changes associated with these reserves may include the lines that reflect the actual sales less production costs for the period prior to sale and the development costs incurred during the same period, with the difference going through the lines Purchases and Sales of Minerals in Place and Net Changes in Income Taxes.

YEAR-END PRICING

In June 2000 and March 2001, the SEC staff issued the following interpretation on the meaning of year-end prices for determining the standardized measure:

> 8. Statement of Financial Accounting Standards 69, paragraph 30.a. requires the following disclosure:
>
> Future cash inflows. These shall be computed by applying year-end prices of oil and gas relating to the enterprise's proved reserves to the year-end quantities of those reserves.
>
> This requires the use of physical pricing determined by the market on the last day of the (fiscal) year. For instance, a west Texas oil producer should determine the posted price of crude (hub spot price for gas) on the last day of the year, apply historical adjustments (transportation, gravity, BS&W, purchaser bonuses, etc.) and use this oil or gas price on an individual property basis for proved reserve estimation and future cash flow calculation (this price is also used in the application of the full cost ceiling test). A monthly average is not the price on the last day of the year, even though that may be the price received for production on the last day of the year. Paragraph 30b) states that future production costs are to be based on year-end figures with the assumption of the continuation of existing economic conditions.

The SEC staff believes the year-end price contemplated by paragraph 30(a) of FAS 69 is the year-end daily posted oil price or daily gas sales price ("spot price") adjusted for oilfield, or gas gathering hub and wellhead price differences (e.g., grade, transportation, gravity, sulfur and BS&W), as appropriate. Consistent use of the year-end price among registrants is critical to preserving comparability of the standardized measure of discounted future net cash flows—a measure important to investing decisions in oil and gas entities. Also, use of a consistent year-end price is critical to the ceiling test evaluation of capitalized costs for companies using the full cost method. The staff has objected to each of the following measures as a proxy for the year-end price under paragraph 30(a) of SFAS 69:

- An average price for any time period
- The producer's monthly contract index price
- The NYMEX futures price[7]

HEDGE-ADJUSTED PRICE

In June 2000, the SEC Division of Corporate Finance issued an interpretation that provides guidance on the use of hedge-adjusted prices for calculation of SMOG:

> Hedging Transactions
> Registrants with financial instruments that are appropriately designated as price hedges of oil and gas quantities under FASB Statement Nos. 80 or 133 (including designation by specific properties) should apply the hedge-adjusted prices to determine proved reserve quantities and the standardized measure of discounted future cash flows. If the impact of the agreements is material to the FASB Statement No. 69 disclosure, the impact should be quantified in a note to the SFAS 69 data. In addition, if hedging activity had a material impact on average oil and gas prices received during the year, the impact should be quantified and discussed in MD&A.[8]

Although the SEC indicated that hedge-adjusted prices should be used for reserves calculations when the reserves qualify for hedge accounting under FAS 133, it later clarified that such prices should not be used in the calculation of SMOG. The effect of hedges on the average prices received during the year must be presented separately and does not affect calculation of SMOG.

USEFULNESS OF DISCLOSURES

The FAS 69 supplemental disclosures are used by stock analysts in several ways:

- SMOG provides a basis to be adjusted to fair value or a comparative valuation benchmark for a publicly-traded E&P company's underlying assets, primarily oil and gas producing properties.[9] An analyst may compare the benchmark value per share to the share's market value. If a company's benchmark value to market value is high compared to that of its peers, this could indicate its stock is a better buy than the stock of its peers. Other factors, such as the quality of management, exploration prospects, or unusual contingent liabilities not reflected in the benchmark value, can also account for a company's high ratio of benchmark value to market value.

- Dividing E&P costs incurred by reserves additions provides one method for determining the amount of finding costs per equivalent barrel. A relatively low ratio of finding costs to discovered or added reserves is an indication of profitable investment by the E&P company. The finding cost ratio may be computed in various ways, either with or without costs and proved reserves attributable to proved property acquisitions. Finding cost per BOE may be based on three or five years' activity, rather than one, since some costs incurred in one year may relate to discoveries in a succeeding year.

- Disclosure of the types of capitalized costs and costs incurred by year helps an analyst assess the unimpaired cost and approximate value of unproved property.

- Disclosures by major geographic area provide the analyst with insights on the general risks of the E&P company's current and near-term operations.

Supplemental disclosures are not required to be audited. As a rule, the proved reserves disclosures and SMOG disclosures are never audited (i.e., incorporated as part of the audited financial statements or subjected to a separate attest examination by a CPA). However, auditing standards do require the auditor to read other information in documents containing audited financial statements to determine whether such information is materially inconsistent with information appearing in the financial statements. Accordingly, auditors typically review SMOG calculations for reasonableness during a financial statement audit. As previously stated, SMOG is, at best, only a rough surrogate for fair value. Nevertheless, analysts generally find the unaudited supplemental disclosures to be important disclosures for their analyses. Indeed, for E&P companies, one leading industry analyst found that net income and the corresponding price earnings ratio were generally meaningless and of far less value than SMOG and a calculated ratio of benchmark value to market value per share. The analyst found market value per share to be more highly correlated with the analyst's benchmark value per share (and with cash provided by operations) than with net income or earnings.

• • •

1   The term SMOG is a popular acronym for standardized measure of oil and gas. It was coined by a major oil company's treasurer about the time FAS 69 was adopted. FAS 69 notes that SMOG is not fair value, but only a rough surrogate for fair market value. The industry feared the public and analysts would mistakenly view SMOG as fair value. In a sense, SMOG presents a rather hazy picture of fair value, much like smog in the air obscures one's view. Hence, the term seemed an appropriate acronym for this required disclosure.

2   FAS 109 amended FAS 69 to replace the outdated term *permanent differences* with the term *tax deductions*.

3   See Chapter 19 for examples of how to apply a short-cut method in calculating income tax effects for the full cost ceiling test.

4   The formula for computing the present value factor for a 10 percent discount, assuming the mid-year convention, is 110 percent raised to the negative power of (the year less a half year). For example, for the second year, it is $110\%^{-1.5}$, which equals 0.8668.

5   Issued by SEC Division of Corporate Finance and published at: http://www.sec.gov/divisions/corpfin/guidance/oilgasletter.htm.

6   The ratio decrease may also be attributable to favorable price increases that extend the economic limit of the field's life, increasing reserves to be produced in later years and decreasing the overall present value ratio. The price change affects reserve revisions and timing changes.

7   Prepared by the accounting staff of the SEC's Division of Corporate Finance, and posted on the web at: http://www.sec.gov/divisions/corpfin/acctdisc.htm and www.sec.gov/divisions/corpfin/guidance/cfactfaq.htm

8   Prepared by the accounting staff of the SEC's division of corporate finance, and posted on the web at http://www.sec.gov/divisions/corpfin/guidance/oilgasletter.htm

9   SMOG, as a *standardized measure*, was intended to be a comparative benchmark value rather than an estimate of fair value. However, an analyst may believe that a better benchmark would incorporate expected prices and cost rates as well as a different discount rate. Thus, the analyst might construct such a benchmark by using SMOG disclosures, reserve disclosures, and other disclosures on historical annual revenues and costs to construct a hypothetical schedule of future production and future annual cash flows from proved reserves at year-end prices and cost rates, held constant. The hypothetical production is adjusted to a point at which the discounted after-tax cash flows match the SMOG disclosure. Then, the analyst has a reasonable base case of annual future cash flows from proved reserves that can be: (1) adjusted for expected changes in prices and cost rates, and (2) discounted by a selected discount rate to compute a benchmark value that the analyst prefers to SMOG.

30

ACCOUNTING FOR BUSINESS COMBINATIONS

Key Concepts:

- Accounting framework for business combinations

- Determining if the acquisition meets the definition of a business

- Conforming accounting policies of the acquired company

- Recording assets acquired and liabilities assumed

- Accounting for acquired goodwill

- Accounting for deferred income taxes

- Presentation of audited financial statements in SEC filings

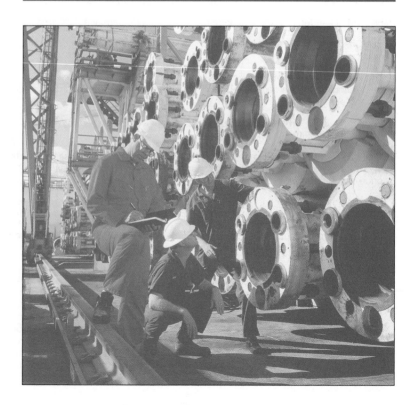

In June 2005, the FASB issued an Exposure Draft proposing a replacement to the Statement of Financial Accounting Standard No. 141, *Business Combinations* (FAS 141). The Exposure Draft proposed a number of significant changes to the manner in which business combinations are currently recorded. Implications of the Exposure Draft are discussed at the end of this chapter. Although FAS 141 provisions are the focus here, readers are encouraged to consult the revised standard when issued and any related changes in SEC staff guidance on how to account for business combinations.

ACCOUNTING FOR BUSINESS COMBINATIONS

In June 2001, the FASB issued FAS 141 (referred to herein as B51 of Current Text). B51 prescribed the overall framework for accounting for business combinations and made them applicable to all business combinations initiated after June 30, 2001. Under this ruling, all business combinations must be accounted for using the purchase method.

B51 states: "a business combination occurs when an entity acquires net assets that constitute a business or acquires equity interests of one or more other entities and obtains control over that entity or entities." The entities involved in a business combination may be either incorporated or unincorporated. Further, B51 applies to all business combinations, regardless of whether the form of consideration given is cash, other assets, a business or subsidiary of the entity, debt, common or preferred shares, or other equity interests. This chapter will focus on certain principles and procedures used in accounting for business combinations by oil and gas companies.

AICPA Practice Aids/Toolkits. Although not authoritative, the following AICPA toolkit can be a helpful source: *The Fair Value Measurement Valuation Toolkit for Financial Accounting Standards Board Statements of Financial Accounting Standards No. 141, "Business Combinations" and No. 142, "Goodwill and Other Intangible Assets."*

DEFINITION OF A BUSINESS

To determine whether a group of net assets constitutes a "business," B51 refers to the Emerging Issues Task Force (EITF) No. 98-3, *Determining Whether a Nonmonetary Transaction Involves Receipt of a Productive Asset or a Business*. EITF 98-3 addresses whether an exchange of net assets (a subset of an entity) constitutes an exchange of productive assets or a business combination and, in doing so, focuses on whether the "transferred set of activities and assets" constitutes a "business." Although EITF 98-3 was developed in the context of transfers of net assets, the FASB staff has indicated the guidance contained in the consensus also should be considered when evaluating whether an entity is a business in applying B51.

When a group of acquired net assets or an acquired entity does not constitute a business, the acquiring entity must account for the acquisition under the provisions of Current Text G40.107 by allocating the entire purchase price to the individual assets acquired and liabilities assumed based on their relative fair values (i.e., no goodwill is recorded). It is common in the oil and gas industry for entities to acquire specific oil and gas properties that might not meet the definition of a business, and thus are outside the scope of B51. Careful consideration must be given to the specific facts of each transaction to determine whether the acquired oil and gas assets constitute a business or an asset, based on the guidance of EITF 98-3.

While EITF 98-3 specifies whether a business exists for accounting purposes, public companies have another consideration. They must determine if the transaction is an acquisition of a business for SEC reporting requirements. If a determination is made that the acquisition is a business for SEC reporting, separate financial statements for the acquired oil and gas assets may be required under Rule 3-05 of Reg. S-X (Rule 3-05).

For purposes of Rule 3-05, the decision on whether a business has been acquired is made in accordance with Rule 11-01 of Reg. S-X (Rule 11-01). The SEC has indicated that an acquisition of a working interest in oil and gas producing properties is deemed to be an acquisition of a business for purposes of Rule 3-05. The determination of whether a business has been acquired may vary between EITF 98-3 and Rule 11-01.

The SEC also has indicated in SAB Topic 2D that working interests and royalties related to developed and undeveloped oil and gas properties are deemed to constitute a business. As a result, when companies acquire oil and gas properties—which for purposes of applying the provisions of B51 are not considered to be the acquisition of a business for U.S. GAAP purposes—the SEC reporting requirements may still apply.

EITF 98-3

EITF 98-3 states that a business is a self-sustaining integrated set of activities and assets (consisting of inputs, processes, and outputs) conducted and managed for the purpose of providing a return to investors. For a transferred set of activities and assets to be a business, it must contain all of the inputs and processes necessary for it to continue to conduct normal operations after the transferred set is separated from the transferor; this includes the ability to sustain a revenue stream by providing its outputs to customers. Key elements to be considered in making an assessment include whether the transferred set contains: (1) long-lived assets including intangible assets, (2) intellectual property, (3) access to necessary materials or rights, (4) employees, (5) management systems and processes, and (6) access to customers.

The determination of whether a transferred set of assets and activities constitutes a business is a three-step process. First, one must identify the elements included in the transferred set. Second, the transferred elements should be compared to the complete set of elements necessary for the transferred set to conduct normal operations. Finally, if there are missing elements, an analysis must be performed to determine whether the missing elements cause the transferred set to not be considered a business. This analysis is based on the degree of difficulty or the level of investment (relative to the fair value of the integrated set of assets transferred) necessary to acquire or obtain access to the missing elements. If the missing elements are considered more than minor, then their absences would lead to a conclusion that the transferred set is not capable of continuing normal operations and is not a business.

If all but a *de minimis* amount of the fair value of the transferred set is represented by a single tangible or identifiable intangible asset, this is an indicator the transferred set is not a business. Further, the transferred set must be "self-sustaining." The intent or capability of the party receiving the integrated set of activities and assets is not considered in the analysis of whether the acquired set of activities and assets is a business. Additionally, the level of financing or working capital necessary to operate the acquired set of activities and assets is not considered relevant.

Quick Facts Regarding Business Combinations in 2006
"There were 912 oil and gas transactions worldwide in 2006. The average value of each transaction was $319 million."
– *O&G Deals Annual Review 2006*, pg. 4, PricewaterhouseCoopers

CONFORMING ACCOUNTING POLICIES OF THE ACQUIRED ENTITY TO THOSE OF THE ACQUIRING ENTITY

Absent justification for different accounting policies, the acquired entity's policies should be conformed to those of the acquiring entity. Although not expected to exist in oil and gas companies, dissimilar operations or dissimilar assets or transactions of the acquired entity may be justification for different accounting policies.

Accounting policies that should be considered for oil and gas transactions include:

- Accounting method for oil and gas properties (successful efforts or full cost)

- Revenue recognition/gas balancing (sales or entitlement method)

- Accounting for impairments under Current Text I08 (conforming policies on assumptions used in determining fair value and aggregation level of identifiable cash flows)

- Accounting for asset retirement obligations (conforming policies on assumptions used)

Consideration also should be given to the accounting for derivative activities. Although not required to account for all derivatives in the same manner (as hedges or as mark-to-market), companies need to determine the treatment for acquired derivatives. Appropriate documentation should be prepared as of the date of the acquisition for derivatives to be accounted for as hedges.

RECORDING ASSETS ACQUIRED AND LIABILITIES ASSUMED

The cost of an acquired entity should be assigned to the assets acquired and liabilities assumed based on their estimated fair values at the date of acquisition. Any excess of cost over the net of the amounts assigned to the assets acquired and liabilities assumed should be recorded as goodwill.

B51 sets forth detailed guidelines for assigning amounts to the individual assets acquired and liabilities assumed. Valuations should be performed by individuals (either internal or external valuation experts) who have the requisite expertise and experience to develop fair value measurements. Such valuations are at best an approximation of fair value.

Assets acquired and liabilities assumed in an oil and gas related acquisition require careful analysis in allocating the purchase price. The following sections highlight some of the considerations in such an acquisition.

OIL AND GAS PROPERTIES

Oil and gas property valuations should be based on reasonable and supportable assumptions. Careful consideration must be given to the underlying geological data; estimates of future prices, costs, and discount rates based on rates commensurate with risks involved in producing and developing the underlying properties; and any other significant assumptions specific to the transaction. Assumptions used in the valuation of oil and gas properties should be compared with recently completed company transactions, other company information (including budgets), or with other comparable transactions.

For additional discussion on valuation techniques commonly used in the oil and gas industry, refer to Chapter 31.

INTANGIBLE ASSETS

B51.138 provides specific criteria for determining whether an acquired intangible asset should be recognized apart from goodwill. Though not an all-inclusive list, the following are examples of intangible assets that may relate to oil and gas transactions:

- Trademarks and trade names

- Internet domain names

- Non-compete agreements

- Customer contracts and relationships

- Lease agreements

- Employment contracts

- Patented and unpatented technology

FINANCIAL DERIVATIVE CONTRACTS

Oil and gas companies often hedge their oil and gas production associated with specific sales points where the underlying properties are located. As a result, upon sale of the related oil and gas properties, the underlying derivative contracts are usually acquired by the purchaser. On the date of acquisition, such derivative contracts are considered new contracts by the acquirer and must be recorded by the acquirer at fair value. As with any new derivative contract, the derivative must meet the hedge criteria at the date of acquisition under D50 (FAS 149, *Amendment of Statement 133 on Derivative Instruments and Hedging Activities*).

In certain situations where a loss contract is recorded, companies must evaluate the contract to determine if an other-than-insignificant financing element exists under D50.142A. When the determination is made that an other-than-insignificant financing element exists, cash flows related to the associated contracts may need to be presented as cash flows from financing activities in the Statement of Cash Flows. Incurring a derivative liability in an acquisition is considered to be an in substance borrowing.

ASSUMED ASSET RETIREMENT OBLIGATIONS

Acquisitions of oil and gas properties often entail an assumption of the associated plugging and abandonment obligations. Consideration must be given to determining the fair value of the assumed asset retirement obligation (ARO). The liability recorded on the acquired company's books is not necessarily the fair value that should be recorded in purchase accounting by the acquirer. The acquiring company's assumptions regarding the cost and timing of plugging and abandonment must be used to determine the fair value of the ARO. Differences between the two entities in credit-adjusted risk-free rates or inflation assumptions and other factors may exist that could significantly affect the fair value of the obligation to be recorded.

ASSUMED LIFTING OBLIGATION RELATED TO OIL AND GAS PROPERTIES BURDENED BY A VPP

Acquisitions involving oil and gas properties burdened by a volumetric production payment (VPP) should be evaluated to determine if the acquiring company is assuming an obligation to deliver the oil and gas associated with the VPP. In situations where the acquirer legally assumed the obligation to deliver oil and gas production under the assumed VPP contract, the future lifting obligation must be recorded at fair value in connection with the transaction. This future lifting obligation generally is amortized over the VPP term through operating revenues. These transactions are often very complex and should be carefully evaluated.

GOODWILL

Under B51, goodwill is measured as the excess of cost over the fair values assigned to the individual assets acquired and liabilities assumed. In a business combination, any acquired intangible assets that do not meet the separate recognition criteria discussed in B51 should be included in the amount of recognized goodwill. In complicated acquisitions where a significant portion of the value is allocated to goodwill, it might be appropriate to engage the assistance of a valuation expert in evaluating the reasonableness of a company's purchase price allocation.

ACQUIRED GOODWILL

In evaluating a company's justification for recording goodwill, consideration must be given to the expected economies of scale in connection with the acquirer's existing operations. Such considerations might include operational synergies (e.g., geographic location), access to new customers, access to capital markets, and favorable government relations. Whether or not goodwill should be recorded depends on the specific facts and circumstances of the transaction.

Goodwill is recorded only after a thorough identification and rigorous valuation of all identifiable intangible assets and acquired proved and unproved properties. For example, a company may expect some operational synergies from a purchase business combination. However, if the fair value of the properties acquired (or other non-current assets) is sufficient to absorb the purchase price, then the entire purchase price is allocated to those assets, and no goodwill is recorded. It also should be recognized that amounts might be properly allocated to goodwill as a result of the mechanics of the application of the purchase method without raising any question about the validity of the values assigned to identifiable assets. The most common example of this is the goodwill that could arise when, in accordance with I27, deferred taxes are not recorded at present value amounts.

Under the G40 accounting model, goodwill and certain intangible assets are not presumed to be wasting assets and are considered to have indefinite useful lives. Goodwill and indefinite lived intangible assets are not to be amortized, but rather are to be tested at least annually for impairment. Intangible assets that have finite useful lives are amortized over their useful lives. G40 provides specific guidance for the testing for impairment of goodwill and intangible assets not being amortized.

When goodwill is recognized, a company should assign the goodwill to a reporting unit. A reporting unit is defined as either an operating segment or one level below an operating segment. This can be a complicated assessment, and, depending on the accounting method utilized by companies for their oil and gas properties and other factors, reporting units may vary significantly. In general, the reporting unit to which goodwill would be allocated for a full cost company is the associated full cost pool. This treatment is typical because operating results, cash flows, segment management reviews, and other reports are not maintained or do not occur at a level lower than the full cost pool. For a successful efforts company, the reporting unit to which goodwill may be allocated might exist at a much lower level than that of a full cost company, since separate distinguishable operating results and cash flows are typically maintained at a lower level.

Once goodwill has been allocated to the appropriate reporting unit, companies should understand how the recoverability of goodwill will be evaluated using the impairment model included in G40.

G40 also requires disclosure of information about goodwill and other intangible assets in the years subsequent to their acquisition. Required disclosures include: (1) information about changes in the carrying amount of goodwill from period to period (in the aggregate and by reportable segment); (2) the carrying amount of intangible assets by major intangible asset class for those assets subject to amortization and those not subject to amortization; and (3) the estimated intangible asset amortization expense for the next five years.

DEFERRED INCOME TAXES

Under B51, the basic model is for each identified asset and liability to be assigned its respective fair value. Frequently, the assigned value will be different than the item's tax basis, resulting in temporary differences under FAS 109. For additional discussion on deferred income taxes associated with business combinations, refer to Chapter 27.

AUDITED STATEMENTS OF GROSS REVENUES AND DIRECT LEASE OPERATING EXPENSES

As discussed previously, under Rule 3-05 full historical financial statements often will be required in filings with the SEC related to acquisitions of oil and gas properties. However, when such properties are acquired, full financial statements might not exist. SAB Topic 2D provides a possible alternative when full financial statements for an oil and gas property are not available. Under SAB Topic 2D, the SEC staff may permit presentation of audited statements of revenues and direct operating expenses for all years in which an income statement would otherwise be required, as determined by the level of significance. Formal clearance with SEC staff is required prior to the utilization of this alternative format.

EXPOSURE DRAFT ON BUSINESS COMBINATIONS

As discussed previously, the FASB issued an exposure draft entitled *Business Combinations: Applying the Acquisition Method*. This project is the second phase of an overall project on business combinations and is a joint project between the FASB and the IASB. (Phase I resulted in the issuance of FAS 141, which was discussed earlier.) In this phase of the project, the boards are reconsidering the existing guidance for applying the purchase method of accounting for business combinations (now called the acquisition method). At the end of this phase, the FASB will issue two standards, FAS 141(R), *Business Combinations*, and FAS 160, *Accounting and Reporting of Noncontrolling Interests in Consolidated Financial Statements (an amendment to ARB No. 51)*.

The primary objective of the joint project is to develop a single high-quality standard of accounting for business combinations that can be used for both domestic and international financial reporting. The new standard would include a common set of principles and related guidance for producing decision-useful information and minimizing allowable exceptions. To achieve these goals and objectives, the exposure draft:

- Clarifies that all assets and liabilities, including those subject to contingencies, should be recognized in the initial accounting for a business combination.

- Requires that the assets acquired, the liabilities assumed, and equity interests be consistently measured using a fair value with limited exception.

- Defines the scope of the standard in a way that ensures that similar economic events are accounted for similarly. (That is, by requiring that all transactions or other events in which an acquirer obtains control of a business be accounted for by applying the acquisition method).

Key provisions in the new standards will significantly impact how companies account for business combinations in the future. The more significant changes proposed are:

- Increasing the number of transactions that will be considered business combinations that require the use of the acquisition method

- Recognizing the full fair value of the business acquired, rather than the accumulated cost approach

- Changing the measurement date for equity consideration from the announcement date to the date control is obtained, generally the closing date

- Expensing acquisition related transaction and restructuring costs

- Recognizing contingent consideration and assets and liabilities subject to contingencies at the their fair values on the acquisition date with changes in the fair value generally recorded through earning each reporting period

- Recognizing adjustments to the initial accounting for a business combination will result in the restatement of any prior period information as if the adjustment had been recorded at the date of the acquisition

- Noncontrolling interests (previously "minority interest") to be recorded as a component of equity

- Recording of "holding" gains and losses in step acquisitions and partial dispositions of subsidiaries when control is obtained or lost

- The treatment of purchases and sales of noncontrolling interests in subsidiary as capital transactions when control is maintained

At the time this book went to print, the FASB was still deliberating some technical points to the exposure draft which may result in changes in the final standard. The final standard is expected to be issued in 2007 with a proposed effective date for annual periods beginning on or after December 15, 2008. Early application of the new standard will not be permitted.

• • •

CHAPTER

31

VALUATION OF PROVED
OIL AND GAS PROPERTIES

Key Concepts:

- General valuation concepts including market, income, and cost approaches

- Methods for determining fair market value of proved oil and gas properties

- Amortization tax benefit calculation

- Other valuation factors to consider

BACKGROUND

The valuation of oil and gas properties is directly related to the ultimate value of petroleum resources that may be extracted from the ground in the future. Due to various geological and economic risks, oil and gas properties present unusual complexities in applying traditional valuation techniques.

This chapter provides an overview of determining the fair market value of proved oil and gas properties. The need for such estimates has increased dramatically in recent years. New accounting standards have driven the changes, as well as a stricter application of fair value concepts in the wake of the Sarbanes-Oxley Act. Proper allocations of fair market value can relate to:

- Allocation of purchase price to individual assets in connection with a business combination accounted for under FAS 141, *Business Combinations*.

- Application of FAS 144 to determine potential asset impairment.

- Allocation of book values in proportion to relative fair values as required for certain property sales as described in Chapter 21.

- Management's use in assessing the acquisition or disposal of proved oil and gas properties.

- Compliance with tax rules[1].

Depending on the purpose for a valuation, the underlying reasoning and valuation methodology may differ. For instance, the determination of fair value used in a purchase price allocation is based on the concept of what a market participant would pay–not what an individual buyer might offer. Assumptions for capital structure, tax rates, and synergies (such as cost savings) are based on circumstances for a typical market buyer. Conversely, a valuation performed in support of a merger or sale would assume a unique buyer with a specific capital structure, tax rate, and synergies.

Valuations of oil and gas properties pursuant to FAS 69, which represents a standardized value for oil and gas properties, reflect "rough estimates" of fair market value[2]. Such valuations often represent data points that can be used to assess the reasonableness of other valuation methods.

This chapter describes several common valuation methods used to determine the fair market value of businesses and properties. Later in the chapter, these concepts are applied specifically to oil and gas proved reserves valuations.

GENERAL VALUATION CONCEPTS

In FAS 144, paragraph 22, the fair value of an asset is defined as "the amount at which the asset could be bought or sold in a current transaction between willing parties, that is, other than in a forced or liquidation sale." An arm's-length transaction refers to a purchase or sale in which the buyer and seller are unrelated and the sales price is presumed to be at a fair value unless available information indicates otherwise. There is a rebuttable presumption that the buyer and seller are both willing and competent parties to the transaction, are under no compulsion to transact, and have a reasonable knowledge of the facts as to the value and utility of the property being sold.

Quoted market prices in active markets are the best evidence of fair value and are used as the basis for the measurement, if available. Frequently, quoted prices in active markets are not available for long-lived assets (asset groups) covered by FAS 144. In these cases, the estimate of fair value is based on the best information available, including prices for similar assets (groups) and results of using other valuation techniques. While paragraph 24 of FAS 144 states that the assumptions to be used should be those of "marketplace participants," if information is not available without undue cost and effort, then the entity uses its own assumptions.

For valuing a business, general valuation methodology recognizes several methods which are commonly classified into three categories:

- Income approach
- Market approach
- Cost approach

For valuing proved oil and gas properties, the income approach is, by far, the primary method used in practice. The market approach, while widely used in general valuations, serves more often as a corroborating method rather than the primary method used by E&P companies. The cost approach is seldom seen in the valuation of oil and gas properties.

While the income method is the most prevalent in the industry, a brief explanation of the general process for each of these methods is provided so that the primary reliance on the income approach will be self-evident. Recent valuation concepts, such as "real options," are also covered.

INCOME APPROACH

The income approach values a business or asset on the basis of future cash flows expected to be produced by the property. The most common income approach is the discounted cash flow analysis (DCF). Using DCF, the fair value is a function of the present value of expected future net cash flows, which are discounted using an appropriate discount rate. The forecast and discount rate are important factors, and each requires the consideration of numerous facts, assumptions, and judgment.

Forecast. In an oil and gas valuation, forecasts are often based on engineering and accounting data readily available for the company or asset being acquired. Production volumes are the building blocks for a forecast. They are accessed from a company's internal reserves ledgers, internal economic runs for particular fields or areas, or reserves reports prepared by independent reserves engineers.

Using basic production volume data, a typical oil and gas cash flow forecast is developed using assumptions for realized oil and gas prices, production, operating and development costs, production taxes, and capital expenditures necessary to produce the oil and gas reserves in the ground.

Since the life of an oil and gas property is generally a fairly finite and known time period, a cash flow forecast can run for the entire life of the asset being valued. Traditional DCF techniques usually call for a finite forecast period (such as 10 years) with a terminal value assumption in the final forecast year that captures all cash flows that are expected to extend past the forecast period.

A common valuation method to determine terminal value is the Gordon Growth Model. It assumes cash flows in the last year of the forecast will continue in perpetuity at a specified growth rate. In an oil and gas environment, the assumption of perpetuity is not realistic, so the Gordon Growth Model is not appropriate. Alternatively, for oil and gas properties the terminal value is often a large cash outflow driven by the cost to plug and abandon wells or other related asset retirement obligations (ARO). Assumptions can be made as to the scrap value of materials and equipment, which are sometimes assumed to offset any ARO (particularly for onshore fields).

Discount Rate. A dollar received or paid in the future is worth less than a dollar received or paid today due to the time value of money. Since a dollar today can be invested and earn interest, it will have a greater value a year from now. In order to determine today's value of a dollar that will not be received until some point in the future, it must be discounted to the current period. To accomplish this, an appropriate discount rate must be selected.

Discount rates can be determined by various means, such as flows to equity (FTE) or the weighted average cost of capital (WACC). The FTE method discounts the cash flows distributable to an equity investor at the levered cost of equity. The WACC method discounts the cash flows to all providers of funds at a blended rate of return. Because WACC is the most prevalent, it is described in more detail.

Cost of capital is the rate of return that a business, asset, or project must earn for a provider of capital (either debt, equity, or both) to invest. Risk is also an important element in investment decision making. The return expected by a debt investor is an interest rate that recognizes the risk of the business, asset, or project. Expected dividend payments, as well as the expected gains in share price, both expressed in percentage terms, are considered by equity investors.

Finally, WACC is simply the weighted average of these returns based on the debt to equity ratio for the business, asset, or project. It takes into account the interest tax shield that is available to providers of debt. While cash flows and the discount rate can be calculated on either a pre-tax or after-tax basis, it is generally accepted that an after-tax DCF analysis is preferable to a pre-tax analysis[3] (see Figure 31-7). Thus, the remainder of examples in this chapter assumes all amounts are after-tax. The formula used to calculate WACC is shown in Figure 31-1.

Figure 31-1
Calculation of Weighted Average Cost of Capital on an After-Tax Basis

$$WACC = R_d (1-T_c) \left[\frac{D}{D+E}\right] + R_e \left[\frac{E}{D+E}\right]$$

Where:

R_d = Pre-tax cost of debt

T_c = Corporate tax rate

R_e = Cost of equity

D = Market value of debt

E = Market value of equity

Deriving the return on debt and equity can be complex and is beyond the scope of this text, although it is an important part of the calculation of WACC.

If a valuation is being performed for purposes of an acquisition or other internal analysis, the company's specific cost of capital (as well as debt and equity ratios) is used to determine the discount rate. However, for a valuation being performed for purchase price allocation, the cost of capital of a typical market participant is assumed (i.e., the discount rate assumes the risks, as well as debt and equity ratios, are the same as a typical market participant, and not a specific entity.)

In the oil and gas industry, reserves information is often discounted at a 10 percent rate for financial statement disclosure purposes. This figure is commonly referred to as PV10. Since it is not a true market value, what discount rates do E&P companies use? Remarkably enough, they use a number very close to 10 percent. Based on recent statistics published by Ibbotson Associates, the median WACC for E&P companies has been 9.48 percent[4]. A similar study by the Society of Petroleum Evaluation Engineers (SPEE) found an average discount rate of 9.3 percent (the SPEE survey included WACC as well as other methods of determining the discount rate)[5].

Once a discount rate is established, cash flows can be discounted back to their present values. To accomplish this, the discount rate is converted into a discount factor: the number used to multiply by each year's cash flow in order to determine its present value. Assuming the outcome, or WACC calculation, yields a 10 percent discount rate, the formula in Figure 31-2 calculates a discount factor for year one, where i equals the discount rate of 10 percent, and t equals the time period of one year.

Figure 31-2
Calculation of Discount Factor

$$\text{Discount Factor} = \frac{1}{(1+i)^t} = \frac{1}{(1+10\%)^1} = 0.909$$

A discount factor is calculated for each year for which a forecast of cash flows has been prepared. The example in Figure 31-2 assumes all cash flows occur at the end of the year. In reality, we know that cash flows are spread across the entire year (sometimes evenly, sometimes not). To address this, a common valuation technique is to assume a mid-year convention; cash flows are earned ratably over the year, which is the same as assuming they were all received at the midpoint of the year. The discount factor formula is adjusted to reflect a mid-year convention as shown in Figure 31-3.

Figure 31-3
Calculation of Discount Factor with Mid-year Convention

$$\text{Discount Factor} = \frac{1}{(1+i)^{(t-0.5)}} = \frac{1}{(1+10\%)^{(1-0.5)}} = \frac{1}{(1.1)^{(0.5)}} = 0.95$$

In the first example, a $1 cash flow is assumed to be received at year-end, and is worth $0.91 today. In the second example, the same $1 is assumed to be earned equally over the year. Since we receive the cash sooner, the same dollar is worth more today at $0.95.

Figure 31-4 shows a simple example of a DCF valuation. Assume a five year production profile, reserves of 4,000 barrels of oil, an expected price for oil based on current NYMEX WTI futures (less assumed transportation and quality differentials), $6 per barrel production costs, $9 per barrel development costs, total abandonment (ARO) costs of $35,000 over a two year period, and a 40 percent income tax rate. Note that in an actual valuation, more detailed assumptions would be made regarding items such as inflation costs and capital spending.

Figure 31-4
Example Discounted Cash Flow Valuations

	Year				
	1	2	3	4	5
Production volume	1,000	1,100	900	600	400
Realized price	$ 55.50	$ 55.00	$ 53.50	$ 52.50	$ 51.00
Revenues	$55,500	$60,500	$48,150	$31,500	$20,400
Production costs	(6,000)	(6,600)	(5,400)	(3,600)	(2,400)
Development costs	(9,000)	(9,900)	(8,100)	(5,400)	(3,600)
Abandonment costs	-	-	-	(15,000)	(20,000)
Cash flow	40,500	44,000	34,650	7,500	(5,600)
Income taxes	(16,200)	(17,600)	(13,860)	(3,000)	2,240
Net cash flow	$24,300	$26,400	$20,790	$ 4,500	$ (3,360)
Discount factor*	0.9535	0.8668	0.7880	0.7164	0.6512
Present value	$23,169	$22,883	$16,382	$ 3,224	$ (2,188)

Sum of Present Values	$63,470
Value/Barrel	$ 15.87

* Using half-year convention

MARKET APPROACH

In many industries, fair value can be estimated as a multiple of historical net income, cash flow, EBITDA, or similar measurement of income for a specified time period. For oil and gas valuations, however, these financial-based multiples are not as common because the timing of future production is more indicative of value than current or historical financial results. Additionally, a multiple in one location may not be indicative of value for another property where the life and decline pattern of future cash flows are substantially different. Instead, other market data are used such as implied value/BOE, or value/BOED production in historical transactions.

Market-based approaches are often used as corroborating measures in oil and gas valuations. In the previous example, the DCF analysis yielded a value of $15.87/barrel. Is this value realistic given the current market? Through the market approach, we can gain an understanding of the value per barrel for comparable property transactions.

The market approach requires that comparable transactions be selected. In order to be regarded as comparable, several factors are analyzed, including but not limited to:

- Geographic location

- Oil and gas weighting of reserves

- Reserves production ratio of reserves

- Geographic location (country or region)

- Geologic profile of reserves (oil sands, onshore, offshore, enhanced recovery areas)

Recent transaction data are plentiful in most domestic markets. However, international transaction data are less abundant, and can be skewed by governmental involvement on the side of either the buyer or the seller. If perfectly comparable transactions cannot be found, certain adjustments are made to convert the resulting transaction values to a more comparable basis. This is often seen in a case where oil and gas weighting or reserves production ratios differ; however, it is difficult to adjust for geographic location.

If the value derived from using the market approach is significantly higher or lower than that from an income-based approach (such as DCF), consideration should be given to weighting both the income and market approaches to determine a final value. Other situations may call for the market approach to be used to place a collar—a high and low value per barrel—on the results from the income approach.

COST APPROACH

The cost approach generally refers to the replacement cost method. Replacement cost rests on the theory that a knowledgeable buyer would pay no more than the cost of constructing a similar asset of like utility as of the valuation date. Asset value is determined by the cost of reproducing or replacing the property as if it were new—less depreciation from physical deterioration, functional obsolescence, and economic obsolescence to the extent they are present and measurable.

Under this method, some appraisers may include consideration of the current property owner's historical cost of acquiring the property. If the property being valued was acquired in an arm's-length transaction by the owner shortly before the valuation date, with no interim exploration or development, then the owner's historical acquisition cost may be a strong indicator of the property's value at the valuation date. However, the historical cost of acquiring and exploring a lease generally is not indicative of the reserves found or the value of such reserves.

As a generalization, replacement cost and historical cost are not useful in determining the value of proved oil and gas properties.

AMORTIZATION TAX BENEFIT

As defined previously, fair value is the value that the highest bidder with a reasonable knowledge of the relevant facts would pay for the asset or business. When using an income approach such as DCF, this value often has two components: (1) the present value of future cash flows generated by an asset or business, and (2) the present value (using the same after-tax discount rate) of the income tax benefits of deducting the purchase price through higher future depreciation, depletion, and amortization charges. This second factor is often referred to as depletion bonus, tax shield, or amortization tax benefit (ATB).

While DD&A expenses are non-cash items, they ultimately impact cash through lower future income taxes. This additional cash flow can be incorporated as a component of an income method when using after-tax cash flows and an after-tax discount rate. Since after-tax cash flows are used by the majority of large E&P companies (see Figure 31-7), this can be a source of value to a potential buyer/owner.

With a basic understanding of the value of an ATB, how is the value determined? The amount of the ATB is dependent on the purchase price, which is dependent on the amount of the ATB, and which implies the need for algebra and solving for a simultaneous equation. While most spreadsheet applications can easily handle a value that includes an ATB component, the following formula can be used[6]:

Value = [PV1 + E * (E% - L%)] / (1 - L%)

Where:

PV1 = present value of a property's future cash flows

E = estimated fair value of fixed assets (excluding oil & gas assets or leasehold)

E% = percent of E that equates to the discounted present value of tax benefits from depreciating $1 of the equipment. E% is also a function of the allowable tax depreciation rates for the equipment asset class, marginal income tax rate, and after-tax discount rate as shown in Figure 31-5.

L% = percent that equates to the discounted present value of tax benefits from depreciating $1 of the leasehold. L% is a function of the percent of reserves to be produced each year (unit-of-production method), marginal income tax rate, and after-tax discount rate as shown in Figure 31-6.

Figure 31-5
Computing E% for the Amortization Tax Benefit

Year	[A] Well Equipment Depreciation Rates	[B] Combined Federal & State Tax Rate	[C] Discount Factor for 10%	[D] E% [A] * [B] * [C]
1	14.29%	40.0%	0.9535	5.45%
2	24.49%	40.0%	0.8668	8.49%
3	17.49%	40.0%	0.7880	5.51%
4	12.49%	40.0%	0.7164	3.58%
5	8.93%	40.0%	0.6512	2.33%
6	8.92%	40.0%	0.5920	2.11%
7	8.93%	40.0%	0.5382	1.92%
8	4.46%	40.0%	0.4893	0.87%
	100%			30.27%

Figure 31-6
Computing L% for the Amortization Tax Benefit

Year	Future Production of Net Reserves (BOE)	[A] % of Reserves Produced	[B] Combined Federal & State Tax Rate	[C] Discount Factor for 10%	[D] L% [A] * [B] * [C]
1	1,000	25.00%	40.0%	0.9535	9.53%
2	1,100	27.50%	40.0%	0.8668	9.53%
3	900	22.50%	40.0%	0.7880	7.09%
4	600	15.00%	40.0%	0.7164	4.30%
5	400	10.00%	40.0%	0.6512	2.60%
	4,000	100.00%			33.06%

Using the information from Figures 31-4, 31-5, and 31-6, and assuming the equipment is allocated at $10,000 of the purchase price, the value of the asset or business would be $94,399 [$63,470 + 10,000*(30.27%-33.06%)] / (1-33.06%). The resulting ATB value is $30,929 [$94,399-63,470], which increases the implied value per BOE from $15.87 (Figure 31-4) to $23.60.

There is vigorous debate over the use of ATB, particularly in purchase price allocations where the value is tied to a theoretical market participant. In some cases, if the most likely market participant would benefit from the ATB, then the value is calculated including the ATB, even if the actual buyer may be a non-taxpaying entity. For other circumstances, consideration of the market approach may show that, even though the DCF value includes value for the ATB, market buyers are not paying for this benefit. In these cases, the market approach could be used as a support for capping the implied value per BOE under the DCF analysis to a level more in line with market transactions. To continue the previous example, an analysis of comparable market transactions might show that buyers are not paying $23.60/BOE for comparable reserves in comparable areas. If the market appears to value such reserves at $17.00/BOE, for example, consideration should be given to which value is most appropriate: $15.87 from the DCF, $17.00/BOE from the market, or a weighting of both.

OIL & GAS SPECIFIC CONCEPTS

Appraisers or others valuing assets will often consider all three approaches mentioned in this chapter. They may quickly dismiss one or two of them as inapplicable or of limited use for a particular valuation. Applicability depends on the nature of the property being valued and the nature and extent of available information. Unlike many businesses where independent appraisals can be obtained for items such as equipment, oil and gas proved reserves are unique assets.

As a rule, most oil and gas valuations are based on a combination of the Income Approach and Market Approach methodologies. This is common when valuations are prepared for purposes of mergers, acquisitions, or purchase price allocations. While valuations of smaller, less complex, or geographically isolated assets may rely on market-based metrics, the larger, more complex, or geographically diverse valuations generally lean towards the income approach. Specific concepts to consider when using these approaches in oil and gas valuations are discussed next.

INCOME APPROACH CONSIDERATIONS

- **Reserves Reports.** The source of many income approach (DCF) models are reserves reports or other internal production or economic models. Reserves reports can provide basic volumes, revenues, operating costs and taxes, capital spending, and future asset retirement costs. From this information, general and administrative costs, interest, income taxes, and other non-operational items are added to prepare a full cash flow forecast.

- **Real or nominal dollars.** Reserves reports prepared for SEC reporting purposes assume current dollars and current costs (i.e., nominal dollars); thus, there is no consideration given to inflation. Based on the assumptions and expectations of the market, inflation may play a large part in determining the value. If cost inflation is expected to far outweigh the expected inflation in commodity prices and revenues, then using purely nominal dollars may yield a misleading valuation.

- **Pricing.** Once a price deck has been determined, assumptions are made for the price differential in order to determine the realized price for a given oil or gas production stream. The differential includes reductions (or additions) for transportation costs (most applicable to natural gas) and product quality (most applicable to oil). If the valuation of an oil property is based on a WTI price deck, and the property produces light WTI oil, then the differential should be predictable and generally consistent from year to year. If the oil produced is something other than WTI, then quality basis differentials will apply. Petroleum accountants should understand that the quality differential does not always have a linear relationship with WTI (or whichever crude is selected as the price deck). Often, the differential is linear within a range of WTI prices, but in higher commodity price environments, the differential can rise disproportionately. In such situations, using the differentials implied in a reserves report based on flat pricing may yield an inaccurate answer.

- **ARO Costs.** ARO costs are sometimes overlooked when preparing an oil and gas valuation. Some reserves reports include estimates for ARO costs, while others may not, usually at the request of the company commissioning the reserves report. If a reserves report that excludes ARO is being used as the source of basic data, ARO costs should be considered.

- **Pre-tax or Post-tax WACC.** Because most reserves reports are prepared on a pre-tax basis, this should be considered in the selection of an appropriate discount rate. If oil and gas properties are being valued individually on a pre-tax basis, then a pre-tax WACC is used. If a larger, taxpaying entity is being valued, and taxes are considered as part of the cash flows, then an after-tax WACC should be calculated. Consistency in one's approach is critical in this regard.

DCF analyses can differ in three ways: (1) the use of real (constant) or nominal (inflated) dollars, (2) use of pre-tax or after-tax cash flows, and (3) risk-adjusting either the cash flows or the discount rate. Figure 31-7 summarizes the practices commonly used by E&P companies.

A large number of E&P companies use some form of DCF analysis. Based on the form of DCF chosen, consistency is key. If pre-tax cash flows are used, then a pre-tax discount rate should also be used. If the cash flows themselves are risked, then the discount rate should not be risked, lest the risk be double counted.

MARKET APPROACH CONSIDERATIONS

- **Timing.** When commodity prices change, it is no secret that market prices are influenced. While market prices do not necessarily react to short term commodity price changes, longer periods of higher commodity prices will translate into higher market prices. Timing of the selected sample of comparable transactions is critical when using a market-based approach.

- **Location.** Oil and gas are commodity products, and their values are often market-dictated. However, product quality and location also affect valuation. When selecting comparable transactions, consideration should be given to the location of the assets covered in an otherwise comparable transaction. The value of oil reserves in a field in New Mexico is different than the value of oil reserves in Alaska due to both quality and transportation differences. If a selection of market transactions yields a $/BOE value, one must be certain that location-related value drivers are appropriately considered.

- **Domestic versus International Properties.** Market-based approaches offer insight into what independent buyers believe are the true market values of particular assets. In North America, an abundance of transactions exist that represent true market values. Elsewhere in the world, transaction volumes may be less available, and prices paid can be more a result of quasi-governmental intervention by either the buyer or seller. Thus, establishing a true market price can be difficult.

- **Oil/Gas Mix.** If a selection of comparable market transactions is chosen based solely on location, an important value driver may have been overlooked. While location is important, the oil and gas mix of the reserves being valued is also key. Although the thermal energy content of one barrel of oil is approximately six times an Mcf of natural gas, the market prices are often very different than the 6:1 ratio for many different reasons. Because the implied value of any transaction is based on the expectations of current and future oil and natural gas prices believed to be true as of the date of the particular transaction, and to the extent that comparable transactions are weighted more heavily towards oil or gas, an adjustment should be made to make them more comparable to the asset being valued.

Figure 31-7
Forms of Discounted Cash Flow (DCF) Used

Survey results from the 2005 Society of Petroleum Evaluation Engineers report:

- 90 percent (23 of 28) of companies used some type of DCF analysis when determining value of property.

Survey results from the *2001 PricewaterhouseCoopers Survey of Petroleum Accounting Practices*:

- 82 percent (23 of 28) of companies used some form of DCF analysis when allocating purchase price among properties acquired.

Selected survey results from the 1993 (most recent) *Current Investment Practices and Procedures: Results of a Survey of U.S. Oil and Gas Producers and Petroleum Consultants*, by Dr. E. L. Dougherty and Ms. Jayati Sarkar:

- 91 percent (94 of 103) of companies used nominal dollars for general analysis.

- After-tax DCF was used in general investment analysis by a:

  - majority (17 of 19) of large companies.

  - majority of midsize and small companies.

  - minority of very small companies.

- Overall, 50.5 percent of the respondents used after-tax DCF exclusively, or used both after-tax and before-tax DCF.

- Only 1 in 18 large companies and 11 of 25 midsize companies reported using before-tax DCF for valuing property acquisitions.

- A slight majority of midsize companies and 74 percent of large companies used a combination of techniques to account for risk, including sensitivity analysis and applying probability factors. Fifty five percent of small and very small companies simply raised the discount rate.

OTHER FACTORS TO CONSIDER

The earlier discussion provides an overview of generally accepted valuation practices, as well as those used more specifically for valuation of oil and gas assets. Yet, the true value of an asset or business can be more or less than the output derived from applying these valuation methodologies. Adjustments to the value may include:

Liquidity or Marketability. A highly liquid asset or equity investment—such as an equity investment in a publicly traded company or an oil or gas asset in an active market—is worth more than an asset or equity investment that is not as liquid. Lack of liquidity arguably results in a delay or higher cost in finding a buyer; the asset or interest may need to be sold at a discount to entice a buyer to purchase it. This is referred to as a liquidity or marketability discount.

Control Premium. When comparing the acquisition of a minority ownership interest in an oil and gas property to the acquisition of a majority or controlling interest, the second type of purchase is clearly more valuable. An owner that controls production volumes, costs, capital decisions, dividends, or cash distributions can influence the ultimate value of that particular asset or business (or arguably so). Some studies suggest investors will pay a premium for the ability to control an asset or company; this has become known as a control premium.

Small Company Premium. Small companies appear to earn returns in excess of the cost of capital, and some practitioners suggest that it is appropriate to make an upward revision to the discount rate when estimating the value of a small company. This is particularly true in the oil and gas industry where sudden downturns in commodity prices can have adverse effects on a small company, especially if it is leveraged heavily to one or two properties.

RECENT VALUATION DEVELOPMENTS

While the three valuation methods discussed in this chapter are commonly accepted and used, the field of valuation is always changing. New theories and methodologies emerge periodically, although they can take years to reach mainstream acceptance.

One such valuation development is the theory of Real Options. Similar to a decision tree, Real Options enables the person preparing the valuation to take into account the value of an investment associated with future opportunities. An example is the option to expand an initial investment if conditions prove favorable. This theory can provide insight into the issues highlighted and better cash flow modeling of future business prospects, which could lead to a more robust valuation.

Real Options addresses some of the shortfalls in the income approach. Primarily, it allows each cash flow stream to be independently risked. This captures a key value component: the value of any property depends on management's flexibility in making decisions and timing project components. Real Options captures the dynamic environment present in most businesses—where value is driven by reactions and changes as new events unfold, and decisions are not made at Point A and left unchanged (the assumption underlying DCF models).

Using Real Options valuation, various parts of an asset or business can be valued separately if they are *independent* properties. An example is drilling in fields in various parts of the country that generally do not impact each other. Decisions can be made separately for these fields. Parts that are *dependent* on one another can be valued together, and information learned from one part can be applied to future go/no-go decisions for the other parts. In these cases, the sum of the whole may far exceed the sum of the parts. This approach captures the value of management's ability (optionality) to make sequential decisions and learn from past mistakes.

Since this theory applies a decision tree type of analysis that captures volatility, risk, and uncertainty of future prices, a risk free discount rate may be appropriate. This removes much of the subjectivity of DCF valuations.

SPEE SURVEY OF ECONOMIC PARAMETERS[7]

The Society of Petroleum Evaluation Engineers (SPEE) conducts an annual survey of economic parameters used in property evaluations and provides a report to participants, SPEE members, and other interested parties. It serves as a limited indicator of price and cost escalations, discount rates, and risk adjustments employed by E&P companies and their consultants in determining the fair value or bid price for proved oil and gas property in general.

The June 2005 SPEE report indicated:

- Respondents were 41 percent producers, 44 percent consultants, nine percent bankers, and six percent other.

- The average WTI posted oil prices were projected to reach $42.29/bbl in 2005, decline to $39.03/bbl in 2009 before increasing to $43.09/bbl in 2015. In actuality, WTI spot prices in the first half of 2005 averaged over $50.00/bbl and escalated to over $60.00/bbl at times in the second half of the year.

- The average projected gas cash prices at Henry Hub in Louisiana were $5.74/MMBtu in 2005, with a decline expected through 2009 to $5.39/MMBtu before escalating to $5.97/MMBtu in 2015. Similar to the oil price response, actual Henry Hub spot gas prices in the first half of 2005 averaged over $6.00/MMBtu, and reached over $14.00/MMBtu at times in the second half of the year.

- Unlike previous years, most respondents believed that costs will generally escalate at rates above the predicted inflation rate, particularly in the next few years. Drilling costs are expected to rise over seven percent in 2005, five percent in 2006, and 4.5 percent in 2007 before declining to the three to four percent range. At the same time, operating costs are expected to escalate over four percent in 2005 before declining to just over three percent through 2015. These rates compared to expected inflation ranging from 2.7 percent in 2005 to 3.2 percent in 2015.

- DCF was used by 90 percent of respondents for determining the value of property, followed by $/BOE multiples from a meager 2.5 percent of respondents.

- The average discount factor was 9.3 percent, down from 11.2 percent the previous year. Of the respondents, over 23 percent determined the discount rate based on professional judgment, 23 percent used a WACC, while the remainder based it on various factors such a blend of the above methods, along with prime lending rates or even industry surveys.

- Concerning risk, 52 percent of respondents did not adjust the discount rate for risk, but rather handled it via reserves adjustment factors. Another 25 percent adjusted for risk in the discount rate, while 23 percent used both methods.

CONCLUSION

In the oil and gas industry, DCF approaches remain the pre-eminent method for determining value, whether for mergers and acquisitions, purchase price allocations, or other valuation needs. Despite studies and research that highlight the many faults of a DCF analysis, the method prevails. As more sophisticated ways to perform valuations become commonly accepted, these theories may work their ways into oil and gas valuations, at least in part.

• • •

1 Tax requirements might affect areas such as: (1) allocation of purchase price among multiple acquired properties, (2) determination of fair value of property contributed to charity or given as a gift to family member(s), and (3) property tax assessments.

2 FAS 69, paragraph 82, states the standardized measure is neither fair market value nor the present value of future cash flows, but "is a rough surrogate for such measures."

3 Since 1974, editions of *Economic Evaluation and Investment Decisions Methods*, a leading textbook on petroleum economic evaluations, have emphasized economic analysis should be done after-tax. The editions are authored by Frank J. Stermole, Colorado School of Mines Professor Emeritus, and his son, John M. Stermole, Adjunct Professor at the Colorado School or Mines, and published by Stermole's Investment Evaluations Corporation.

4 Source: *Cost of Capital 2004 Yearbook*, published by Ibbotson Associates for SIC Code 13 - Oil and Gas Extraction. It summarized 114 companies in the oil and gas extraction industry.

5 Source: *The Twenty-Fourth Annual Survey of Economic Parameters Used in Property Evaluations* published by SPEE in June 2005.

6 Formula for derivation and further explanation of the tax shield concept can be found in SPE Paper 19858, *Understanding Minimum Sales Price and Maximum Purchase Price* by G. C. Daley and D. R. Elmer of ARCO (1989).

7 SPEE *Twenty-Fourth Annual Survey*, June 2005.

CHAPTER

32

OFFSHORE OPERATIONS AND ENHANCED RECOVERY

Key Concepts:

- Leasing and drilling considerations in offshore locations

- Accounting issues including unproved properties, G&G, exploratory drilling, DD&A, and removal and restoration

- Enhanced recovery methods and related accounting issues

The physical activities involved in offshore exploration and production can be much different from typical onshore projects. This chapter addresses the diverse aspects of offshore operations and enhanced recovery methods and analyzes the special accounting issues created.

OFFSHORE OPERATIONS

Within U.S. territorial waters, oil and gas operators can acquire mineral leases either from state governments or the federal government. On the Atlantic and Pacific coasts, state governments own mineral rights to a distance of three miles from shore; however, in the Gulf of Mexico state ownership extends for nine miles. Beyond these perimeters, the federal government controls the leasing rights.

Leases are obtained from state or federal authorities through a process of competitive bidding. Typically, announcements of available offshore tracts contain a minimum royalty rate per acre and a fixed royalty rate on production. Companies make competitive bonus bids for the tracts involved. Authorities in some cases have asked for competitive royalty bids with a fixed bonus or, less frequently, have required net-profit-sharing leases.

LEASING

Jurisdiction and ownership of mineral rights in most of the outer continental shelf (OCS) areas of the world were agreed upon in the Geneva Convention of the High Seas of 1958. Procedures for leasing OCS areas from the federal government were set up in the OCS Lands Act of 1953-1954. The Minerals Management Service (MMS) of the U.S. Department of the Interior administers federal oil and gas leases.

Offshore leasing guidelines seek to balance the needs of the federal government for environmental protection, resource development, and a fair return, while also creating a reasonable and practical system. Offshore blocks generally cover 5,760 acres (nine square miles), apply a royalty rate of 16.67 percent (one-sixth) based on the fair market value of production, possess a primary term of five years, and charge an annual rent that is due unless drilling or production operations are underway. Recognizing the additional risks associated with water depths greater than 400 meters, deep-water blocks can have eight- or ten-year terms and a royalty rate of 12.5 percent (one-eighth).

Federal leasing procedures include the following:

1. To allow time for seismic surveys or other prospecting, the MMS publishes lists of available tracts several years in advance.

2. The MMS gives 30 days advance notice in the *Federal Register* of a lease sale to be held in a particular area. Companies can submit bids on any unleased blocks in the area, unless a section has been excluded by the MMS for a specific reason. An environmental impact statement is prepared prior to the sale, and a hearing is held.

3. On the bid date, the MMS opens sealed bids on a block-by-block basis, revealing the name (or names, since companies often make joint bids) of each bidder and the amount of the bid.

4. After opening the bids, the MMS determines a confidential minimum acceptable bid level for each unleased block.

5. Two months after opening the bids, the MMS awards the lease to the highest bidder if the bid exceeds the minimum acceptable amount.

Offshore operations and onshore work employ the same types of exploration methods. Magnetic, gravimetric, and seismic equipment are commonly utilized. Because many of the first offshore oil and gas prospects in the Gulf of Mexico involved salt domes, gravitational exploration methods became especially important. Marine seismic exploration uses an air gun that discharges air under high pressure. A resulting high-pressure bubble oscillates, and seismic waves are generated and reflected. Hydrophones at the water's surface record the reflected sound waves. Seismic surveys are generally cheaper per acre offshore than on land due to the lack of surface impediments and greater ease in obtaining permits. 3-D seismic has become a common type of offshore survey.

DRILLING

Early offshore drilling was merely an extension of onshore activities. Some of the first offshore drilling was done from piers stretching out hundreds of feet from the beach at Santa Barbara, California. In the marshes of Louisiana in the 1920s and 1930s, drilling platforms were constructed by dredging channels, moving in barges, and sinking them in water four to eight feet deep. The barges were fastened into place by wooden pilings. In bays along the coast of the Gulf of Mexico, wooden platforms were constructed on the tops of wooden pilings. If the wells were successful, production equipment was installed and oil was transported by flow lines to an onshore tank battery.

As production moved to deeper water, however, drilling methods changed. Massive platforms rising hundreds of feet from the ocean floor to the water's surface were required along with special production facilities. A single producing well could rarely extract enough oil or gas to justify the facilities cost. Instead, carefully planned programs of exploratory drilling, evaluation or appraisal drilling, and development drilling were implemented.

Mobile rigs perform the exploratory and evaluation drilling today, and these wells are usually abandoned even if oil or gas is discovered. Development wells are drilled from huge platforms with room for drilling numerous wells—generally eight to 30 drill slots, but possibly as many as 60 slots for deep-water platforms when a second platform for a large field is cost-prohibitive. Production facilities on the platform handle output from all wells.

As discussed in Chapter 8, several types of mobile exploratory drilling rigs are used:

- Submersible rigs

- Jack-up rigs

- Semi-submersible rigs

- Drilling barges and drilling ships

Physical conditions in the environment—such as water depth, weather, and distance from port or shore—largely determine the type of exploratory rig to be used. Related factors are the positioning capabilities of the rig, support requirements (including living accommodations), and mobilization problems of getting the rig on location.

Submersible rigs are similar to sunken barges and were among the earliest offshore exploratory rigs. A submersible rig has both a lower and upper hull. The lower hull provides buoyancy when floating the unit from one location to another, and the upper hull provides working space and crew's quarters. When a rig has been moved to a site, the lower hull is flooded and the rig sinks until it rests on the seabed. After drilling operations cease, ballast water is forced out of the lower hull, and the unit is re-floated to prepare for a move to a new location. The difficulty of moving a submersible rig is a major disadvantage. Most submersible rigs operate in shallow water (less than 50 feet), although some can operate in 100 foot depths. Few submersible rigs are being constructed today.

Jack-up rigs, which are relatively inexpensive, are used in much deeper water than submersible rigs. The depth limit is generally 350 feet, but Gorilla class jack-ups can work in water up to 550 feet in the Gulf of Mexico and 400 feet in the North Sea. A jack-up rig has a watertight hull, and while it is in transit the legs are retracted above the hull. When the rig is moved to the drill site, its legs are jacked down to the seabed and its hull is lifted above the water's surface. In this way, tides and waves will not interfere with operations. Jack-up rigs are quite stable, but are difficult to tow. The legs must be shortened or removed for long trips, and several accidents have occurred in jacking platforms up or down.

In deeper waters, submersible rigs and jack-up rigs cannot be used. Semi-submersible rigs (or semis, pronounced sem'-ize) operate in depths generally up to 2,000 feet. (However, PetroBras drilled a well from a semi in 8,022 feet of water at Marlim field.) A semi's hull is floated and submerged just below the water's surface. The rig has a working deck similar to a jack-up, but it is stabilized by ballasting pontoons and columns to a predetermined depth. Older model semis are generally kept over the drill site by anchoring. Newer rigs are self-propelled and are kept in place above the drill site, without anchoring, through the use of Dynamic Positioning (DP). DP technology employs electrically powered propeller thrusters that direct their thrusts in the desired directions. Semi-submersibles are especially useful in deep, rough water such as the North Sea. A major disadvantage is their limited cargo and storage capacity and heavy dependence on supply ships and tugboats.

Drilling ships (drill ships) are seagoing vessels that serve as exploratory drilling platforms. They can work in greater depths than semis. Drill ships are much like traditional ocean-going vessels and are self-propelled. Because they require a sailing crew, operating costs are high. On the plus side, drill ships can move rapidly between work sites and store large quantities of material (thus requiring fewer support ships). Ballasting systems, as well as thrusters, are used to provide stability and secure the ship over the drill site.

Drilling barges are not self-propelled and must be moved by tugboats, thus increasing travel time. Like submersibles, barges are moved to the drilling location and ballasted so they rest on the bottom. Barges typically work in water depths of less than ten feet and are best suited for protected areas such as the marshlands of South Louisiana or parts of Nigeria.

DRILLING OPERATIONS

The drilling operations of an offshore rig are almost identical to those of onshore rigs. Additional technology is used for the work performed on floaters—the semi-submersibles and drill ships mentioned previously. Despite anchoring or dynamic positioning, a significant amount of movement must be managed, particularly the up and down wave action known as heave. Motion compensators act to isolate the drill string from the heave. Marine riser systems guide the drill stem from the drilling vessel to the subsea wellhead and conduct the drilling fluid between the well and the vessel. Emergency disconnect equipment is used in case the vessel is forced off-location by an approaching hurricane, loss of power, broken anchor chains, or collision with another ship. In this way, the well can be re-entered safely.

A special problem in offshore drilling is the installation of blowout preventers. On a nonfloating rig, the blowout preventer is almost identical to the type used onshore. It is installed beneath the rig floor. Floating rig blowout preventers are installed at the wellhead on the sea floor to maintain control of the well during an emergency disconnect. Subsea blowout preventers are similar to regular blowout preventers, but are equipped for remote control operation via electrical or hydraulic power.

Interesting Offshore Facts and Sources

Which state has the highest number of offshore oil and gas rigs? The answer is Louisiana. Baker Hughes, Inc., one of the world's largest oilfield service companies, has published worldwide and North American rig counts since 1944. These rig counts are available on the web at www.bakerhughes.com/investor/rig. According to their website, "Since 1940 the highest [total] weekly U.S. rig count was 4,530 recorded on December 28, 1981. The lowest rig count of 488 was recorded on April 23, 1999."

Baker Hughes Rig Count
www.bakerhughes.com/investor/rig

Offshore Rigs by State

	as of 5-11-07	as of 5-12-06
California	1	6
Louisiana	64	80
Texas	12	14
Total U.S.	77	100

What type of rig is used most frequently? The answer is jack-up rigs. Rigzone (www.rigzone.com) provides statistics on worldwide offshore fleets, utilization rates, and regional counts by rig type, operator, and other categories.

Worldwide Offshore Rigs by Type

Statistics for the primary segments of the competitive offshore rig fleet.*

	Rigs Contracted	Rig Fleet	Utilization %
Drillships	29	35	82.9%
Jack-ups	319	354	90.1%
Semi-submersibles	139	155	89.7%

* Source: http://www.rigzone.com/data/; May 23, 2007

EVALUATION AND DEVELOPMENT WELLS

The platforms and related development wells to handle deep-water offshore reservoirs can cost hundreds of millions of dollars. Many fields must have proved reserves of 200 million equivalent barrels of oil or more before the cost of development can be economically justified. Because a single well will not prove up this quantity of reserves, several evaluation wells are drilled to assess the probability of adequate reserves to justify development. Such wells also aid in determining the precise location for constructing a permanent platform.

Evaluation wells use the same type of drilling equipment as exploratory wells, and—especially if drilled in deep water—are rarely expected to be completed even though they verify the existence of proved reserves. Evaluation wells not used for future development are termed expendable wells, although evaluation wells can sometimes be temporarily abandoned and later tied into the production platform.

Once evaluation wells confirm the existence of adequate reserves, platform construction begins. Fixed platforms are made of concrete or steel, and are designed to withstand severe environmental conditions such as hurricanes, icy seas, earthquakes, and strong winds. Many factors determine the type of platform to be used and its structural details. Fabricated onshore, the platform is either floated or transported on barges to the permanent location where it is erected. To facilitate drilling multiple wells, the platform has drilling slots arranged in rows, forming a rectangle. The drilling derrick is movable and is skidded from one drilling slot to another as drilling is completed. The wells are directional and extend away from the platform (see Figure 8-8).

An example of the type of deepwater drilling being conducted today is the Jack #2 well located in the Gulf of Mexico. In September 2006, Chevron (the operator of a three-member joint venture) announced production tests had been successful to depths of more than 27,000 feet. Further well testing is expected to be done in 2007.

PRODUCTION AND TRANSPORTATION

Production techniques for offshore activities are similar to those onshore. Gas, oil, and water are funneled by separators that resemble those used in onshore drilling. Many jurisdictions require water from the well site to be treated for impurities before it can be discharged into the sea or reinjected into the reservoir. Additional equipment is installed on the platform or in tender ships to properly handle the water. Gas is gathered and transported to shore by pipelines; oil is either accumulated in storage tanks for subsequent transport by tanker or transferred directly from separators and treaters into a tanker. If an oil pipeline has been constructed, the oil may be pumped from treating equipment directly into it.

Offshore pipelines are laid by pipe-laying barges. The pipeline is continuously welded and placed along the bed. On softer and shallower bottoms, the pipeline is buried. Some pipe-laying barges are semi-submersible to minimize the effects of wind and waves in rough water. In recent years, flexible pipelines laid by reel barges have been developed.

REMOVAL AND RESTORATION

As discussed in Chapter 20, a major cost of offshore operations is incurred after oil and gas production ceases—removal of the equipment and platform and clean-up of the ocean bed. Reclamation requirements vary across the globe, but often cost much more than the original platform and facilities, particularly when oil storage facilities are a part of the structure.

Offshore platforms are often an oasis for marine life. Small fish find protection in the shallower, sunlit water depths. Offshore platforms, particularly in the Gulf of Mexico, are a popular destination for sport fishermen. Government authorities sometimes allow these structures to be removed from the seabed, towed to designated areas outside of shipping lanes, and sunk, forming artificial reefs. In rare instances, operators are allowed to cut off the tops of platforms to a certain water depth (perhaps 40 meters) and leave the substructure in place.

ACCOUNTING ISSUES RELATED TO OFFSHORE ACTIVITIES

Many of the challenges in accounting for onshore operations are compounded by offshore work. These complications are recognized in Oi5 and Reg. S-X Rule 4-10 and have been presented in previous chapters of the book where noted. In this section, several topics are highlighted for special consideration by petroleum accountants.

Unproved Properties. Acquisition costs of offshore properties are handled in the same way as for onshore leases. The bonus paid to the state or federal government is capitalized, as are incidental acquisition costs. Offshore properties are large, and the bonus costs are unusually high, often exceeding $10 million. The costs of unproved offshore leases are typically assessed on a property-by-property basis for successful efforts impairment (Chapter 7). For full cost accounting, the costs of acquiring unproved offshore property are usually initially excluded from the full cost amortization base (Chapter 19).

Because offshore leases are large, both in area and cost, Oi5.120 allows a portion of the leasehold cost to be transferred to proved property accounts if proved reserves are found on only a part of the lease and if exploration is continuing on the remainder of the property. Oi5.120 indicates the allocable portion is to be "determined on the basis of geological structural features or stratigraphic conditions." This language suggests a lease is large only if it is believed to have more than one structural feature to be explored.

Oi5.120 is silent about whether the allocation can be based on relative surface acreage, but that approach seems reasonable. For instance, if a successful exploratory well finds proved reserves in a structural feature under an estimated 5,000 acres on a largely unexplored 50,000-acre lease, then perhaps 10 percent of the lease acquisition cost could be reclassified to proved property. However, if G&G studies indicate the 50,000-acre lease contains only five geological structural features with possible oil and gas reserves under a total of 20,000 surface acres, it is more reasonable to allocate 5/20ths, or 25 percent, of the lease acquisition costs to proved properties.

Support Facilities. When a company engages in offshore operations, the costs of acquiring and operating support facilities are likely to be much higher than onshore sites. Port facilities, docks, transportation vessels, helicopters, midget submarines, and supply centers are very expensive. In addition, these facilities often service a project throughout its life cycle. Thus, a major accounting consideration is to develop procedures to charge costs to the appropriate activity, whether exploration, acquisition, drilling, development, or production. This is especially important because most operator-owned facilities are used in joint operations.

Recognizing this problem, the Council of Petroleum Accountants Societies (COPAS) has issued several publications related to accounting procedures for offshore operations, including: *Model Form Interpretation No. 5* (MFI-5), MFI-45, and MFI-46. Although the COPAS documents are intended primarily for use in joint operations, they provide guidance in classifying and recording costs and in allocating costs to specific activities.

Under Reg. S-X Rule 4-10(a)(17)(ii), the depreciation and amortization of support facilities, as well as their applicable operating costs, become exploration, development, or production costs and are accounted for as such.

G&G Costs. The accounting rules for G&G costs incurred offshore are identical to those for onshore activities, although offshore costs are likely to be greater. As discussed in previous chapters, the accounting for G&G costs depends on whether such costs are exploratory or development costs. For successful efforts companies, all exploratory G&G costs are expensed as incurred, whereas development G&G costs are capitalized. If the G&G costs relate to both a proved area and an unproved area, then such costs would be allocated on a reasonable basis. A full cost company capitalizes all such costs as part of the cost pool in the cost center.

Exploratory Drilling. Offshore exploratory drilling is likely to be much more expensive than onshore drilling to the same depth. As previously discussed, offshore platforms, barges, and ships must be used. Offshore rigs are costly to construct and move. Enormous cash resources are required for: transportation of the materials, supplies, and workforce; provision of lodging and food for the crews; and construction and maintenance of onshore support facilities.

Many offshore exploratory wells are drilled with no intention for the well to be completed as productive, even if proved reserves are discovered. Such wells are stratigraphic test wells, which are defined by Reg. S-X 4-10(a)(13) as:

> ...a drilling effort, geologically directed, to obtain information pertaining to a specific geologic condition. Such wells customarily are drilled without the intention of being completed for hydrocarbon production. This classification also includes tests identified as core tests and all types of expendable holes related to hydrocarbon exploration. Stratigraphic test wells are classified as (i) *exploratory-type* if not drilled in a proved area, or (ii) *development-type* if drilled in a proved area.

The costs of offshore exploratory wells are accounted for in the same way as onshore exploratory wells. Under the successful efforts method, wells that find proved reserves are capitalized, and unsuccessful ones are charged to expense. A full cost company capitalizes all exploratory well costs.

A troublesome point for successful efforts companies relates to accounting for evaluation wells. Before production begins, a permanent platform must be built in order to drill development wells and install production equipment and storage. Before the high costs of construction can be justified, however, evaluation wells (usually stratigraphic wells) are drilled to determine whether adequate reserves are present. As discussed in Chapter 9 and under Oi5.125, companies using the successful efforts method may continue to defer costs of stratigraphic test wells that find oil and gas reserves in an area requiring a major capital expenditure (usually additional test wells and a production platform) before production can begin, only as long as: (1) the well has found a sufficient quantity of reserves to justify its completion as a producing well, and (2) the enterprise is making sufficient progress assessing the reserves and the economic and operating viability of the project. Otherwise, the stratigraphic test well is assumed to be impaired, and the cost is expensed.

Development Costs. The same rules of capitalization apply to offshore and onshore development costs. Again, a major difference is the magnitude of costs incurred and substantial costs of service facilities to be allocated to various offshore activities. Another difference is the timeline of offshore operations; from lease acquisition to first production, it often takes years rather than months.

Offshore development costs include stratigraphic test wells drilled into proved areas (whether or not successful). Stratigraphic test wells are frequently drilled to assist in determining the most favorable location for a permanent platform.

Depreciation, Depletion, and Amortization. To estimate the total quantity of proved reserves from an offshore project, wells may be drilled over several years from the permanent platform. Production from the earliest wells can commence long before the entire drilling program is completed. Under both the successful efforts and full cost methods, this extended development period raises a question about the time when both the capitalized acquisition, exploration, and development costs and related proved reserves should enter into the DD&A calculation.

Oi5.126 and Reg. S-X Rule 4-10(c)(3)(ii) provide rules for transferring such costs to the amortization base for successful efforts companies and full cost companies, respectively, as addressed in Chapters 17 and 19.

Removal and Restoration. One of the most interesting and important accounting issues related to offshore activities is the accrual of costs related to platform removal and reclamation. (See Chapter 20.) A number of factors cause accounting policies related to removal and restoration to differ among companies. Requirements vary in different parts of the world, and international requirements have not been firmly established. In addition, because of the long (and often uncertain) period between the time of installation of a facility and its ultimate removal, it is difficult to estimate the total cost.

Production Costs. Offshore production costs are charged to expense as incurred. A major element of such expenses can be the cost of operating support facilities both onshore and offshore. An offshore production cost not found in onshore activities is the cost of transporting the oil or gas to shore by pipeline, barge, or ship. Reg. S-X Rule 4-10(a)(1)(c) points out:

> ...the oil and gas production function shall normally be regarded as terminating at the outlet valve on the lease or field storage tank; if unusual physical or operational circumstances exist, it may be appropriate to regard the production functions as terminating at the first point at which oil, gas, or gas liquids are delivered to a main pipeline, a common carrier, a refinery, or a marine terminal.

Thus, the cost of transporting the product from the platform or well to shore and perhaps the costs of terminal facilities onshore are appropriately treated as production expenses.

Shared Facilities. It is common for the operator of a platform to sublet platform space or services to operators of smaller platforms in the area. For example, the operator of a marginal field may enter into an agreement for a nearby platform to handle or process fluids, or for a nearby operator to provide daily oversight.

ENHANCED RECOVERY[1]

Oil and gas recovery methods can be classified as two types: primary recovery and enhanced recovery. A broad definition of primary recovery includes all production when the reservoir's natural drive mechanism (water drive, dissolved gas drive, or gas cap drive) is the only source of energy, causing the reservoir contents to flow into the well bore.[2] Once in the well bore, primary production may: (1) flow freely up the well, (2) be pumped up, or (3) be lifted up utilizing natural gas lift. Enhanced recovery represents the production that results from an artificial reservoir drive, such as water flooding or gas injections, causing the reservoir contents to flow into the well bore.

Enhanced recovery methods are sometimes further divided into *secondary* and *tertiary* recovery.[3] The distinction between these two classes is rather inexact. Although for purposes of this chapter the distinction is not important, a secondary recovery project is defined as the first installation of an artificial drive mechanism to force the reservoir contents into the well bore. Tertiary recovery projects are those involving installation of a second artificial drive mechanism.

The efficiency of a reservoir's primary drive mechanism is dependent on many factors, including the:

1. physical geometry of the reservoir

2. physical and chemical composition of the reservoir rock and fluids

3. depth, temperature, and pressure of the reservoir

4. physical characteristics of the wells penetrating the reservoir

5. historical manner in which the reservoir has been produced

In oil reservoirs, it is rare for the primary recovery factor (the ratio of oil produced to original oil in place) to exceed 50 percent, and the average is probably around 25 to 30 percent. Enhanced oil recovery projects often result in a doubling of the recovery factor and occasionally result in total recovery factors in excess of 75 percent. Natural gas reservoirs routinely exceed 70 percent recovery factors and occasionally exceed 90 percent without any enhanced recovery techniques applied. Enhanced recovery efforts on gas reservoirs typically target additional gas liquids or condensate contained in the gas rather than the gas itself.

Enhanced recovery methods are capital-intensive and usually require an extended period of time from the first investment until additional production occurs. These techniques are not without risk. Projects may perform below expectations despite supportive engineering studies prior to the projects' implementation.

ENHANCED RECOVERY METHODS

Artificial stimulation of oil reservoirs has been used since the early twentieth century. Initial methods involved injection of water or natural gas into the reservoir. Later methods have included injection of chemicals, steam, and carbon dioxide (CO_2), and *in situ* combustion (a fire is started within the reservoir). A brief review of commonly encountered techniques will make the accounting issues more evident.

Water Injection. Water injection is a simple method of improving recovery from a reservoir. It may be put into effect as soon as production begins from the reservoir under pressure maintenance programs. If the water injection (called waterflooding) is begun before natural reservoir pressure declines significantly, it does not represent a true secondary recovery method.

Water injection serves two functions: (1) it provides a means for disposing of water produced from the reservoir along with the oil and gas, and (2) it increases total productivity by flushing oil out of the rock. Water is forced through properly located injection wells into the reservoir and through the reservoir rock into the productive wells, carrying oil along with it. Waterflood projects commonly use a five-spot pattern, which is depicted in Figure 32-1.

Water injected (or reinjected) into the reservoir must be similar or identical to the water found in the reservoir and must be clear, noncorrosive, and free of materials that might plug the oil-bearing formation. If water produced from the reservoir or other subsurface sources is used, it contains little oxygen, and minimal treatment is required. However, if surface water is used, it may be high in oxygen content and also contain incompatible chemicals. Thus, the facilities needed for a water injection program may include not only injection wells and pumps, but also systems for deaeration, filtration, chemical treatment, and testing.[4]

Chemical Injection. Water flows through a reservoir more easily than oil due to its lower viscosity. In waterflood situations, injected water can sometimes channel past the oil, greatly reducing the effectiveness of the waterflood project. In this case, long-chain polymers called viscosifiers can be added to the water. The thickened water does not push past the oil as easily and results in better sweep efficiency of the oil in the reservoir. Due to the cost and quantity of chemical additives needed, and the narrow range of conditions where such projects are feasible, polymer floods, as they are commonly known, are relatively rare.

Figure 32-1
Five-Spot Waterflood Pattern

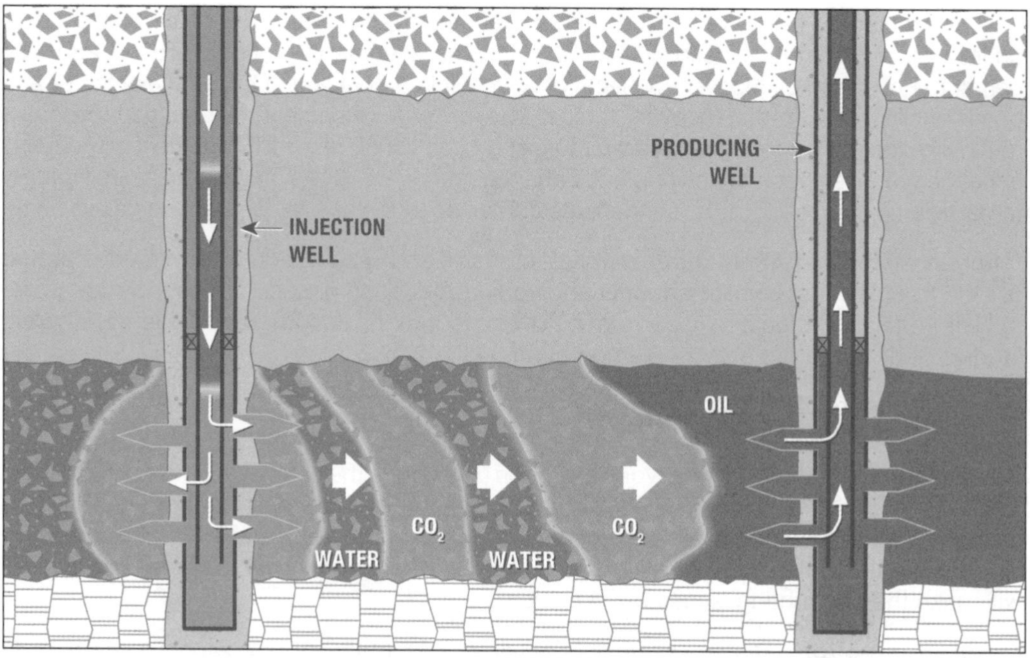

Gas Injection. Gas produced from a reservoir can be reinjected into the reservoir if there is no market for the gas or if it will increase the ultimate recovery of oil or condensate. If no pipeline exists and regulators will not allow the gas to be flared, operators often reinject it. (See Chapter 11 for additional details.)

Reinjection enhances the current production of valuable oil or condensate. An advantage is the gas can be produced at a future time when a pipeline may exist. In some situations, the reinjection of gas maintains an oil reservoir's pressure above a critical threshold called the bubble point. The bubble point is dependent on the pressure, temperature, and chemical composition of the oil and gas in a particular reservoir. When pressure is above the bubble point, all gas in the reservoir is absorbed in the crude oil and is said to be in solution. When pressure falls below the bubble point, gas bubbles out of the solution, much like the bubbles that form when a carbonated beverage is opened. If reservoir pressure can be maintained above the bubble point, ultimate oil recoveries are generally much higher.

In gas reservoirs that contain condensate, the corollary to the bubble point is called the dew point. Above the dew point, all condensate in the reservoir exists as gas. When the reservoir pressure falls below the dew point, the condensate can liquefy in the reservoir, reducing the ultimate recovery of both condensate and gas. In a gas cycling operation, the lean gas (the resulting gas stream after it has passed through the separators and condensate has been removed) is reinjected into the reservoir where it maintains pressure and absorbs condensate, increasing the ultimate recovery.

In both examples, the reinjected gas can be part or all of the production, or additional gas can be obtained to provide the necessary volume. At some point, the incremental recovery of oil or condensate does not cover the additional expense of the compressors and related facilities necessary for reinjection. The process will cease and any excess gas is sold. This is often called the blowdown phase.

Enriched Gas and Miscible Injection. Propane or butane mixed with natural gas (known as enriched gas) or carbon dioxide (CO_2) can be injected into an oil reservoir. Enriched gas or CO_2 acts as a **miscible solvent** when it contacts oil. The oil absorbs the rich gas or CO_2, reducing the oil's viscosity and enhancing the oil's ability to flow. Reduced viscosity and increased pressure from injection increase the ultimate recovery factor. The solvent is usually removed during separation and reinjected. The cost of propane or butane limits the number of enriched gas projects. Miscible CO_2 projects are also expensive, but are relatively common in areas where they have been shown to work well, particularly in West Texas and New Mexico. A common technique is known as WAG (water and gas, or water alternating gas), in which a volume of CO_2 is injected, followed by a volume of water to displace it. This procedure achieves the desired effect at a lower cost.

Thermal Stimulation. In reservoirs containing oil with high viscosity (generally heavy oil with high density such as API gravity below 20 degrees), it may be possible to stimulate production by heating the contents of the reservoir. Hot water or steam is injected as depicted in Figure 32-1. The water or steam lowers the viscosity and flushes the oil to the producing well. Steam may be continuously injected, or a cyclic steam injection process can be used called huff-and-puff. In huff-and-puff, steam is injected periodically into the reservoir. As the steam condenses, the resulting hot water thins the oil and drives it to the well bore. Another injection of steam follows and the huff-and-puff cycle continues until the reservoir is heated. Continuous steam flooding and huff-and-puff steam injection are quite common in fields containing heavy oil near Bakersfield, California. Steam flooding operations provide significant markets for natural gas. The gas is burned in co-generation facilities that generate: (1) heat to convert water to steam, and (2) electricity used onsite or sold to a local electric utility.

Another thermal process is *in situ* (or fireflooding) combustion. Air is injected into the reservoir, and a fire is ignited that burns some of the oil residing in it. As the reservoir heats up, the heavy oil is supposed to flow into the producing well. *In situ* combustion is used only when other stimulation methods are not feasible, as results have been relatively poor.

Other Methods. The enhanced recovery methods discussed in this chapter are used on most projects around the world, but not all of them. Other types that might be encountered include heating of the reservoir by electrical currents, introduction of anaerobic bacteria to convert a portion of the hydrocarbons to gases to repressurize the reservoir, or repressurization using nitrogen or combustion flue gases.

ACCOUNTING ISSUES RELATED TO ENHANCED RECOVERY

Two major accounting issues derive from the use of enhanced recovery techniques: (1) determining when the related reserves are to be included in the reserves disclosures and amortization calculation, and (2) accounting for material injected into the reservoir. Costs incurred to install enhanced recovery facilities, including the cost to drill injection wells, are properly capitalized as wells and related equipment and facilities. These costs are amortized as the related reserves are produced. In computing amortization of enhanced recovery facilities, a successful efforts company includes such costs in the property or field's total developed costs to be amortized over the cost center's total proved developed reserves (which have been increased by the incremental proved developed reserves added by the enhanced recovery operation).

Reg. S-X Rule 4-10(a)(2), (3), and (4) place limits on recognizing proved reserves from enhanced recovery techniques:

> ...Reserves which can be produced economically through application of improved recovery techniques (such as **fluid injection** [bold added]) are included in the "proved" classification when successful testing by a pilot project, or the operation of an installed program in the reservoir, provides support for the engineering analysis on which the project or program was based....Additional oil and gas expected to be obtained through the application of fluid injection or other improved recovery techniques for supplementing the natural forces and mechanisms of primary recovery should be included as "proved developed reserves" only after testing by a pilot project or after the operation of an installed program has confirmed through production response that increased recovery will be achieved....Under no circumstances should estimates for proved undeveloped reserves be attributable to any acreage for which an application of fluid injection or other improved recovery technique is contemplated, unless such techniques have been proved effective by actual tests in the area and in the same reservoir.

The reference to "in the area and in the same reservoir" seems to mean simply in the same reservoir based on SEC staff interpretations that such language, consistent with Reg. S-X Rule 4-10(a), paragraph (2)(ii), limits the comparable program to one in the same reservoir. As noted in Chapter 16, the Society of Petroleum Engineers' definition of proved undeveloped reserves requires only that such tests or operations have been successful in a reservoir in the immediate area with similar rock and fluid properties. However, the industry definition of proved undeveloped reserves remains unacceptable to the SEC and for financial reporting under FAS 25, which requires the SEC definition in Reg. S-X Rule 4-10 to be used.

For a full cost company, enhanced recovery facilities are amortized as part of the total cost of the countrywide cost pool. It is appropriate to exclude the capital costs of recovery projects from the amortization calculation until the reserves to be added by the project have been classified as proved or when the project is considered unsuccessful.

Problems in accounting for materials injected into the reservoir have been discussed in Chapter 13. If none of the materials are recoverable, these costs may be charged to expense at the same time they are injected, or if they are deemed to be of benefit over the life of the entire project, the costs may be capitalized and amortized along with the wells and related facilities. If some part of the materials is recoverable, the portion of cost related to the recoverable product can be treated separately as an inventory item. This type of cost is not charged immediately to expense and is not amortized. As the injected product is deemed to be produced, its costs are then charged to expense. Another approach is to treat the cost of the recoverable material in the same way as the nonrecoverable material. Both approaches are used in practice.

In the long run it is almost certain that oil added through enhanced recovery will become a more important part of U.S. oil supplies.

TAX INCENTIVES FOR ENHANCED RECOVERY

As discussed at the end of Chapter 26, Section 43 of the Internal Revenue Code provides for an enhanced oil recovery tax credit equal to 15 percent of qualified EOR costs for tertiary recovery projects in U.S. oil fields. If EOR credits are claimed, the otherwise deductible costs associated with the EOR are reduced by the amount of the EOR tax credit. Thus, if a taxpayer's tax rate is 35%, a $100,000 EOR tax credit is partially offset by taking away $100,000 in deductions (causing an increase in taxes of $35,000). This results in an ultimate reduction of taxes of $65,000, not $100,000.

• • •

---

1 The authors acknowledge the contributions of ARCO engineer D.J. Charlton, former manager of the Dallas Projects Group, ARCO Resources Technology, to the section of this chapter dealing with the technical aspects of enhanced recovery.

2 In rare instances, gravity can be a significant natural drive mechanism.

3 Secondary recovery is often viewed as water flooding, whereas more exotic recovery methods classified as tertiary recovery may be employed in some reservoirs that were never subjected to secondary recovery.

4 Deaeration reduces the water's oxygen content to reduce corrosion.

33

RISK MANAGEMENT ACTIVITIES

Key Concepts:

• Overview of risk management issues

• Enterprise-wide risk management

• Risk frameworks

• Areas of risk for E&P companies

• Types of derivatives and associated risks in E&P companies

Understanding and addressing the inherent risks in various business environments are critical components of strategic leadership. This chapter provides an overview of enterprise-wide risk management, its importance to E&P organizations, and the consequences for petroleum accounting.

Successful risk management includes an appropriate assessment of the accounting and information needs of a company and its stakeholders. Yet, risk management involves much more than a simple focus on internal controls. Chapter 3 can be referenced for a discussion of internal control and audit frameworks with E&P companies.

RISK

The *Merriam Webster Dictionary* defines risk as "exposure to possible loss or injury." In reality, the term risk is used in different ways depending on the activity under discussion.

Every organization faces some level of uncertainty. Uncertainty creates both risks and opportunities, which can either erode the value of a company or enhance it. This is especially true for E&P companies that seek to manage a plethora of risks: exploration, competitive, market, financial, operating, technology, environmental, regulatory, litigation, and political.

WHAT IS RISK MANAGEMENT?

The ability to develop processes and controls that minimize the negative impact of risks is commonly referred to as risk management. An organization can focus on individual elements of risk, such as financial risk management or political risk management, or it can take a more holistic approach. Enterprise Risk Management (ERM) is a comprehensive, systematic approach for helping organizations identify, measure, and prioritize their risks, and respond to the risks that could challenge critical objectives and operations.

ERM helps a company decide how much risk it can manage, or wants to manage, given the needs of its stakeholders. It provides enhanced capabilities to align risk appetite with the organization's strategy. By successfully managing risks, an organization can improve its performance and better protect itself from pitfalls. Thus, ERM is an integral and essential component of a risk and value-based management framework.

RISK FRAMEWORKS FOR PETROLEUM ACCOUNTANTS

In 2004, the accounting industry was presented with an official framework for applying ERM by The Committee of Sponsoring Organizations of the Treadway Commission (COSO). COSO's Integrated Framework describes the essential components, principles and concepts of ERM. A holistic approach, it applies to the activities at all levels within the organization.

ERM utilizes a portfolio view of the organization and its risks. The three-dimensional framework begins by identifying the organization's objectives in terms of Strategic, Operational, Reporting and Compliance goals. Figure 33-1 illustrates these objectives along with the eight interrelated components of the framework. Descriptions of the framework's eight components are summarized in Figure 33-2.

In May 2002, U.S. energy companies announced the formation of The Committee of Chief Risk Officers (CCRO). "The Committee is composed of Chief Risk Officers from leading companies that are active in both physical and financial energy trading and marketing. They are committed to opening channels of communication and establishing best practices for risk management in the industry."
– www.ccro.org, June 11, 2007

Figure 33-1
COSO Risk Management Framework

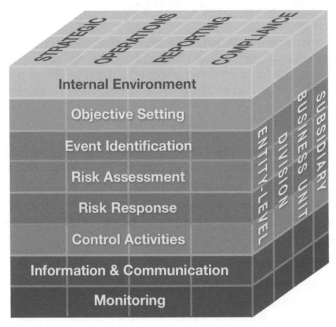

Figure 33-2
Components of COSO Framework

Component	Purpose
Internal Environment	A successful ERM program sets a tone from the top of the organization; it establishes and communicates a risk management philosophy that becomes the entity's risk culture.
Objective Setting	Management must first specify the objectives of the risk management program before it can identify risks and take the necessary actions to manage them. Objectives should align with the entity's mission and strategy, and be consistent with its risk appetite and risk tolerance level. Measurable objectives are set at the strategic level, establishing a basis for operations, reporting, and compliance objectives.
Event Identification	While identified events can range from the obvious to the obscure, they are equally important. Internal or external incidences that could affect strategy and achievement of objectives are identified. The distinction between risk and opportunity is made during event identification.
Risk Assessment	Risk assessment is perhaps the most critical aspect of the framework. Risks are assessed from two perspectives—likelihood and impact (or significance). Likelihood represents the possibility a given event will occur, while impact represents its effects. The likelihood of an event can be expressed in: (1) qualitative terms such as high, medium and low or other judgmental scales; or (2) as a quantitative measure such as a percentage, frequency of occurrence, or other numerical metric. The impact of an event can be described in terms such as expected or worst-case value, or a range or distribution. Units of measure for assessing risks should be the same units used for measuring related objectives (see Figure 33-3).

Component	Purpose
Risk Response	The next step involves identifying and evaluating possible responses to risk. Typical responses include risk avoidance, reduction, sharing, and acceptance. The evaluation of risk responses are based on: (1) assessment of the cost versus the benefit of potential risk responses, and (2) the effect of potential risk responses on risk likelihood and their impacts.
Control Activities	Control activities involve the policies and procedures that help ensure the risk responses are carried out. All levels of the organization should participate in developing and implementing these policies and procedures.
Information and Communication	All relevant information should be identified, captured, and communicated. The form and timeframe used should enable people to carry out their responsibilities. Information can originate from internal and external sources, and include both financial and non-financial aspects. It should be appropriate, timely, current, accurate, and accessible.
Monitoring	A monitoring program to observe and measure the effectiveness of the ERM components allows management to evaluate and improve upon its risk management activities. The monitoring program should be an ongoing process.

Figure 33-3
Risk Assessment Likelihood and Impact

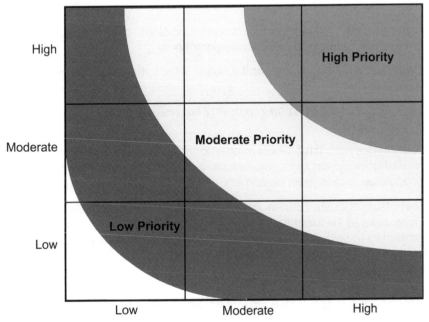

RISK IN AN EXPLORATION & PRODUCTION COMPANY

Many business decisions are driven by an assessment of risks. For an E&P company, risk-taking is an asset, and like all assets, it should be managed.

An E&P company buys many leases expecting to drill successful wells and some dry holes. It strives to discover enough oil and gas to be sold at an adequate profit for the overall exploration and production effort. Leases (and the associated risks) are purchased on the assumption that opportunities will outweigh hazards. Buying several leases and entering into joint venture agreements reduce the risk of little or no success. However, exposure to unexpected events is always present, such as the occurrence of a well blowout or local citizens who rally to keep a company's new offshore discovery from being produced.

Risk is inherent in virtually every business action and inaction. It cannot be eliminated entirely and is a natural part of business success. In fact, a risk-averse organization frequently does not survive as new markets, products, and responses quickly pass it by.

AREAS OF RISK

Broad areas of risk exist for every company and its stakeholders. Risks must be recognized in order to be managed, and recognition requires an awareness of stakeholders who may be affected.

A stakeholder is defined as any group or individual that affects or is affected by achievement of a company's objectives. Stakeholders include shareholders, creditors, employees, governments, communities in which a company operates, and even the world when a company's activities have an impact on general prosperity. The long-term viability of a company partly depends on intelligent, balanced service to its stakeholders.

Risks can be categorized in a variety of ways. The most common risks found in petroleum companies include:

- *Strategic risks* arising from corporate decisions on mergers, acquisitions, geographic focus, and other strategic actions.

- *Financial risks* concerning capital costs, information systems, and employee fraud.

- *Operational risks* occurring in property acquisition, exploration, development, and production.

- *Compliance risks* which exist in attempting to conduct business according to myriad government laws, regulations, and contracts dealing with exploration, production, employees, customers, taxation, and environmental safety.

The petroleum industry continues to experience significant changes, and each one brings new risks to be identified and addressed. Trends such as globalization have led U.S. companies to seek business in areas of the world where opportunities exist for major discoveries. Yet, kidnappings and guerilla warfare can be among the hazards of doing business in these areas.

IMPORTANCE OF RISK MANAGEMENT TO THE E&P INDUSTRY

The foundation of the E&P industry is the management of risks. As wells deplete and dry holes occur, new reserves must be found. A typical E&P company must focus on adding reserves value in order to be successful. There are many strategies for managing risks to add reserves value including:

- Acquisition of lease rights in promising areas to improve opportunities for exploratory success

- Use of the most suitable exploration technology

- Spreading risk and gaining expertise via joint venture arrangements

- Hedging oil and gas prices in line with management directives

- Sophisticated approaches to valuing reserves

- Strong engineering oversight of production

- Geological, engineering, and management personnel with technical, financial, and risk management perspectives

- Creative and assorted financing arrangements to provide capital at the lowest cost for the degree of retained risks of property ownership

Given the: (a) core nature of the industry to explore, (b) volatility of petroleum prices and exploratory success, (c) industry issues of globalization and global warming, and (d) rapid and substantial technology changes, a strong risk management process throughout an E&P company should be of significant benefit and importance.

IMPACT OF RISK MANAGEMENT ON PETROLEUM ACCOUNTING

Risk management drives many of the events and transactions petroleum accountants must address, including:

- Use of joint venture arrangements to manage risk at the expense of complicating petroleum accounting

- Globalization to enhance corporate opportunities at the expense of requiring additional or specialized accounting systems and policies for new foreign locations

- Creative financing arrangements such as conveyances of volumetric production payments, which can necessitate special petroleum accounting

- Development and use of standardized forms, contracts, and joint venture protocols, such as COPAS accounting exhibits, gas balancing agreements, EDI (Electronic Data Interchange) standards, joint venture audits, and material transfer accounting procedures

- Enhanced, secure internet communications of accounting transactions

- Hedge accounting

- Internal and external financial and tax reporting

- Internal auditing

Petroleum accounting is a key element of risk management for an E&P company. As a company's risk management program increases in importance and sophistication, so should the company's accounting department.

DERIVATIVES IN A RISK MANAGEMENT PROGRAM

Exploration and production, marketing, pipeline, refining, and utility companies, as well as large industrial consumers, use derivatives in their operations. Energy derivatives are widely used to hedge risks associated with oil and gas pricing. Investors and companies that speculate on the movement of commodity prices also utilize them.

Derivatives are financial instruments whose values are derived from the value of an underlying asset, reference rate, or index. Oil and gas companies typically use futures, forwards, options, and swaps. Derivatives designed specifically for the energy industry have existed for several years. The New York Mercantile Exchange (NYMEX) crude oil and natural gas futures contracts have been in existence since 1983 and 1990, respectively.

The media and regulators have paid a great deal of attention to derivatives in recent years. Several prominent companies have generated significant losses in the industry. In 2001, the world saw the collapse of one of the largest commodity derivates dealers—Enron Corporation.

> "The story of derivatives in the energy industry and the accounting for them is incomplete without an examination of the ways in which Enron and other companies have used derivatives for purposes other than risk management, such as managing reported earnings, and for other financial engineering goals, such as hiding debt. Such accounting and financial engineering objectives may have been responsible for at least some of the explosive growth in the derivatives markets in the late 1990s.... Since the Enron debacle, the SEC, the FERC, and debt-service agencies such as Moody's have required energy traders to disclose information about transactions.... As a result, it is likely that the potential for abuse of derivatives to hide loans will be considerably reduced in the future."
>
> – *Energy Information Administration, "Derivatives and Risk Management in the Petroleum, Natural Gas, and Electricity Industries," http://www.eia.doe.gov/oiaf/servicerpt/derivative/chapter5.html*

COMMON TYPES OF COMMODITY-BASED DERIVATIVE INSTRUMENTS

FUTURES

A **futures contract** can be defined as an exchange-traded legal contract to buy or sell a standard quantity and quality of a commodity at a specified future date and price. Both crude oil and natural gas futures contracts are traded on NYMEX, with other exchanges developing similar contracts. A standard NYMEX crude oil futures contract is for 1,000 bbls for delivery in Cushing, Oklahoma, while a standard NYMEX natural gas futures contract is for 10,000 MMBtu for delivery at the Henry Hub in southern Louisiana.

Futures contracts protect against adverse price changes or losses on existing assets. They may be used to speculate on upward and downward price movements of underlying commodities. Futures contracts are subject to regulation by the Commodities Futures Trading Commission (CFTC).

The purchaser of a futures contract has a long position, and the seller of a futures contract has a short position. Buyers/sellers of futures contracts can easily liquidate their positions by selling/buying an offsetting contract for the same delivery month. Most crude oil and gas futures contracts are settled in this manner, as opposed to delivering or receiving oil or gas at the exchange delivery points. Buyers/sellers may also settle their futures positions by exchanging for physicals as discussed in Chapter 12.

Transactions are typically executed through a commodity futures brokerage firm. Initial margin deposits of cash or cash equivalents are required for futures contracts. If the value of the futures contract decreases by a significant amount, the customer must deposit additional funds to restore the original margin account amount. The exchange acts as a clearinghouse between buyers and sellers of futures contracts, guarantees contract performance, and assumes all counterparty credit risk.

FORWARD CONTRACTS

Like a futures contract, a **forward contract** is a legal contract between two parties to purchase and sell a specific quantity and quality of a commodity at a specified price, with delivery and settlement at a specified future date.[1] Oil and gas forward contracts, however, are not traded on regulated commodity exchanges. The contracts are privately negotiated agreements referred to as over-the-counter (OTC) contracts. Consequently, they lack the liquidity and minimal credit risk exposure offered by exchange-traded futures contracts. However, forward contracts are more flexible than futures contracts because they can be tailored to specific quantities, settlement dates, and delivery points. Like futures contracts, forward contracts can be used for both hedging and speculating.

OPTIONS

Option contracts give the holder a right, but not an obligation, to buy (call) or sell (put) a specified item at a fixed price (exercise or strike price) during a specified period (exercise period). The buyer (holder) pays a nonrefundable fee (premium) to the seller (writer). Options are either exchange-traded (such as NYMEX options on the NYMEX crude oil futures contract) or OTC contracts. OTC options expose the holder to counterparty default. Options can be used for both hedge and speculative purposes.

Call Example. On June 1, 2005, Optimistic Oil, Inc., pays Pessimistic Corporation a $500 premium for an over-the-counter call option to buy from Pessimistic by May 1, 2006, 1,000 barrels of West Texas Intermediate (WTI) crude oil at $60 per barrel. If by May 1, 2006, the spot price of WTI remains less than $60 per barrel, Optimistic's call is unexercised and expires as worthless. Alternatively, assume on April 15, 2006, the spot price is $62 per barrel. Optimistic, as holder, exercises the call option by paying $60,000 to Pessimistic (the call option writer) in return for the 1,000 barrels worth $62,000. In that case, the call option costing Optimistic $500 would provide, upon exercise, a profit to Optimistic of $1,500 before transaction expenses. Pessimistic loses a net $1,500 from writing the exercised call option. Usually, option contracts are settled on a net cash basis without physical delivery of the commodity.

Put Example. Assume GoingUp, Inc., sold an OTC put option for 1,000 barrels of WTI crude at $60 per barrel exercisable on or before May 1, 2006. GoingDown, Inc., pays a $400 premium to buy the put option. It gives GoingDown the right to sell 1,000 barrels to GoingUp for $60,000. On March 18, 2006, assuming the WTI price had fallen to $58/bbl, GoingDown exercises the put option by selling 1,000 barrels of WTI to GoingUp for $60,000 for a net profit of $1,600 after the $400 cost of the premium.

The option buyer's risk is limited to the amount of premium paid. Because an option is a right and not an obligation, the holder can profit from favorable price movements in the item underlying the option. The writer of an option bears the risk of an unfavorable change in the price of the item underlying the option. Similarly, the writer of a naked option (i.e., the writer does not own the item underlying the option) is exposed to losses substantially greater than the premium received.

Naked Option Example. Paul Pessimistic writes a naked call option on crude oil at a price of $60 per barrel and receives a premium of $1 per barrel. When war breaks out in a key oil-producing region and the price of crude oil goes up to $70 per barrel, the option is exercised. Paul Pessimistic must buy crude oil at $70 per barrel, sell it for $60 per barrel, and take a loss (after the $1/bbl premium) of $9 per barrel.

There are several terms unique to the use of options. Depending on whether a call option's strike price is less than, equal to, or greater than the commodity's current price, the call option is considered to be in-the-money, at-the-money, or out-of-the-money, respectively. In contrast, when a put option's strike price is less than, equal to, or greater than the commodity's price, then the put option is considered to be out-of-the-money, at-the-money, or in-the-money, respectively.

The value of an option is derived primarily from its intrinsic and time values as well as the underlying commodity's volatility. The extent to which an option is in-the-money is its intrinsic value. Consequently, intrinsic value is never a negative amount. The time value of an option represents the portion of the premium in excess of the option's intrinsic value due to the possibility the option can move in-the-money during the exercise period. Volatility refers to the amount a commodity's price fluctuates. More volatile commodities are more likely to move in-the-money during an exercise period. Higher intrinsic values, longer exercise periods, and greater price volatility of the underlying commodity result in higher option premiums and risks. American options can be exercised at any time during the exercise period. European options are exercised only at the end of the exercise period. A payoff for Asian options is linked to the average value of the underlying commodity on a specific set of dates during the life of the option.

SWAPS

Swaps are contracts between two parties to exchange variable and fixed-rate payment streams based on a specified contract principal or notional amount. For instance, two companies may enter into a natural gas price swap which requires one company (the fixed-price payor) to pay a fixed price and another company (the variable-price payor) to pay based upon a published gas index or futures contract settlement price. The volume of gas (e.g., 1,000 MMBtu per month for six months) used to calculate the variable and fixed-rate payment is the contract principal or notional amount. The settlement amount of these contracts is typically calculated as the difference between the fixed and variable prices multiplied by the notional volume. A net payment is made to one of the parties.

Swap contracts are more flexible than futures contracts because they can be tailored for specific quantities, settlement dates, and locations. Swap agreements are OTC contracts and therefore expose the parties to counterparty credit risk (i.e., the other party may be unable to pay or honor the contract). Consequently, parties to swap agreements may require margin deposits. Swaps are used primarily for hedging purposes or to alter the terms of an existing agreement.

Swap Example. On January 1, 2006, Lockin, Inc., seeks to lock in its sale of gas to third parties for 2006 and 2007. Skyhigh, Inc., has previously agreed to sell its natural gas production at a fixed price to a cogeneration facility over the next two years; however, now it is optimistic that gas prices will increase substantially.

On January 1, 2006, Lockin and Skyhigh agree to enter into a natural gas swap for 2006 and 2007 with the following terms:

- Volume: 10,000 MMBtu per day

- Fixed price: $6.60/MMBtu

- Variable price: average monthly spot price published by a third party

- Skyhigh will pay Lockin the fixed price and Lockin will pay Skyhigh the variable price.

- Payments are made at the end of the month following the month of gas sales.

As a result of the agreement, Skyhigh will pay cash to Lockin for the excess of the $6.60/MMBtu fixed price over the average monthly spot price. Alternatively, Lockin will pay cash to Skyhigh for the excess of the average monthly spot price over the $6.60/MMBtu fixed price.

On January 31, 2007, the average monthly spot price for January 2007 settled to $7.00:

Fixed Price	Average Monthly Spot Price for January 2007	Difference	Payment by Lockin to Skyhigh
$6.60/MMBtu	$7.00/MMBtu	$.40/MMBtu	$124,000 **

** $124,000 = [($7.00/MMBtu average monthly spot price - $6.60/MMBtu fixed price) x 10,000 MMBtu/day x 31 days]

Lockin will pay Skyhigh $124,000 for the settlement of the swap by February 28, 2007. If Lockin sells 10,000 MMBtu at $7.00/MMBtu to its third parties, the swap would reduce Lockin's effective price to $6.60/MMBtu as follows:

Sales to third parties ($7.00/MMBtu x 10,000 MMBtu x 31 days)	$ 2,170,000
Settlement of swap	(124,000)
Net sales for Lockin	$ 2,046,000
Net sales for Lockin per MMBtu ($2,046,000/31 days/10,000 MMBtu)	$6.60

If Skyhigh sold 10,000 MMBtu at $6.60/MMBtu to the cogeneration plant, the swap would increase Skyhigh's effective price to $7.00/MMBtu as follows:

Sale to cogeneration facility ($6.60/MMBtu x 10,000 MMBtu x 31 days)	$ 2,046,000
Settlement of swap	124,000
Net sales for Skyhigh	$ 2,170,000
Net sales for Skyhigh per MMBtu ($2,171,000/31 days/10,000 MMBtu)	$7.00

If on February 28, 2007, the average monthly spot price for February 2007 settled at $6.10, then the following would occur:

Fixed Price	Average Monthly Spot Price for February 2007	Difference	Payment by Skyhigh to Lockin
$6.60/MMBtu	$6.10/MMBtu	$.50/MMBtu	$140,000 **

** $140,000 = [($6.10/MMBtu average monthly spot price - $6.60/MMBtu fixed price) x 10,000 MMBtu/day x 28 days]

Skyhigh will pay Lockin $140,000 for the settlement of the swap by March 31, 2007. If Lockin sold 10,000 MMBtu at $6.10/MMBtu to its third parties, the swap would increase Lockin's effective price to $6.60/MMBtu as follows:

Sales to third parties ($6.10/MMBtu x 10,000 MMBtu x 28 days)	$ 1,708,000
Settlement of swap	140,000
Net sales for Lockin	$ 1,848,000
Net sales for Lockin per MMBtu ($1,848,000/28 days/10,000 MMBtu)	$6.60

If Skyhigh sold 10,000 MMBtu at $6.60/MMBtu to the cogeneration plant, the swap would decrease Skyhigh's effective price to $6.10/MMBtu as follows:

Sale to cogeneration facility ($6.60/MMBtu x 10,000 MMBtu x 28 days)	$ 1,848,000
Settlement of swap	(140,000)
Net sales for Skyhigh	$ 1,708,000
Net sales for Skyhigh per MMBtu ($1,708,000/28 days/10,000 MMBtu)	$6.10

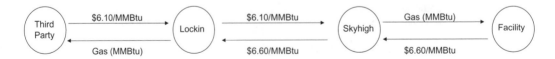

In conclusion, the swap effectively locks in a $6.60/MMBtu price for Lockin on 10,000 MMBtu/day for two years, whereas Skyhigh effectively receives a price that fluctuates with spot gas prices.

USES OF DERIVATIVES IN THE ENERGY INDUSTRY

Exploration and production companies that sell their production at index prices can protect a portion of their oil and gas reserves from downward price movements by effectively fixing the sales price of their reserves production using futures, forwards, and swaps. Producers create floors by purchasing put options that guarantee minimum oil or gas prices. E&P companies also create **collars** by selling a call option and buying a put option on their production. A collar effectively fixes the realized price between the strike prices of the put and call options. When the premium received for the call equals the premium paid for the put, the collar is known as a zero-cost collar.

FLOOR EXAMPLE

Lowrisk, Inc., buys a put option for $5,000 to sell 10,000 WTI oil barrels at $58.00/bbl when the spot price of such oil is $60.00/bbl. If the spot price drops to $56.00/bbl Lowrisk's production would be sold at $56.00/bbl, except that Lowrisk can exercise the put option to sell 10,000 barrels for $58.00/bbl. After the $5,000 cost of the put ($.50 per contract barrel), Lowrisk has created a $57.50 net floor price for 10,000 barrels of its production.

ZERO-COST COLLAR EXAMPLE

In addition to buying the put option, suppose Lowrisk sold a call option for $5,000 allowing the holder to buy 10,000 barrels at $63.00/bbl from Lowrisk. Now Lowrisk receives a $0.50/bbl call premium offset by the $0.50/bbl cost of the put option, and Lowrisk has created a ceiling price of $63.00/bbl for 10,000 barrels of production. If the price goes above $63.00/bbl, the call holder exercises the call and pays only $63.00/bbl to Lowrisk for the 10,000 barrels. By buying a put for $5,000 and selling a call for $5,000 to create a zero-cost collar, Lowrisk has reduced the price range for 10,000 barrels of production to a range of $58.00 to $63.00 per barrel. If prices are very volatile, both options might be exercised over the exercise time period: Lowrisk would sell 10,000 barrels at $58.00/bbl and an additional 10,000 barrels at $63.00/bbl, for an average price of $60.50/bbl.

Companies enter into these types of transactions for several reasons:

- to maintain a desired level of profitability during periods of falling prices
- to achieve a desired internal rate of return on investments
- to obtain additional financing from financial institutions

Derivatives are popular instruments for marketing, pipeline, refining, and utility companies, as well as large industrial consumers. For instance, a gas marketing company, which buys gas from producers at spot prices, may offer its customers fixed-price sales contracts. The company is exposed to price risk because an increase in supply spot prices in excess of the fixed sales contract prices results in losses. It can effectively fix its supply cost by purchasing futures contracts or using other derivative financial instruments. Likewise, pipeline, refining, and utility companies as well as large industrial consumers effectively fix their fuel costs by using derivative contracts.

RISKS ASSOCIATED WITH DERIVATIVES

Although derivatives can be effectively used to protect companies from adverse commodity price movements, significant risks are associated with them.

PRICE RISK

Because of the volatility of oil and gas prices, producers are exposed to the risk that prices will decline. If derivatives are used to hedge this exposure, risk management activities should be performed by knowledgeable personnel with good understanding of a company's price risks and the terms of the derivatives/financial instruments used to reduce this risk. Poor risk management strategy can result in increased exposure to volatile oil and gas prices.

CREDIT RISK

Similar to other financial instruments, derivatives expose a company to credit risk. Credit risk is the risk a loss may occur from the failure of another party (counterparty) to perform according to contract terms. It includes not only the net payable or receivable outstanding, but also the cost of replacing a derivative contract if the counterparty defaults. Counterparty credit risk is further concentrated when companies enter into multiple derivative contracts with the same counterparty or counterparties in the same geographic location or industry. Credit risk is generally lower if the derivative is an exchange-traded contract. Exposure to credit risk can be further minimized by requiring collateral or margin deposits.

LIQUIDITY RISK

Liquidity risk results from the inability to easily purchase or sell derivative contracts in required quantities at a fair price. Fair prices may not be available when there are large discrepancies between the bid price (buyer's price) and the asking price (seller's price). Exchange-traded derivatives are generally more liquid than over-the-counter derivatives.

CORRELATION RISK

Correlation risk is a risk the commodity price in the derivative contract will not move in tandem with the commodity price being hedged. Consequently, an increase in the value of a derivative transaction might not fully offset the decrease in the value of the hedged item, or vice versa. When deciding whether to hedge a risk, a key factor is whether there is an expected high correlation between anticipated changes in the market value of the hedging instrument and market value of the hedged item, and whether that correlation is likely to continue throughout the hedging period.

BASIS

Basis is the difference between the spot price of a hedged item and the price of the hedging instrument. Basis is sometimes referred to as the spread. Because the prices received for oil and gas vary by location, quality, local supply/demand conditions, and other factors, the commodity price of a hedge contract frequently does not equal the spot price received for the production.

ACCOUNTING GUIDANCE

In June 1998, the FASB issued Statement of Financial Accounting Standards No. 133 (FAS 133), *Accounting for Derivative Instruments and Hedging Activities*. It represents a comprehensive framework of accounting rules that standardizes and creates uniform accounting for derivatives. All entities and all types of derivatives are subject to the rules of FAS 133.

Under FAS 133, all derivatives must be recognized on the balance sheet at fair value with an offsetting entry related to unrealized gains and (or) losses reflected either: (1) as part of current earnings, or (2) in other comprehensive income, which is a component of stockholders' equity. These modifications eliminate the practice of synthetic-instrument and off-balance sheet accounting.

The ultimate goal of the FASB was to increase the visibility of derivatives and require hedge ineffectiveness to be recorded in earnings. The adoption of FAS 133 resulted in an increase in earnings and equity volatility as well as an increase in the number of derivative contracts included in the balance sheet accounts for many E&P entities.

As a result of the complexity of FAS 133, FASB created the Derivatives Implementation Group (DIG). DIG was a task force to assist the FASB in answering questions as companies implemented and interpreted FAS 133. The objective in forming the group was to establish a mechanism to identify and resolve significant implementation questions in advance of adoption of the standard by many companies.

In June 2000, the FASB issued FAS 138, *Accounting for Certain Derivative Instruments and Certain Hedging Activities, an Amendment to FASB Statement No. 133*. For E&P companies, a notable provision of FAS 138 is to allow certain contracts to avoid being considered derivatives. Contracts that contain net settlement provisions qualify for the normal purchases and sales exception if it is probable at inception, and throughout the term of the individual contract, the contract will not settle net and will result in physical delivery. In April 2003, FASB issued FAS 149, *Amendment of Statement 133 on Derivative Instruments and Hedging Activities*, which amends and clarifies FAS 133 for certain decisions made by the FASB as part of the DIG process.

DEFINITION OF A DERIVATIVE

A derivative is defined as a financial instrument or other contract that possess all three of the following characteristics:

1. Value changes by direct reference to: (1) one or more underlyings, and (2) one or more notional amounts or payment provisions or both

2. No initial net investment (or a small investment for time value)

3. Settled net or by delivery of an asset readily convertible to cash

The three concepts of underlying, notional amount, and payment provision are key to defining a derivative. An underlying in a derivative is a specified commodity price, interest rate or security price, or some other variable. It may be a price or rate of interest, but not the asset or liability itself. Thus, the underlying generally is the referenced index that determines whether or not the derivative has a positive or negative value.

The notional amount is a number representing the barrels of crude oil, natural gas MMBtu, pounds, bushels, currency units, shares, or other units specified in a contract. Settlement of a derivative is determined by the interaction of the notional amount with the value of the underlying. This interaction may consist of simple multiplication or it may involve a more complex formula.

A payment provision specifies a fixed or determinable settlement that is to be made if the underlying behaves in a certain manner. For the energy industry, the payment provision is the most problematic component as the commodity (such as crude oil and natural gas) is produced and sold in liquid markets.

The net settlement requirement can be accomplished in three ways:

1. Net settlement explicitly required or permitted by the contract (i.e., symmetrical liquidating damage clause)

2. Net settlement by a market mechanism outside the contract (i.e., futures exchange)

3. Delivery of a derivative or an asset that is readily convertible to cash

Based on these concepts, the definition of a derivative has been expanded to include not only the typical financial instruments that have been viewed in the past as derivatives, but may also include traditional physical commodity contracts which do not meet the normal purchase and sale exclusion provided for in FAS 133. FAS 149 allows contracts that contain net settlement provisions to qualify for the normal purchases and sales exception if it is probable at inception and throughout the term of the individual contract that the contract will not settle net and will result in physical delivery. The FASB and DIG have provided additional interpretive guidance pertaining to the new settlement criteria.

EXCLUSIONS

Examples of types of exclusions include: normal purchases and sales, contingent consideration resulting from a business combination, certain insurance contracts, and employee compensation arrangements that are indexed to an entity's own stock and classified as part of stockholders' equity. Contracts, which meet the definition of a derivative and qualify for one of the exclusions, are not subject to the guidance for accounting for derivatives.

EMBEDDED DERIVATIVES

An embedded derivative is a provision in a contract through its implicit or explicit terms that contains the characteristics of a free-standing derivative which ultimately affect the cash flows or value of other exchanges required by a contract. Thus, the combination of a host contract and an embedded derivative is referred to as a hybrid instrument. Examples of an embedded derivative include a purchase or sale contract subject to a cap, floor or collar. An embedded derivative should be separated from the host contract and accounted for separately in the financial statements if all of the following criteria are met:

- The embedded characteristic in the contract meets the definition of a derivative.
- Characteristics and risks of the embedded derivative are not clearly and closely related to the host contract.
- The host contract is not measured at fair value.

Judgment is required to interpret the phrase "clearly and closely related." It implies the economic features of an embedded derivative and host contract are somewhat interdependent, and the fair value of the embedded derivative and the host contract are impacted by the same variables, and vice versa. The FASB and DIG have provided interpretive guidance to assist in the determination of what is "clearly and closely related" (reference the DIG Statement 133 Implementation Issue No. B36, April 2, 2003; http://www.fasb.org/derivatives/issueb36.shtml).

TYPES OF HEDGES

Income statement recognition of changes in the fair value of derivatives depends on the intended use of the derivatives. If a derivative does not qualify as a hedging instrument or is not designated as such, gain or loss on the derivative must be recognized currently in earnings. To qualify for hedge accounting, the derivative must qualify either as a fair value hedge, cash flow hedge, or foreign currency hedge.

A fair value hedge represents the hedge of an exposure to changes in the fair value of an asset, liability, or an unrecognized firm commitment that is attributable to a particular risk. An example of a fair value hedge is a forward contract pertaining to an unrecognized firm commitment (fixed price sales and purchase contracts), or an interest rate swap contract associated with fixed rate debt. A fair value hedge is reflected in the financial statements at market value each reporting period, and the associated unrealized gain or loss incurred with respect to such instrument is included in earnings.

Changes in the fair value of the corresponding unrecognized firm commitment or asset/liability being hedged are also recognized in the financial statements each reporting period. As a result, both the income statement and balance sheet of an organization are increased for these transactions. The only component that affects net income, in any given reporting period, is any ineffectiveness identified as part of the effectiveness assessment made by the organization.

A cash flow hedge is a hedge of an exposure to variability in cash flows that is attributable to a particular risk associated with an existing recognized asset or liability (floating rate debt) or a forecasted transaction (future production of crude oil or natural gas). Some common examples include the use of futures, swaps, or costless collar arrangements associated with future crude oil and natural gas productions, or an interest rate swap associated with variable rate debt. A cash flow hedge is reflected in the financial statements at market value each reporting period, and the associated unrealized gain or loss incurred with respect to such instrument is included in other comprehensive income. The amount that is deferred in other comprehensive income is always the lesser of (in absolute value terms): (1) estimated changes in the expected future cash flows of the hedged item that are attributable to the hedged risk, or (2) cumulative gain or loss on the derivative instrument. The corresponding forecasted transaction or recognized asset/liability is not reflected in the financial statements. In a given reporting period, the only component that affects net income is any ineffectiveness identified as part of the effectiveness assessment made by the organization.

FAS 133 generally retained the FAS 52 hedge accounting provisions. In this regard, it includes a narrow scope of transactions for which hedge accounting may be applied to foreign currency/operations activities. A foreign currency hedge is the hedge of a foreign currency exposure to an unrecognized firm commitment, available-for-sale security, forecasted transaction, or net investment in a foreign operation. Foreign currency hedges can have the dynamics of a fair value transaction, cash flow transaction, or foreign currency hedge of a net investment in a foreign operation—depending on the nature of the underlying physical transaction(s). They are accounted for in a manner consistent with the general provisions of a fair value hedge or cash flow hedge as previously described.

EFFECTIVENESS

Certain criteria must be met for a derivative financial instrument to fall within one of the hedging categories described above. Some criteria are similar to the determination of hedge accounting at present, while others formalize a process which may already be in place. First, an entity indicates what it is doing with the derivative financial instrument through formal documentation of the hedge relationship and risk management objective and strategy at the beginning of the contract term. This documentation encompasses a specific designation of the hedge instrument and related items, nature of the risk being hedged, and the method of assessing effectiveness. A hedging item should be consistent with the respective risk management policy, and is expected to be highly effective at inception and on an ongoing basis throughout the term of the contract.

The FASB declined to quantify the term "highly effective"; however, DIG provided interpretive guidance on this matter. An assessment of effectiveness is required to be performed at least every three months and whenever financial statements or earnings are reported to the public. The method for assessing effectiveness should be included as part of the initial documentation requirements. Hedge effectiveness must be achieved initially and on an ongoing basis. Measurement of hedge effectiveness is prospective, as well as retrospective. Ordinarily, it is expected an entity will assess effectiveness for similar hedges in a similar manner; use of different methods for similar hedges must be justified.

Effectiveness allows an entity to utilize hedge accounting; however, ineffectiveness must still be measured and recorded in the financial statements. If a derivative has been determined to be highly effective, some ineffectiveness is likely to occur, and some gain or loss will be reflected in earnings. Items which may generate ineffectiveness include: (1) different maturity or repricing dates, (2) different underlying (e.g., hedging jet fuel inventory with heating oil futures), (3) location and quality differentials (San Juan Basin gas versus NYMEX or sweet versus sour barrels), and (4) credit differences. As it relates to cash flow hedges, the amount deferred in other comprehensive income is the lesser of (in absolute value terms): (1) estimated changes in the expected future cash flows of the hedged item that are attributable to the hedged risk, and (2) cumulative gain or loss on the derivative instrument. In essence, there is a limitation of the amounts pertaining to unrealized gains and/or losses that may be accumulated in other comprehensive income. Therefore, the cumulative gain or loss on the derivative in excess of the estimated changes in expected future cash flows is recorded in the income statement as ineffectiveness.

Any changes an entity makes to its method of assessing effectiveness has to be justified and applied prospectively by a discontinuance of the existing hedging relationship and a new designation of the relationship through the use of the improved method. In addition, if an enterprise changes the method of assessing effectiveness on a hedged item, the enterprise also changes the method of assessment for similar hedges.

DISCONTINUANCE OF HEDGE ACCOUNTING

The discontinuance of hedge accounting occurs in two situations: (1) a failure to meet any of the qualifying hedge criteria, and (2) the derivatives were to expire or be sold, terminated, exercised, or simply de-designated as a hedging instrument.

DISCLOSURES

The disclosure requirements in financial statements for derivatives and hedging activities are quite extensive. Qualitative disclosures should include the objective and strategy, risk management policy, and description of hedged items. In addition, FAS 133 expands the disclosure pertaining to derivatives to include the amount of ineffectiveness reflected in earnings, earnings impact from discontinued hedges, amount of gains and losses included in other comprehensive income to be included in earnings within the next twelve months, and the purpose of derivatives that do not qualify as a hedging instrument.

RECENT FASB STATEMENT ON FAIR VALUE MEASUREMENTS

On September 15, 2006, the FASB issued Statement of Financial Accounting Standards No. 157 (FAS 157), *Fair Value Measurements*. The ruling provides guidance for using fair value to measure assets and liabilities. FAS 157 applies to situations when other standards require (or permit) assets or liabilities to be measured at fair value. It defines fair value, establishes a framework for measuring fair value, and expands disclosures about fair value measurements. Where applicable, FAS 157 simplifies and codifies related guidance within generally accepted accounting principles (GAAP).

Prior to FAS 157, there were different definitions of fair value and limited guidance for applying those definitions in GAAP. Fair value definitions were dispersed among many accounting pronouncements, which created inconsistencies and added to the complexity in applying GAAP. In developing FAS 157, the Board considered the need for increased consistency and comparability in fair value measurements and for expanded disclosures about fair value measurements. Under FAS 157, fair value is defined as the price that would be received to sell an asset or paid to transfer a liability in an orderly transaction between market participants at the measurement date.

The changes to current practice resulting from the application of FAS 157 relate to the definition of fair value, the methods used to measure fair value, and the expanded disclosures about fair value measurements.

• • •

---

1 A forward is similar to the prepaids described in Chapter 22; however, for prepaids the cash is paid up-front and presumably discounted for the time value of money.

Appendices

REGULATION S-X RULE 4-10

(reprinted as of May 2, 2007)

Regulation S-X Rule 4-10 prescribes the financial accounting and reporting standards for oil and gas producing activities of SEC registrants. The subsections are listed below for easier reference.

Regulation S-X Article 4

Rule 4-10   Financial accounting and reporting for oil and gas producing activities pursuant to the Federal Securities Laws and the Energy Policy and Conservation Act of 1975

This section prescribes financial accounting and reporting standards for registrants with the Commission engaged in oil and gas producing activities in filings under the federal securities laws and for the preparation of accounts by persons engaged, in whole or in part, in the production of crude oil or natural gas in the United States, pursuant to Section 503 of the Energy Policy and Conservation Act of 1975 ("EPCA") and Section 11(c) of the Energy Supply and Environmental Coordination Act of 1974 ("ESECA"), as amended by Section 505 of EPCA. The application of this section to those oil and gas producing operations of companies regulated for rate-making purposes on an individual-company-cost-of-service basis may, however, give appropriate recognition to differences arising because of the effect of the rate-making process.

Exemption. Any person exempted by the Department of Energy from any recordkeeping or reporting requirements pursuant to Section 11(c) of ESECA, as amended, is similarly exempted from the related provisions of this section in the preparation of accounts pursuant to EPCA. This exemption does not affect the applicability of this section to filings pursuant to the federal securities laws.

DEFINITIONS

(a) Definitions. The following definitions apply to the terms listed below as they are used in this section:

(1) Oil and gas producing activities.

(i) Such activities include:

(A) The search for crude oil, including condensate and natural gas liquids, or natural gas ("oil and gas") in their natural states and original locations.

(B) The acquisition of property rights or properties for the purpose of further exploration and/or for the purpose of removing the oil or gas from existing reservoirs on those properties.

(C) The construction, drilling and production activities necessary to retrieve oil and gas from its natural reservoirs, and the acquisition, construction, installation, and maintenance of field gathering and storage systems -- including lifting the oil and gas to the surface and gathering, treating, field processing (as in the case of processing gas to extract liquid hydrocarbons) and field storage. For purposes of this section, the oil and gas production function shall normally be regarded as terminating at the outlet valve on the lease or field storage tank; if unusual physical or operational circumstances exist, it may be appropriate to regard the production functions as terminating at the first point at which oil, gas, or gas liquids are delivered to a main pipeline, a common carrier, a refinery, or a marine terminal.

(ii) Oil and gas producing activities do not include:

(A) The transporting, refining and marketing of oil and gas.

(B) Activities relating to the production of natural resources other than oil and gas.

(C) The production of geothermal steam or the extraction of hydrocarbons as a by-product of the production of geothermal steam or associated geothermal resources as defined in the Geothermal Steam Act of 1970.

(D) The extraction of hydrocarbons from shale, tar sands, or coal.

(2) <u>Proved oil and gas reserves</u>. Proved oil and gas reserves are the estimated quantities of crude oil, natural gas and natural gas liquids which geological and engineering data demonstrate with reasonable certainty to be recoverable in future years from known reservoirs under existing economic and operating conditions, i.e., prices and costs as of the date the estimate is made. Prices include consideration of changes in existing prices provided only by contractual arrangements, but not on escalations based upon future conditions.

(i) Reservoirs are considered proved if economic producibility is supported by either actual production or conclusive formation test. The area of a reservoir considered proved includes (A) that portion delineated by drilling and defined by gas-oil and/or oil-water contacts, if any, and (B) the immediately adjoining portions not yet drilled, but which can be reasonably judged as economically productive on the basis of available geological and engineering data. In the absence of information on fluid contacts, the lowest known structural occurrence of hydrocarbons controls the lower proved limit of the reservoir.

(ii) Reserves which can be produced economically through application of improved recovery techniques (such as fluid injection) are included in the "proved" classification when successful testing by a pilot project, or the operation of an installed program in the reservoir, provides support for the engineering analysis on which the project or program was based.

(iii) Estimates of proved reserves do not include the following: (A) oil that may become available from known reservoirs but is classified separately as "indicated additional reserves"; (B) crude oil, natural gas, and natural gas liquids, the recovery of which is subject to reasonable doubt because of uncertainty as to geology, reservoir characteristics, or economic factors; (C) crude oil, natural gas, and natural gas liquids, that may occur in undrilled prospects; and (D) crude oil, natural gas, and natural gas liquids, that may be recovered from oil shales, coal, gilsonite and other such sources.

(3) <u>Proved developed oil and gas reserves</u>. Proved developed oil and gas reserves are reserves that can be expected to be recovered through existing wells with existing equipment and operating methods. Additional oil and gas expected to be obtained through the application of fluid injection or other improved recovery techniques for supplementing the natural forces and mechanisms of primary recovery should be included as "proved developed reserves" only after testing by a pilot project or after the operation of an installed program has confirmed through production response that increased recovery will be achieved.

(4) <u>Proved undeveloped reserves</u>. Proved undeveloped oil and gas reserves are reserves that are expected to be recovered from new wells on undrilled acreage, or from existing wells where a relatively major expenditure is required for recompletion. Reserves on undrilled acreage shall be limited to those drilling units offsetting productive units that are reasonably certain of production when drilled. Proved reserves for other undrilled units can be claimed only where it can be demonstrated with certainty that there is continuity of production from the existing productive formation. Under no circumstances should estimates for proved undeveloped reserves be attributable to any acreage for which an application of fluid injection or other improved recovery technique is contemplated, unless such techniques have been proved effective by actual tests in the area and in the same reservoir.

(5) <u>Proved properties</u>. Properties with proved reserves.

(6) <u>Unproved properties</u>. Properties with no proved reserves.

(7) <u>Proved area</u>. The part of a property to which proved reserves have been specifically attributed.

(8) <u>Field</u>. An area consisting of a single reservoir or multiple reservoirs all grouped on or related to the same individual geological structural feature and/or stratigraphic condition. There may be two or more reservoirs in a field that are separated vertically by intervening impervious strata, or laterally by local geologic barriers, or by both. Reservoirs that are associated by being in overlapping or adjacent fields may be treated as a single or common operational field. The geological terms "structural feature" and "stratigraphic condition" are intended to identify localized geological features as opposed to the broader terms of basins, trends, provinces, plays, areas-of-interest, etc.

(9) <u>Reservoir</u>. A porous and permeable underground formation containing a natural accumulation of producible oil and/or gas that is confined by impermeable rock or water barriers and is individual and separate from other reservoirs.

(10) <u>Exploratory well</u>. A well drilled to find and produce oil or gas in an unproved area, to find a new reservoir in a field previously found to be productive of oil or gas in another reservoir, or to extend a known reservoir. Generally, an exploratory well is any well that is not a development well, a service well, or a stratigraphic test well as those items are defined below.

(11) <u>Development well</u>. A well drilled within the proved area of an oil or gas reservoir to the depth of a stratigraphic horizon known to be productive.

(12) <u>Service well</u>. A well drilled or completed for the purpose of supporting production in a existing field. Specific purposes of service wells include gas injection, water injection, steam injection, air injection, salt-water disposal, water supply for injection, observation, or injection for in-situ combustion.

(13) <u>Stratigraphic test well</u>. A drilling effort, geologically directed, to obtain information pertaining to a specific geologic condition. Such wells customarily are drilled without the intention of being completed for hydrocarbon production. This classification also includes tests identified as core tests and all types of expendable holes related to hydrocarbon exploration. Stratigraphic test wells are classified as (i) "exploratory-type," if not drilled in a proved area, or (ii) "development-type," if drilled in a proved area.

(14) <u>Acquisition of properties</u>. Costs incurred to purchase, lease or otherwise acquire a property, including costs of lease bonuses and options to purchase or lease properties, the portion of costs applicable to minerals when land including mineral rights is purchased in fee, brokers' fees, recording fees, legal costs, and other costs incurred in acquiring properties.

(15) <u>Exploration costs</u>. Costs incurred in identifying areas that may warrant examination and in examining specific areas that are considered to have prospects of containing oil and gas reserves, including costs of drilling exploratory wells and exploratory-type stratigraphic test wells. Exploration costs may be incurred both before acquiring the related property (sometimes referred to in part as prospecting costs) and after acquiring the property. Principal types of exploration costs, which include depreciation and applicable operating costs of support equipment and facilities and other costs of exploration activities, are:

(i) Costs of topographical, geographical and geophysical studies, rights of access to properties to conduct those studies, and salaries and other expenses of geologists, geophysical crews, and others conducting those studies. Collectively, these are sometimes referred to as geological and geophysical or "G&G" costs.

(ii) Costs of carrying and retaining undeveloped properties, such as delay rentals, ad valorem taxes on properties, legal costs for title defense, and the maintenance of land and lease records.

(iii) Dry hole contributions and bottom hole contributions.

(iv) Costs of drilling and equipping exploratory wells.

(v) Costs of drilling exploratory-type stratigraphic test wells.

(16) Development costs. Costs incurred to obtain access to proved reserves and to provide facilities for extracting, treating, gathering and storing the oil and gas. More specifically, development costs, including depreciation and applicable operating costs of support equipment and facilities and other costs of development activities, are costs incurred to:

(i) Gain access to and prepare well locations for drilling, including surveying well locations for the purpose of determining specific development drilling sites, clearing ground, draining, road building, and relocating public roads, gas lines, and power lines, to the extent necessary in developing the proved reserves.

(ii) Drill and equip development wells, development-type stratigraphic test wells, and service wells, including the costs of platforms and of well equipment such as casing, tubing, pumping equipment, and the wellhead assembly.

(iii) Acquire, construct and install production facilities such as lease flow lines, separators, treaters, heaters, manifolds, measuring devices, and production storage tanks, natural gas cycling and processing plants, and central utility and waste disposal systems.

(iv) Provide improved recovery systems.

(17) Production costs. (i) Costs incurred to operate and maintain wells and related equipment and facilities, including depreciation and applicable operating costs of support equipment and facilities and other costs of operating and maintaining those wells and related equipment and facilities. They become part of the cost of oil and gas produced. Examples of production costs (sometimes called lifting costs) are:

(A) Costs of labor to operate the wells and related equipment and facilities.

(B) Repairs and maintenance.

(C) Materials, supplies, and fuel consumed and supplies utilized in operating the wells and related equipment and facilities.

(D) Property taxes and insurance applicable to proved properties and wells and related equipment and facilities.

(E) Severance taxes.

(ii) Some support equipment or facilities may serve two or more oil and gas producing activities and may also serve transportation, refining, and marketing activities. To the extent that the support equipment and facilities are used in oil and gas producing activities, their depreciation and applicable operating costs become exploration, development or production costs, as appropriate. Depreciation, depletion, and amortization of capitalized acquisition, exploration, and development costs are not production costs but also become part of the cost of oil and gas produced along with production (lifting) costs identified above.

SUCCESSFUL EFFORTS METHOD

(b) A reporting entity that follows the successful efforts method shall comply with the accounting and financial reporting disclosure requirements of Statement of Financial Accounting Standards No. 19, as amended.

FULL COST METHOD

(c) Application of the full cost method of accounting. A reporting entity that follows the full cost method shall apply that method to all of its operations and to the operations of its subsidiaries, as follows:

(1) Determination of cost centers. Cost centers shall be established on a country-by-country basis.

(2) Costs to be capitalized. All costs associated with property acquisition, exploration, and development activities (as defined in paragraph (a) of this section) shall be capitalized within the appropriate cost center. Any internal costs that are capitalized shall be limited to those costs that can be directly identified with acquisition, exploration, and development activities undertaken by the reporting entity for its own account, and shall not include any costs related to production, general corporate overhead, or similar activities.

(3) Amortization of capitalized costs. Capitalized costs within a cost center shall be amortized on the unit-of-production basis using proved oil and gas reserves, as follows:

(i) Costs to be amortized shall include (A) all capitalized costs, less accumulated amortization, other than the cost of properties described in paragraph (ii) below; (B) the estimated future expenditures (based on current costs) to be incurred in developing proved reserves; and (C) estimated dismantlement and abandonment costs, net of estimated salvage values.

(ii) The cost of investments in unproved properties and major development projects may be excluded from capitalized costs to be amortized, subject to the following:

(A) All costs directly associated with the acquisition and evaluation of unproved properties may be excluded from the amortization computation until it is determined whether or not proved reserves can be assigned to the properties, subject to the following conditions: (1) Until such a determination is made, the properties shall be assessed at least annually to ascertain whether impairment has occurred. Unevaluated properties whose costs are individually significant shall be assessed individually. Where it is not practicable to individually assess the amount of impairment of properties for which costs are not individually significant, such properties may be grouped for purposes of assessing impairment. Impairment may be estimated by applying factors based on historical experience and other data such as primary lease terms of the properties, average holding periods of unproved properties, and geographic and geologic data to groupings of individually insignificant properties and projects. The amount of impairment assessed under either of these methods shall be added to the costs to be amortized. (2) The costs of drilling exploratory dry holes shall be included in the amortization base immediately upon determination that the well is dry. (3) If geological and geophysical costs cannot be directly associated with specific unevaluated properties, they shall be included in the amortization base as incurred. Upon complete evaluation of a property, the total remaining excluded cost (net of any impairment) shall be included in the full cost amortization base.

(B) Certain costs may be excluded from amortization when incurred in connection with major development projects expected to entail significant costs to ascertain the quantities of proved reserves attributable to the properties under development (e.g., the installation of an offshore drilling platform from which development wells are to be drilled, the installation of improved recovery programs, and similar major projects undertaken in the expectation of significant additions to proved reserves). The amounts which may be excluded are applicable portions of (1) the costs that relate to the major development project and have not previously been included in the amortization base, and (2) the estimated future expenditures associated with the development project. The excluded portion of any common costs associated with the development project should be based, as is most appropriate in the circumstances, on a comparison of either (i) existing proved reserves to total proved reserves expected to be established upon completion of the project, or (ii) the number of wells to which proved reserves have been assigned and total number of wells expected to be drilled. Such costs may be excluded from costs to be amortized until the earlier determination of whether additional reserves are proved or impairment occurs.

(C) Excluded costs and the proved reserves related to such costs shall be transferred into the amortization base on an ongoing (well-by-well or property-by-property) basis as the project is evaluated and proved reserves established or impairment determined. Once proved reserves are established, there is no further justification for continued exclusion from the full cost amortization base even if other factors prevent immediate production or marketing.

(iii) Amortization shall be computed on the basis of physical units, with oil and gas converted to a common unit of measure on the basis of their approximate relative energy content, unless economic circumstances (related to the effects of regulated prices) indicate that use of units of revenue is a more appropriate basis of computing amortization. In the latter case, amortization shall be computed on the basis of current gross revenues (excluding royalty payments and net profits disbursements) from production in relation to future gross revenues, based on current prices (including consideration of changes in existing prices provided only by contractual arrangements), from estimated production of proved oil and gas reserves. The effect of a significant price increase during the year on estimated future gross revenues shall be reflected in the amortization provision only for the period after the price increase occurs.

(iv) In some cases it may be more appropriate to depreciate natural gas cycling and processing plants by a method other than the unit-of-production method.

(v) Amortization computations shall be made on a consolidated basis, including investees accounted for on a proportionate consolidation basis. Investees accounted for on the equity method shall be treated separately.

(4) Limitation on capitalized costs:

(i) For each cost center, capitalized costs, less accumulated amortization and related deferred income taxes, shall not exceed an amount (the cost center ceiling) equal to the sum of: (A) the present value of estimated future net revenues computed by applying current prices of oil and gas reserves (with consideration of price changes only to the extent provided by contractual arrangements) to estimated future production of proved oil and gas reserves as of the date of the latest balance sheet presented, less estimated future expenditures (based on current costs) to be incurred in developing and producing the proved reserves computed using a discount factor of ten percent and assuming continuation of existing economic conditions; plus (B) the cost of properties not being amortized pursuant to paragraph (i)(3)(ii) of this section; plus (C) the lower of cost or estimated fair value of unproven properties included in the costs being amortized; less (D) income tax effects related to differences between the book and tax basis of properties referred to in paragraphs (i)(4)(i)(B) and (C) of this section.

(ii) If unamortized costs capitalized within a cost center, less related deferred income taxes, exceed the cost center ceiling, the excess shall be charged to expense and separately disclosed during the period in which the excess occurs. Amounts thus required to be written off shall not be reinstated for any subsequent increase in the cost center ceiling.

(5) Production costs. All costs relating to production activities, including workover costs incurred solely to maintain or increase levels of production from an existing completion interval, shall be charged to expense as incurred.

(6) Other transactions. The provisions of paragraph (h) of this section, "Mineral property conveyances and related transactions if the successful efforts method of accounting is followed," shall apply also to those reporting entities following the full cost method except as follows:

(i) Sales and abandonments of oil and gas properties. Sales of oil and gas properties, whether or not being amortized currently, shall be accounted for as adjustments of capitalized costs, with no gain or loss recognized, unless such adjustments would significantly alter the relationship between capitalized costs and proved reserves of oil and gas attributable to a cost center. For instance, a significant alteration would not ordinarily be expected to occur for sales involving less than 25% of the reserve quantities of a given cost center. If gain or loss is recognized on such a sale, total capitalized costs within the cost center shall be allocated between the reserves sold and reserves retained on the same basis used to compute amortization, unless there are substantial economic differences between the properties sold and those retained, in which case capitalized costs shall be allocated on the basis of the relative fair values of the properties. Abandonments of oil and gas properties shall be accounted for as adjustments of capitalized costs, that is, the cost of abandoned properties shall be charged to the full cost center and amortized (subject to the limitation on capitalized costs in paragraph (b) of this section).

(ii) Purchases of reserves. Purchases of oil and gas reserves in place ordinarily shall be accounted for as additional capitalized costs within the applicable cost center; however, significant purchases of production payments or properties with lives substantially shorter than the composite productive life of the cost center shall be accounted for separately.

(iii) Partnerships, joint ventures and drilling arrangements.

(A) Except as provided in subparagraph (i)(6)(i) of this section, all consideration received from sales or transfers of properties in connection with partnerships, joint venture operations, or various other forms of drilling arrangements involving oil and gas exploration and development activities (e.g., carried interest, turnkey wells, management fees, etc.) shall be credited to the full cost account, except to the extent of amounts that represent reimbursement of organization, offering, general and administrative expenses, etc., that are identifiable with the transaction, if such amounts are currently incurred and charged to expense.

(B) Where a registrant organizes and manages a limited partnership involved only in the purchase of proved developed properties and subsequent distribution of income from such properties, management fee income may be recognized provided the properties involved do not require aggregate development expenditures in connection with production of existing proved reserves in excess of 10% of the partnership's recorded cost of such properties. Any income not recognized as a result of this limitation would be credited to the full cost account and recognized through a lower amortization provision as reserves are produced.

(iv) <u>Other services</u>. No income shall be recognized in connection with contractual services performed (e.g., drilling, well service, or equipment supply services, etc.) in connection with properties in which the registrant or an affiliate (as defined at Rule 1-02(b)) holders an ownership or other economic interest, except as follows:

(A) Where the registrant acquires an interest in the properties in connection with the service contract, income may be recognized to the extent that cash consideration received exceeds the related contract costs plus the registrant's share of costs incurred and estimated to be incurred in connection with the properties. Ownership interests acquired within one year of the date of such a contract are considered to be acquired in connection with the service for purposes of applying this rule. The amount of any guarantees or similar arrangements undertaken as part of this contract should be considered as part of the costs related to the properties for purposes of applying this rule.

(B) Where the registrant acquired an interest in the properties at least one year before the date of the service contract through transactions unrelated to the service contract, and that interest is unaffected by the service contract, income from such contract may be recognized subject to the general provisions for elimination of intercompany profits under generally accepted accounting principles.

(C) Notwithstanding the provisions of (A) and (B) above, no income may be recognized for contractual services performed on behalf of investors in oil and gas producing activities managed by the registrant or an affiliate. Furthermore, no income may be recognized for contractual services to the extent that the consideration received for such services represents an interest in the underlying property.

(D) Any income not recognized as a result of these rules would be credited to the full cost account and recognized through a lower amortization provision as reserves are produced.

(7) <u>Disclosures</u>. Reporting entities that follow the full cost method of accounting shall disclose all of the information required by paragraph (k) of this section, with each cost center considered as a separate geographic area, except that reasonable groupings may be made of cost centers that are not significant in the aggregate. In addition:

(i) For each cost center for each year that an income statement is required, disclose the total amount of amortization expense (per equivalent physical unit of production if amortization is computed on the basis of physical units or per dollar of gross revenue from production if amortization is computed on the basis of gross revenue).

(ii) State separately on the face of the balance sheet the aggregate of the capitalized costs of unproved properties and major development projects that are excluded, in accordance with paragraph (i)(3) of this section, from the capitalized costs being amortized. Provide a description in the notes to the financial statements of the current status of the significant properties or projects involved, including the anticipated timing of the inclusion of the costs in the amortization computation. Present a table that shows, by category of cost, (A) the total costs excluded as of the most recent fiscal year; and (B) the amounts of such excluded costs, incurred (1) in each of the three most recent fiscal years and (2) in the aggregate for any earlier fiscal years in which the costs were incurred. Categories of cost to be disclosed include acquisition costs, exploration costs, development costs in the case of significant development projects and capitalized interest.

INCOME TAXES

(d) <u>Income taxes</u>. Comprehensive interperiod income tax allocation by a method which complies with generally accepted accounting principles shall be followed for intangible drilling and development costs and other costs incurred that enter into the determination of taxable income and pretax accounting income in different periods.

• • •

ADDENDUM: EXCERPTS FROM SEC REG. S-K AND FINANCIAL REPORTING POLICIES

REGULATION S-K EXCERPT REGARDING FAS 69:

§229.302

(b) *Information about oil and gas producing activities.* Registrants engaged in oil and gas producing activities shall present the information about oil and gas producing activities (as those activities are defined in Regulation S-X, § 210.4-10(a)) specified in paragraphs 9-34 of Statement of Financial Accounting Standards ("SFAS") No. 69, "Disclosures about Oil and Gas Producing Activities," if such oil and gas producing activities are regarded as significant under one or more of the tests set forth in paragraph 8 of SFAS No. 69 [For an additional test, see the excerpt below from FRR Codification §406.02 d.i.].

Instructions to Paragraph (b).

1. (a) SFAS No. 69 disclosures that relate to annual periods shall be presented for each annual period for which an income statement is required, (b) SFAS No. 69 disclosures required as of the end of annual period shall be presented as of the date of each audited balance sheet required, and (c) SFAS No. 69 disclosures required as of the beginning of an annual period shall be presented as of the beginning of each annual period for which an income statement is required.

2. This paragraph, together with §210.4-10 of Regulation S-X, prescribes financial reporting standards for the preparation of accounts by persons engaged, in whole or in

part, in the production of crude oil or natural gas in the United States, pursuant to Section 503 of the Energy Policy and Conservation Act of 1975 (42 U.S.C. 6383) ("EPCA") and Section 11(c) of the Energy Supply and Environmental Coordination Act of 1974 (15 U.S.C. 796) ("ESECA") as amended by Section 506 of EPCA. The application of this paragraph to those oil and gas producing operations of companies regulated for ratemaking purposes on an individual-company-cost-of-service basis may, however, give appropriate recognition to differences arising because of the effect of the ratemaking process.

3. Any person exempted by the Department of Energy from any recordkeeping or reporting requirements pursuant to Section 11(c) of ESECA, as amended, is similarly exempted from the related provisions of this paragraph in the preparation of accounts pursuant to EPCA. This exemption does not affect the applicability of this paragraph to filings pursuant to the federal securities laws.

EXCERPTS FROM THE SEC'S CODIFICATION OF FINANCIAL REPORTING POLICIES:

406. Oil and Gas Producing Activities

406.01.c. Full Cost Method

406.01.c.i. Exclusion of Capitalized Costs

. . . Since unevaluated properties are required to be assessed periodically for impairment and to have value at least equal to their carrying costs (including any capitalized interest), exclusion from immediate amortization should not distort future income statements by postponing the recognition of non-productive costs. . . .

With respect to the assessment of impairment generally, the Commission also sees merit in the suggestion that an aggregate assessment of impairment be permitted on individually insignificant properties, and the final rules have been revised to permit, but not require, that approach. The rules do not include any specific guidance on the determination of "significance." However, the Commission believes that in general individual properties or projects would be expected to be individually significant if their costs exceed 10% of the net capitalized costs of the cost center. Where individual properties or projects with costs representing less than 10% of the cost center are involved, the Commission believes it is still appropriate to test impairment on an individual basis but will permit companies to aggregate such properties for purposes of this assessment . . .

While the final rules permit the general exclusion of all unevaluated costs from immediate amortization, the Commission emphasizes that as soon as it can be determined whether or not proved reserves can be assigned, the related costs should be included in the amortization base. Once these costs are included in the amortization base, they lose their identity for all future accounting purposes. Consequently, individual cost elements cannot subsequently be removed from this base. . . .

406.01.c.iii. Limitation on Capitalized Costs

. . . If application of the rules, as a result of an unusual event or transaction such as major purchase of proved properties, would require a writedown when the fair value of the properties in a cost center clearly exceeds the unamortized costs, the registrant may request an exemption from the general rule. In such cases, the registrant should be prepared to demonstrate that the additional value clearly exists beyond reasonable doubt.

The rules specify that the cost center ceiling is to be computed giving consideration to income tax effects. The Commission believes that unusual tax relationships may exist in certain instances, as a result of the expiration of operating loss carryforwards, change in tax rates, etc. In these circumstances, it will be necessary to consider tax effects in computing the ceiling limitation.

406.01.c.iv. Mineral Property Conveyances

The rules dealing with mineral property conveyances specify that a sale of oil and gas reserves shall be accounted for as an adjustment of capitalized costs, unless the adjustment causes a significant alteration of the relationship between remaining capitalized costs and proved reserves attributable to the cost center. A significant alteration would not normally be expected to result from a sale involving less than 25 percent of the total reserve quantities of the cost center.

The rules provide that costs should be allocated between cost center assets sold and retained except where estimated relative fair values should be used in order to reflect other substantial economic difference between the properties sold and those retained.

406.01.c.v. Consolidated Financial Statements

The rules specify that a registrant must apply its accounting method to the operations of its subsidiaries. Rule 4-10(c)(3)(v) requires that amortization rates be determined on a consolidated basis even though this may result in a consolidated amortization provision that is not equal to the sum of the expenses for the individual members of the consolidated group. This same concept applies to the determination of the limitation on capitalized costs within cost centers.

406.01.d. Accounting Changes

. . . The Commission expects registrants to comply with GAAP in making an accounting change to or from successful efforts or full costs. Since GAAP expresses a preference for successful efforts, no justification for the change to successful efforts is necessary nor is a preferability letter required by Rule 10-01(b)(6) of Regulation S-X. However, in view of SFAS 25, any change to full cost must be justified as being preferable in the registrant's circumstances and a preferability letter describing those circumstances must be filed with the Commission.

. . . [E]stimates of quantities of oil and gas reserves that had been made in prior years shall not currently be revised in retrospect.

For reporting entities following the full cost method of accounting, retroactive application of Rule 4-10(c)(4), "Limitations on capitalized costs," shall be applied as follows:

(a) If unamortized costs capitalized within a cost center do not exceed the cost center ceiling as of the beginning of the fiscal period in which the rules are initially adopted, then no provisions shall be made for past periods when application of the rules based on information known during those periods might have resulted in unamortized capitalized costs being in excess of the cost center ceiling.

(b) If unamortized costs capitalized within a cost center exceed the cost center ceiling as of the beginning of the fiscal year in which the rules are initially adopted, then this excess shall be recognized retroactively through a charge to expense in the periods in which the excess initially arose.

406.02. Supplemental Disclosures

406.02.b Summary of Operations on the Basis of Reserve Recognition Accounting

By conforming its disclosure requirements with those of the FASB standard, the Commission is eliminating its requirement for a supplemental presentation of an earnings summary based on Reserve Recognition Accounting ("RRA").

406.02.c. Separate Disclosure of Undiscounted Future Net Revenues

. . . [T]he Commission will no longer require separate disclosure of the first three years of future net revenues on an undiscounted basis.

. . . The Commission continues to believe that this sort of information may in some circumstances be essential to an understanding of a company's financial position and results of operations. Accordingly, the Commission reminds registrants that disclosures of undiscounted future cash flows from oil and gas operations may be necessary in the Management's Discussion and Analysis of the financial statements. Such disclosures would ordinarily be expected where near-term cash flows are likely to be negative or only at a break-even level, and may be appropriate in other circumstances.

406.02.d.i. Significance Criteria

The Commission believes that in most instances the significance criteria of SFAS 69 will identify the same enterprises as the Commission's proposed tests.[1] Accordingly, in view of its commitment to conform its rules wherever practicable with those of the private sector, the Commission is not adopting its separate proposed significance tests. However, in those circumstances where the discounted present value of a registrant's oil and gas reserves is significantly in excess of ten percent of consolidated total assets, the Commission expects that the general requirement for disclosure of material amounts will require that some disclosures be made, even if the stated SFAS 14 tests are not met.

406.02.d.ii Applicability of Commission Requirements

The final rules also specify that the subject supplemental disclosures shall be presented whenever required by the terms of the applicable Federal securities form. The SFAS 69 requirements apply to enterprises which are "publicly traded" as defined by the standard. This FASB definition is both broader and narrower than the class of enterprises currently required to provide supplemental oil and gas disclosures in Commission filings. The FASB definition includes certain small enterprises which although "traded" may not be required to file reports under either the Securities Act or the Securities Exchange Act. However, the FASB definition would not apply to other enterprises filing reports with the Commission such as certain limited partnerships, nor would it apply to companies providing information to investors under the Regulation D exemptions. The Commission recognizes that it has a different constituency and must retain the specific requirements of its various filing forms.

406.02.d.iii. Limited Partnerships

Topic 12-A-3-C of the Staff Accounting Bulletin series currently states that in certain circumstances the staff will not take exception to omission of the value based RRA disclosures required by Regulation S-X for limited partnerships engaged in oil and gas producing activities. This waiver applies only to value-based disclosures in periodic reports filed on Form 10-K where (1) the partnership agreement contains a buyout provision under which the general partner agrees to purchase the limited partnership interests that are offered for sale, based upon a specified valuation formula, and (2) some form of reserve value information is available to the limited partners pursuant to the partnership agreement. The staff anticipates that this policy will continue to apply to the comparable "standardized measure" disclosures specified in paragraphs 30-34 of SFAS 69. It should be noted, however, that the waiver in the Staff Accounting Bulletin extends only to value-based disclosures and not to reserve quantity disclosures or historical cost based information. In addition, the waiver was not intended to apply to limited partnerships where owners and buyers do not have some sort of value-based information otherwise automatically provided.

• • •

---

1 Author's note: Such criteria are quite similar to the three FAS 131 tests for significant industry segments.

FASB CURRENT TEXT SECTION Oi5

Sources: FASB Statement 19; FASB Statement 25; FASB Statement 69; FASB Statement 95; FASB Statement 109; FASB Statement 131; FASB Statement 143; FASB Statement 145; FASB Statement 153; FASB Statement 154; FASB Interpretation 36; FASB Staff Position FAS 19-1

[**Note:** Additional guidance with respect to implementation of this section is presented in paragraphs .801 through .813. A list of AICPA Accounting Standards Executive Committee (AcSEC) pronouncements that provide supplemental guidance for this section is presented in paragraph .2000.]

Financial Accounting Standards Board (FASB) Current Text Industry Standards
Oi5 Oil and Gas Producing Activities
Publish Date: January 10, 2006

Summary

An enterprise with oil and gas producing activities shall classify production payments payable in cash as debt and shall apply comprehensive income tax allocation like other enterprises. Both publicly traded and other enterprises shall disclose the method of accounting for costs incurred in oil and gas producing activities and the manner of disposing of related capitalized costs.

Publicly traded enterprises with significant oil and gas activities, when presenting a complete set of annual financial statements, are to disclose the following as supplementary information, but not as a part of the financial statements:

   a. Proved oil and gas reserve quantities

   b. Capitalized costs relating to oil and gas producing activities

   c. Costs incurred in oil and gas property acquisition, exploration, and development activities

   d. Results of operations for oil and gas producing activities

   e. A standardized measure of discounted future net cash flows relating to proved oil and gas reserve quantities.

In addition, this section describes a preferable, but not required, form of the successful efforts method of accounting for oil and gas producing activities. Under that method, costs shall be accounted for as follows:

   a. Geological and geophysical costs and costs of carrying and retaining undeveloped properties are charged to expense as incurred.

   b. Costs of drilling exploratory wells and exploratory-type stratigraphic test wells that do not find proved reserves are charged to expense when the wells do not find proved reserves.

   c. Costs of acquiring properties, costs of drilling development wells and development-type stratigraphic test wells, and costs of drilling successful exploratory wells and exploratory-type stratigraphic test wells are capitalized.

d. The capitalized costs of wells and related equipment are amortized as the related oil and gas reserves are produced.

e. Costs of unproved properties are assessed periodically, and a loss is recognized if the properties are impaired.

Scope

.101 This section [presents] standards of financial accounting and reporting for the **oil and gas producing activities** of a business enterprise. Those activities involve the acquisition of mineral interests in properties, exploration (including prospecting), development, and production of crude oil, including condensate and natural gas liquids, and natural gas (hereinafter collectively referred to as oil and gas producing activities). [FAS19, ¶1] This section applies only to *oil and gas producing activities*; it does not address financial accounting and reporting issues relating to the transporting, refining, and marketing of oil and gas. Also, this section does not apply to activities relating to the production of other wasting (nonregenerative) natural resources; nor does it apply to the production of geothermal steam or to the extraction of hydrocarbons as a by-product of the production of geothermal steam and associated geothermal resources as defined in the *Geothermal Steam Act of 1970*; nor does it apply to the extraction of hydrocarbons from shale, tar sands, or coal. [FAS19, ¶6]

.102 [Compliance with the accounting standards contained in paragraphs .103 through .132 and .135 through .139 is not required although those standards have been issued by the FASB and remain in existence] for purposes of applying [FAS25, ¶4] Section A07, "Accounting Changes and Error Corrections," paragraphs .111 through .113. [FAS154, ¶C9] [Enterprises registered with the Securities and Exchange Commission (SEC), however, are required to apply either those standards or a form of full cost accounting specified in the SEC's rules. The accounting and reporting standards contained in paragraphs .133, .134, .140 through .142, and .156 are required of all enterprises with oil and gas producing activities. In addition, **publicly traded enterprises** that have significant oil and gas producing activities shall make disclosures described in paragraphs .157 and .160 through .184 as supplementary information.]

.103 An enterprise's oil and gas producing activities involve certain special types of assets. Costs of those assets shall be capitalized when incurred. Those types of assets broadly defined are:

a. *Mineral interests in properties* (hereinafter referred to as properties), that include fee ownership or a lease, concession, or other interest representing the right to extract oil or gas subject to such terms as may be imposed by the conveyance of that interest. Properties also include royalty interests, production payments payable in oil or gas, and other nonoperating interests in properties operated by others. Properties include those agreements with foreign governments or authorities under which an enterprise participates in the operation of the related properties or otherwise serves as producer of the underlying reserves (refer to paragraph .163); but properties do not include other supply agreements or contracts that represent the right to purchase (as opposed to extract) oil and gas. Properties shall be classified as proved or unproved as follows:

    (1) Unproved properties—properties with no **proved reserves**.

    (2) Proved properties—properties with proved reserves.

b. Wells and related equipment and facilities,[1] the costs of which include those incurred to:

    (1) Drill and equip those **exploratory wells** and **exploratory-type stratigraphic test wells** that have found proved reserves.

    (2) Obtain access to proved reserves and provide facilities for extracting, treating, gathering, and storing the oil and gas, including the drilling and equipping of **development wells** and **development-type stratigraphic test wells** (whether those wells are successful or unsuccessful) and **service wells**.

c. Support equipment and facilities used in oil and gas producing activities (such as seismic equipment, drilling equipment, construction and grading equipment, vehicles, repair shops, warehouses, supply points, camps, and division, district, or field offices).

d. Uncompleted wells, equipment, and facilities, the costs of which include those incurred to:

    (1) Drill and equip wells that are not yet completed.

    (2) Acquire or construct equipment and facilities that are not yet completed and installed.

[FAS19, ¶11]

.104 The costs of an enterprise's wells and related equipment and facilities and the costs of the related proved properties shall be amortized as the related oil and gas reserves are produced. That amortization plus production (lifting) costs becomes part of the cost of oil and gas produced. Unproved properties shall be assessed periodically, and a loss [shall be] recognized if those properties are impaired. [FAS19, ¶12]

.105 Some costs incurred in an enterprise's oil and gas producing activities do not result in acquisition of an asset and, therefore, shall be charged to expense. Examples include geological and geophysical costs, the costs of carrying and retaining undeveloped properties, and the costs of drilling those exploratory wells and exploratory-type stratigraphic test wells that do not find proved reserves. [FAS19, ¶13]

Accounting at the Time Costs Are Incurred

Acquisition of Properties

.106 Costs incurred to purchase, lease, or otherwise acquire a property (whether unproved or proved) shall be capitalized when incurred. They include the costs of lease bonuses and options to purchase or lease properties, the portion of costs applicable to minerals when land including mineral rights is purchased in fee, brokers' fees, recording fees, legal costs, and other costs incurred in acquiring properties. [FAS19, ¶15]

Exploration

.107 Exploration involves (a) identifying areas that may warrant examination and (b) examining specific areas that are considered to have prospects of containing oil and gas reserves, including drilling exploratory wells and exploratory-type stratigraphic test wells. Exploration costs may be incurred both before acquiring the related property (sometimes referred to in part as prospecting costs) and after acquiring the property. [FAS19, ¶16]

.108 Principal types of exploration costs, which include depreciation and applicable operating costs of support equipment and facilities (refer to paragraph .117) and other costs of exploration activities, are:

    a.   Costs of topographical, geological, and geophysical studies, rights of access to properties to conduct those studies, and salaries and other expenses of geologists, geophysical crews, and others conducting those studies. Collectively, those are sometimes referred to as geological and geophysical, or *G&G*, costs.

    b.   Costs of carrying and retaining undeveloped properties, such as delay rentals, *ad valorem* taxes on the properties, legal costs for title defense, and the maintenance of land and lease records.

    c.   Dry hole contributions and bottom hole contributions.

    d.   Costs of drilling and equipping exploratory wells.

    e.   Costs of drilling exploratory-type stratigraphic test wells.[2]

[FAS19, ¶17]

.109 Geological and geophysical costs, costs of carrying and retaining undeveloped properties, and dry hole and bottom hole contributions shall be charged to expense when incurred. [FAS19, ¶18]

.110 The costs of drilling exploratory wells and the costs of drilling exploratory-type stratigraphic test wells shall be capitalized as part of the enterprise's uncompleted wells, equipment, and facilities pending determination of whether the well has found proved reserves. If the well has found proved reserves (refer to paragraphs .122 through .125), the capitalized costs of drilling the well shall become part of the enterprise's wells and related equipment and facilities (even though the well may not be completed as a producing well); if, however, the well has not found proved reserves, the capitalized costs of drilling the well, net of any salvage value, shall be charged to expense. [FAS19, ¶19]

.111 An enterprise sometimes conducts G&G studies and other exploration activities on property owned by another party, in exchange for which the enterprise is contractually entitled to receive an interest in the property if proved reserves are found or to be reimbursed by the owner for the G&G and other costs incurred if proved reserves are not found. In that case, the enterprise conducting the G&G studies and other exploration activities shall account for those costs as a receivable when incurred and, if proved reserves are found, they shall become the cost of the proved property acquired. [FAS19, ¶20]

Development

.112 Development costs are incurred to obtain access to proved reserves and to provide facilities for extracting, treating, gathering, and storing the oil and gas. More specifically, development costs, including depreciation and applicable operating costs of support equipment and facilities (refer to paragraph .117) and other costs of development activities, are costs incurred to:

    a.   Gain access to and prepare well locations for drilling, including surveying well locations for the purpose of determining specific development drilling sites, clearing ground, draining, road building, and relocating public roads, gas lines, and power lines, to the extent necessary in developing the proved reserves.

b. Drill and equip development wells, development-type stratigraphic test wells, and service wells, including the costs of platforms and of well equipment such as casing, tubing, pumping equipment, and the wellhead assembly.

c. Acquire, construct, and install production facilities such as lease flow lines, separators, treaters, heaters, manifolds, measuring devices, and production storage tanks, natural gas cycling and processing plants, and utility and waste disposal systems.

d. Provide improved recovery systems.

[FAS19, ¶21]

.113 Development costs shall be capitalized as part of the cost of an enterprise's wells and related equipment and facilities. Thus, all costs incurred to drill and equip development wells, development-type stratigraphic test wells, and service wells are development costs and shall be capitalized, whether the well is successful or unsuccessful. Costs of drilling those wells and costs of constructing equipment and facilities shall be included in the enterprise's uncompleted wells, equipment, and facilities until drilling or construction is completed. [FAS19, ¶22]

Production

.114 Production involves lifting the oil and gas to the surface and gathering, treating, **field** processing (as in the case of processing gas to extract liquid hydrocarbons), and field storage. For purposes of this section, the production function shall normally be regarded as terminating at the outlet valve on the lease or field production storage tank; if unusual physical or operational circumstances exist, it may be more appropriate to regard the production function as terminating at the first point at which oil, gas, or gas liquids are delivered to a main pipeline, a common carrier, a refinery, or a marine terminal. [FAS19, ¶23]

.115 Production costs are those costs incurred to operate and maintain an enterprise's wells and related equipment and facilities, including depreciation and applicable operating costs of support equipment and facilities (refer to paragraph .117) and other costs of operating and maintaining those wells and related equipment and facilities. They become part of the cost of oil and gas produced. Examples of production costs (sometimes called lifting costs) are:

a. Costs of labor to operate the wells and related equipment and facilities

b. Repairs and maintenance

c. Materials, supplies, and fuel consumed and services utilized in operating the wells and related equipment and facilities

d. Property taxes and insurance applicable to proved properties and wells and related equipment and facilities

e. Severance taxes.

[FAS19, ¶24]

.116 Depreciation, depletion, and amortization of capitalized acquisition, exploration, and development costs also become part of the cost of oil and gas produced along with production (lifting) costs identified in paragraph .115. [FAS19, ¶25]

Support Equipment and Facilities

.117 The cost of acquiring or constructing support equipment and facilities used in oil and gas producing activities shall be capitalized. Examples of support equipment and facilities include seismic equipment, drilling equipment, construction and grading equipment, vehicles, repair shops, warehouses, supply points, camps, and division, district, or field offices. Some support equipment or facilities are acquired or constructed for use exclusively in a single activity—exploration, development, or production. Other support equipment or facilities may serve two or more of those activities and may also serve the enterprise's transportation, refining, and marketing activities. To the extent that the support equipment and facilities are used in oil and gas producing activities, their depreciation and applicable operating costs become an exploration, development, or production cost, as appropriate. [FAS19, ¶26]

Disposition of Capitalized Costs

.118 The effect of paragraphs .106 through .117, which deal with accounting at the time costs are incurred, is to recognize as assets: (a) unproved properties; (b) proved properties; (c) wells and related equipment and facilities (that consist of all development costs plus the costs of drilling those exploratory wells and exploratory-type stratigraphic test wells that find proved reserves); (d) support equipment and facilities used in oil and gas producing activities; and (e) uncompleted wells, equipment, and facilities. Paragraphs .119 through .132 deal with disposition of the costs of those assets after capitalization. Among other things, those paragraphs provide that the acquisition costs of proved properties and the costs of wells and related equipment and facilities be amortized to become part of the cost of oil and gas produced; that impairment of unproved properties be recognized; and that the costs of an exploratory well or exploratory-type stratigraphic test well be charged to expense if the well is determined not to have found proved reserves. [FAS19, ¶27]

Assessment of Unproved Properties

.119 Unproved properties shall be assessed periodically to determine whether they have been impaired. A property would likely be impaired, for example, if a dry hole has been drilled on it and the enterprise has no firm plans to continue drilling. Also, the likelihood of partial or total impairment of a property increases as the expiration of the lease term approaches if drilling activity has not commenced on the property or on nearby properties. If the results of the assessment indicate impairment, a loss shall be recognized by providing a valuation allowance. Impairment of individual unproved properties whose acquisition costs are relatively significant shall be assessed on a property-by-property basis, and an indicated loss shall be recognized by providing a valuation allowance. When an enterprise has a relatively large number of unproved properties whose acquisition costs are not individually significant, it may not be practical to assess impairment on a property-by-property basis, in which case the amount of loss to be recognized and the amount of the valuation allowance needed to provide for impairment of those properties shall be determined by amortizing those properties, either in the aggregate or by groups, on the basis of the experience of the enterprise in similar situations and other information about such factors as the primary lease terms of those properties, the average holding period of unproved properties, and the relative proportion of such properties on which proved reserves have been found in the past. [FAS19, ¶28]

Reclassification of an Unproved Property

.120 A property shall be reclassified from unproved properties to proved properties when proved reserves are discovered on or otherwise attributed to the property; occasionally, a single property, such as a foreign lease or concession, covers so vast an area that only the portion of the property to which the proved reserves relate—determined on the basis of geological structural features or stratigraphic conditions—should be reclassified from unproved to proved. For a property whose impairment has been assessed individually in accordance with paragraph .119, the *net* carrying amount (acquisition cost minus valuation allowance) shall be reclassified to proved properties; for properties amortized by providing a valuation allowance on a group basis, the gross acquisition cost shall be reclassified. [FAS19, ¶29]

Amortization (Depletion) of Acquisition Costs of Proved Properties

.121 Capitalized acquisition costs of proved properties shall be amortized (depleted) by the unit-of-production method so that each unit produced is assigned a pro rata portion of the unamortized acquisition costs. Under the unit-of-production method, amortization (depletion) may be computed either on a property-by-property basis or on the basis of some reasonable aggregation of properties with a common geological structural feature or stratigraphic condition, such as a **reservoir** or field. If an enterprise has a relatively large number of royalty interests whose acquisition costs are not individually significant, they may be aggregated, for the purpose of computing amortization, without regard to commonality of geological structural features or stratigraphic conditions; if information is not available to estimate reserve quantities applicable to royalty interests owned (refer to paragraph .160), a method other than the unit-of-production method may be used to amortize their acquisition costs. The unit cost shall be computed on the basis of the total estimated units of **proved oil and gas reserves**. (Joint production of both oil and gas is discussed in paragraph .129.) Unit-of-production amortization rates shall be revised whenever there is an indication of the need for revision but at least once a year; those revisions shall be accounted for prospectively as changes in accounting estimates— [FAS19, ¶30]—refer to paragraphs .119 through .122 of Section A07. [FAS154, ¶C8(a)]

Accounting When Drilling of an Exploratory Well or an Exploratory-Type Stratigraphic Well Is Completed

.122 As specified in paragraph .110, the costs of drilling an exploratory well or an exploratory-type stratigraphic well are capitalized as part of the enterprise's uncompleted wells, equipment, and facilities pending the determination of whether the well has found proved reserves. If proved reserves are found, the capitalized costs of drilling the well shall be reclassified as part of the costs of the enterprise's wells and related equipment and facilities at that time. If proved reserves are not found, the capitalized costs of drilling the well shall be charged to expense. However, an exploratory well or an exploratory-type stratigraphic well may be determined to have found oil and gas reserves, but those reserves cannot be classified as proved when drilling is completed. In those cases, the capitalized drilling costs shall continue to be capitalized if the well has found a sufficient quantity of reserves to justify its completion as a producing well[2aa] *and* the enterprise is making sufficient progress assessing the reserves and the economic and operating viability of the project.[2ab] (Refer to paragraphs .123 through .125 for guidance on assessing whether an enterprise is making sufficient progress on assessing the reserves and the economic and operating viability of the project.) [FSP FAS 19-1, ¶9]

.122A If either of those criteria is not met, or if an enterprise obtains information that raises substantial doubt about the economic or operational viability of the project, the exploratory well or exploratory-type stratigraphic well shall be assumed to be impaired and its costs, net of any salvage value, shall be charged to expense. Further, an enterprise shall not continue to capitalize exploratory well costs on the chance that (a) current market conditions will change (for example, an increase in the market price of oil or gas), or (b) technology will be developed to make the development of the project economically and operationally viable. [FSP FAS 19-1, ¶9]

Progress on Assessing Reserves

.123   All relevant facts and circumstances shall be evaluated when determining whether an enterprise is making sufficient progress on assessing the reserves and the economic and operating viability of the project. The following are some indicators, among others, that an enterprise is making sufficient progress. No single indicator is determinative. An entity should evaluate indicators in conjunction with all other relevant facts and circumstances.

     a.   Commitment of project personnel who are at the appropriate levels and who have the appropriate skills

     b.   Costs are being incurred to assess the reserves and their potential development

     c.   An assessment process covering the economic, legal, political, and environmental aspects of the potential development is in progress

     d.   Existence (or active negotiations) of sales contracts with customers for the oil and gas

     e.   Existence (or active negotiations) of agreements with governments, lenders, and venture partners

     f.   Outstanding requests for proposals for development of any required facilities

     g.   Existence of firm plans, established timetables, or contractual commitments, which may include seismic testing and drilling of additional exploratory wells

     h.   Progress is being made on contractual arrangements that will permit future development

     i.   Identification of existing transportation and other infrastructure that is or will be available for the project (subject to negotiations for use).

[FSP FAS 19-1, ¶9]

.124   Long delays in the assessment or development plan (whether anticipated or unexpected) may raise doubts about whether the enterprise is making sufficient progress to continue the capitalization of exploratory well or exploratory-type stratigraphic well costs after the completion of drilling. The longer the assessment process for the reserves and the project, the more difficult it is to conclude that the enterprise is making sufficient progress to continue the capitalization of those exploratory well or exploratory-type stratigraphic well costs. [FSP FAS 19-1, ¶9]

.125   If an enterprise has not engaged in substantial activities to assess the reserves or the development of the project in a reasonable period of time after the drilling of the well is completed or activities have been suspended, any capitalized costs associated with that well shall be expensed net of any salvage value. After a reasonable period of time, the planning of future activities without engaging in substantial activities is not sufficient to continue the capitalization of exploratory well or exploratory-type stratigraphic well costs. However, brief interruptions in activities required to assess the reserves or the project, or other delays resulting from governmental or other third-party evaluation of a proposed project, do not require capitalized exploratory well or exploratory-type stratigraphic well costs to be expensed. [FSP FAS 19-1, ¶9]

Amortization and Depreciation of Capitalized Exploratory Drilling and Development Costs

.126 Capitalized costs of exploratory wells and exploratory-type stratigraphic test wells that have found proved reserves and capitalized development costs shall be amortized (depreciated) by the unit-of-production method so that each unit produced is assigned a pro rata portion of the unamortized costs. It may be more appropriate, in some cases, to depreciate natural gas cycling and processing plants by a method other than the unit-of-production method. Under the unit-of-production method, amortization (depreciation) may be computed either on a property-by-property basis or on the basis of some reasonable aggregation of properties with a common geological structural feature or stratigraphic condition, such as a reservoir or field. The unit cost shall be computed on the basis of the total estimated units of **proved developed reserves**, rather than on the basis of all proved reserves, which is the basis for amortizing acquisition costs of proved properties. If significant development costs (such as the cost of an offshore production platform) are incurred in connection with a planned group of development wells before all of the planned wells have been drilled, it will be necessary to exclude a portion of those development costs in determining the unit-of-production amortization rate until the additional development wells are drilled. Similarly, it will be necessary to exclude, in computing the amortization rate, those proved developed reserves that will be produced only after significant additional development costs are incurred, such as for improved recovery systems. However, in no case should future development costs be anticipated in computing the amortization rate. (Joint production of both oil and gas is discussed in paragraph .129.) Unit-of-production amortization rates shall be revised whenever there is an indication of the need for revision but at least once a year; those revisions shall be accounted for prospectively as changes in accounting estimates [FAS19, ¶35]—refer to paragraphs .119 through .122 of Section A07. [FAS154, ¶C8(b)]

Depreciation of Support Equipment and Facilities

.127 Depreciation of support equipment and facilities used in oil and gas producing activities shall be accounted for as exploration cost, development cost, or production cost, as appropriate (refer to paragraph .117). [FAS19, ¶36]

Dismantlement Costs and Salvage Values

.128 Obligations for dismantlement, restoration, and abandonment costs shall be accounted for in accordance with the provisions of Section A50, "Asset Retirement Obligations." Estimated residual salvage values shall be taken into account in determining amortization and depreciation rates. [FAS143, ¶23]

Amortization of Costs Relating to Oil and Gas Reserves Produced Jointly

.129 The unit-of-production method of amortization requires that the total number of units of oil or gas reserves in a property or group of properties be estimated and that the number of units produced in the current period be determined. Many properties contain both oil and gas reserves. In those cases, the oil and gas reserves and the oil and gas produced shall be converted to a common unit of measure on the basis of their approximate relative energy content (without considering their relative sales values). However, if the relative proportion of gas and oil extracted in the current period is expected to continue throughout the remaining productive life of the property, unit-of-production amortization may be computed on the basis of one of the two minerals only; similarly, if either oil or gas clearly dominates both the reserves and the current production (with dominance determined on the basis of relative energy content), unit-of-production amortization may be computed on the basis of the dominant mineral only. [FAS19, ¶38]

Information Available after the Balance Sheet Date

.130 Information that becomes available after the end of the period covered by the financial statements but before those financial statements are issued shall be taken into account in evaluating conditions that existed at the balance sheet date, for example, in assessing unproved properties (refer to paragraph .119) and in determining whether an exploratory well or exploratory-type stratigraphic test well had found proved reserves (refer to paragraphs .122 through .125). [FAS19, ¶39] If an exploratory well or exploratory-type stratigraphic test well is in progress at the end of a period and the well is determined not to have found proved reserves before the financial statements for that period are issued, the costs incurred through the end of the period, net of any salvage value, shall be charged to expense for that period. Previously issued financial statements shall not be retroactively restated. [FIN36, ¶2]

Surrender or Abandonment of Properties

.131 When an unproved property is surrendered, abandoned, or otherwise deemed worthless, capitalized acquisition costs relating thereto shall be charged against the related allowance for impairment to the extent an allowance has been provided; if the allowance previously provided is inadequate, a loss shall be recognized. [FAS19, ¶40]

.132 Normally, no gain or loss shall be recognized if only an individual well or individual item of equipment is abandoned or retired or if only a single lease or other part of a group of proved properties constituting the amortization base is abandoned or retired as long as the remainder of the property or group of properties continues to produce oil or gas. Instead, the asset being abandoned or retired shall be deemed to be fully amortized, and its cost shall be charged to accumulated depreciation, depletion, or amortization. When the last well on an individual property (if that is the amortization base) or group of properties (if amortization is determined on the basis of an aggregation of properties with a common geological structure) ceases to produce and the entire property or property group is abandoned, gain or loss shall be recognized. Occasionally, the partial abandonment or retirement of a proved property or group of proved properties or the abandonment or retirement of wells or related equipment or facilities may result from a catastrophic event or other major abnormality. In those cases, a loss shall be recognized at the time of abandonment or retirement. [FAS19, ¶41]

Mineral Property Conveyances and Related Transactions

.133 Mineral interests in properties are frequently conveyed to others for a variety of reasons, including the desire to spread risks, to obtain financing, to improve operating efficiency, and to achieve tax benefits. Conveyances of those interests may involve the transfer of all or a part of the rights and responsibilities of operating a property (operating interest). The transferor may or may not retain an interest in the oil and gas produced that is free of the responsibilities and costs of operating the property (a nonoperating interest). A transaction may, on the other hand, involve the transfer of a nonoperating interest to another party and retention of the operating interest. [FAS19, ¶42]

.134 Certain transactions, sometimes referred to as conveyances, are in substance borrowings repayable in cash or its equivalent and shall be accounted for as borrowings. The following are examples of such transactions:

a. Enterprises seeking supplies of oil or gas sometimes make cash advances to operators to finance exploration in return for the right to purchase oil or gas discovered. Funds advanced for exploration that are repayable by offset against purchases of oil or gas discovered, or in cash if insufficient oil or gas is produced by a specified date, shall be accounted for as a receivable by the lender and as a payable by the operator.

b. Funds advanced to an operator that are repayable in cash out of the proceeds from a specified share of future production of a producing property, until the amount advanced plus interest at a specified or determinable rate is paid in full, shall be accounted for as a borrowing. The advance is a payable for the recipient of the cash and receivable for the party making the advance. Such transactions, as well as those described in paragraph .138(a), are commonly referred to as production payments. The two types differ in substance, however, as explained in paragraph .138(a).

[FAS19, ¶43]

.135 In a [FAS153, ¶3(a)] pooling of assets in a joint undertaking intended to find, develop, or produce oil or gas from a particular property or group of properties, [FAS145, ¶9(d)] gain or loss shall not be recognized at the time of conveyance. [FAS153, ¶3(a)]

.136 In the following types of conveyances, gain shall not be recognized at the time of the conveyance:

a. A part of an interest owned is sold and substantial uncertainty exists about recovery of the costs applicable to the retained interest.

b. A part of an interest owned is sold and the seller has a substantial obligation for future performance, such as an obligation to drill a well or to operate the property without proportional reimbursement for that portion of the drilling or operating costs applicable to the interest sold.

[FAS19, ¶45]

.137 If a conveyance is not one of the types described in paragraphs .135 and .136, gain or loss shall be recognized unless there are other aspects of the transaction that would prohibit such recognition under accounting principles applicable to enterprises in general. [FAS19, ¶46]

.138 In accordance with paragraphs .135 through .137, the following types of transactions shall be accounted for as indicated in each example.[3] No attempt has been made to include the many variations of those arrangements that occur, but paragraphs .135 through .137 shall, where applicable, determine the accounting for those other arrangements as well.

a. Some production payments differ from those described in paragraph .134(b) in that the seller's obligation is not expressed in monetary terms but as an obligation to deliver, free and clear of all expenses associated with operation of the property, a specified quantity of oil or gas to the purchaser out of a specified share of future production. Such a transaction is a sale of a mineral interest for which gain shall not be recognized because the seller has a substantial obligation for future performance. The seller shall account for the funds received as unearned revenue to be recognized as the oil or gas is delivered. The purchaser of such a production payment has acquired an interest in a mineral property that shall be recorded at cost and amortized by the unit-of-production method as delivery takes place. The related reserve estimates and production data shall be reported as those of the purchaser of the production payment and not of the seller (refer to paragraphs .160 through .167).

b.   An assignment of the operating interest in an unproved property with retention of a nonoperating interest in return for drilling, development, and operation by the assignee is a pooling of assets in a joint undertaking for which the assignor shall not recognize gain or loss. The assignor's cost of the original interest shall become the cost of the interest retained. The assignee shall account for all costs incurred as specified by paragraphs .106 through .132 and shall allocate none of those costs to the mineral interest acquired. If oil or gas is discovered, each party shall report its share of reserves and production (refer to paragraphs .160 through .167).

c.   An assignment of a part of an operating interest in an unproved property in exchange for a "free well" with provision for joint ownership and operation is a pooling of assets in a joint undertaking by the parties. The assignor shall record no cost for the obligatory well; the assignee shall record no costs for the mineral interest acquired. All drilling, development, and operating costs incurred by either party shall be accounted for as provided in paragraphs .106 through .132. If the conveyance agreement requires the assignee to incur geological or geophysical expenditures instead of, or in addition to, a drilling obligation, those costs shall likewise be accounted for by the assignee as provided in paragraphs .106 through .132. If reserves are discovered, each party shall report its share of reserves and production (refer to paragraphs .160 through .167).

d.   A part of an operating interest in an unproved property may be assigned to effect an arrangement called a *carried interest* whereby the assignee (the carrying party) agrees to defray all costs of drilling, developing, and operating the property and is entitled to all of the revenue from production from the property, excluding any third-party interest, until all of the assignee's costs have been recovered, after which the assignor will share in both costs and production. Such an arrangement represents a pooling of assets in a joint undertaking by the assignor and assignee. The carried party shall make no accounting for any costs and revenue until after recoupment (payout) of the carried costs by the carrying party. Subsequent to payout, the carried party shall account for its share of revenue, operating expenses, and (if the agreement provides for subsequent sharing of costs rather than a carried interest) subsequent development costs. During the payout period the carrying party shall record all costs, including those carried, as provided in paragraphs .106 through .132 and shall record all revenue from the property including that applicable to the recovery of costs carried. The carried party shall report as oil or gas reserves only its share of proved reserves estimated to remain after payout, and unit-of-production amortization of the carried party's property cost shall not commence prior to payout. Prior to payout, the carrying party's reserve estimates and production data shall include the quantities applicable to recoupment of the carried costs (refer to paragraphs .160 through .167).

e.   A part of an operating interest owned may be exchanged for a part of an operating interest owned by another party. The purpose of such an arrangement, commonly called a joint venture in the oil and gas industry, often is to avoid duplication of facilities, diversify risks, and achieve operating efficiencies. No gain or loss shall be recognized by either party at the time of the transaction. In some joint ventures which may or may not involve an exchange of interests, the parties may share different elements of costs in different proportions. In such an arrangement, a party may acquire an interest in a property or in wells and related equipment that is disproportionate to the share of costs borne by it. As in the case of a carried interest or a free well, each party shall account for its own cost under the provisions of this section. No gain shall be recognized for the acquisition of an interest in joint assets, the cost of which may have been paid in whole or in part by another party.

f. In a unitization, all the operating and nonoperating participants pool their assets in a producing area (normally a field) to form a single unit and in return receive an undivided interest (of the same type as previously held) in that unit. Unitizations generally are undertaken to obtain operating efficiencies and to enhance recovery of reserves, often through improved recovery operations. Participation in the unit is generally proportionate to the oil and gas reserves contributed by each. Because the properties may be in different stages of development at the time of unitization, some participants may pay cash and others may receive cash to equalize contributions of wells and related equipment and facilities with the ownership interests in reserves. In those circumstances, cash paid by a participant shall be recorded as an additional investment in wells and related equipment and facilities, and cash received by a participant shall be recorded as a recovery of cost. The cost of the assets contributed plus or minus cash paid or received is the cost of the participant's undivided interest in the assets of the unit. Each participant shall include its interest in reporting reserve estimates and production data (refer to paragraphs .160 through .167).

g. If the entire interest in an unproved property is sold for cash or cash equivalent, recognition of gain or loss depends on whether, in applying paragraph .119, impairment had been assessed for that property individually or by amortizing that property as part of a group. If impairment was assessed individually, gain or loss shall be recognized. For a property amortized by providing a valuation allowance on a group basis, neither gain nor loss shall be recognized when an unproved property is sold unless the sales price exceeds the original cost of the property, in which case gain shall be recognized in the amount of such excess.

h. If a part of the interest in an unproved property is sold, even though for cash or cash equivalent, substantial uncertainty usually exists as to recovery of the cost applicable to the interest retained. Consequently, the amount received shall be treated as a recovery of cost.[4] However, if the sales price exceeds the carrying amount of a property whose impairment has been assessed individually in accordance with paragraph .119, or exceeds the original cost of a property amortized by providing a valuation allowance on a group basis, gain shall be recognized in the amount of such excess.

i. The sale of an entire interest in a proved property that constitutes a separate amortization base is not one of the types of conveyances described in paragraph .135 or .136. The difference between the amount of sales proceeds and the unamortized cost shall be recognized as a gain or loss.

j.   The sale of a part of a proved property, or of an entire proved property constituting a part of an amortization base, shall be accounted for as the sale of an asset, and a gain or loss shall be recognized, since it is not one of the conveyances described in paragraph .135 or .136. The unamortized cost of the property or group of properties, a part of which was sold, shall be apportioned to the interest sold and the interest retained on the basis of the fair values of those interests. However, the sale may be accounted for as a normal retirement under the provisions of paragraph .132 with no gain or loss recognized if doing so does not significantly affect the unit-of-production amortization rate.

k.   The sale of the operating interest in a proved property for cash with retention of a nonoperating interest is not one of the types of conveyances described in paragraph .135 or .136. Accordingly, it shall be accounted for as the sale of an asset, and any gain or loss shall be recognized. The seller shall allocate the cost of the proved property to the operating interest sold and the nonoperating interest retained on the basis of the fair values of those interests.[5]

l.   The sale of a proved property subject to a retained production payment that is expressed as a fixed sum of money payable only from a specified share of production from that property, with the purchaser of the property obligated to incur the future costs of operating the property, shall be accounted for as follows:

  (1) *If satisfaction of the retained production payment is reasonably assured.* The seller of the property, who retained the production payment, shall record the transaction as a sale, with recognition of any resulting gain or loss. The retained production payment shall be recorded as a receivable, with interest accounted for in accordance with the provisions of Section I69, "Interest: Imputation of an Interest Cost." The purchaser shall record as the cost of the assets acquired the cash consideration paid plus the present value (determined in accordance with Section I69) of the retained production payment, which shall be recorded as a payable. The oil and gas reserve estimates and production data, including those applicable to liquidation of the retained production payment, shall be reported by the purchaser of the property (refer to paragraphs .160 through .167).

  (2) *If satisfaction of the retained production payment is not reasonably assured.* The transaction is in substance a sale with retention of an overriding royalty that shall be accounted for in accordance with paragraph .138(k).

m.   The sale of a proved property subject to a retained production payment that is expressed as a right to a specified quantity of oil or gas out of a specified share of future production shall be accounted for in accordance with paragraph .138(k).

[FAS19, ¶47]

Accounting for Income Taxes

.139   Some costs incurred in an enterprise's oil and gas producing activities enter into the determination of taxable income and pretax accounting income in different periods. A principal example is intangible drilling and development costs, which are deductible in determining taxable income when incurred but which, for successful exploratory wells and for all development wells, are capitalized and amortized for financial accounting purposes under the provisions of this section. As another example, some geological and geophysical costs, which are charged to expense when incurred under the provisions of this section, are deferred and deducted in subsequent periods for income tax purposes. [FAS19, ¶60]

.140   Comprehensive [recognition of deferred taxes] [FAS19, ¶61] as described in Section I27, "Income Taxes," [FAS109, ¶288(o)] shall be followed by oil and gas producing companies for intangible drilling and development costs and other costs incurred that enter into the determination of taxable income and pretax accounting income in different periods. [FAS19, ¶61]

.141   In applying the comprehensive interperiod income tax allocation provision of the preceding paragraph, the possibility that statutory depletion in future periods will reduce or eliminate   [FAS19, ¶62] taxable income in future years shall be considered in determining whether it is more likely than not that the tax benefits of deferred tax assets will not be realized. However, the tax benefit of the [FAS109, ¶288(o)] excess of statutory depletion over cost depletion for tax purposes [FAS19, ¶62] shall not be recognized until [FAS109, ¶288(o)] the period in which the excess is deducted for income tax purposes. [FAS19, ¶62]

Impairment Test for Proved Properties and Capitalized Exploration and Development Cost

.141A   The provisions of paragraphs .139 through .161 of Section I08 are applicable to the costs of an enterprise's wells and related equipment and facilities and the costs of the related proved properties. The impairment provisions relating to unproved properties referred to in paragraphs .104, .118 through .120, .122(b), .124, .131, .138(g), and .138(h) of this section remain applicable to unproved properties. [FAS144, ¶C25]

Capitalizing Interest under Full Cost Method

.142   [Section I67, "Interest: Capitalization of Interest Costs," paragraph .108, provides guidance on accounting for interest costs for enterprises that use the full cost method of accounting for oil and gas producing activities.]

.143-.155   [Deleted 11/82 because of FASB Statement 69, *Disclosures about Oil and Gas Producing Activities*.]

NOTES TO Oi5 OIL AND GAS PRODUCING ACTIVITIES

[1]   Often referred to in the oil and gas industry as *lease and well equipment* even though, technically, the property may have been acquired other than by a lease. [FAS19, ¶11, fn1]

[2]   [Although] the costs of drilling stratigraphic test wells are sometimes considered to be geological and geophysical costs, they are accounted for separately in this section. [FAS19, ¶17, fn2]

2aa   To meet this criterion, an enterprise is not required to complete the exploratory or exploratory-type stratigraphic well as a producing well. [FSP FAS 19-1, ¶9]

2ab   For purposes of determining whether capitalized drilling costs shall continue to be capitalized pending the determination of proved reserves, a project may include more than one exploratory well or exploratory-type stratigraphic well if the reserves are intended to be extracted in a single, integrated producing operation (for example, the producing wells will operate with shared infrastructure). [FSP FAS 19-1, ¶9]

2a   [Deleted 4/02 because of FASB Statement 145, *Rescission of FASB Statements No. 4, 44, and 64, Amendment of FASB Statement No. 13, and Technical Corrections*.]

[3]   Costs of unproved properties are always subject to an assessment for impairment as required by paragraph .119. [FAS19, ¶47, fn3]

[4]   The carrying amount of the interest retained shall continue to be subject to the assessment for impairment as required by paragraph .119. [FAS19, ¶47, fn4]

[5]   A retained production payment denominated in money is not a mineral interest (refer to paragraphs .103 and .134). [FAS19, ¶47, fn5]

Disclosures

.156 All enterprises engaged in oil and gas producing activities shall disclose in their financial statements the method of accounting for costs incurred in those activities and the manner of disposing of capitalized costs relating to those activities

.157 In addition, publicly traded enterprises[6] that have significant oil and gas producing activities shall disclose with **complete sets of annual financial statements**[7] the information required by paragraphs .160 through .184. Those disclosures relate to the following and are considered to be supplementary information:

  a. Proved oil and gas reserve quantities

  b. Capitalized costs relating to oil and gas producing activities

  c. Costs incurred for property acquisition, exploration, and development activities

  d. Results of operations for oil and gas producing activities

  e. A standardized measure of discounted future net cash flows relating to proved oil and gas reserve quantities.

[FAS69, ¶7]

.158 For purposes of this section, an enterprise is regarded as having significant oil and gas producing activities if it satisfies one or more of the following tests. The tests shall be applied separately for each year for which a complete set of annual financial statements is presented.

  a. Revenues from oil and gas producing activities, as defined in paragraph .175 (including both sales to unaffiliated customers and sales or transfers to the enterprise's other operations), are 10 percent or more of the combined revenues (sales to unaffiliated customers and sales or transfers to the enterprise's other operations) of all of the enterprise's **industry segments**.[8]

  b. Results of operations for oil and gas producing activities, excluding the effect of income taxes, are 10 percent or more of the greater of:

    (1) The combined operating profit of all industry segments that did not incur an operating loss

    (2) The combined operating loss of all industry segments that did incur an operating loss [FAS69, ¶8]

  c. The identifiable assets of oil- and gas-producing activities (tangible and intangible enterprise assets that are used by oil- and gas-producing activities, including an allocated portion of assets used jointly with other operations) are 10 percent or more of the assets of the enterprise, excluding assets used exclusively for general corporate purposes. [FAS131, ¶133(b)]

.159 The disclosures set forth in this section are not required in interim financial reports. However, interim financial reports shall include information about a major discovery or other favorable or adverse event that causes a significant change from the information presented in the most recent annual financial report concerning oil and gas reserve quantities. [FAS69, ¶9]

Disclosure of Proved Oil and Gas Reserve Quantities

.160 Net quantities of an enterprise's interests in proved reserves and proved developed reserves of (a) crude oil (including condensate and natural gas liquids)[9] and (b) natural gas shall be disclosed as of the beginning and the end of the year. "Net" quantities of reserves include those relating to the enterprise's operating and nonoperating interests in properties as defined in paragraph .103(a). Quantities of reserves relating to royalty interests owned shall be included in "net" quantities if the necessary information is available to the enterprise; if reserves relating to royalty interests owned are not included because the information is unavailable, that fact and the enterprise's share of oil and gas produced for those royalty interests shall be disclosed for the year. "Net" quantities shall not include reserves relating to interests of others in properties owned by the enterprise. [FAS69, ¶10]

.161 Changes in the net quantities of an enterprise's proved reserves of oil and of gas during the year shall be disclosed. Changes resulting from each of the following shall be shown separately with appropriate explanation of significant changes:

   a. *Revisions of previous estimates.* Revisions represent changes in previous estimates of proved reserves, either upward or downward, resulting from new information (except for an increase in proved acreage) normally obtained from development drilling and production history or resulting from a change in economic factors.

   b. *Improved recovery.* Changes in reserve estimates resulting from application of improved recovery techniques shall be shown separately, if significant. If not significant, such changes shall be included in revisions of previous estimates.

   c. *Purchases of minerals in place.*

   d. *Extensions and discoveries.* Additions to proved reserves that result from (1) extension of the proved acreage of previously discovered (old) reservoirs through additional drilling in periods subsequent to discovery and (2) discovery of new fields with proved reserves or of new reservoirs of proved reserves in old fields.

   e. *Production.*

   f. *Sales of minerals in place.*

   [FAS69, ¶11]

.162 If an enterprise's proved reserves of oil and of gas are located entirely within its home country, that fact shall be disclosed. If some or all of its reserves are located in foreign countries, the disclosures of net quantities of reserves of oil and of gas and changes in them required by paragraphs .160 and .161 shall be separately disclosed for (a) the enterprise's home country (if significant reserves are located there) and (b) each **foreign geographic area** in which significant reserves are located. Foreign geographic areas are individual countries or groups of countries as appropriate for meaningful disclosure in the circumstances. [FAS69, ¶12]

.163 Net quantities disclosed in conformity with paragraphs .160 through .162 shall not include oil or gas subject to purchase under long-term supply, purchase, or similar agreements and contracts, including such agreements with governments or authorities. However, quantities of oil or gas subject to such agreements with governments or authorities as of the end of the year, and the net quantity of oil or gas received under the agreements during the year, shall be separately disclosed if the enterprise participates in the operation of the properties in which the oil or gas is located or otherwise serves as the "producer" of those reserves, as opposed, for example, to being an independent purchaser, broker, dealer, or importer. [FAS69, ¶13]

.164 In determining the reserve quantities to be disclosed in conformity with paragraphs .160 through .163:

a. If the enterprise issues consolidated financial statements, 100 percent of the net reserve quantities attributable to the parent company and 100 percent of the net reserve quantities attributable to its consolidated subsidiaries (whether or not wholly owned) shall be included. If a significant portion of those reserve quantities at the end of the year is attributable to a consolidated subsidiary(ies) in which there is a significant minority interest, that fact and the approximate portion shall be disclosed.

b. If the enterprise's financial statements include investments that are proportionately consolidated, the enterprise's reserve quantities shall include its proportionate share of the investees' net oil and gas reserves.

c. If the enterprise's financial statements include investments that are accounted for by the equity method, the investees' net oil and gas reserve quantities shall *not* be included in the disclosures of the enterprise's reserve quantities. However, the enterprise's (investor's) share of the investees' net oil and gas reserve quantities shall be separately disclosed as of the end of the year.

[FAS69, ¶14]

.165 In reporting reserve quantities and changes in them, oil reserves and natural gas liquids reserves shall be stated in barrels, and gas reserves in cubic feet. [FAS69, ¶15]

.166 If important economic factors or significant uncertainties affect particular components of an enterprise's proved reserves, explanation shall be provided. Examples include unusually high expected development or lifting costs, the necessity to build a major pipeline or other major facilities before production of the reserves can begin, and contractual obligations to produce and sell a significant portion of reserves at prices that are substantially below those at which the oil or gas could otherwise be sold in the absence of the contractual obligation. [FAS69, ¶16]

.167 If a government restricts the disclosure of estimated reserves for properties under its authority, or of amounts under long-term supply, purchase, or similar agreements or contracts, or if the government requires the disclosure of reserves other than proved, the enterprise shall indicate that the disclosed reserve estimates or amounts do not include figures for the named country or that reserve estimates include reserves other than proved. [FAS69, ¶17]

Disclosure of Capitalized Costs Relating to Oil and Gas Producing Activities

.168 The aggregate capitalized costs relating to an enterprise's oil and gas producing activities (refer to paragraph .103) and the aggregate related accumulated depreciation, depletion, amortization, and valuation allowances shall be disclosed as of the end of the year. Section D40, "Depreciation," paragraph .105, requires disclosure of "balances of major classes of depreciable assets, by nature or function." Thus, separate disclosure of capitalized costs for asset categories (a) through (d) in paragraph .103 or for a combination of those categories often may be appropriate. [FAS69, ¶18]

.169 If significant, capitalized costs of unproved properties shall be separately disclosed. Capitalized costs of support equipment and facilities may be disclosed separately or included, as appropriate, with capitalized costs of proved and unproved properties. [FAS69, ¶19]

.170 If the enterprise's financial statements include investments that are accounted for by the equity method, the enterprise's share of the investees' net capitalized costs relating to oil and gas producing activities as of the end of the year shall be separately disclosed. [FAS69, ¶20]

Disclosure of Costs Incurred in Oil and Gas Property Acquisition, Exploration, and Development Activities

.171 Each of the following types of costs for the year shall be disclosed (whether those costs are capitalized or charged to expense at the time they are incurred under the provisions of paragraphs .106 through .113):[10]

    a. Property acquisition costs

    b. Exploration costs

    c. Development costs

[FAS69, ¶21]

.172 If some or all of those costs are incurred in foreign countries, the amounts shall be disclosed separately for each of the geographic areas for which reserve quantities are disclosed (refer to paragraph .162). If significant costs have been incurred to acquire mineral interests that have proved reserves, those costs shall be disclosed separately from the costs of acquiring unproved properties. [FAS69, ¶22]

.173 If the enterprise's financial statements include investments that are accounted for by the equity method, the enterprise's share of the investees' property acquisition, exploration, and development costs incurred in oil and gas producing activities shall be separately disclosed for the year, in the aggregate and for each geographic area for which reserve quantities are disclosed (refer to paragraph .162). [FAS69, ¶23]

Disclosure of the Results of Operations for Oil and Gas Producing Activities

.174 The results of operations for oil and gas producing activities shall be disclosed for the year. That information shall be disclosed in the aggregate and for each geographic area for which reserve quantities are disclosed (refer to paragraph .162). The following information relating to those activities shall be presented:[11]

    a. Revenues

    b. Production (lifting) costs

    c. Exploration expenses[12]

    d. Depreciation, depletion, and amortization, and valuation provisions

    e. Income tax expenses

    f. Results of operations for oil and gas producing activities (excluding corporate overhead and interest costs)

[FAS69, ¶24]

.175 Revenues shall include sales to unaffiliated enterprises and sales or transfers to the enterprise's other operations (for example, refineries or chemical plants). Sales to unaffiliated enterprises and sales or transfers to the enterprise's other operations shall be disclosed separately. Revenues shall include sales to unaffiliated enterprises attributable to net working interests, royalty interests, oil payment interests, and net profits interests of the reporting enterprise. Sales or transfers to the enterprise's other operations shall be based on market prices determined at the point of delivery from the producing unit. Those market prices shall represent prices equivalent to those that could be obtained in an arm's-length transaction. Production or severance taxes shall not be deducted in determining gross revenues, but rather shall be included as part of production costs. Royalty payments and net profits disbursements shall be excluded from gross revenues. [FAS69, ¶25]

.176 Income taxes shall be computed using the statutory tax rate for the period, applied to revenues less production (lifting) costs, exploration expenses, depreciation, depletion, and amortization, and valuation provisions. Calculation of income tax expenses shall reflect [FAS69, ¶26] tax deductions, [FAS109, ¶288(u)] tax credits and allowances relating to the oil and gas producing activities that are reflected in the enterprise's consolidated income tax expense for the period. [FAS69, ¶26]

.177 Results of operations for oil and gas producing activities are defined as revenues less production (lifting) costs, exploration expenses, depreciation, depletion, and amortization, valuation provisions, and income tax expenses. General corporate overhead and interest costs[13] shall not be deducted in computing the results of operations for an enterprise's oil and gas producing activities. However, some expenses incurred at an enterprise's central administrative office may not be general corporate expenses, but rather may be operating expenses of oil and gas producing activities, and therefore should be reported as such. The nature of an expense rather than the location of its incurrence shall determine whether it is an operating expense. Only those expenses identified by their nature as operating expenses shall be allocated as operating expenses in computing the results of operations for oil and gas producing activities. [FAS69, ¶27]

.178 The amounts disclosed in conformity with paragraphs .174 through .177 shall include an enterprise's interests in proved oil and gas reserves (refer to paragraph .160) and in oil and gas subject to purchase under long-term supply, purchase, or similar agreements and contracts in which the enterprise participates in the operation of the properties on which the oil or gas is located or otherwise serves as the producer of those reserves (refer to paragraph .163). [FAS69, ¶28]

.179 If the enterprise's financial statements include investments that are accounted for by the equity method, the investees' results of operations for oil and gas producing activities shall not be included in the enterprise's results of operations for oil and gas producing activities. However, the enterprise's share of the investees' results of operations for oil and gas producing activities shall be separately disclosed for the year, in the aggregate and by each geographic area for which reserve quantities are disclosed (refer to paragraph .162). [FAS69, ¶29]

Disclosure of a Standardized Measure of Discounted Future Net Cash Flows Relating to Proved Oil and Gas Reserve Quantities

.180 A standardized measure of discounted future net cash flows relating to an enterprise's interests in (a) proved oil and gas reserves (refer to paragraph .160) and (b) oil and gas subject to purchase under long-term supply, purchase, or similar agreements and contracts in which the enterprise participates in the operation of the properties on which the oil or gas is located or otherwise serves as the producer of those reserves (refer to paragraph .163) shall be disclosed as of the end of the year. The standardized measure of discounted future net cash flows relating to those two types of interests in reserves may be combined for reporting purposes. The following information shall be disclosed in the aggregate and for each geographic area for which reserve quantities are disclosed in accordance with paragraph .162:

a. *Future cash inflows.* These shall be computed by applying year-end prices of oil and gas relating to the enterprise's proved reserves to the year-end quantities of those reserves. Future price changes shall be considered only to the extent provided by contractual arrangements in existence at year-end.

b. *Future development and production costs.* These costs shall be computed by estimating the expenditures to be incurred in developing and producing the proved oil and gas reserves at the end of the year, based on year-end costs and assuming continuation of existing economic conditions. If estimated development expenditures are significant, they shall be presented separately from estimated production costs.

c. *Future income tax expenses.* These expenses shall be computed by applying the appropriate year-end statutory tax rates, with consideration of future tax rates already legislated, to the future pretax net cash flows relating to the enterprise's proved oil and gas reserves, less the tax basis of the properties involved. The future income tax expenses shall give effect to [FAS69, ¶30] tax deductions, [FAS109, ¶288(u)] tax credits and allowances relating to the enterprise's proved oil and gas reserves.

d. *Future net cash flows.* These amounts are the result of subtracting future development and production costs and future income tax expenses from future cash inflows.

e. *Discount.* This amount shall be derived from using a discount rate of 10 percent a year to reflect the timing of the future net cash flows relating to proved oil and gas reserves.

f. *Standardized measure of discounted future net cash flows.* This amount is the future net cash flows less the computed discount.

[FAS69, ¶30]

.181 If a significant portion of the economic interest in the consolidated standardized measure of discounted future net cash flows reported is attributable to a consolidated subsidiary(ies) in which there is a significant minority interest, that fact and the approximate portion shall be disclosed. [FAS69, ¶31]

.182 If the financial statements include investments that are accounted for by the equity method, the investees' standardized measure of discounted future net cash flows relating to proved oil and gas reserves shall not be included in the disclosure of the enterprise's standardized measure. However, the enterprise's share of the investees' standardized measure of discounted future net cash flows shall be separately disclosed for the year, in the aggregate and by each geographic area for which quantities are disclosed (refer to paragraph .162). [FAS69, ¶32]

.183 The aggregate change in the standardized measure of discounted future net cash flows shall be disclosed for the year. If individually significant, the following sources of change shall be presented separately:

a. Net change in sales and transfer prices and in production (lifting) costs related to future production

b. Changes in estimated future development costs

c. Sales and transfers of oil and gas produced during the period

d. Net change due to extensions, discoveries, and improved recovery

e. Net change due to purchases and sales of minerals in place

f. Net change due to revisions in quantity estimates

g. Previously estimated development costs incurred during the period

h. Accretion of discount

i. Other—unspecified

j. Net change in income taxes

In computing the amounts under each of the above categories, the effects of changes in prices and costs shall be computed before the effects of changes in quantities. As a result, changes in quantities shall be stated at year-end prices and costs. The change in computed income taxes shall reflect the effect of income taxes incurred during the period as well as the change in future income tax expenses. Therefore, all changes except income taxes shall be reported pretax. [FAS69, ¶33]

.184 Additional information necessary to prevent the disclosure of the standardized measure of discounted future net cash flows and changes therein from being misleading also shall be provided. [FAS69, ¶34]

NOTES TO Oi5 DISCLOSURES

[5a] [FAS69, ¶6] [6]For purposes of this section, a publicly traded enterprise is a business enterprise (a) whose securities are traded in a public market on a domestic stock exchange or in the domestic over-the-counter market (including securities quoted only locally or regionally) or (b) whose financial statements are filed with a regulatory agency in preparation for the sale of any class of securities in a domestic market. [FAS69, ¶1, fn2]

    [5a] [Paragraphs .811 and .813 contain additional disclosure requirements.]

[7   Editorial deletion, 6/97.]

[8]   For purposes of this section, an industry segment is a component of an enterprise engaged in providing a product or service or a group of related products or services primarily to external customers (that is, customers outside the enterprise) for a profit. [FAS131, ¶133(a)]

[9]   If significant, the reserve quantity information shall be disclosed separately for natural gas liquids. [FAS69, ¶10, fn5]

[10] As defined in the paragraphs cited, exploration and development costs include depreciation of support equipment and facilities used in those activities and do not include the expenditures to acquire support equipment and facilities. [FAS69, ¶21, fn6]

[11] If oil and gas producing activities represent substantially all of the business activities of the reporting enterprise and those oil and gas activities are located substantially in a single geographic area, the information required by paragraphs .174 through .179 need not be disclosed if that information is provided elsewhere in the financial statements [FAS69, ¶24, fn7] If oil- and gas-producing activities constitute an operating segment, as discussed in paragraphs .109 through .123 of Section S30, "Segment Disclosures and Related Information," information about the results of operations required by paragraphs .174 through .179 of this section may be included with segment information disclosed elsewhere in the financial report. [FAS131, ¶133(c)]

[12] Generally, only enterprises utilizing the successful efforts accounting method will have exploration expenses to disclose, since enterprises utilizing the full cost accounting method generally capitalize all exploration costs when incurred and subsequently reflect those costs in the determination of earnings through depreciation, depletion, and amortization, and valuation provisions. [FAS69, ¶24, fn8]

[13] The disposition of interest costs that have been capitalized as part of the cost of acquiring qualifying assets used in oil and gas producing activities shall be the same as that of other components of those assets' costs. [FAS69, ¶27, fn9]

Summaries and Illustrations of Certain Disclosures about Oil and Gas Producing Activities

.185 Following are summaries and illustrations of certain of the disclosure requirements for oil and gas producing activities required by this section.

	Disclosure Illustration
Accounting Method	
Method of accounting for costs incurred and the manner of disposing of capitalized costs relating to oil and gas producing activities	—
Capitalized Costs	
Aggregate amount of capitalized costs and related accumulated depreciation, depletion, and amortization, and valuation allowances (If significant, capitalized costs of unproved properties shall be separately disclosed.)	1
Enterprise's share of equity method investees' capitalized costs in the aggregate at the end of the year	1
Costs Incurred in Oil and Gas Property Acquisition, Exploration, and Development	
Costs incurred in oil and gas producing activities in the aggregate, by type, and by geographic area during the year (If significant, costs of acquiring existing mineral interests that have proved reserves shall be disclosed separately from the costs of acquiring unproved properties.)	2
Enterprise's share of equity method investees' costs incurred in the aggregate and by geographic area during the year	2
Results of Operations	
Results of operations for the year from oil and gas producing activities and the major components of those activities in the aggregate and by geographic area	3
Enterprise's share of equity method investees' results of operations for the year from oil and gas producing activities in the aggregate and by geographic area	3
Reserve Quantity Information	
Net quantities of proved reserves and proved developed reserves at the beginning and end of the year and changes in proved reserves in the aggregate, by type, and by geographic area	4
Reserves subject to purchase under supply agreements with governments or authorities in which the enterprise acts as producer, and reserves received under those agreements during the year in the aggregate and by geographic area	4
Enterprise's share of equity method investees' proved reserves at the end of the year in the aggregate and by geographic area	4
Approximate portion of reserve quantities at the end of the year attributable to a consolidated subsidiary(ies) in which there is a significant minority interest	4
Important economic factors and significant uncertainties affecting an enterprise's proved reserves	—
Governmental restrictions on reporting reserve information	—

Standardized Measure of Discounted Future Net Cash Flows

Standardized measure of discounted future net cash flows and major components of that calculation relating to proved reserve quantities (including those relating to long-term supply agreements for which the enterprise acts as producer) at the end of the year in the aggregate and by geographic area, based on year-end prices, costs, and statutory tax rates (adjusted for [FAS69, ¶40] tax deductions [FAS109, ¶288(u)]) and a 10-percent annual discount rate   5

Enterprise's share of equity method investees' standardized measure of discounted future net cash flows in the aggregate and by geographic area   5

Approximate portion of economic interests in the consolidated standardized measure of discounted future net cash flows at the end of the year attributable to a consolidated subsidiary(ies) in which there is a significant minority interest   5

Summary of changes in the standardized measure of discounted future net cash flows during the year in the aggregate   5

Additional information concerning the standardized measure of discounted future net cash flows required to prevent the information from being misleading   —

[FAS69, ¶40]

.186 The following illustrations present formats that may be used to disclose certain information required by this section when a complete set of annual financial statements is presented for one year.

Illustration 1

Capitalized Costs Relating to Oil and Gas Producing Activities at December 31, 20XX

	Total
Unproved oil and gas properties	$X
Proved oil and gas properties	X
	X
Accumulated depreciation, depletion, and amortization, and valuation allowances	X
Net capitalized costs	$X
Enterprise's share of equity method investees' net capitalized costs	$X

Illustration 2

Costs Incurred in Oil and Gas Property Acquisition, Exploration, and Development Activities for the Year Ended December 31, 20XX

	Total	United States	Foreign Geographic Area A	Foreign Geographic Area B	Other Foreign Geographic Areas
Acquisition of properties					
- Proved	$X	$X	$X	$X	$X
- Unproved	X	X	X	X	X
Exploration costs	X	X	X	X	X
Development costs	X	X	X	X	X
Enterprise's share of equity method investees' costs of property acquisition, exploration, and development	X	X	X	X	X

Illustration 3

Results of Operations for Producing Activities for the Year Ended December 31, 20XX

	Total	United States	Foreign Geographic Area A	Foreign Geographic Area B	Other Foreign Geographic Areas
Revenues					
Sales	$ X	$ X	$ X	$ X	$ X
Transfers	X	X	X	X	X
Total	X	X	X	X	X
Production costs	(X)	(X)	(X)	(X)	(X)
Exploration expenses	(X)	(X)	(X)	(X)	(X)
Depreciation, depletion, and amortization, and valuation provisions	(X)	(X)	(X)	(X)	(X)
	X	X	X	X	X
Income tax expenses	(X)	(X)	(X)	(X)	(X)
Results of operations from producing activities (excluding corporate overhead and interest costs)	$ X	$ X	$ X	$ X	$ X
Enterprise's share of equity method investees' results of operations for producing activities	$ X	$ X	$ X	$ X	$ X

Illustration 4

Reserve Quantity Information*
for the Year Ended December 31, 20XX

	Total		United States		Foreign Geographic Area A		Foreign Geographic Area B		Other Foreign Geographic Areas	
	Oil	Gas	Oil	Gas	Oil	Gas	Oil	Gas	Oil	Gas
Proved developed and undeveloped reserves:										
Beginning of year	X	X	X	X	X	X	X	X	X	X
Revisions of previous estimates	X	X	X	X	X	X	X	X	X	X
Improved recovery	X	X	X	X	X	X	X	X	X	X
Purchases of minerals in place	X	X	X	X	X	X	X	X	X	X
Extensions and discoveries	X	X	X	X	X	X	X	X	X	X
Production	(X)	(X)	(X)	(X)	(X)	(X)	(X)	(X)	(X)	(X)
Sales of minerals in place	(X)	(X)	(X)	(X)	(X)	(X)	(X)	(X)	(X)	(X)
End of year	X†	X	X	X	X	X	X	X	X	X
Proved developed reserves:										
Beginning of year	X	X	X	X	X	X	X	X	X	X
End of year	X	X	X	X	X	X	X	X	X	X
Oil and gas applicable to long-term supply agreements with governments or authorities in which the enterprise acts as producer:										
Proved reserves—end of year	X	X			X	X				
Received during the year	X	X			X	X				
Enterprise's proportional interest in reserves of investees accounted for by the equity method—end of year	X	X	X	X	X	X	X	X	X	X

* Oil reserves stated in barrels; gas reserves stated in cubic feet.
† Includes reserves of X barrels attributable to a consolidated subsidiary in which there is an X-percent minority interest.

Illustration 5

Standardized Measure of Discounted Future Net Cash Flows and Changes Therein Relating to Proved Oil and Gas Reserves at December 31, 20XX

	Total	United States	Foreign Geographic Area A	Foreign Geographic Area B	Other Foreign Geographic Areas
Future cash inflows*	$ X	$ X	$ X	$ X	$ X
Future production and development costs*	(X)	(X)	(X)	(X)	(X)
Future income tax expenses*	(X)	(X)	(X)	(X)	(X)
Future net cash flows	X	X	X	X	X
10% annual discount for estimated timing of cash flows	(X)	(X)	(X)	(X)	(X)
Standardized measure of discounted future net cash flows	$ X†	$ X	$ X	$ X	$ X
Enterprise's share equity method investees' standardized measure of discounted future net cash flows	$ X	$ X	$ X	$ X	$ X

The following are the principal sources of change in the standardized measure of discounted future net cash flows during 20XX:

Sales and transfers of oil and gas produced, net of production costs	$(X)
Net changes in prices and production costs	X
Extensions, discoveries, and improved recovery, less related costs	X
Development costs incurred during the period	(X)
Revisions of previous quantity estimates	X
Accretion of discount	X
Net change in income taxes	X
Other	X

[FAS69, ¶41]

---

* Future net cash flows were computed using year-end prices and costs, and year-end statutory tax rates (adjusted for [FAS69, ¶41] tax deductions [FAS109, ¶288(u)]) that relate to existing proved oil and gas reserves in which the enterprise has mineral interests, including those mineral interests related to long-term supply agreements with governments for which the enterprise serves as the producer of the reserves.

† Includes $X attributable to a consolidated subsidiary in which there is an X-percent minority interest. [FAS69, ¶41]

Glossary

.400 Complete set of financial statements. A set of financial statements (including necessary footnotes) that present financial position, results of operations, and [FAS69, ¶1, fn3] cash flows [FAS95, ¶152(g)] in conformity with generally accepted accounting principles. [FAS69, ¶1, fn3]

.401 Development well. A well drilled within the **proved area** of an oil or gas reservoir to the depth of a stratigraphic horizon known to be productive. [FAS19, ¶274]

.402 Exploratory well. A well that is not a development well, a service well, or a stratigraphic test well, as those terms are defined in this section. [FAS19, ¶274]

.403 Field. An area consisting of a single reservoir or multiple reservoirs all grouped on or related to the same individual geological structural feature or stratigraphic condition, or both. There may be two or more reservoirs in a field which are separated vertically by intervening impervious strata, or laterally by local geologic barriers, or by both. Reservoirs that are associated by being in overlapping or adjacent fields may be treated as a single or common operational field. The geological terms *structural feature* and *stratigraphic condition* are intended to identify localized geological features as opposed to the broader terms of *basins, trends, provinces, plays, areas of interest,* etc. [FAS19, ¶272]

.403A Foreign geographic area. Individual countries or groups of countries as appropriate for meaningful disclosure in the circumstances. [FAS69, ¶12]

.403B Industry segment. A component of an enterprise engaged in providing a product or service or a group of related products or services primarily to external customers (that is, customers outside the enterprise) for a profit. [FAS131, ¶133(a)]

.403C Oil and gas producing activities. Those activities [that] involve the acquisition of mineral interests in properties, exploration (including prospecting), development, and production of crude oil, including condensate and natural gas liquids, and natural gas. [FAS19, ¶1]

.404 Proved area. The part of a property to which proved reserves have been specifically attributed. [FAS19, ¶275]

.405 Proved reserves.[401]

  a. *Proved oil and gas reserves.* The estimated quantities of crude oil, natural gas, and natural gas liquids which geological and engineering data demonstrate with reasonable certainty to be recoverable in future years from known reservoirs under existing economic and operating conditions, that is, prices and costs as of the date the estimate is made. Prices include consideration of changes in existing prices provided only by contractual arrangements but not on escalations based upon future conditions.

  (1) Reservoirs are considered proved if economic producibility is supported by either actual production or conclusive formation test. The area of a reservoir considered proved includes (a) that portion delineated by drilling and defined by gas-oil or oil-water contacts, if any, or both, and (b) the immediately adjoining portions not yet drilled, but which can be reasonably judged as economically productive on the basis of available geological and engineering data. In the absence of information on fluid contacts, the lowest known structural occurrence of hydrocarbons controls the lower proved limit of the reservoir.

(2) Reserves that can be produced economically through application of improved recovery techniques (such as fluid injection) are included in the *proved* classification if successful testing by a pilot project, or the operation of an installed program in the reservoir, provides support for the engineering analysis on which the project or program was based.

(3) Estimates of proved reserves do not include the following: (a) oil that may become available from known reservoirs but is classified separately as *indicated additional reserves*; (b) crude oil, natural gas, and natural gas liquids, the recovery of which is subject to reasonable doubt because of uncertainty as to geology, reservoir characteristics, or economic factors; (c) crude oil, natural gas, and natural gas liquids that may occur in undrilled prospects; and (d) crude oil, natural gas, and natural gas liquids that may be recovered from oil shales, coal, gilsonite, and other such sources.

b. *Proved developed oil and gas reserves.* Proved developed oil and gas reserves are reserves that can be expected to be recovered through existing wells with existing equipment and operating methods. Additional oil and gas expected to be obtained through the application of fluid injection or other improved recovery techniques for supplementing the natural forces and mechanisms of primary recovery should be included as *proved developed reserves* only after testing by a pilot project or after the operation of an installed program has confirmed through production response that increased recovery will be achieved.

c. *Proved undeveloped reserves.* Proved undeveloped oil and gas reserves are reserves that are expected to be recovered from new wells on undrilled acreage, or from existing wells for which a relatively major expenditure is required for recompletion. Reserves on undrilled acreage should be limited to those drilling units offsetting productive units that are reasonably certain of production when drilled. Proved reserves for other undrilled units can be claimed only if it can be demonstrated with certainty that there is continuity of production from the existing productive formation. Under no circumstances should estimates for proved undeveloped reserves be attributable to any acreage for which an application of fluid injection or other improved recovery technique is contemplated, unless such techniques have been proved effective by actual tests in the area and in the same reservoir. [FAS25, ¶34]

.405A **Publicly traded enterprise.** A business enterprise (a) whose securities are traded in a public market on a domestic stock exchange or in the domestic over-the-counter market (including securities quoted only locally or regionally) or (b) whose financial statements are filed with a regulatory agency in preparation for the sale of any class of securities in a domestic market. [FAS69, ¶1, fn2]

.406 **Reservoir.** A porous and permeable underground formation containing a natural accumulation of producible oil or gas that is confined by impermeable rock or water barriers and is individual and separate from other reservoirs. [FAS19, ¶273]

.407 **Service well.** A service well is a well drilled or completed for the purpose of supporting production in an existing field. Wells in this class are drilled for the following specific purposes: gas injection (natural gas, propane, butane, or flue gas), water injection, steam injection, air injection, salt-water disposal, water supply for injection, observation, or injection for combustion. [FAS19, ¶274]

.408 **Stratigraphic test well.** A stratigraphic test is a drilling effort, geologically directed, to obtain information pertaining to a specific geologic condition. Such wells customarily are drilled without the intention of being completed for hydrocarbon production. This classification also includes tests identified as core tests and all types of expendable holes related to hydrocarbon exploration. For purposes of this section, stratigraphic test wells (sometimes called expendable wells) are classified as follows:

a. *Exploratory-type stratigraphic test well.* A stratigraphic test well not drilled in a proved area.

b. *Development-type stratigraphic test well.* A stratigraphic test well drilled in a proved area.

[FAS19, ¶274]

NOTES TO Oi5 GLOSSARY

[401]The following definitions of proved reserves are those developed by the Department of Energy for its Financial Reporting System and adopted by the SEC on December 19, 1978 in Accounting Series Release 257. Reference should be made to the SEC's reporting requirements for revisions that may have been made since the issuance of ASR 257. [FAS25, ¶34]

Supplemental Guidance: FASB Staff Positions (FSPs)

802 For purposes of paragraphs .810 through .813, a project may include more than one exploratory well or exploratory-type stratigraphic well if the reserves are intended to be extracted in a single integrated producing operation (for example, the producing wells will operate with shared infrastructure). [Posted 4/4/05.] [FSP FAS 19-1]

NOTES TO SUPPLEMENTARY GUIDANCES

801 Exploratory wells and exploratory-type stratigraphic wells, as defined in paragraphs .402 and .408 of this section are referred to collectively as exploratory wells for purposes of paragraphs 809 through .813. [Posted 4/4/05.] [FSP FAS 19-1]

.801 This section contains FASB Staff Positions (FSPs) related to the topic of this section. An FSP that is issued at the direction of the Board is issued after an exposure period and discussion at a public meeting and is considered an official position of the FASB. FSPs, other than those issued at the direction of the Board, are written by the FASB staff and express their positions and opinions. While this type of FSP is issued after an exposure period if the Board does not object to its issuance, this type of FSP is not an official position of the FASB.

Accounting for Suspended Well Costs

.802 Questions have arisen as to whether there are circumstances that would permit the continued capitalization of exploratory well[801] costs beyond one year, other than when additional exploration wells are necessary to justify major capital expenditures and those wells are under way or firmly planned for the near future. [Posted 4/4/05.][FSP FAS 19-1]

.803 The Board directed the FASB staff to provide guidance on the accounting for exploratory well costs and to propose an amendment to FASB Statement No. 19, *Financial Accounting and Reporting by Oil and Gas Producing Companies*, accordingly. The guidance in paragraphs .809 through .813 applies to enterprises that use the successful efforts method of accounting as described in this section. [Posted 4/4/05.][FSP FAS 19-1]

Background

.804 Paragraph .110 of this section requires costs of drilling exploratory wells to be capitalized pending determination of whether the well has found proved reserves. If the well has found proved reserves, the capitalized costs become part of the enterprise's wells, equipment, and facilities; if, however, the well has not found proved reserves, the capitalized costs of drilling the well are expensed, net of any salvage value. [Posted 4/4/05.] [FSP FAS 19-1]

.805 In certain circumstances, an exploratory well finds reserves but those reserves cannot be classified as proved when drilling is completed. To meet the classification of proved reserves, the geological and engineering data must support with reasonable certainty that the quantities of reserves are recoverable under *existing economic and operating conditions* (typically, prices and costs at the date that the estimate is made). For example, after reserves are found, an enterprise may be required to obtain additional geological information, government approvals, sales contracts, and project financing before the enterprise can classify the reserves as proved. [Posted 4/4/05.] [FSP FAS 19-1]

.806 Paragraphs 31 through 34 of Statement 19 provide guidance on whether exploratory well costs can continue to be capitalized when the well finds reserves but those reserves cannot be classified as proved when drilling is completed. If reserves cannot be classified as proved in an area requiring a major capital expenditure, paragraphs 31(a) and 34 of Statement 19 require that the cost be carried as an asset provided that (a) there have been sufficient reserves found to justify completion as a producing well if the required capital expenditure is made, and (b) drilling of the additional exploratory wells is under way or firmly planned for the near future. If either of those two criteria is not met, the enterprise must expense the exploratory well costs. [Posted 4/4/05.] [FSP FAS 19-1]

.807 For all other exploratory wells not addressed in paragraphs 31(a) and 34 of Statement 19, paragraph 31(b) of Statement 19 requires the capitalized costs to be expensed if the reserves cannot be classified as proved after one year following the completion of drilling. [Posted 4/4/05.] [FSP FAS 19-1]

.808 Application of paragraphs 31 and 34 of Statement 19 to the facts and circumstances commonly faced by oil- and gas-producing companies in the current exploration and development environment has become a concern. For example, exploration activities are frequently performed in more remote areas, to greater depths, and in more complex geological formations than the exploration activities that occurred when the FASB issued Statement 19 in 1977. These changes in exploration activities have resulted in an increased frequency of exploratory wells that successfully find reserves that cannot be recognized as proved when drilling is completed and a lengthened evaluation period for determining whether the reserves qualify as proved. There are diverse views on how an enterprise should evaluate the criteria in paragraphs 31 and 34 of Statement 19 in this changed environment—specifically, the one-year capitalization period. [Posted 4/4/05.] [FSP FAS 19-1]

FASB Staff Position

.809 The FASB staff believes that exploratory well costs should continue to be capitalized when the well has found a sufficient quantity of reserves to justify its completion as a producing well and the enterprise is making sufficient progress assessing the reserves and the economic and operating viability of the project.[802] [Posted 4/4/05.] [FSP FAS 19-1]

Amendment to Statement 19

.810   The Board has agreed to replace paragraphs 31 through 34 of Statement 19 with the following:

Accounting When Drilling of an Exploratory Well or an Exploratory-type Stratigraphic Well Is Completed

31. As specified in paragraph 19, the costs of drilling an exploratory well or an exploratory-type stratigraphic well are capitalized as part of the enterprise's uncompleted wells, equipment, and facilities pending the determination of whether the well has found proved reserves. If proved reserves are found, the capitalized costs of drilling the well shall be reclassified as part of the costs of the enterprise's wells and related equipment and facilities at that time. If proved reserves are not found, the capitalized costs of drilling the well shall be charged to expense. However, an exploratory well or an exploratory-type stratigraphic well may be determined to have found oil and gas reserves, but those reserves cannot be classified as proved when drilling is completed. In those cases, the capitalized drilling costs shall continue to be capitalized if the well has found a sufficient quantity of reserves to justify its completion as a producing well[2a] *and* the enterprise is making sufficient progress assessing the reserves and the economic and operating viability of the project.[2b] (Refer to paragraphs 32–34 for guidance on assessing whether an enterprise is making sufficient progress on assessing the reserves and the economic and operating viability of the project.)

31A. If either of those criteria is not met, or if an enterprise obtains information that raises substantial doubt about the economic or operational viability of the project, the exploratory well or exploratory-type stratigraphic well shall be assumed to be impaired and its costs, net of any salvage value, shall be charged to expense. Further, an enterprise shall not continue to capitalize exploratory well costs on the chance that (a) current market conditions will change (for example, an increase in the market price of oil or gas), or (b) technology will be developed to make the development of the project economically and operationally viable.

Progress on assessing reserves

32. All relevant facts and circumstances shall be evaluated when determining whether an enterprise is making sufficient progress on assessing the reserves and the economic and operating viability of the project. The following are some indicators, among others, that an enterprise is making sufficient progress. No single indicator is determinative. An entity should evaluate indicators in conjunction with all other relevant facts and circumstances.

a.   Commitment of project personnel who are at the appropriate levels and who have the appropriate skills

b.   Costs are being incurred to assess the reserves and their potential development

c.   An assessment process covering the economic, legal, political, and environmental aspects of the potential development is in progress

d.   Existence (or active negotiations) of sales contracts with customers for the oil and gas

e. Existence (or active negotiations) of agreements with governments, lenders, and venture partners

f. Outstanding requests for proposals for development of any required facilities

g. Existence of firm plans, established timetables, or contractual commitments, which may include seismic testing and drilling of additional exploratory wells

h. Progress is being made on contractual arrangements that will permit future development

i. Identification of existing transportation and other infrastructure that is or will be available for the project (subject to negotiations for use).

33. Long delays in the assessment or development plan (whether anticipated or unexpected) may raise doubts about whether the enterprise is making sufficient progress to continue the capitalization of exploratory well or exploratory-type stratigraphic well costs after the completion of drilling. The longer the assessment process for the reserves and the project, the more difficult it is to conclude that the enterprise is making sufficient progress to continue the capitalization of those exploratory well or exploratory-type stratigraphic well costs.

34. If an enterprise has not engaged in substantial activities to assess the reserves or the development of the project in a reasonable period of time after the drilling of the well is completed or activities have been suspended, any capitalized costs associated with that well shall be expensed net of any salvage value. After a reasonable period of time, the planning of future activities without engaging in substantial activities is not sufficient to continue the capitalization of exploratory well or exploratory-type stratigraphic well costs. However, brief interruptions in activities required to assess the reserves or the project, or other delays resulting from governmental or other third-party evaluation of a proposed project, do not require capitalized exploratory well or exploratory-type stratigraphic well costs to be expensed.

2a To meet this criterion, an enterprise is not required to complete the exploratory or exploratory-type stratigraphic well as a producing well.

2b For purposes of determining whether capitalized drilling costs shall continue to be capitalized pending the determination of proved reserves, a project may include more than one exploratory well or exploratory-type stratigraphic well if the reserves are intended to be extracted in a single, integrated producing operation (for example, the producing wells will operate with shared infrastructure).

[Posted 4/4/05.] [FSP FAS 19-1]

Disclosures

.811 The objective of the disclosures required in this paragraph is to provide users of financial statements with information about management's evaluation of capitalized exploratory well costs. The guidance in paragraphs .809 and .810 requires management to apply more judgment than was [previously] required in evaluating whether the costs meet the criteria for continued capitalization. Accordingly, this paragraph requires the following disclosures in the notes to the annual financial statements to provide information for users of financial statements about management's application of judgment in its evaluation of a project's capitalized exploratory well costs. These disclosures are not required routinely in interim financial statements; however, interim financial statements should include information about significant changes from the information presented in the most recent annual financial statements. Any impairment of capitalized exploratory well costs that were capitalized for a period of greater than one year after the completion of drilling at the most recent annual balance sheet date shall be considered significant for purposes of determining whether the change should be disclosed in interim financial statements.

a.   An enterprise shall disclose the amount of capitalized exploratory well costs that is pending the determination of proved reserves. An enterprise also shall separately disclose for each annual period that an income statement is presented changes in those capitalized exploratory well costs resulting from (1) additions to capitalized exploratory well costs that are pending the determination of proved reserves, (2) capitalized exploratory well costs that were reclassified to wells, equipment, and facilities based on the determination of proved reserves, and (3) capitalized exploratory well costs that were charged to expense. This disclosure should not include amounts that were capitalized and subsequently expensed in the same annual period.

b.   An enterprise shall disclose the amount of exploratory well costs that have been capitalized for a period of greater than one year after the completion of drilling at the most recent balance sheet date and the number of projects to which those costs relate. Additionally, for exploratory well costs that have been capitalized for periods greater than one year at the most recent balance sheet date, an enterprise shall provide an aging of those amounts by year, or by using a range of years, and the number of projects to which those costs relate.

c.   For exploratory well costs that continue to be capitalized for more than one year after the completion of drilling at the most recent balance sheet date, an enterprise shall describe the projects and the activities that it has undertaken to date in order to evaluate the reserves and the projects, and the remaining activities required to classify the associated reserves as proved.

[Posted 4/4/05.] [FSP FAS 19-1]

Effective Date and Transition

.812   The guidance in paragraphs .809 through .811 shall be applied to the first reporting period beginning after April 4, 2005. The guidance should be applied prospectively to existing and newly capitalized exploratory well costs. Any capitalized exploratory well costs that are expensed upon the application of this guidance shall be recognized in income from continuing operations and either shall be presented as a separate component of operations or shall be disclosed in the notes to the financial statements. An enterprise shall quantify and describe the projects to which those costs relate. Capitalization of exploratory well costs that were previously expensed is not permitted. Early application of this guidance is permitted in periods for which financial statements have not yet been issued. [Posted 4/4/05.] [FSP FAS 19-1]

Disclosures for transition and periods preceding the adoption of paragraphs .809 through .812

.813   An enterprise shall provide the disclosures required by paragraphs .811(a) through .811(c) of this section in the period of adoption, including an interim period. An enterprise also shall provide the disclosures required by paragraphs .811(a) and .811(b) of this section for annual periods preceding the adoption of paragraphs .809 through .811 of this section. Those disclosures shall be provided in each prior period for which an income statement is presented and shall be presented based on the previous accounting method. Exhibit 813A follows. [Posted 4/4/05.] [FSP FAS 19-1]

Exhibit 813A

Example Disclosures in the Year of Adoption

As of January 1, 2005, the Company adopted FASB Staff Position FAS 19-1, "Accounting for Suspended Well Costs." Upon adoption of paragraphs of the FSP, the Company evaluated all existing capitalized exploratory well costs under the provisions of the FSP. As a result, the Company determined that $175 of capitalized costs related to two separate projects was impaired and, therefore, the Company expensed those costs upon adoption of the FSP. (The Company also shall provide a description of those projects.) This expense is included in income from continuing operations. The following table reflects the net changes in capitalized exploratory well costs during 2005, 2004, and 2003, and does not include amounts that were capitalized and subsequently expensed in the same period. Capitalized exploratory well costs for fiscal years ending December 31, 2004, and December 31, 2003, are presented based on the Company's previous accounting policy.

	2005	2004	2003
Beginning balance at January 1	$ 975	$ 850	$ 800
Capitalized exploratory well costs charged to expense upon the adoption of FSP FAS 19-1	(175)	—	—
Additions to capitalized exploratory well costs pending the determination of proved reserves	375	500	350
Reclassifications to wells, facilities, and equipment based on the determination of proved reserves	(200)	(225)	(150)
Capitalized exploratory well costs charged to expense	(75)	(150)	(150)
Ending balance at December 31	$ 900	$ 975	$ 850

The following table provides an aging of capitalized exploratory well costs based on the date the drilling was completed and the number of projects for which exploratory well costs have been capitalized for a period greater than one year since the completion of drilling:

	2005	2004	2003
Capitalized exploratory well costs that have been capitalized for a period of one year or less	$ 375	$ 500	$ 350
Capitalized exploratory well costs that have been capitalized for a period greater than one year	525	475	500
Balance at December 31	$ 900	$ 975	$ 850
Number of projects that have exploratory well costs that have been capitalized for a period greater than one year	8	10	9

Included in the amount of exploratory well costs that have been capitalized for a period of greater than one year since the completion of drilling are costs of $45 and $95 that have been capitalized since 2001 and 2000, respectively, related to 2 projects. (The Company also shall provide the disclosures required by paragraph 10(c) of the FSP for those costs that at December 31, 2005, have been capitalized for a period of greater than one year following the completion of drilling.)

[Posted 4/4/05.] [FSP FAS 19-1]

Supplemental Guidance: AICPA Accounting Standards Executive Committee (AcSEC)

.2000   [Listed below is an AcSEC pronouncement that provides supplemental guidance for this section.

Statement of Position 94-6, *Disclosure of Certain Significant Risks and Uncertainties*]

• • •

Illustrative Chart of Accounts

The Illustrative Chart of Accounts is a comprehensive document: it includes categories used by both the successful efforts and full cost methods of accounting. Accounts unique to successful efforts companies are noted by an SE in the left margin, while FC denotes accounts unique to full cost companies. Figure 4-3 located in Chapter 4 presents a condensed version of this chart.

ABC Oil Company
Chart of Accounts

100-109	**Cash**
101	Cash in First National Bank
102	Cash in First State Bank
105	Special Deposits
106	Payroll Account
107	Petty Cash

110-119	**Short-Term Investments**
110	Marketable Securities
111	Overnight Interest-Bearing Accounts

120 - 129	**Accounts Receivable**
120	Accounts Receivable—Oil and Gas Sales
121	Accounts Receivable—Gas Imbalances (if using entitlement method)
122	Accounts Receivable—Gas Marketing
123	Accounts Receivable—Joint Interest Billings
124	Accounts Receivable—Employees
126	Accounts Receivable—Other Receivables
127	Accrued Receivables
127.001	Oil and Gas Sales
127.002	Accrued Interest
127.003	Other
129	Allowance for Doubtful Accounts

130 -139	**Inventories**
130	Inventory of Crude Oil (account used infrequently)
131	Inventory of Natural Gas Held in Storage
132	Inventory of Materials and Supplies
132.001	Field Yards (detailed by location and type of material)
132.002	Trucking Yards (detailed by location and type of material)
132.003	Warehouse Inventories (detailed by location and type of material)
132.004	Lower-of-Cost-or-Market Reserve

140-149	**Other Current Assets**
140	Prepaid Expenses
141	Current Portion of Long-Term Receivables
142	Margin Accounts for Futures Trading
143	Other

210-219	**Unproved Property Acquisition Costs***
210	Unproved Property Purchase Suspense (detailed by project)
211	Unproved Property Acquisition Costs
211.001	Lease Bonus
211.002	Commissions
211.003	Landman Services and Expenses

	211.004	Abstracting Fees
	211.005	Capitalized Interest
FC	211.006	Delay Rentals
FC	211.007	Other Carrying Costs
	211.999	Transfers to Proved Mineral Interests
219		Allowance for Impairment of Unproved Properties
		(detailed by property or by groups of properties as appropriate)

Additional unproved property accounts may be used for other types of economic interests, such as Account 212 for fee interests, Account 213 for royalty interests, Account 214 for overriding royalty interests, Account 215 for net profits interests, and Account 216 for volume production payments.

*Note: The conventional term "unproved property" refers to unevaluated property. Once a property is evaluated as not having proved reserves, the capitalized acquisition costs are either: (1) expensed under the successful efforts method to Account 800, Exploration Expenses, or (2) reclassified using full cost accounting to Account 227, Abandoned and Worthless Property.

220-226   Proved Property Acquisition Costs

221   Proved Property Acquisition Costs (detailed by lease)

Additional proved property accounts may be used for other types of economic interests, such as Account 222 for fee interests, Account 223 for royalty interests, and Account 224 for overriding royalty interests.

	225	Proved Production Payments
SE	226	Accumulated Amortization of Proved Property Acquisition Costs
		(detailed by property interest or by geological structure)

227-229   Capitalized Costs of Unsuccessful Efforts

FC	227	Abandoned and Worthless Properties
FC	228	Impairment of Unproved Properties
FC	229	Unsuccessful Exploration Costs

230- 239   Proved Property Well and Development Costs

	230		Capitalized Asset Retirement Obligations (ARO) at Inception
	231		Intangible Costs of Wells and Development (detailed by well or field)
FC		231.001	Well Drilling and Completion
SE		231.001	Successful Exploratory Wells
SE		231.002	Successful Development Wells
SE		231.003	Development Dry Holes
		231.004	Intangible Capitalizable Workover Costs (infrequently used; workovers are generally repairs that are expensed as production costs)
		231.005	Enhanced Recovery Projects
		231.006	Other Intangibles
SE	232		Accumulated Amortization of Intangible Costs of Wells and Development
	233		Tangible Costs of Wells and Development (detailed by well or field)
FC		233.001	Well Drilling and Completion
SE		233.001	Successful Exploratory Wells
SE		233.002	Successful Development Wells
SE		233.003	Development Dry Holes
		233.004	Tangible Workover Costs (infrequently used)
		233.005	Development Support Equipment and Facilities
		233.006	Gas Processing Facilities (may be a separate section)
		233.007	Enhanced Recovery Projects
		233.008	Other Field Equipment
		233.009	Allocated Tangible Cost of Acquired Properties
SE	234		Accumulated Amortization of Tangible Costs of Wells and Development
	235		Accumulated Amortization of Capitalized ARO Costs
FC	236		Accumulated Amortization of Oil and Gas Property Acquisition, Exploration, and Development

FC	237	Accumulated Impairment of Oil and Gas Property Cost Centers (by country)
FC	238	Deferred Losses (Gains) on Sales of Properties

240-249		**Work in Progress**
240		Work in Progress—Geological and Geophysical Exploration (detailed by project or AFE)
	240.001	Geological and Geophysical Contract Work
	240.002	Geological and Geophysical Services Other
	240.003	Field Party Salaries and Wages
	240.004	Field Party Supplies
	240.005	Other Field Party Expenses
	240.006	Charges for Support Facilities
	240.007	Shooting Rights and Damages
	240.008	Mapping Expenses
	240.009	Equipment Rental
	240.010	Other Geological and Geophysical Costs
	240.011	Purchased Geological and Geophysical Data
	240.012	Overhead
	240.015	Transfers to Exploration Expense
241		Work in Progress—Intangible Costs of Wells and Related Development (detailed by AFE)
	241.001	Drilling Contract
	241.002	Site Preparation, Roads, Pits
	241.003	Bits, Reamers, Tools
	241.004	Labor, Company
	241.005	Labor, Other
	241.006	Fuel, Power, Water
	241.007	Drilling Supplies
	241.008	Mud and Chemicals
	241.009	Drill Stem Tests
	241.010	Coring, Analysis
	241.011	Electric Surveys, Logs
	241.012	Geological and Engineering
	241.013	Cementing
	241.014	Completion, Fracturing, Acidizing, Perforating
	241.015	Rig Transportation, Erection, Removal
	241.016	Environmental and Safety
	241.017	Other Services
	241.018	Overhead
	241.019	Miscellaneous
	241.025	Capitalized Interest
	241.028	Transfers to Exploration Expense—Dry Holes
	241.029	Transfers to Proved Property Well and Development Costs
243		Work In Progress—Tangible Costs of Wells and Related Development
	243.030	Tubular Goods
	243.031	Wellhead and Subsurface Equipment
	243.032	Pumping Units
	243.033	Tanks
	243.034	Separators and Heater-Treaters
	243.035	Engines and Power Equipment
	243.036	Flow Lines
	243.037	Miscellaneous
	243.038	Installation Costs—Surface Equipment
	243.045	Capitalized Interest
	243.048	Transfers to Exploration Expense—Dry Holes
	243.049	Transfers to Proved Well and Development Costs
244		Work in Progress—Workovers^ (usually a production expense)
245		Work in Progress—Support Equipment and Facilities^
246		Work in Progress—Gas Processing Facilities^
247		Work in Progress—Enhanced Recovery Projects^
248		Work in Progress—Other Field Equipment
		(^ Subaccounts are not illustrated.)

258-259	**General Support Equipment and Facilities**
258	Cost of General Support Equipment and Facilities (detailed by facility or unit)
259	Accumulated Depreciation of General Support Equipment and Facilities (detailed by facility or unit)

260-269	**Other Plant and Equipment** (detailed by asset and location)
261	Autos
262	Office Equipment
263	Buildings
264	Land
268	Other
269	Accumulated Depreciation (detailed by type of equipment and by asset)

270-279	**Notes Receivable**
270	Notes Receivable—Trade
271	Notes Receivable—Production Payments
272	Notes Receivable—Co-owners
273	Notes Receivable—Officers and Employees
274	Notes Receivable—Other

280-289	**Other Assets**
280	Pipeline Demand Charges
281	Stock of Subsidiaries
282	Other Stock Investments
283	Cash Surrender Value of Life Insurance
284	Investments in Hedging Instruments
289	Other

290-299	**Deferred Charges**
290	Deferred Tax Asset
291	Deferred Loss on Hedging of Future Production
292	Deferred Expenses Recoverable Under Foreign Production Sharing Contracts
293	Other Deferred Charges

300-349	**Current Liabilities** (appropriately detailed in subaccounts)
301	Vouchers Payable
302	Revenue Distributions Payable
303	Lease Bonuses Payable
304	Revenues Held in Suspense
305	Advances from Joint Interest Owners
306	Gas Imbalance Payables (if using entitlement method)
307	Accrued Liabilities
310	Short-Term Debt
311	Current Portion of Long-Term Debt
320	Production Taxes Payable
321	Ad Valorem Taxes Payable
330	Federal Income Taxes Payable
331	State Income Taxes Payable
332	Payroll Taxes Payable
335	Other Current Liabilities

350-369	**Clearing, Apportionment, and Control Accounts**
350	District Expenses
351	Region Expenses
352	Support Facility Expenses
360	Revenue Control Account

361	Billing Control Account

400-409   Long-Term Debt

401	Notes Payable
402	Mortgages Payable
403	Bonds Payable
404	Production Payments Payable as Debt
405	Commercial Paper
406	Capitalized Lease Obligations
407	Debt Premium
408	Debt Discount
409	Portion Reclassified as Current

410-419   Other Long-Term Liabilities

410	Asset Retirement Obligation (ARO)
411	Other Environmental Liabilities
412	Accrued Pension Liability

420   Deferred Income Taxes

430-439   Other Deferred Credits

430	Deferred Revenue for Prepaids
431	Deferred Revenue for Volume Production Payments
432	Deferred Gain (for future commitments on certain property sales)
433	Deferred Gain on Hedging of Future Production

500-599   Stockholders' Equity

500	Preferred Stock
501	Common Stock
505	Additional Paid-In Capital
525	Retained Earnings
530	Dividends

600-699   Revenues (typically presented net of royalties due to others)

601	Crude Oil Revenues
602	Gas Revenues
603	NGL Revenues
604	Royalty Oil Revenues
605	Royalty Gas Revenues
606	Royalty NGL Revenues
607	Revenues from Net Profits Interests
610	Gain (Loss) on Hedging the Company's Revenues (using futures, options, derivatives, etc.)
615	Gain (Loss) on Trading of Futures, Options, and Derivatives (speculative trades)
620	Gains on Property Sales (rarely used for full cost method)
625	Interest Income
630	Other Income

701-709   Marketing Expenses

701	Oil Marketing Expenses
702	Gas Marketing Expenses
703	NGL Marketing Expenses

710   Lease Operating Expenses

710	Lease Operating Expenses
710.001	Salaries and Wages
710.002	Employee Benefits
710.003	Contract Pumping Services
710.004	Well Services and Workovers
710.005	Repairs and Maintenance of Surface Equipment

	710.006	Fuel, Water, and Lubrication
	710.007	Supplies
	710.008	Auto and Truck Expenses
	710.009	Supervision
	710.010	Ad Valorem Taxes
	710.011	Production Taxes and Severance Taxes
	710.012	Other Taxes
	710.013	Compressor Rentals
	710.014	Insurance
	710.015	Salt Water Disposal
	710.016	Treating Expenses
	710.017	Environment and Safety
	710.018	Overhead
	710.019	Shut-in and Minimum Royalties
	710.020	Other Royalties (where appropriate)
	710.021	Pressure Maintenance
	710.022	Other

	725-749		**DD&A**
FC	725		Depreciation, Depletion, and Amortization
SE	726		Amortization of Proved Property Acquisition Costs
SE	732		Amortization of Intangible Costs of Wells and Development
SE	734		Amortization of Tangible Costs of Wells and Development
	735		Amortization of Capitalized Asset Retirement Obligations
	739		Depreciation of General Support Equipment and Facilities
	749		Depreciation of Other Plant and Equipment

	760-761		**Loss on Impairment of Long-Lived Assets**
	760		Loss on Impairment of Long-Lived Assets
FC	761		Provision for Impairment of Oil and Gas Assets

SE	**800-899**		**Exploration Expenses**
SE	801		Geological and Geophysical Expenses
SE		801.001	Geological and Geophysical Contract Work
SE		801.002	Geological and Geophysical Services Other
SE		801.003	Field Party Salaries and Wages
SE		801.004	Field Party Supplies
SE		801.005	Other Field Party Expenses
SE		801.007	Shooting Rights and Damages
SE		801.008	Mapping Expenses
SE		801.009	Equipment Rental
SE		801.010	Other Geological and Geophysical Costs
SE		801.011	Purchased Geological and Geophysical Data
SE		801.012	Overhead
SE	802		Carrying and Retaining Undeveloped Properties
SE		802.001	Rentals (also called Delay Rentals)
SE		802.002	Ad Valorem Taxes
SE		802.003	Title Defense
SE		802.004	Record Maintenance
SE	803		Test Well Contributions
SE		803.001	Dry Hole Costs
SE		803.002	Bottom-Hole Costs
SE	804		Unsuccessful Exploratory Wells (i.e., Dry Holes)
SE		804.001	Intangibles
SE		804.002	Tangibles
SE	805		Unsuccessful Exploratory Stratigraphic Test Wells
SE		805.001	Intangibles
SE		805.002	Tangibles
SE	806		Impairment, Amortization and Abandonment of Unproved Properties

900-919	**General and Administrative Expenses**
901	Officers' Salaries
902	Other Salaries
903	Employee Benefits
904	Rent
905	Office Supplies
906	Utilities
907	Dues and Subscriptions
908	Travel and Entertainment
909	Legal and Auditing
910	Insurance
911	Taxes Other Than Income
912	Contributions
918	Miscellaneous G&A Expense
919	Operator's Overhead Recovery

920-929	**Interest Expense**
920	Interest on Debts
921	Other Interest
922	Gain (Loss) on Hedging of Interest Expense
923	Transfer for Interest Capitalized
924	Accretion Cost on Asset Retirement Obligations

930	**Losses on Sales of Property**

931	**Provisions for Restructuring**

933	**Casualty Loss**

940-949	**Income Tax Provision**
940	Current Federal Income Taxes
941	Current State and Local Income Taxes
942	Current Foreign Income Taxes
945	Deferred Federal Income Taxes
946	Deferred State and Local Income Taxes
947	Deferred Foreign Income Taxes

960	**Extraordinary Items**

Note: Revenues, taxes, and lease activities often must be tracked or summarized by state. The American Petroleum Institute (API) designated the following standardized numerical codes to facilitate such tracking:

API CODE
FOR THE UNITED STATES AND OFFSHORE FEDERAL WATERS

01	Alabama	21	Michigan	41	Tennessee
02	Arizona	22	Minnesota	42	Texas
03	Arkansas	23	Mississippi	43	Utah
04	California	24	Missouri	44	Vermont
05	Colorado	25	Montana	45	Virginia
06	Connecticut	26	Nebraska	46	Washington
07	Delaware	27	Nevada	47	West Virginia
08	District of Columbia	28	New Hampshire	48	Wisconsin
09	Florida	29	New Jersey	49	Wyoming
10	Georgia	30	New Mexico	50	Alaska
11	Idaho	31	New York	51	Hawaii
12	Illinois	32	North Carolina	55	Alaska Offshore
13	Indiana	33	North Dakota	56	Pacific Coast Offshore
14	Iowa	34	Ohio	60	Northern Gulf of Mexico
15	Kansas	35	Oklahoma	61	Atlantic Coast Offshore
16	Kentucky	36	Oregon		
17	Louisiana	37	Pennsylvania		
18	Maine	38	Rhode Island		
19	Maryland	39	South Carolina		
20	Massachusetts	40	South Dakota		

• • •

OTHER REFERENCE SOURCES

SOURCES OF PETROLEUM ACCOUNTING INFORMATION

COPAS Publications and Videos. The Council of Petroleum Accountants Societies publishes COPAS Bulletins, Interpretations, Research Papers, Guidebooks, videos and other educational resources. Ordering information is available at: **www.copas.org**.

2001 PricewaterhouseCoopers Survey of U.S. Petroleum Accounting Practices. The *Survey* collects information on industry accounting practices, especially those not typically disclosed in annual reports. Respondents are categorized in three ways: (1) integrated and independent, (2) successful efforts and full cost, and (3) public and private. For copies of the latest survey, contact the Institute of Petroleum Accounting at **www.unt.edu/ipa**. Telephone: (940) 565-3170. A new release is expected in 2007.

Petroleum Accounting and Financial Management Journal (formerly titled the *Journal of Extractive Industries Accounting*, and *Journal of Petroleum Accounting*). The *Journal* is published three times a year by the Institute of Petroleum Accounting, University of North Texas. It contains general, technical, and research articles concerning accounting, economics, environmental issues, finance, taxation, and government regulation of the U.S. and global petroleum, energy, and extractive industries. Each year, the spring issue contains a cumulative topical index of articles published since 1982. The *Journal's* tables of contents also can be accessed on the website: **www.unt.edu/ipa**.

Audit and Accounting Guide: ***Audits of Entities with Oil and Gas Producing Activities.*** Published by the American Institute of Certified Public Accountants (AICPA), the guide summarizes applicable practices and delivers advice for handling most types of financial statements. It describes relevant matters, conditions, and procedures unique to the oil and gas industry. Financial statements and reports are illustrated in order to caution auditors and accountants about unusual problems. CD-ROM subscriptions are available by calling (888) 777-7077; online orders can be placed at: **www. cpa2biz.com**. Annual subscriptions include up to three update discs, and multi-user versions are available.

IASB Extractive Industries Project. The International Accounting Standards Board (IASB) is engaged in a project to develop an International Accounting Standard for extractive activities, which include mining and oil and gas. An updated summary of the project can be found on the IASB website: **www.iasb.org/Current+Projects/IASB+Projects/Extractive+Activities/Summary**.

ACCOUNTING REGULATIONS

Financial Accounting Standards Board (FASB). The FASB establishes standards for financial accounting and reporting. Its work is considered authoritative by the SEC and AICPA. Stakeholders, such as investors, creditors, auditors and the general public, rely on financial information prepared in accordance with FASB standards. The organization's website is: **www.fasb.org**.

OTHER INDUSTRY SOURCES

American Petroleum Institute (API). API is the primary trade association of the oil and gas industry in the U.S. Its website (**www.api.org**) contains technical information about the field, along with related trends, issues, and developments.

Energy Information Administration (EIA). The U.S. Department of Energy's Energy Information Administration is the government source for industry statistics and information. Price, production, trade, and sector overviews are available on a monthly or annual basis. EIA's website is: **www.eia.doe.gov**.

• • •

GLOSSARY

(Glossary words noted with an asterisk are informational
terms and may not be found in the chapter material.)

AAPL — (abbrev.) American Association of Professional Landmen (formerly the American Association of Petroleum Landmen).

ABANDON — To cease attempts to produce oil or gas from a well or lease, and to plug the reservoir in accordance with regulatory requirements and recover equipment.

ABSORBER* — Field equipment, usually a tower, that removes oil or water from a gas stream using absorption (as opposed to adsorption). In absorption, the removed liquid changes by mixing with another liquid. For example, a triethylene glycol (TEG) absorber removes water from a gas stream in a process where wet gas enters at the bottom of the unit, passes through a TEG stream, and exits dry at the top. The resulting wet glycol is dried in a reboiler to remove the water.

ACIDIZE — To increase the flow of oil from a well by introducing acid into a carbonate formation (such as limestone) to open passages through which oil can flow into the well bore. Acidizing may be called an acid job.

ACQUISITION COSTS — Direct and indirect costs incurred to acquire legal rights to wasting natural resources.

ACQUISITION WELL* — A well drilled in exchange for a mineral interest in a property. It also can be called an obligation well.

ACRE-FOOT — Reservoir analysis measure of volume equaling 43,560 cubic feet, or 7,758 barrels. One acre-foot represents the volume that would cover one acre to a depth of one foot.

ACT or LACT SYSTEM — (abbrev.) See LACT UNIT.

AD VALOREM TAXES — Local taxes, such as county and school district taxes, paid and based on the individual property value.

ADSORPTION PLANT* — Field equipment for removing liquid from a gas stream by adsorption (as opposed to absorption as explained above). In adsorption, the removed liquid is unchanged, but clings to the surface of a solid adsorbent such as activated charcoal.

ADVANCE ROYALTY* or ADVANCED ROYALTY — Generally, a royalty that must be paid regardless of production and revenue levels, such as a minimum royalty or a shut-in royalty, for which future production royalties may or may not be reduced.

AFE (AUTHORIZATION OR AUTHORITY FOR EXPENDITURE) — Budgeting and approval form used during the planning process for a well about to be drilled (and for other projects). It includes an estimate of costs to be incurred in the IDC category and in the tangible equipment category. Costs are shown in total with accompanying breakdowns. The AFE form represents: (1) a budget for the project against which actual expenditures are compared, and (2) a joint venture form for evidencing agreement by joint interest owners to participate in the budgeted project.

AIR DRILLING* — Use of compressed air as a substitute for drilling mud in rotary drilling.

AIR/GAS LIFT* — Method of raising oil from the formation by injecting air or gas directly into the fluid in the casing.

ALLOWABLE* — Amount of oil or gas that a well or lease can produce during a given time period according to government regulations.

AMI — (abbrev.) Area of mutual interest.

ANGLE OF DEFLECTION* — In directional drilling, the angle expressed in degrees at which a well is deflected from the vertical by means of a whipstock or other deflecting tool.

ANNULAR SPACE (ANNULUS)—Space surrounding a cylindrical object within a cylinder. The space around a pipe suspended in a wellbore is often termed the annulus, and its outer wall may be either the wall of the borehole or the casing.

ANTICLINES—Underground mountain-shaped strata covered with a cap rock or an impervious rock layer.

API—(abbrev.) American Petroleum Institute.

API GRAVITY or °API—Standard industry measure of gravity (i.e., density) of a liquid petroleum product. The formula for API gravity in terms of specific gravity (g) is (141.5 ÷ g at 60°F) – 131.5. Very light crude oils and gasoline have API gravity in the range of 50° to 60°. The API gravity for light crude oils ranges from about 35° to 45°. Heavy (dense) crude oils have an API Gravity range from about 6° to 25°. In comparison, water has an API gravity of 10° and a specific gravity of 1.

API WELL NUMBER*—Distinct twelve digit number assigned to a U.S. well. Digits 1 and 2 are state codes, digits 3 through 5 are county/parish or offshore codes, digits 6 through 10 identify the well, and digits 11 and 12 identify special well conditions such as a sidetracking.

APO—(abbrev.) After payout. Used with working interests and net revenue interests to indicate ownership after payout (see PAYOUT) versus before payout (see BPO).

AREA OF INTEREST—Federal income tax term used in allocating GEOPHYSICAL AND GEOLOGICAL COSTS to certain properties. A large-scale geophysical survey may indicate several areas of interest. Costs of the survey must be allocated to each area of interest, and when leases are obtained, the geophysical costs become part of the basis of the property

AREA OF MUTUAL INTEREST (AMI)—A term found in joint venture agreements designating a geographic area around the joint venture's leases. The agreement provides that any joint venture participant obtaining new property rights within the AMI must offer such rights to the joint venture.

ASSIGNEE—In law, generally a transferee; a recipient of an interest in property or a contract. In oil and gas law, the term commonly means, but is not limited to, the transferee of an oil and gas lease.

ASSIGNMENT—In law, generally a transfer. In oil and gas law, usually a transfer of a property interest or of a contract. The most common usage refers to the assignment of an oil and gas lease.

ASSIGNOR—In law, generally a transferor; the party who conveys a right, title or interest in property or a contract. In oil and gas law, the term commonly means, but is not limited to, the conveyor of an oil and gas lease.

ASSOCIATED GAS—Natural gas, occurring in the form of a gas cap, overlying an oil zone (as opposed to NONASSOCIATED GAS from a gas reservoir with no oil, and CASINGHEAD GAS contained in the reservoir's crude oil gas).

AUTHORIZATION FOR EXPENDITURE—See AFE.

AUTOMATIC CUSTODY TRANSFER SYSTEM—See LACT UNIT.

BACK-IN INTEREST*—ORRI or carried interest which converts to a working interest at a specific time or event, such as one year from well completion or completion of a payout provision (e.g., 300 percent payout).

BAFFLE*—Device which changes the direction of flow of fluids.

BARREL (BBL)—Standard measure of volume for crude oil and liquid petroleum products. One barrel equals 42 U.S. gallons.

BASIC SEDIMENT & WATER (OR BS&W)—Impurities contained in produced oil. Purchasing companies will ordinarily not accept oil having more than one percent of BS&W. If the fluid as produced contains more than this proportion of foreign matter, some of the impurities such as sand and water may be removed from the crude after settling in the bottom of the lease storage tank.

BATTERY—Group of lease storage tanks.

BBL—(abbrev.) Bbl or bbl; barrel of oil.

BBL/D*—(abbrev.) Barrels per day.

BCF—(abbrev.) Billion cubic feet.

BEAM WELL*—A well from which oil is lifted by use of a walking beam pump unit.

BEHIND-PIPE RESERVES—Oil or gas reserves (proved or unproved) that cannot be produced until future perforation of casing at the depth of that reservoir. Generally, these are reserves in reservoirs above currently producing zones.

BENCHMARK CRUDE*—Oil for an area that is used to set the standard for quality and price. In the U.S., West Texas Intermediate is used in crude oil futures contracts on the New York Mercantile Exchange. OPEC's benchmark is Saudi Arabian Light, and Europe's benchmark is North Sea Brent.

BENCHMARK PRICING*—An agreement between parties to sell and buy oil or gas in the future at a percentage or function of a future published oil or gas price routinely determined by another party. The benchmark might be another party's posted price for crude oil (or a published average spot gas price) at a specified location on the date of sale. One of four methods is used to price gas or five methods for oil for Federal royalty purposes. Benchmark pricing generally is used in processed gas sales.

BHP—(abbrev.) Bottom-hole pressure (or sometimes brake horse power).

BIT—Cutting or boring element used in drilling oil and gas wells. Bits are designed on two basic and different principles: the cable tool bit which moves up and down to pulverize, and the rotary bit which revolves to grind.

BLEED*—To drain off liquid or gas slowly through a valve called a bleeder.

BLOW BY*—Escape of gas with the liquid from a separator.

BLOWOUT OR BLOW OUT—Sudden, violent expulsion of oil, gas, and mud (and sometimes water) from a drilling well followed by an uncontrolled flow from the well. It can occur when high pressure gas is encountered in the hole, and sufficient precautions—such as increasing the weight of the mud—have not been taken.

BLOWOUT PREVENTER—Heavy casinghead control filled with special gates or rams which can be closed around the drill pipe, or which completely close the top of the casing.

BLUE SKY LAW*—Statute that regulates the issuance and sale of securities. The term is usually restricted to state statutes; the corresponding federal statute and regulations are the Federal Securities Act and SEC regulations.

BOE—(abbrev.) Barrels of oil equivalent. Amount of energy resource equal to one barrel of oil on energy basis. A barrel is equivalent to 42 U.S. gallons. Typically calculated on a conversion of 6 Mcf: 1 bbl.

BONUS—Consideration paid by the lessee to the lessor upon execution of an oil and gas lease.

BOPD*—(abbrev.) Barrels of oil per day.

BOREHOLE—Wellbore; the hole made by drilling or boring a well.

BOTTOM-HOLE CONTRIBUTIONS—Money or property paid to an operator for use in drilling a well on property in which the payer has no property interest. The contributions are payable when the well reaches a predetermined depth, regardless of whether the well is productive or nonproductive. The payer may receive proprietary information on the well's potential productivity.

BOTTOM-HOLE LETTER* OR CONTRACT—An agreement by which an operator contemplating the drilling of a well on his own land secures the promise of another to contribute to the cost of the well, usually in return for proprietary information on the well's potential productivity. In contrast to the dry hole letter, the bottom-hole letter requires payment upon drilling and testing the well at a specified depth or formation even if the well does not produce.

BOTTOM-HOLE PRESSURE—Reservoir or rock pressure at the bottom of the hole, whether measured under flowing conditions or not. If measured under flowing conditions, pressure readings are usually taken at different rates of flow in order to compute a theoretical value for maximum productivity. Decline in pressure furnishes a guide, in some reservoirs, to the amount of depletion from the reservoir and the amount of remaining proved reserves.

BPO—(abbrev.) Before payout. Used with working interests and net revenue interests to indicate ownership before payout (see PAYOUT) versus after payout (APO).

BRITISH THERMAL UNIT (BTU)—Measure of the amount of heat required to raise the temperature of one pound of water by one degree Fahrenheit. The energy values of petroleum products per barrel (million Btu/bbl) are approximately as follows: average U.S. crude petroleum is 5.8; residual fuel oil is 6.29; distillate fuel oil is 5.83; gasoline is 5.35; jet fuel (kerosene type) is 5.67; jet fuel (naphtha type) is 5.36; and kerosene is 5.67. Dry natural gas averages 1.03 MMBtu/Mcf; wet natural gas is 1.110 MMBtu/Mcf. Natural gas in pipelines has from .95 to 1.05 MMBtu/Mcf. An average oil barrel has the energy content of approximately 5.6 Mcf dry natural gas of 1.03 MMBtu/Mcf.

BS&W (or BS)— (abbrev.) See BASIC SEDIMENT AND WATER.

BTU—(abbrev.) See BRITISH THERMAL UNIT.

BULLET PERFORATOR*—Perforator that fires bullets through the casing in order to provide holes through which the well fluids may enter.

BUTANE—A hydrocarbon gas (C4H10) extracted as a NATURAL GAS LIQUID from natural gas. It is used as a gasoline ingredient increasing volatility and improving cold engine starts. Liquefied petroleum gas may contain some butane, but generally consists of propane.

CABLE-TOOL DRILLING—Using a cable tool rig to drill a well by pounding the chisel-shaped bit up and down thereby pulverizing the rock. This original well drilling method is now largely replaced by rotary drilling where the drill bit rotates to grind, rather than pulverize, the rock.

CAPACITY—Maximum volume a well is capable of producing in a unit of time. Generally expressed as an amount per hour. Capacity may also refer to a maximum volume of fluid for a given container or reservoir.

CARRIED INTEREST AGREEMENT OR ARRANGEMENT—An agreement under which one party (carrying party) agrees to pay for a specified portion or for all of the development and operating costs of another party (carried party) on a property in which both own a portion of the working interest. The carrying party may be able to recover a specified amount of costs from the carried party's share of the revenue from the production of petroleum, if any, from the property.

CARRIED PARTY—Party for whom funds are advanced in a carried interest arrangement.

CARRYING PARTY—Party advancing funds in a carrying interest arrangement.

CARVED-OUT INTEREST*—Non-operating interest carved-out of a working interest. It is often an overriding royalty (ORRI) and sometimes can be a production payment. For example, the owner of a 20 percent working interest (WI), with a 15 percent net revenue interest (NRI), may carve-out and convey to a key employee an ORRI with one percent NRI. This leaves the WI owner with a 20 percent share of well costs and a 14 percent share of revenues.

CASH BALANCING—Method of paying cash, in lieu of delivering gas, to eliminate a gas imbalance. Terms for cash balancing may be set out in a separate gas balancing agreement or in the joint operating agreement.

CASING — Steel pipe placed in an oil or gas well as drilling and completion progresses. The function of casing is to prevent the wall of the hole from caving in during drilling and to facilitate safe oil and gas production if the well is productive.

CASINGHEAD GAS — Wet gas produced along with crude oil from oil wells. The DISSOLVED GAS is dissolved in the reservoir's crude oil but bubbles out of the oil when exposed to normal atmospheric pressures. Casinghead refers to the top of the well's casing.

CASING POINT — Point in a drilling project when well drilling operations cease, and the well owners must decide whether well COMPLETION should begin or whether the well should be plugged and abandoned. At the casing point, the well has been drilled to the objective depth. Well logs, drill stem tests, and other tests of productivity are analyzed to judge whether probable production is sufficient to economically justify completion costs, including the installation of production casing. A joint venture owner that is carried to casing point does not pay drilling costs, only completion costs. Casing point may also refer to the depth to which casing is set in a well.

CEMENTING — Pumping cement slurry down the well bore to fill the space created between the rock walls and the casing. Various types of cementing jobs include primary, secondary, squeeze, plug-back or multi-stage.

CENTRIFUGE — Machine in which samples of oil are placed and spun at high speed to break out sediment.

CHECKERBOARD ACREAGE* — Mineral interests situated in a checkerboard pattern.

CHRISTMAS TREE — A descriptive term applied to the well-head (i.e., the valves and fittings assembled at the top of a well to control the flow of production).

CLEAN-OUT COSTS — Costs incurred to clean-out a well in order to maintain its productive capacity or restore it to original capacity.

CLEARING ACCOUNTS — Accounts used to accumulate expenses during a period. Any clearing account balances are allocated to other accounts on a predetermined basis at period-end.

COALBED METHANE* — High-methane natural gas adsorbed to underground coal. It was not substantially produced until the late 1980s when available IRC Section 29 tax credits sparked a drilling boom.

COLLAR — Financial position created when an E&P company sells a call option and buys a put option on its production. A collar effectively fixes the realized price between the strike prices of the put and call options. When the premium received for the call equals the premium paid for the put, the collar is known as a zero-cost collar.

COMPLETION — Refers to the work performed and the installation of permanent equipment for production of oil or gas from a recently drilled well.

COMPRESSOR — Equipment on a gas pipeline to raise gas pressure to keep gas flowing.

CONDENSATE — A light hydrocarbon liquid (generally natural gasolines C5 to C10) that condenses to a liquid as the wet gas is sent through a mechanical separator near the well.

CONTIGUOUS LEASES — Leases which have a common boundary line.

CONTINUING INTEREST* — Any interest in mineral property that lasts for the entire period of the lease contract with which it is associated.

CONVEYANCE — Assignment or transfer of mineral rights to another person.

COPAS — (abbrev.) Council of Petroleum Accountants Societies.

COPAS ACCOUNTING PROCEDURE JOINT OPERATIONS EXHIBIT — An Operating Agreement exhibit that establishes joint venture accounting practices using one of several standard forms developed by COPAS.

CORE—Cylindrical sample of rock taken from a formation during drilling for purposes of determining the formation's permeability, porosity, hydrocarbon saturation, and other characteristics of petroleum productivity.

CORE ANALYSIS—Study of the CORE in a laboratory to determine the following properties of the formation from which the core was taken: porosity, permeability, fluid content, angle of dip, geological age, lithology, and probable productivity.

COST CEILING—Limit placed on the carrying value of oil and gas property in a cost center pursuant to FASB standards or SEC rules.

COST CENTER—Geological, geographical, or legal unit by which costs and revenues are identified and accumulated. Examples are the lease, the field, and the country.

CROSS-SECTION MAPPING*—Maps of cross-section of underground formations.

CRUDE OIL—Liquid petroleum as it comes out of the ground, as distinguished from oil which has been processed in a refinery. Crude oil is also referred to as, simply, crude. It varies radically in its properties, including specific gravity and viscosity. Depending on the chemical nature of its chief constituents, crude oil is classified as paraffin base, asphaltic base, or mixed base.

CYCLING—Primary recovery method by which condensate is recovered from gas produced from a condensate gas reservoir. The residue gas is compressed and returned to the reservoir from which it was originally produced. The return of the residue gas serves to maintain the reservoir pressure so that the condensate remains in a gaseous state in the reservoir. If reservoir pressure drops low enough for the condensate to liquefy in the reservoir, substantially less condensate may be recovered.

DAILY DRILLING REPORT*—Twenty-four hour on-site report indicating all important events which occurred in drilling a well.

DAMAGE PAYMENTS—Payments made to the surface landowner by the oil or gas operator for damages to the land, growing crops, streams, or other assets of the landowner.

DAY RATE CONTRACT—Agreement between a drilling rig contractor and an operator wherein an agreed upon amount of money per day will be paid to the drilling contractor until a well is drilled to an agreed upon depth.

DEAD MAN*—Buried anchor to which guy wires are tied to steady the derrick, boiler stacks, or other equipment.

DECLINE CURVE—Graph of oil and/or gas production plotted over a period of time. Used to extrapolate the expected future production of a well for estimating proved reserves.

DEFERRED BONUS—Lease bonus payable in installments over a period of years. A deferred bonus is distinguishable from a delay rental in that a deferred bonus payment is due even if the lease is dropped, whereas a delay rental is not.

DEHYDRATION—Process of removing water content from a gas stream to reduce the formation of hydrates (solid, crystalline compounds of water [90%] and hydrocarbons [10%] that can disrupt natural gas movement). Usually performed at the well site by use of a dehydrator which may treat commingled gas from several wells.

DELAY RENTAL—Amounts paid to a lessor (subsequent to the payment of any bonus) for the privilege of deferring the commencement of a well or of commercial production on the lease. Normally, rentals are paid prospectively on an annual basis.

DELINEATION WELL—See FIELD EXPLORATORY WELL.

DELIVERY—Flow of gas or oil through a meter.

DELIVERY PRESSURE*—Pressure of the gas from a well to be delivered into a pipeline. This amount is set out in the sales contract and stated in terms of PSI.

DEPLETION—Federal income tax term regarding allowable income tax deduction related to exhaustion of mineral reserves, or element of amortization referring to the portion of the carrying value prorated in each accounting period. Two methods exist for computing a depletion allowance: cost depletion and the percentage method.

DEPRECIATION—Financial accounting principle that recognizes the expense of a capital asset over its estimated useful life. Depreciation also can be an income tax deduction for a tangible cost whereby part of the purchase price is deducted every year over the asset's assigned useful life. E&P company support facilities — trucks, field units, warehouses — and equipment may be subject to depreciation.

DERIVATIVES—Financial instruments used by oil and gas companies to help manage the risk of price fluctuations in the market. The types of derivates utilized include futures contracts, forward contracts, options, and swaps. FAS 133 provides authoritative guidance on accounting for derivatives.

DETAILED SURVEY*—Intensive geological and geophysical exploration of an area of interest.

DEVELOPED PROPERTY—Property where wells have been drilled, and production equipment has been installed.

DEVELOPED PROVED RESERVES (or DRILLED RESERVES)—Crude oil or gas reserves which can be produced from existing facilities.

DEVELOPMENT COSTS—Costs incurred to obtain access to proved reserves and to construct facilities for producing, treating, and storing the hydrocarbons.

DEVELOPMENT WELL—A well drilled within the proved area of an oil or gas reservoir to the depth of a stratigraphic horizon known to be productive

DEVIATED WELL*—A well drilled at an angle from the vertical.

DIRECTIONAL DRILLING—Technique for drilling a well at an angle from the vertical to access a specific part of the reservoir.

DISCOVERY WELL—Exploratory well which discovers a new oil field.

DISMANTLEMENT, RESTORATION, AND ABANDONMENT (DR&A) COSTS—Costs to remove equipment and facilities and restore the site to its pre-existing condition at the end of the productive life of an oil or gas field.

DISPOSAL WELL—A well used for the disposal of waste fluids or salt water that were produced along with the oil and gas. Disposal wells are commonly subject to regulatory requirements to avoid ground water contamination.

DISSOLVED GAS—Natural gas mixed with crude oil in a producing formation.

DIVISION ORDER—Contract between the owners of an oil and gas property and the company purchasing production from the property. The division order sets forth the interest of each owner and serves as the basis for payment of each owner's respective share of oil and gas proceeds.

DOGHOUSE*—Small house on the rig floor used for keeping records, storage, and other functions.

DOME—Geological formation associated with the accumulation of oil where a portion of the underground strata has been thrust upward and has deformed the overlying layers of rock. A dome can trap oil above the anticline formed, alongside it, and even below the formation.

DOUBLE*—Two lengths or joints of drill or other pipe joined together.

DRILLING PERMIT—A permit issued by a governmental body (usually a state) which gives permission to drill on a specified location to a specified depth, and which commits the operator to conform to all other regulatory drilling requirements.

DRILLING RIG—Unit consisting of a derrick, drawworks, and related surface equipment of a drilling or workover unit.

DRY GAS—Natural gas composed of over 90 percent (some say 95 percent) methane and suitable for use by customers of local gas distribution companies.

DRY HOLE—Exploratory or development well that does not produce oil or gas in commercial quantities.

DRY HOLE CONTRIBUTIONS—Money or property paid by property owners to an operator drilling a well on adjacent property in which the payers have no property interest. Such contributions are payable only in the event the well reaches an agreed depth and is found to be dry. The payers may be entitled to proprietary information on the well.

DUAL COMPLETION—A well that simultaneously drains two reservoirs of oil or gas at different depths with the production from each zone separated by tubing.

ECONOMIC INTEREST—Interest in minerals in-place which the owner has acquired by investment, and which secures income derived from the extraction of such minerals.

EDQ—(abbrev.) Equal daily quantities. An average daily volume used for pricing crude oil by allocating volumes from multiple run tickets in a month.

EFFECTIVE DATE—Date a lease, acquisition, or assignment is first in force. The balance sheet date for which a reserve estimate or ceiling test applies.

ENHANCED RECOVERY—Any method used to drive oil from reservoirs into a well in excess of that which could be produced through natural reservoir pressure, energy, or drive (primary recovery). (See SECONDARY and TERTIARY RECOVERY.) Pumping units that lift crude oil up the well are not considered enhanced recovery.

EQUALIZATION—Adjustment clause within a unitization agreement providing that participants with undeveloped leases will pay cash to participants with fully or partially developed leases in order to make the capital contributions for wells and equipment equivalent.

ETHANE—Hydrocarbon gas (C2H6) extracted as a NATURAL GAS LIQUID from natural gas. Ethane can be used as a fuel and as a refrigerant.

EXEMPT OWNER—Owner whose interest is exempt when calculating production, severance, or ad valorem taxes. Usually a government interest is exempt.

EXPLOITATION ENGINEERING*—Engineering related to subsurface geology, the recovery of fluids from reservoirs, and drilling and development of oil and gas reserves.

EXPLORATION COSTS—Costs incurred in identifying areas that may warrant examination and in examining specific areas for oil and gas resources. These costs include drilling exploratory wells and exploratory stratigraphic type test wells.

EXPLORATION RIGHTS—Permission granted by landowners allowing others to enter their property to conduct geological and geophysical surveys.

EXPLORATORY WELL—A well drilled to find and produce oil or gas in an unproved area, find a new reservoir in a field previously found to be productive in another reservoir, or extend a known reservoir.

FARMOUT—Transfer of all or part of the operating rights from a working interest owner to an assignee, who assumes all or some of the burden of development in return for an interest in the property. The assignor usually retains an overriding royalty but may retain any type of interest.

FASB—(abbrev.) Financial Accounting Standards Board.

FAULTS—Oil and gas traps formed by the breaking and shearing of strata resulting from significant moving or shifting of the earth's surface.

FEE INTEREST—Ownership of both surface and mineral rights in a property.

FERC—(abbrev.) Federal Energy Regulatory Commission.

FIELD—Area consisting of a single reservoir or multiple reservoirs all grouped on or related to the same individual geologic structural feature and/or stratigraphic feature.

FIELD EXPLORATORY WELL—A well drilled just outside the proved limits of a reservoir. Also known as a delineation well.

FIELD FACILITY*—Oil and gas production equipment serving more than one lease (e.g., separator or extraction unit).

FIELD PROCESSING—Treatment of oil or gas before it is delivered to a gas plant or refinery.

FIRE WALL*—Earthen dike built around an oil tank to contain the petroleum in the event of a tank rupture.

FISH—Any object accidentally dropped or stuck in the wellbore during drilling, completion, or workover operations. Activities to recover the object are called fishing.

FLARE—To burn unmarketable gas from a lease.

FLASH GAS—High BTU content gas which is vented from a low-pressure separator.

FLOW CHART—(1) a circular paper chart that records metered gas differential pressure and static pressure, and is used to determine gas volume flowing through the meter; (2) a schematic of how gas flows from point to point.

FLOW LINES—Pipes carrying produced emulsion (oil, gas, or water) from wells to lease treatment and storage facilities.

FLOW TANK—Tank for storing oil after it has been being produced.

FLOW TREATER*—Equipment that separates oil and gas, heats oil, and treats oil and water.

FLOWING WELL—A well that lifts oil and gas to the surface using natural reservoir pressure.

FLUID INJECTION—Inducing gas or liquids into a reservoir to move oil toward the well bore.

FLUSH PRODUCTION*—Large flow of production from a well immediately after being drilled.

FOOTAGE-RATE DRILLING CONTRACT—Drilling contract providing for payment of a specified price per foot for drilling a well to a certain depth.

FORCE MAJEURE CLAUSE—Lease or contract provision whereby a lessee is not in violation of the agreement in the event the lessee is incapable of fulfilling the terms due to conditions or events beyond the lessee's control.

FORMATION—Bed or deposit composed substantially of the same minerals throughout.

FORMATION PRESSURE—Bottom-hole pressure of a shut-in well.

FORMATION TESTING*—Procedures to determine potential productivity before installing casing in a well.

FORMULA PRICING—Methodology that ties a particular crude oil stream to one or more widely traded crude oil streams for determining a trade price. Adjustments are made for quality and market differentials.

FORWARD CONTRACT—Financial instrument which provides for two parties to purchase and sell a specific quantity and quality of oil or gas at a set price with delivery and settlement at a selected future date. Forward contracts are over-the-counter products used to manage pricing risks in an E&P company.

FRACTURING—Procedure to stimulate production by forcing a mixture of fluid (usually diesel oil or water) and proppant (usually sand) into the formation under high pressure. Fracing creates artificial fractures in the reservoir rock to increase permeability and porosity. The size of a frac job is expressed in terms of the pounds of proppant used, which might range from 20,000 to one million pounds of sand.

FREE WELL AGREEMENT—Sharing arrangement in which one party drills one or more wells completely free of costs to a second party in return for some type of economic interest in property.

FULL COST—Method of accounting which can be elected by an E&P company. As described in Reg. S-X Rule 4-10(c), a full cost company capitalizes all costs incurred in property acquisition, exploration, and development.

FUTURES CONTRACT—Financial instrument that is an exchange-traded legal contract to buy or sell a standard quantity and quality of a commodity at a specified date and price. Future contacts serve to protect an E&P company from pricing risks.

G&G (GEOLOGICAL AND GEOPHYSICAL) COSTS—Exploratory costs of topographical, geological, and geophysical surveys along with costs incurred to obtain the rights to make these surveys. Salaries and other expenses of the personnel required to carry out the surveys are also included.

GAS BALANCING AGREEMENT (GBA)—Contract between two or more parties to account for any differences between measured volumes and confirmed nominations of gas deliveries at a particular date, such as monthly. The GBA provides for the rights and obligations of the joint venture's working interest owners regarding producer imbalances and generally forms a part of the joint operating agreement.

GAS CAP— Free gas overlying an oil zone and occurring within the same producing formation as oil. It can provide the primary drive mechanism for the recovery of oil in the reservoir.

GAS CHROMATOGRAPH—Analytical instrument that separates gases from each other. The gases are carried by a carrier, an inert gas that is usually nitrogen or helium, through a column filled with either a solid or liquid that is called the stationary phase or packing. This separates the gases into individual components depending on their affinity for the stationary phase. More volatile, lighter, and less polar compounds pass through the column the fastest. A gas chromatograph is composed of a sample preparation, sample valve, column, detector, and signal recorder. The sample is introduced into the gas chromatograph with a syringe where it is immediately vaporized by heat. The separated compounds are identified by flame ionization or by a thermal conductivity detector and are recorded on the gas chromatogram.

GAS IMBALANCE—An imbalance that occurs when: (1) one or more producers sells or utilizes an amount of natural gas above its respective share (producer-producer imbalance); (2) when a pipeline receives an amount of natural gas that is larger or smaller than the amount it redelivers to a customer (producer-pipeline imbalance).

GAS LIFT—Artificial means of extracting oil whereby gas is injected down the hole between the casing and production tubing. The injected gas aerates the liquid and floats up the tubing to the surface. Gas lifts are commonly used on offshore wells.

GAS-OIL RATIO*—Measure of the volume of gas produced along with oil from the same well.

GAS PAYMENT*—Production payment payable out of gas produced.

GAS PLANT PRODUCTS*—NATURAL GAS LIQUIDS removed from natural gas in refineries or field facilities.

GAS SETTLEMENT STATEMENT—Record of the amount of gas transferred from a well to a pipeline. Statements generally include purchaser and seller identification, well identification, volume accepted, BTU content, pressure base, water content (i.e., saturated or dry), and gross value due to the seller.

GAS WELL—A well primarily producing natural gas.

GATHERING SYSTEM—Group of small pipelines which moves the oil (or gas) from several wells into a major pipeline (or in the case of oil, a single tank battery).

GAUGE TICKET*—Form on which the measurement of oil in lease tanks is recorded.

GAUGER—Individual responsible for the measurement of quantity and quality of oil and gas on a lease.

GBA—(abbrev.) See GAS BALANCING AGREEMENT.

GENERAL PARTNERSHIP—Legal form of organization in which all of the partners are general partners and have the right to participate in management.

GEOLOGICAL AND GEOPHYSICAL STUDIES—Processes which seek surface or subterranean indications of earth structure or formations where experience has shown mineral deposits may exist.

GEOLOGICAL SURVEY—Exploratory program directed to examination of rocks and sediments obtained by boring or drilling, or by inspection of surface outcroppings.

GEOLOGY—Science of the history, development, and structure of the earth, especially the earth's crust.

GEOPHYSICAL SURVEY—Study of the configuration of the earth's crust in a given area as determined by the use of seismic, gravity, magnetic, and geochemical procedures.

GEOPHYSICS—Study of the physics of the earth.

GPM—(abbrev.) NGL gallons per one Mcf of gas. Also used as an abbreviation for gallons per minute.

GRAVITY—A shortened term for API gravity which expresses the density of a given petroleum fluid.

GRAVITY METER*—Instrument measuring variations in the gravitational pull of the earth.

GROSS WELLS*—Total number of wells participated in, regardless of the amount of interest owned. For example, a company owning a 10 percent interest in each of 20 wells is said to have 20 gross wells or two net wells (20 wells x 10% = 2.0 net wells)

HOLE—Wellbore. Shallow bores under the derrick in which the kelly joint and joints of pipe are temporarily suspended while making a connection are called the mouse hole and rat hole.

HORIZON—Underground geological formation which is a portion of the larger formation possessing sufficient porosity and permeability to constitute a reservoir

HORIZONTAL ASSIGNMENT*—Assignment of an interest in the minerals above, below, or between specified depths, or in a given stratum or horizon.

HORIZONTAL DRILLING—Deviation drilling that becomes horizontal or near horizontal to increase the length of the well bore penetrating the target formation.

HYDROCARBON—An organic compound of hydrogen and carbon (i.e., oil, gas, and NGL).

IDC (INTANGIBLE DRILLING COST)—Federal income tax term that refers to any cost which in itself has no salvage value, but is necessary for and incident to the drilling of wells and getting them ready for production. IDC can also occur when deepening or plugging back a previously drilled oil or gas well, or an abandoned well, to a different formation. Examples of IDC are labor, fuel, repairs, transportation, and supplies.

IGNEOUS ROCK—Rock that is formed directly from the molten state.

IN SITU COMBUSTION—Process of setting fire to some oil in the reservoir and creating a burning front of gases intended to drive oil ahead of it to the well bore.

INDEPENDENT PRODUCER—Oil company that engages in exploration, drilling, and/or producing, but does not engage in transportation, refining, or retail sales. Independent producers may process and market natural gas to gas consumers using third party pipelines to transport it.

INITIAL PRODUCTION*—Figure given to a well indicating its capability to produce. Abbreviated as IP, it may be the first full day's production, or a fraction thereof, multiplied to the equivalent of a day.

INJECTION OR INPUT WELLS—A well used to inject gas, water, or LPG under high pressure into a producing formation to maintain sufficient pressure to produce the recoverable reserves.

INSTALLMENT BONUS—See DEFERRED BONUS.

INTEGRATED OIL COMPANY—Petroleum company that engages in exploration, production, and significant refining, transportation, or retail operations in the petroleum industry.

INTERMEDIATE CASING STRING*—String of casing set in a well after the surface casing and before the production casing. It serves to protect the well bore as the well is deepened and to seal off problem formations such as high pressure areas.

INTERMEDIATE CRUDE OIL—Crude oil with an API gravity greater than 18 degrees and less than 36 degrees, and located in the spectrum between sour and sweet crude. West Texas Intermediate (WTI) is a well-known benchmark in oil pricing and is the underlying commodity of the New York Mercantile Exchange oil futures contracts.

INTERRUPTIBLE GAS*—Gas sold or transported without a pipeline's prior guarantee to move the gas.

IPAA—(abbrev.) Independent Petroleum Association of America.

ISOPACH MAPS*—Maps showing variations in the thickness of a particular sedimentary bed and the interval between one sedimentary bed and another.

JOINT—Single length of drill pipe or casing that is usually 20 to 30 feet in length.

JOINT INTEREST OR JOINT VENTURE—Association of two or more persons or companies to drill, develop, and operate jointly owned properties. Each owner has an undivided interest in the properties.

JOINT OPERATING AGREEMENT—Contractual agreement between two or more lease owners that provides for the operation of the lease. One party typically operates the lease with all owners sharing in the cost.

KEEP-WHOLE AGREEMENT—Processing agreement where the producer receives 100 percent of the attributable residue gas and consideration for the attributable plant volume reduction (PVR). Payment for the PVR either can be equivalent Btus of additional residue gas or a cash payment. The processor generally keeps 100 percent of the liquids extracted as payment for processing.

KELLY—Heavy square or hexagonal steel member that turns the drill string. It is suspended from a swivel through the rotary table and is connected to the drill pipe.

KILL A WELL—Industry term meaning to stop formation fluids, which are usually under dangerous high pressure, from coming up a well. The stopping process uses mud (or water) to halt production rather than closing well-head valves.

LACT UNIT (LEASE AUTOMATIC CUSTODY TRANSFER UNIT)—Automatic device for moving and measuring oil from lease storage to the pipeline. The process also requires a pump, an oil meter, and a BS&W measuring device.

LANDMAN—Person employed by an E&P company responsible for identifying, negotiating, acquiring, retaining, or disposing of oil and gas leases. May also manage the company's internal land department. The term also refers to an independent broker for identifying, negotiating, and acquiring leases. Landman, whether referring to a male or female, continues to be more commonly used than the term Landperson.

LEASE—(1) A contract in which the owner of minerals gives an E&P company temporary and limited rights to explore for, develop, and produce minerals from the property. (2) Any transfer where the owner of a mineral interest assigns all or a part of the operating rights to another party but retains a continuing nonoperating interest in production from the property.

LEASE AND WELL EQUIPMENT—Capital investment in equipment used in a well or on a lease, and having a potential salvage value. Such items can include the cost of casing, tubing, well head assemblies, pumping units, lease tanks, treaters and separators.

LEASE CONDENSATE—See CONDENSATE.

LEASE OPERATING EXPENSES—Costs of operating the wells and equipment on a producing lease, many of which are recurring.

LEASEHOLD INTEREST—See WORKING INTEREST.

LEASE USE—Gas or natural gasoline used at a well site to operate production equipment.

LESSEE—Individual or company entitled to exploit the mineral deposits under an oil or gas lease.

LESSOR—Owner of the mineral rights of a property with an executed an oil or gas lease.

LIFTING COSTS—Costs of operating wells for the production of oil and gas (producing costs).

LIMITED PARTNERSHIP—Legal form of organization of a business that consists of one or more general partners providing management services, and one or more limited partners with no management role and no authority to incur obligations on behalf of the entity. E&P limited partnerships may adopt either the successful efforts or full cost method of accounting.

LOCATION—Site for a well to be drilled or at which a well has been drilled.

LOGGING—Process of taking and recording physical measurements about formations being drilled.

MAGNETIC METER*—Instrument measuring the magnetic fields of the earth.

MAKE UP GAS—Gas taken in a later period that was paid for previously under a TAKE-OR-PAY contract.

MAKING A TRIP—Act of hoisting the drilling string out of and returning it into a wellbore.

MANAGING PARTNER—Partner in a general partnership that performs overall management duties, including maintaining business records, filing tax returns, and providing an accounting to partners.

MARGINAL WELL*—A well with limited production that has become barely profitable to operate.

MASS SPECTROMETER*—Instrument used to determine molecular weights and relative abundances of isotopes in a substance. The molecular components are ionized and disassociated by electronic bombardment. Positive ions are then accelerated in an electric field and separated magnetically by mass. A mass spectrometer is often used for gas analysis because it is fast and accurate. It can determine the amount of methane, ethane, propane, isobutane, N-butane, pentanes, hexanes, heptanes, and heavier hydrocarbons along with carbon dioxide, hydrogen sulfide, nitrogen, and helium content. A mass spectrometer also can calculate the Btu content of gas.

MCF—(abbrev.) Standard measure of volume for natural gas which is 1,000 cubic feet.

METAMORPHIC ROCKS—Rocks developed as a result of sedimentary rocks subjected to heat and pressure.

MINERAL INTEREST—Economic interest in underground minerals, such as a MINERAL RIGHT, WORKING INTEREST, or ORRI.

MINERAL RIGHTS—Rights of ownership of gas, oil, and other minerals beneath the surface which can be conveyed by deed.

MINIMUM ROYALTY—Obligation of a lessee to pay a lessor a periodic fee sum of money after production occurs, regardless of the amount of production. Such minimum royalty may or may not be chargeable against the royalty owner's share of future production.

MISCIBLE SOLVENT—Tertiary recovery process similar to a water flood, but involving the injection of a solvent that mixes with crude oil.

MMBTU— (abbrev.) Measure of one million British thermal units; also, a measurement of the energy released when natural gas is burned.

MMCF—(abbrev.) Measure of volume for natural gas which is one million cubic feet of gas.

MOBILE DRILLING RIG—Type of drilling rig consisting of either: (1) a small land rig mounted on a truck used for shallow wells, or (2) a drilling rig used offshore that can be floated from one drill site to another. Drill ships, jack-ups, and semi-submersibles are all considered mobile rigs.

MOUSE HOLE*—Hole drilled under the derrick floor (which is temporarily cased) where a length of drill pipe is temporarily suspended for later connection to the drill string.

MUD—Drilling fluid circulated through the drill pipe and back to the surface during rotary drilling and workovers.

MULTIPLE COMPLETION WELL—A well that is producing oil and/or gas from different zones at different depths in the same well bore with separate tubing strings for each zone. This type of well differs from a commingled well, which uses just one tubing string.

NATURAL GAS—Light hydrocarbons existing in a gaseous state in the earth's crust under certain atmospheric and temperature conditions. Natural gas often is found in association with oil.

NATURAL GAS LIQUIDS (NGL)—Hydrocarbons which can be extracted from wet natural gas and become liquid under various combinations of increasing pressure and lower temperature. NGL consists primarily of ethane, propane, butane, and natural gasolines.

NATURAL GASOLINES—Hydrocarbons found in natural gas and consisting of propane, butane, pentane, hexane, and heptane (C5H12 to C10H22). Natural gasolines are recovered from the natural gas stream in refineries primarily by means of absorption or compression technologies.

NET-BACK PRICING—Method of pricing oil or gas by subtracting transportation costs (and sometimes processing and refining costs) from the downstream price received for the oil or gas.

NET-BACK METHOD—Sale of produced wet natural gas for a price determined in part by proceeds from the sale of extracted NGL.

NET PROFITS INTEREST—Interest in production created from the working interest and measured by a certain percentage of the net profits (as defined in the contract) from the operation of the property.

NET REVENUE—For the full cost ceiling, the proceeds of an oil or gas sale less the production and severance taxes, marketing and transportation costs, royalties and overriding royalties, and operating expenses.

NET WELLS—Aggregate of fractional interests an owner has in more than one well. (See GROSS WELLS.)

NEW FIELD WILDCAT*—A well drilled in an area where there had been no previous production of oil or gas.

NOMINATION—Anticipated volume a producer expects to deliver into a pipeline in the next month as communicated to the pipeline company for confirmation. Nominations are changed and confirmed as necessary.

NONASSOCIATED GAS—Natural gas (usually dry) not in contact with crude oil in a reservoir.

NONCONSENT—Common provision in a joint operating agreement that allows certain working interest owners to not participate in the drilling, reworking, or completion of a well (also referred to as "going nonconsent"). The parties interested in participating must absorb all costs of the drilling operation, including any dry hole costs, and are permitted to recoup a percentage of those costs out of the future production attributable to the interests of the nonconsenting parties. The percentage recovery is specified in the joint operating agreement and may range from 100 to 800 percent.

NONCONTINUING INTEREST*—An interest in a mineral property whose life is limited in terms of dollars, units of product, or time.

NONOPERATING INTEREST*—An interest in minerals for which the holder does not have the responsibility to bear the cost of developing and producing the minerals. Examples are royalties, overriding royalties, and volume production payments.

NONOPERATOR—An E&P joint venture participant that is not the operator managing the joint venture.

OFFSET WELL—Type of well drilled on a well spacing unit adjacent to a producing well spacing unit; a well drilled on a lease to minimize drainage of reserves by wells on an adjacent lease.

OIL POOL*—Underground reservoir containing oil in sedimentary rocks.

OIL SAND—Any porous reservoir (generally sandstone) containing oil. The term oil sands may refer to formations close to the surface containing heavy hydrocarbons whereby the sands are mined and processed to produce synthetic crude oil.

OIL SEEP*—Area where tiny amounts of petroleum have migrated to the earth's surface.

OIL WELL—A well which can and does produce crude oil with minimal natural gas. Most state regulations classify a well as an oil well (not a gas well) if it produces less than 15 Mcf of gas per barrel of oil.

OIL-WELL GAS—See CASINGHEAD GAS.

OPERATING AGREEMENT—Legal instrument that defines the rights and obligations of the co-owners of a working interest in a lease concerning the joint development and operation of the lease.

OPERATOR—Participant in an E&P joint venture that serves to manage the joint venture, pay venture expenses, and bill the nonoperators for their respective shares of joint venture costs.

OPTION CONTRACT—Financial instrument that gives the holder (buyer) a right, but not an obligation, to buy (call) or sell (put) a specified amount of oil at a fixed price during a specified period. The holder pays a nonrefundable fee (premium) to the seller. Options are sold either on public exchanges or over-the-counter.

ORIFICE METER—Instrument used to measure the volume of flowing natural gas in a pipe.

OUTPOST WELL—A well drilled outside well locations offsetting a producing well, but within the possible or probable extent of the reservoir. (See STEP-OUT WELL.)

OVERRIDING ROYALTY INTEREST (ORRI)—Royalty interest which is created out of the operating or working interest. Its term is coextensive with that of the operating interest.

PARTICIPATION FACTORS—Set of undivided interests in the total area covered by a unitization agreement. Factors may be classified as either operating or non-operating depending on the type of property contributed. Also, percentages could be revised as more information about the contributed reserves becomes available.

PAY—Oil- or gas-saturated rock that is capable of producing oil or gas.

PAYOUT—A condition that occurs when revenues to a given interest in a well equal all land, acquisition, drilling, completing, and operating costs allocated to that interest.

PERCENTAGE DEPLETION—Federal income tax term referring to a deduction based on the gross income from mineral properties. (It is also known as statutory depletion.) Percentage depletion is computed on a property-by-property basis and is subject to certain limitations.

PERMEABILITY—Measure of the relative ease that oil can move through a reservoir.

PETROLEUM—Oil or gas obtained from the rocks of the earth, usually by drilling down into a reservoir and producing the hydrocarbons to the surface.

PIG*—A scraping instrument for cleaning a pipeline.

PLUG AND ABANDON—Act of sealing off a well, and often abbreviated as P&A. Cement plugs are inserted in the hole, and the property is abandoned.

PLUG BACK—Act of sealing off a lower formation in a well bore in order to produce from a higher formation.

POOL*—Underground reservoir having a common accumulation of oil or gas.

POOLING—Provision in an oil or gas lease that allows the operator to combine the leased property with properties owned by others. (Pooling is also called unitization.) The separate tracts are joined to form a drilling unit which can result in cost savings. Ownership shares are issued according to the acreage contributed or, for fields in later stages of development, by the production capabilities of each producing well.

POROSITY—Relative volume of the pore space in a reservoir compared to its total bulk volume.

POSTED FIELD PRICE*—Published price a crude oil purchaser will pay for a specific grade of crude at the point it is delivered by the seller and accepted by the purchaser on or after a stated date.

PRESSURE MAINTENANCE—Injection of gas, water, or other material to re-pressure an oil field.

PRESSURE REGULATOR*—Instrument for maintaining pressure in a pipeline downstream from the valve.

PRICE BULLETIN—Posting of the price per barrel a purchaser will pay for each grade of crude oil in a geographic area.

PRIMARY RECOVERY—Oil which is forced into the well bore by natural reservoir pressure, energy, or drive.

PRODUCTION COSTS—Costs of activities that involve lifting oil and gas to the surface, and operating and maintaining wells and related equipment and facilities.

PRODUCTION PAYMENT—Obligation to pay or receive a specified portion of production proceeds or to deliver a specified portion of certain production before the production is expected to cease.

PRODUCTION STRING—Last and deepest string of casing set in a well through which oil or gas will be produced.

PRODUCTION TAXES—Statutory amounts levied by state governments on mineral production based on the value and/or quantity of production. Also called severance taxes.

PRODUCTIVITY TEST*—Test of the maximum or other rates at which a well can produce.

PROJECT AREA*—Large territory a taxpayer determines can be explored advantageously in a single integrated operation.

PROPANE—A hydrocarbon gas (C3H8) extracted as a NATURAL GAS LIQUID from natural gas. Propane, also called liquefied petroleum gas (LPG), is stored in a liquid state under pressure. LPG is the fuel used in portable gas grills.

PROPERTY—Aggregate economic interests owned through a lease or acquisition of a mineral interest, as defined for financial accounting purposes. For income tax reporting, property refers to each separate interest owned by a taxpayer in each mineral deposit in each separate tract or parcel of land. Certain interests for tax purposes may be combined to form a property.

PROPERTY ACQUISITION COSTS—See ACQUISITION COSTS.

PROVED DEVELOPED RESERVES—Reserves which can be expected to be recovered through existing wells with existing equipment and operating methods.

PROVED PROPERTY—Property with PROVED RESERVES.

PROVED RESERVES—Quantities of reserves that appear with reasonable certainty to be recoverable in the future from known oil and gas reserves based on geologic and engineering data and under existing economic and operating conditions.

PROVED UNDEVELOPED RESERVES—Reserves expected to be recovered from new wells on undrilled proved acreage or from existing wells where a relatively major expenditure is required for completion.

PROVEN PROPERTIES—For federal income tax purposes, a property whose principal value has been demonstrated by exploration, discovery, or development. For financial accounting purposes, a property containing proved reserves.

PUMPER—Individual responsible for all equipment contained on the lease.

QUARTER SECTION*—A one fourth section of land. It measures one-half mile on a side and equals 160 acres. (A full section is 640 acres and is one mile wide).

RABBIT*—Line cleaning instrument consisting of a small plug which is run through a line.

RAT HOLE*—A hole from 30 to 35 feet deep with casing that projects above the derrick floor, where the kelly is placed when hoisting operations are in progress.

RECOMPLETION*—As defined in the AAPL Model Form Operating Agreement, recompletion is "an operation whereby a completion in one zone is abandoned in order to attempt a completion in a different zone within the existing wellbore." (See WORKOVER.)

RESERVES—See PROVED RESERVES, PROVED UNDEVELOPED RESERVES and PROVED DEVELOPED RESERVES.

RESERVOIR—Porous and permeable underground formation that contains a natural accumulation of producible oil or gas. The formation is confined by impermeable rock or water barriers and is individual and separate from other reservoirs.

RESIDUE GAS—Gas produced at the tail gate of a gas processing plant after all natural gas liquids and natural gas liquid products have been removed.

RETAINED INTEREST*—Interest kept by the grantor when selling or assigning an interest to another party.

REVERSIONARY INTEREST—Portion of an economic interest that will be returned to its former owner after a predetermined amount of production or income has been produced.

ROYALTY or ROYALTY INTEREST—Landowner's (lessor's) share of oil or gas production, typically in increments of 1/8, 1/6, or 1/4, and free of costs, but subject to severance taxes (unless the lessor is a government agency).

RUN TICKET—Record of the quantity of oil removed from a stock tank into a pipeline or tank truck. A run ticket will generally have opening and closing volumes, observed gravity and temperature, BS&W, and date and time of delivery. It is usually made in triplicate and filled out by the gauger employed by the purchaser. Sometimes the entries will be witnessed by the pumper as a subcontractor or an employee of the E&P company operating the well.

SECONDARY RECOVERY—See WATER FLOODING. (This term used to refer to any process of injecting water or gas into a formation to build up pressure in order to produce additional oil otherwise unobtainable by primary recovery.)

SECONDARY RESERVES*—Reserves recoverable by secondary recovery.

SEDIMENTARY ROCKS—Rocks formed by the accumulation of sediment at the bottom of a body of water that is compressed over time.

SEISMIC—Exploration method of sending energy waves or sound waves into the earth and recording the wave reflections to indicate the type, size, shape, and depth of subsurface rock formations. 2-D seismic provides two dimensional information, and 3D seismic provides three dimensional pictures. 4-D seismic produces 3-D pictures over time and is used to indicate fluid movement in producing reservoirs.

SEISMOGRAPH*—Device for detecting vibrations in the earth. It is used in prospecting for probable oil-bearing structures.

SEPARATOR—Cylindrical or spherical device located at the well site to separate commingled oil and gas by means of gravity and centrifugal force. In the process, the oil drops out of the mix, and the gas rises and escapes through separate outlets.

SHOOTING—Employing seismic processes in a zone. The term can also mean exploding nitroglycerin or other high explosives in a well hole to shatter the rock and increase the flow of oil.

SHUT-IN WELL—A well that is capable of producing oil or gas, but which is not on production.

SLIM HOLE*—Small diameter well, generally drilled to achieve less expensive exploration or limited development. A slim hole development well generally cannot be recompleted or as easily repaired as a normal diameter well. If a producing slim hole well has behind-pipe reserves, a second well normally must be drilled to produce them.

SMOG—(abbrev.) FAS 69 disclosure called the standardized measure of discounted future net cash flows relating to proved oil and gas reserves.

SOUR OIL or SOUR GAS—Oil or gas with a high sulfur content.

SPACING—Regulation concerning the number of wells which can be drilled on a given area of land. Depending on the depth of the reservoir, one well may be allowed on a small area of five acres or on an area up to 640 acres. Typical spacing is 40 acres for oil wells and 640 acres for gas wells. However, spacing for tight sands gas production may be 20 acres.

SPLIT CONNECTION*—One gas well that is connected to more than one pipeline. It occurs when two or more working interest owners usr different pipeline companies.

SPUD—Commencement of actual drilling operations.

STEP-OUT WELL—A well drilled beyond the proven limits of a field, but within the possible or probable extent of the reservoir. (See OUTPOST WELL.)

STIMULATION—Mechanical or chemical process designed to increase production by changing the characteristics of the portion of the reservoir near a well. (See ACIDIZE, FRACTURING, and WORKOVER.)

STRATIGRAPHIC TEST WELL—A well drilled to obtain information about geologic conditions.

STRIP A WELL*—Act of pulling both the rods and tubing from a well simultaneously.

STRIPPER WELL*—A well with marginally economic production.

STRUCTURAL MAPS*—Maps that indicate the contours of the subsurface.

SUCCESSFUL EFFORTS ACCOUNTING METHOD—Financial reporting accounting method under which costs incurred in searching for, acquiring, and developing oil and gas reserves are capitalized if they result directly in acquiring, finding, or developing proved reserves. All other costs are expensed as incurred.

SWAB—Device that fits tightly inside the tubing of a well, and when pulled through the tubing, it lifts out fluid.

SWAP—Financial instrument that enables two parties to exchange variable and fixed-rate payment streams based on a specified contract principal or notional amount (i.e., one company may pay a fixed price, and the other company may pay based on a published price index or futures contract settlement price)

SWEET CRUDE OIL or SWEET GAS—Oil or gas containing a relatively small amount of sulfur.

TAKE OR PAY CONTRACT—Agreement where the purchaser of gas agrees to take a minimum quantity of gas per year—if it is not prevented from doing so by circumstances beyond control and if the gas is available for delivery. If the purchaser does not take the minimum quantity, it is required to pay for that minimum quantity at the contract price. The purchaser may make up deficiency amounts in future years if it purchases in excess of minimum amounts. (New take or pay contracts became rare in the 1990s after gas purchasers suffered substantial losses in older contracts when gas prices unexpectedly declined.)

TANGIBLE COSTS—Costs of assets that, in themselves, have salvage value.

TANK BATTERY—Group of storage tanks to which crude oil flows from producing oil wells.

TANK STRAPPER—Individual who measures a tank and prepares the tank table.

TANK TABLE—Table showing the volume of a tank at various levels based on one-fourth-inch intervals.

TCF—(abbrev.) Trillion cubic feet.

TD—(abbrev.) Total depth to the bottom of a well.

TEMPORARILY ABANDONED WELL*—A well, which is deemed nonproductive, but which is not permanently plugged. An intent exists to use it for some other purpose or to re-establish production if economics improve.

TERTIARY RECOVERY—Use of sophisticated techniques to increase the production of oil or gas, such as flooding the reservoir with steam.

THIEF—Device for extracting oil samples from a tank.

TIGHT HOLE*—A drilling or completed well for which the operator refuses to release information to interested parties.

TOP LEASE—Lease provision granting a new oil or gas lease prior to the termination of an existing one. The new lease becomes effective upon expiration of the old lease.

TUBING — Small diameter pipe suspended in a well through which gas or oil is produced.

TURNKEY WELL — Completed, producing well which is drilled and equipped by a contractor for a fixed price.

UNDEVELOPED PROPERTY — Property that has not been drilled or equipped for production.

UNITIZATION — See POOLING. Unitization is a contractual or legal consolidation of multiple areas or blocks to permit the field or a pool to be efficiently developed.

UNIT-OF-PRODUCTION METHOD — Method of computing depreciation or depletion provisions based on quantities produced in relation to reserves.

VALVE — Device used to control the rate of flow in a line, open or shut off a line completely, or serve as an automatic or semi-automatic safety device.

VISCOSITY — Ability of a fluid to flow as a result of its physical characteristics.

WATER WELL* — A well drilled to obtain a supply of water for drilling or operating use.

WATER FLOODING — Secondary recovery method in which water is forced down injection wells laid out in various patterns around the producing wells. The injected water displaces the oil and forces it to the producing wells.

WELL — Hole drilled in the ground to obtain geological information, find and produce oil or gas, or provide service to the operation of an oil or gas property.

WELLHEAD — Equipment located at the top of a well casing that is used to maintain the surface control of a well.

WET GAS — Gas that contains a large quantity of liquids.

WILDCAT* — Exploratory well that is particularly risky (e.g., information from seismic data or nearby producing fields is not available to support the prospect).

WORKING INTEREST — Interest in the oil and gas in-place with responsibility for the cost of development and operation of the property. It is also called the operating interest.

WORKOVER — Major remedial operations on a completed well to restore, maintain, or improve the well's production. Workovers use workover rigs and can take many forms such as acidizing or fracing the well or removal of sand or paraffin build-up. The term workover is also used for deepening an existing well or plugging back to produce from a shallower formation. Costs to explore to an unproved formation are exploration costs. Costs to access a proved formation are development costs. The term workover excludes minor repairs or well servicing such as repair or replacement of downhole equipment.

ZONE — Stratigraphic interval containing one or more reservoirs.

• • •

INDEX
Terms in bold are defined in the Glossary.

* This supplemental term defined in the Glossary is not used in the chapters or appendices.